Applications of Model Theory to Algebra, Analysis, and Probability

Applications of Model Theory to Algebra, Analysis, and Probability

Edited by W. A. J. LUXEMBURG

California Institute of Technology

HOLT, RINEHART and WINSTON

New York Chicago San Francisco Atlanta Dallas

Montreal Toronto London Sydney

Library of Congress Catalog Card Number: 69-11203

SBN: 03-072175-X

Printed in the United States of America

01234 22 98765432

Preface

This volume constitutes the Proceedings of the International Symposium on the Applications of Model Theory to Algebra, Analysis, and Probability. The Symposium was held under the direction of W. A. J. Luxemburg at the California Institute of Technology, from May 23 to 26, 1967, under the sponsorship of the Office of Naval Research (Contract Nr-041-339).

The papers in this volume are the texts, at times considerably expanded and revised, of addresses presented by invited speakers to the Symposium. Several papers that were presented by some of the participants by title only are also included in this volume.

The origin of the subject matter of the papers in this volume can be traced to an article of Thoralf Skolem entitled "Ueber die Nicht-charakterisierbarkeit der Zahlenreihe mittels endlich oder abzählbar unendlich vieler Aussagen mit ausschliesslich Zahlen variablen," which appeared in 1934 in volume 23 of the Fundamenta Mathematicae. In this article Skolem showed that there exist proper extensions of the natural number system which have, in some sense, "the same properties" as the natural numbers. This means, as expressed in the title of Skolem's paper, that no axiomatic system specified in a formal language can characterize the natural numbers categorically. An interest in the properties of the structures whose existence Skolem had established came only at a later date. In fact, about 15 years later, an intensive study of these and similar structures began and became known as the study of nonstandard models of arithmetic.

A whole new development began in 1960 when Abraham Robinson applied similar ideas to analysis. This development led to the establishment of new structures which are proper extensions of the real number system. This enabled Robinson to give the complete solution for the century-old problem of introducing infinitely small and infinitely large numbers in the Differential and Integral Calculus which was so strongly advocated by Leibniz and later discarded as unsound and replaced by Weierstrass by the ϵ,δ-method. Going beyond this, Robinson showed that this new method, which has become known as nonstandard analysis, can be applied fruitfully to other mathematical structures. The Symposium stressed, in particular, this fact. So that the Proceedings should be of interest to a broad section of the mathematical community.

The interested reader who wishes to become more familiar with the logical foundations of the new method is referred to the recent book of Abraham Robinson entitled "Non-Standard Analysis" which appeared in the series "Studies in Logic" of the North-Holland Publishing Company, and to the first chapter of the article of the editor in this volume entitled "A general theory of monads."

The editor wishes to thank all participants for their prompt and enthusiastic cooperation. Special thanks are due to Abraham Robinson for his continuing support and for being a continuing source of inspiration during the preparation of the Symposium.

The editor wishes to express his gratitude to the California Institute of Technology for its support and to the Office of Naval Research for its generous financial support.

Finally, the editor wishes to commend Holt, Rinehart and Winston, Inc., for undertaking the publication of the Proceedings.

W. A. J. Luxemburg

Pasadena, California
December 1968

Contents

Applications of Model Theory to Algebra, Analysis, and Probability

Topics in Nonstandard Algebraic Number Theory

by ABRAHAM ROBINSON[1]

1. Introduction

Nonstandard analysis was put forward originally as a consistent framework for the development of the calculus and of other branches of analysis in terms of infinitely small and infinitely large quantities. Later, the basic ideas of this method were extended to other branches of mathematics, in particular, to general topology (see [6]). The present paper is one of a series (compare [7–9]) in which the nonstandard approach is applied to algebraic number theory and to related topics. The paper falls into two parts. In Sections 2–4 we consider the theory of entire ideals in an infinite algebraic number field; that is, in an infinite algebraic extension of the field of rational numbers. One of the difficulties that arises in the classical multiplicative theory of these ideals is that the cancellation rule no longer applies to it. We shall show how this situation can be alleviated by our nonstandard approach.

In Sections 5 and 6 we continue the development of class field theory for infinite algebraic number fields which was begun in [9]. We show how the main result obtained there can be related to the classical theory of Chevalley and Weil.

We shall now give an informal introduction to the basic ideas of nonstandard analysis as applied to the problems studied in the present paper. The reader may consult [6] and [8] for details.

[1] The author acknowledges with thanks that the research leading to the present paper was supported in part by the National Science Foundation. He also wishes to express his appreciation of the support given by the Office of Naval Research to a program in nonstandard analysis which was conducted at the California Institute of Technology during the academic year 1967–1968 and in which he participated during the winter term. Finally, the author thanks David Cantor for an instructive discussion in connection with the problems considered here.

Let F be an infinite algebraic extension of the field of rational numbers Q. We consider the properties of F in a higher-order language L, which includes symbols for all individuals (that is, numbers) of F, all subsets of F, all relations of two, three, $\cdots$ variables between individuals of F, all functions from individuals to individuals of F, and, more generally, all relations and functions of finite type (for example, functions from sets of numbers into relations between numbers) that can be defined beginning with the individuals of F. Let K be the set of all sentences formulated in L which hold (are true) in F. Then there exists a structure $^*F$ with the following properties.

1.1. $^*F$ is a model of K "in Henkin's sense." That is, all sentences of K hold in $^*F$, provided, however, that we interpret all quantifiers other than those referring to individuals in a nonstandard fashion, as follows. Within the class of all entities of any given type other than 0 (the type of individuals), there is distinguished a certain subclass of entities called *internal*. And, for such a type, the quantifiers "for all x" and "there exists an x" are to be interpreted as "for all *internal* x," "there exists an *internal* x" (of the given type). F can be injected into $^*F$, and so $^*F$ may, and will, be regarded as an extension of F.

1.2. Every concurrent binary relation $R(x, y)$ in F possesses a bound in $^*F$.

The relation $R(x, y)$, of any type, called *concurrent* if for any $a_1, \cdots, a_n$, $n \geq 1$, for which there exists $b_1, \cdots, b_n$ such that $R(a_1, b_1)$, $\cdots$, $R(a_n, b_n)$ hold in F, there also exists a b such that $R(a_1, b), \cdots$, $R(a_n, b)$ hold in F. And the entity b_R in $^*F$ is called a *bound* for $R(x, y)$ if $R(a, b_R)$ holds in $^*F$ for any a for which there exists a b such that $R(a, b)$ holds in F.

Any structure $^*F$ which satisfies 1.1 and 1.2 is called an *enlargement* of F. In particular, $^*F$ can be constructed as an ultrapower of F. (See [3] and [4] for the notions of an ultrapower.) Enlargements which are ultrapowers have special properties that will be used implicitly in Sections 5 and 6 on the theory of idèles. On the other hand, the arguments of Sections 2–4 on ideal theory in infinite number fields apply to enlargements in general. Moreover, the reader will check that we shall have to rely on the existence of bounds only for a few concurrent relations. For all these cases, the existence of bounds is ensured already for any ultrapower of F that is based on a free ultrafilter in a countable index set. Thus *all* results of the present paper hold for such ultrapowers (compare [9]).

We stated earlier that there is an embedding of F into $^*F$. For the case of an ultrapower, this is obtained by identifying any entity a of F with the entity of $^*F$ which corresponds to the constant function $f(x) \equiv a$ on the index set of $^*F$. In terms of the language L, an entity b of $^*F$ corresponds to an entity a of F if it is denoted by the same symbol in L. The entities of $^*F$ which occur in this correspondence are called *standard* entities. If no confusion is likely to arise, we shall refer to entities of F also as standard. Notice, however, that if entities of F and $^*F$ correspond as indicated, then they are not, in general, extensionally the same. For example, if N is the set of natural numbers in F, then the corresponding set in $^*F$, to be denoted by $^*N$, contains, in addition to the standard natural numbers $0, 1, 2, \cdots$ also certain nonstandard, or infinite, natural numbers. To see that there must be such infinite numbers in $^*N$, consider the relation $R(x, y)$, which is defined by the condition "x and y are natural numbers and $x < y$." It is easy to verify that $R(x, y)$ is concurrent. Let b_R be a bound for R in $^*F$. Then b_R is a natural number in $^*F$; that is, an element of $^*N$ and, moreover, $0 < b_R$, $1 < b_R$, $2 < b_R$, and so on. This proves that b_R is a nonstandard, "infinite" natural number in $^*F$. More generally, it is not difficult to see that if A and $^*A$ are corresponding sets in F and $^*F$, then $^*A$ is a proper extension of A if and only if A is infinite.

Let B be the set of all finite sets of a given type in F. On passing to $^*F$, B is extended to a set $^*B$ whose elements will be called *star-finite*. An internal set A in $^*F$ is star-finite if and only if there is an internal one-to-one correspondence between the elements of A and a set of natural numbers $\{x \mid 0 \leq x \leq n\}$, where n is a finite or infinite element of $^*N$.

2. Ideals in Infinite Algebraic Number Fields

Let the fields F and Q be defined as in Section 1. On passing from F to an enlargement $^*F$, Q is extended to a subfield $^*Q$ of $^*F$. Let Q^i and F^i be the rings of integers in Q and F so that $Q^i = Z$, the ring of rational integers, and let $^*Q^i = {}^*Z$ and $^*F^i$ be the corresponding rings in the enlargement. Let $\Phi = \{F_n\}$ be a tower of subfields of F,

$$Q = F_0 \subset F_1 \subset F_2 \subset \cdots$$

such that all the F_n are finite extensions of Q and such that $\bigcup_n F_n = F$. Then the corresponding entity in $^*F$, $^*\Phi$, is a mapping from $^*N$ into the set of subfields of $^*F$, $^*\Phi = \{H_n\}$, say. For finite n, $H_n = {}^*F_n$, while for any infinite $n = \omega$, we have $F_m \subset H_\omega$ for any finite m. We conclude that $F = \bigcup_n F_n \subset H_\omega$, where n ranges only over finite subscripts. Thus $F \subset H_\omega \subset {}^*F$. Put $H_\omega = H$.

H is a *star-finite* extension of $^*Q$. That is to say, there exists an $\alpha \in {}^*F$

such that $H = {}^*Q(\alpha)$, where α is algebraic over ${}^*Q$ and where the symbol ${}^*Q(\alpha)$ and the term *algebraic* both have to be interpreted in the nonstandard sense. Thus the degree ω of α may well be (and actually is, for infinite F, as assumed) infinite; that is, n is an infinite natural number.

Let $S = \{J\}$ be the set of ideals in F^i, and let ${}^*S$ be the corresponding set in ${}^*F^i$. Thus ${}^*S$ consists of all internal sets of numbers of ${}^*F$ which are entire ideals in ${}^*F^i$. Let S_ω be the set of internal and entire ideals in H^i, where $H^i = H \cap {}^*F_i$. For any $J \in S$ we have the canonical mapping $J \to {}^*J$ into ${}^*S$. On the other hand, for any ideal $J \in {}^*S$, we define $\varphi(J) = J_H$ by $J_H = J \cap H_\omega$. Then $\varphi({}^*J) \cap F = J$. The ring of integers in H will be denoted by H^i, so that $H^i = {}^*F^i \cap H$. Let S_H be the set of internal ideals in H^i. Then the ideals of S_H are either principal or they have two-element bases, since this is true for the ideal of any finite algebraic number field.

Two different ideals $J_1, J_2 \in S_H$ may have the same intersection with F^i. However, to any $J \in S$ there corresponds a unique ideal $J_H \in S_H$ by the mapping $\psi(J)$ which is defined by $\psi(J) = \varphi({}^*J) = J_H$. The inverse of this map is simply $\psi^{-1}(J_H) = J_H \cap F^i$.

If $J \in S$ is prime, so is ${}^*J$, since the property of being prime can be expressed within the language L. Also, if any $J \in {}^*S$ is prime, so are the restrictions of J to H and to F. It follows that if $J \in S$ is prime, so is $J_H = \psi(J)$. At the same time, if any $J \in S_H$ is prime, so is its restriction to F.

The mapping ψ is not, in general, multiplicative. To see this, let F be the field of all algebraic numbers and let $J \in S$ be given by

$$J = (2^{2^{-1}}, 2^{2^{-2}}, \cdots, 2^{2^{-k}}, \cdots),$$

where $k = 1, 2, \cdots$ ranges over the finite positive integers. Then $J^2 = J$. But $1 \notin J$, so that J is not the unit ideal in F, and so $1 \notin J_H = \psi(J)$, J_H is not the unit ideal in H. It follows that $J_H{}^2 \neq J_H$, in other words, $(\psi(J))^2 \neq \psi(J)$. For, since the cancellation rule applies in H, $J_H{}^2 = J_H$ would imply that J_H is the unit ideal in H.

For any subset A of (the set of individuals of) ${}^*F$, we define the *standard part* of A, ${}^0A$, by ${}^0A = A \cap F$, and we write $\sigma(A) = {}^0A$ or

$$A \xrightarrow{\sigma} {}^0A.$$

Now let J_1 and J_2 be ideals in S_H and let

$$J_1 \xrightarrow{\sigma} {}^0J_1, \qquad J_2 \xrightarrow{\sigma} {}^0J_2, \qquad J_1J_2 \xrightarrow{\sigma} J,$$

so that $J = {}^0(J_1J_2)$. Then any $c \in {}^0J_1{}^0J_2$ can be written in the form

$$c = a_1b_1 + \cdots + a_kb_k,$$

where k is a finite positive integer and $a_i \in {}^0J_1$, $b_1 \in {}^0J_2$, $i = 1, \cdots, k$. Hence ${}^0J_1{}^0J_2 \subset J$. In general, the sign of inclusion in this relation cannot be replaced by $=$. However, if we add the assumption that there exist ideals K_1, K_2 in S such that $J_1 = \psi(K_1) = K_{1H}$, $J_2 = \psi(K_2) = K_{2H}$, then

$$*K_1{*K_2} = *(K_1K_2)$$

Hence
$$K_{1H}K_{2H} \subset (*(K_1K_2))$$

and so
$${}^0(K_{1H}K_{2H}) \subset {}^0(*(K_1K_2)) = K_1K_2;$$

that is,
$$J = {}^0(J_1J_2) \subset {}^0J_1{}^0J_2.$$

Thus ${}^0J_1{}^0J_2 = {}^0(J_1J_2)$ in this case. A corresponding conclusion applies for any finite number of ideals $J_i \in S_H$ such that $J_i = \psi(K_i)$, $K_i \in S$. We have proved

***Theorem* 2.1.** *Let $K_1, \cdots, K_m$ be any finite number of ideals in S, $m \in N$. Then*

$${}^0(\psi(K_1)){}^0(\psi(K_2)) \cdots {}^0(\psi(K_m)) = {}^0(\psi(K_1)\psi(K_2) \cdots \psi(K_m)).$$

By a familiar result of commutative ring theory, any maximal ideal in S is prime (excluding the unit ideal, as usual). Conversely, let P be any prime ideal in S, $P \neq 0$, $P \neq F^i$; then the following nonstandard argument shows that P *is maximal.*

Since P is prime and since the property that an ideal is prime can be expressed in L, $*P$ also must be prime. Hence $P_H = \psi(P)$ is prime. If P is not maximal, then it is included in a maximal ideal Q in S, $P \subset Q \subset F^i$, $P \neq Q$, $Q \neq F^i$. Since $F^i - Q$ is not empty, $H^i - Q_H$ cannot be empty either, and so Q_H is a proper ideal which is a proper extension of P_H. But this is impossible, since any prime ideal in H must be maximal, as is the case for all finite algebraic number fields. Hence P is maximal, as asserted.

Let J be any proper ideal in S; that is, $J \neq 0$, $J \neq F^i$. A familiar argument shows that J possesses at least one prime divisor. We shall call J *primary* if it possesses exactly one prime divisor, P. Then $J_H \subset P_H$ and so there exists an ideal $Q \in S_H$ such that $J_H = P_HQ$. Suppose now that J_H possesses, in addition to P_H, another prime divisor P'. Then $1 \notin P'$ and so $1 \notin {}^0P'$ and at the same time $J \subset {}^0P'$. Assuming that J is primary, we conclude that either ${}^0P' = F^i$ or ${}^0P' = P$. But the former possibility is ruled out by $1 \notin {}^0P'$ and so ${}^0P' = P$. It follows that all prime divisors of J_H have the same standard part.

Now let J be any proper ideal in S, so that $J_H = \psi(J)$ is a proper ideal in S_H. Then J_H can be decomposed into a product of powers of distinct prime ideals,

$$J_H = P_1^{n_1} \cdots P_k^{n_k}, \qquad k \geq 1, \quad n_j \geq 1 \qquad \text{for } j = 1, \cdots, k,$$

where k and the n_j may be finite or infinite. Suppose that all the P_j have the same standard part, P. Then

$$J_H = \bigcap_j P_j^{n_j}$$

and so

$$J = \bigcap_j {}^0(P_j^{n_j}).$$

Now let Q be any proper prime ideal in S which divides J. Then $\psi(Q) = Q_H$ is a proper prime ideal which divides J_H. Accordingly, Q_H coincides with one of the P_j, and so $Q = {}^0Q_H = {}^0P_j = P$. We have proved

Theorem 2.2. *A proper ideal $J \in S$ is primary if and only if the prime divisors of $\psi(J)$ all have the same standard part.*

3. The Ring Δ_H

Let μ be the subset of $^*F^i$ which is defined by

3.1. $\mu = \{x \mid x \in {}^*F^i$ *any x is divisible by all nonzero standard rational integers*$\}$.

Then μ is an external ideal in $^*F^i$. We shall study the quotient ring $\Delta = {}^*F^i/\mu$. A corresponding investigation for the case that F is a finite algebraic number field or, more generally, a Dedekind ring has been carried out in [7–9].

The elements of μ are characterized also by the property that they are divisible by all nonzero elements of F^i. For if $a \in F^i$, $a \neq 0$, and Na is the norm of a, then $a \mid Na$, a divides Na, and so $Na \mid x$ implies $a \mid x$. Yet another equivalent condition is that for every standard rational prime p there exists an infinite natural number n such that $p^n \mid x$.

Let δ be the canonical mapping

$$\delta \colon {}^*F^i \to \Delta.$$

Then δ injects $F^i \subset {}^*F^i$ into Δ, since μ does not contain any standard elements other than 0. Let $\mu_H = \mu \cap H$; then we may identify $H^i/\mu_H = \Delta_H$ with a subring of Δ. Let δ_H be the restriction of δ to H, so that δ_H maps H on Δ_H and injects F^i into Δ_H.

Theorem 3.2. *Let $a \in F^i$, $a \neq 0$. Then $\delta_H(a)$ is invertible in Δ_H if and only if all prime ideals $P_j \in S_H$ which divide the ideal $(a)_H$ generated by a in H have norms NP_j that are powers of nonstandard primes.*

Remark. If F is a finite algebraic number field, then any proper internal prime ideal P in $^*F^i$ is standard if and only if its norm is a power of a standard rational prime. Even if P is not standard, its norm must be a *finite* power f of a rational prime (which is then infinite), since f is bounded by the degree of F over Q. In the case under consideration here, where F is an infinite extension of Q, we first pass from $^*F^i$ to H^i to be able to apply the results of standard ideal theory. Even in H^i, the norm of a proper internal prime ideal must be a power of a rational prime.

Proof of Theorem 3.2. For any $a \in H$, $N_H a$ shall denote throughout the norm of a in H over $^*Q$.

The conclusion of the theorem is satisfied if and only if Na, which is a rational integer, is divisible only by *infinite* prime numbers. For let

$$(a) = P_1^{k_1} \cdots P_l^{k_l}$$

be the prime power decomposition of the ideal $(a) \in S_H$. Then

$$|N_H a| = (N_H P_1)^{k_1} \cdots (N_H P_l)^{k_l},$$

where $N_H P_j$, $j = 1, \cdots, l$, is a finite or infinite power of the unique prime number contained in it.

Now let $b \neq 0$ be a rational integer such that all prime divisors of b are nonstandard. Let p be the smallest positive prime divisor of b so that p is infinite. Then b and $(p - 1)!$ are coprime, and so there exist rational integers k and l such that

$$k(p - 1)! + lb = 1.$$

Thus

3.3. $$lb \equiv 1 \bmod (p - 1)!$$

Suppose now that a satisfies the hypothesis of the theorem and put $b = N_H a = aa'$, where $a' \in H^i$. Then

$$aa'l \equiv 1 \bmod (p - 1)!$$

by 3.3. But $(p - 1)! \in \mu_H$, and so

$$\delta_H(a)\delta(a'l) = 1,$$

which shows that $\delta_H(a)$ is invertible in Δ_H.

Conversely, suppose that δ_H is invertible in Δ_H. Then there exists a number $a' \in H^i$ such that $aa' - 1 \in \mu_H$. Thus $aa' - 1$ is divisible by $n!$ for all finite natural numbers n. A basic argument of nonstandard analysis now shows that $aa' - 1$ must be divisible also by ω for some infinite natural number ω. To sketch the argument briefly, let $A \subset {}^*N$

be the set of natural numbers n, finite or infinite, such that $n!$ does not divide $aa' - 1$. A is internal. If A is empty, then we have finished. Now it is a fact concerning standard natural numbers, which can be expressed as a sentence of K, that every nonempty set of natural numbers possesses a smallest element, and the same must therefore be true in $^*N$. Hence, if A is not empty, then it has a smallest element, $\omega + 1$, say, where ω is infinite, and $aa' - 1$ is then divisible by ω. Thus

$$aa' = 1 + k\omega!$$

where $k \in H^i$, and so

3.4. $$N_H a N_H a' = 1 + l\omega!$$

where l must now be a rational integer. Suppose that the standard prime number q divides $N_H a$. Since q also divides $\omega!$, it would then follow from 3.4 that q also divides 1, which is impossible. This completes the proof of Theorem 3.2.

Theorem 3.5. *Let $J \in S_H$. Then δ_H maps J on a principal ideal J' in Δ_H.*

Proof. Let $J \in S_H$. If $J = (0)$, then $J' = (0)$ and we have finished. If $J \neq (0)$ and $a \in J$, $a \neq 0$, then for any infinite natural number ω, J contains also the number $a\omega!$ By a standard result, which applies also in H, there exists a $b \in J$ such that $J = (b, a\omega!)$. Hence $J' = \delta_H(J) = (\delta_H(b), \delta_H(a\omega!))$. But $\delta_H(a\omega!) \in \mu_H$, and so $J' = (\delta_H(b))$, as asserted.

Theorem 3.6. *Let $J \in S_H$ and suppose that J contains a standard number $a \neq 0$. If there exist numbers $b \in H^i$, $c \in H^i$ such that*

$$J' = \delta_H(J) = (\delta_H(b)) = (\delta_H(c)),$$

then $\delta_H(b)$ and $\delta_H(c)$ are associated elements in Δ_H. That is, there exist invertible *elements m' and n' of Δ_H such that $\delta_H(b) = m'\delta_H(c)$ and $\delta_H(c) = n'\delta_H(b)$.*

Proof. Suppose that b and c satisfy the assumptions of the theorem. Then there exists an $m' \in \Delta_H$ such that $\delta_H(b) = m'\delta_H(c)$. Choose $m \in H^i$ such that $m' = \delta_H(m)$. Then $\delta_H(b - mc) = 0$, and so

$$b - mc \in \mu_H.$$

Similarly, there exists an $n \in H^i$ such that

$$c - nb \in \mu_H.$$

Hence $$nb - nmc \in \mu_H.$$

3.7. $$(1 - nm)c \in \mu_H.$$

By assumption, there exists a standard number $a \in J$, $a \neq 0$. Then $\delta(a) \in J'$ and so $\delta(a) = k'\delta(c)$ for some $k' \in \Delta_H$. But $k' = \delta_H(k)$ for some $k \in H^i$ and, for such k, $\delta_H(a) - \delta_H(k)\delta_H(c) = 0$ and hence

$$a - kc \in \mu_H,$$

$$(1 - nm)a - (1 - nm)kc \in \mu_H,$$

and, taking into account 3.7,

3.8. $$(1 - nm)a \in \mu_H.$$

Now it is easy to see that if $q \in \mu_H$ and γ is a standard positive integer, then $q/\gamma \in \mu_H$. But $a \mid Na$ (where Na is now the standard norm of the standard number a) and so $q/a = (q/Na)(Na/a)$ also belongs to μ_H. Hence, dividing $(1 - nm)a$ by a, we obtain, from 3.8,

$$1 - nm \in \mu_H$$

and so $$\delta_H(n)\delta_H(m) = 1.$$

Hence $m' = \delta_H(m)$ and $n' = \delta_H(n)$ are invertible, proving the theorem.

Theorem 3.9. *Let $J \in S_H$ and suppose that J contains a standard number $a \neq 0$. Suppose further that $J = (b, m)$, where $m \in \mu_H$. Then there exists an ideal $D \in S_H$ such that $JD = (b)$, where all prime divisors of $N_H D$ are nonstandard.*

Proof. Given J, a, and b with the specified properties there exists an ideal $D \in S_H$ such that $JD = (b)$, by standard ideal theory in finite algebraic number fields. Also, $\mu_H \subset J$, since any number of H_i which is divisible by all standard positive integers is divisible also by a.

Suppose now that D has a prime divisor $P \in S_H$ whose norm $N_H P$ is a power of a standard prime number p; p is the unique rational prime number contained in P. Then $ap \in JP$ and so, as above, $\mu_H \subset JP$ and, in particular, $m \in JP$. Also, $JP \supset JD = (b)$ and so $b \in JP$ and $J = (b, m) \subset JP$. But $J \supset JP$, and so $J = JP$. But this implies $P = H^i$, by standard ideal theory—which contradicts our assumptions and proves the theorem.

In particular, the conditions of 3.4 apply if the ideal J considered in Theorem 3.5 contains a standard element different from 0.

4. Topological Considerations

Let $T \subset S$ be the set of proper prime ideals in F^i. The *Krull topology* of T [5] is defined as follows. A subset A of T is *open* if for any $J \in A$ there exists a subfield F' of F which is finite (that is, a finite algebraic extension of Q) such that all $J' \in T$ for which $J' \cap F' = J \cap F$ also belong to A. In other words, for any $J \in T$, a fundamental system of neighborhoods of J is defined by the set of ideals of T which coincide with J on some finite subfield of F.

Passing to the enlargement $^*F$, we recall that the *monad* $\mu(J)$ of any $J \in T$ in the sense of nonstandard topology [6] is defined as the set $\bigcap_\nu {}^*A_\nu$ where A_ν ranges over the open neighborhoods of J in T. To define $\mu(J)$ more directly in terms of the algebraic situation we introduce $\lambda(F)$ as the set $\bigcup_\nu {}^*F_\nu$ where F_ν ranges over all finite subfields of F. It is not difficult to see that $\lambda(F)$ is a field that contains H. However, $\lambda(F)$ must be a proper subfield of $^*F$. For, on the one hand, all elements of $\lambda(F)$ are algebraic over $^*Q$ in the standard sense; that is, their degrees over $^*Q$ are finite natural numbers. On the other hand, since F is infinite over Q, the degrees of its elements are unbounded. It follows that $^*F$ contains elements of infinite degree over $^*Q$ and so $\lambda(F) \neq {}^*F$.

Theorem 4.1. *Let* $J \in T$. *Then* $\mu(J)$ *consists of all* $J' \in {}^*T$ *such that* $J' \cap \lambda(F) = {}^*J \cap \lambda(F)$.

Proof. Let A be any open set that includes J and suppose that $J' \cap \lambda(F) = {}^*J \cap \lambda(F)$. By assumption, there exists a finite field $F' \subset F$ such that A contains all ideals of T with the same restrictions to F' as J. It follows that $^*A$ contains all ideals of $^*T$ that have the same restrictions to $^*F'$ as $^*J$. This is true of J', since $\lambda(F)$ includes $^*F'$.

Conversely, suppose that $J' \in \mu(J)$, but that $J' \cap \lambda(F) \neq {}^*J \cap \lambda(F)$. It follows that $((J' - {}^*J) \cup ({}^*J - J'))$ has a nonempty intersection with $\lambda(F)$ and hence has a nonempty intersection with $^*F'$ for some finite subfield F' of F. Define A as the set of all ideals of T that coincide with J on F'. Then $J \in A$ and A is open and so $^*A \supset \mu(J)$. But $J' \in {}^*A$, since J' does not coincide with $^*J$ on $^*F'$. This completes the proof of 4.1.

As usual in nonstandard analysis, we may derive certain standard properties of T from results about $^*T$. For example, 4.1 shows immediately that an ideal of $^*T$ cannot belong to the monads of two distinct ideals of T. It follows [6] that T is a Hausdorff space.

5. Theory of Idèles

From now on, let F be a finite algebraic extension of the field of rational numbers, Q, and let F_{P_ν} be the completions of F, where P_ν ranges over the finite and infinite (or Archimedean) primes in F. Let $M = \Pi_\nu F_{P_\nu}$ be the strong direct product of the completions of F and let $I \subset H$ be the group of idèles over F. Thus I consists of the elements of M whose components are different from zero and are nonunits for a finite number of finite primes P_ν only. We may regard the F_{P_ν} as extensions of F (given a particular injection of F into F_{P_ν} for each ν). The diagonal injection of F into M then yields an embedding of F', the multiplicative group of F, into I. The idèle class group C is defined as the quotient group $C = I/F'$.

It has been shown in [9] (compare [8]) that M is isomorphic to the quotient ring F_0/μ, where F_0 and μ consist of all elements of $^*F$ whose absolute values are finite or infinitesimal, respectively, in the valuations associated with all the standard P_ν. Equivalently, F_0 consists of the elements of $^*F$ that are finite in all Archimedean valuations and whose orders are nonnegative, or negative but finite, for all standard finite primes; and μ consists of the elements of $^*F$ that are infinitesimal in all Archimedean valuations and whose orders are positive and infinite for the standard finite primes.

Let H be the set of entire or functional internal ideals J in $^*F$ such that $J \neq (0)$ and $\text{ord}_{P_\nu} J = 0$ for all standard finite primes P_ν. In other words, H consists of the nonzero ideals whose prime power decomposition does not contain any standard prime ideals. Let H_0 be the set of principal ideals in $^*F$, which can be written $J = (a)$, where a is positive in all real Archimedean valuations and $\text{ord}_{P_\nu} (a - 1)$—the order of $a - 1$ for the prime P_ν—is positive infinite for all standard finite primes. H_0 is a subset of H, as can be seen from the equation

$$\begin{aligned}\text{ord}_{P_\nu} J = \text{ord}_{P_\nu} a = \text{ord}_{P_\nu} (a - 1 + 1) \\ = \min(\text{ord}_{P_\nu} (a - 1), \text{ord}_{P_\nu} 1) = 0.\end{aligned}$$

Moreover, H_0 is multiplicatively closed, since

$$\begin{aligned}\text{ord}_{P_\nu} (ab - 1) &= \text{ord}_{P_\nu} ((a - 1)b + (b - 1)) \\ &\geq \min(\text{ord}_{P_\nu} (a - 1)b, \text{ord}_{P_\nu} (b - 1)).\end{aligned}$$

This shows that if $\text{ord}_{P_\nu} (a - 1)$ and $\text{ord}_{P_\nu} (b - 1)$ are infinite, and hence $\text{ord}_{P_\nu} b = 0$, then $\text{ord}_{P_\nu} (ab - 1)$ also is infinite. Finally, H_0 is closed with respect to inversion, since $J^{-1} = (1/a)$ for $J = (a)$ and

$$\text{ord}_{P_\nu} \left(\frac{1}{a} - 1\right) = \text{ord}_{P_\nu} (a - 1) - \text{ord}_{P_\nu} a,$$

which is infinite if $\text{ord}_{P_\nu} (a - 1)$ is infinite and $\text{ord}_{P_\nu} a = 0$.

Having verified that H_0 is a multiplicative subgroup of H, we consider next the quotient group $D = H/H_0$. *We propose to show that D is a homomorphic image of the idèle class group C.*

For this purpose, we have to construct an epimorphism from C to

D. Let β be the canonical epimorphism from I to C, and let c be any element of C. Let b and b' be corresponding elements of I, so that $c = \beta b = \beta b'$. Then $b' = fb$ for some $f \in F'$ (and, conversely the existence of an $f \in F'$ such that $b' = fb$ shows that $\beta b = \beta b'$).

As mentioned earlier, there is an epimorphism, to be called here α, from the ring F_0 onto $M = \Pi_\nu F_{P_\nu}$, where the kernel of α is the set μ introduced above. We may assume that the embedding of F into M has been determined in such a way that for any $f \in F$, F being regarded as a subset of F_0, $\alpha f = f$. Moreover (see [9], sec. 5), if α_ν is the P_ν-component of αa for $a \in F_0$, then a is infinitesimal for any given Archimedean P_ν if and only if $a_\nu = 0$; for standard finite P_ν, $\text{ord}_{P_\nu} a$ is infinite if and only if $a_\nu = 0$, and if $\text{ord}_{P_\nu} a$ is finite, then it is equal to $\text{ord}_{P_\nu} a_\nu$. It follows that $a \in F_0$ belongs to $\alpha^{-1}I$ if and only if a is not infinitesimal for any Archimedean valuation while the number of standard prime divisors of (a) and the (positive or negative) powers in which they appear in (a) are all finite. This condition shows immediately that $G = \alpha^{-1}I$ is a multiplicative group.

For any $b \in I$ and for any $a \in b$ such that $b = \alpha a$, we may have at the same time $b = \alpha a'$ if and only if $a' = a + m$ for some $m \in \mu$. Thus, if $a \xrightarrow{\alpha} b$ and $f \in F'$, $m \in \mu$, then

$$fa + m \xrightarrow{\alpha} fb.$$

And if at the same time $b \xrightarrow{\beta} c$ and so $a \xrightarrow{\beta\alpha} c$, then

$$fa + m \xrightarrow{\beta\alpha} c.$$

Conversely, if $a \in G$ and $a \xrightarrow{\beta\alpha} c$ and at the same time $a' \xrightarrow{\beta\alpha} c$ for some $a' \in G$, then we claim that there exist $f \in F'$ and $m \in \mu$ such that $a' = fa + m$. Indeed, let $b = \alpha a$, $b' = \alpha a'$ so that $c = \beta b = \beta b'$. Then we know already that there exists an $f \in F'$ such that $b' = fb$. It follows that $b' = \alpha(fa)$ and so $fa - a' \in \mu$; that is, $a' = fa + m$ for some $m \in \mu$, as asserted.

Next, we introduce a homomorphism γ from G into H in the following way. For any $a \in G$ consider the representation of (a) as a product of powers of prime ideals in $^*F$.

5.1. $$(a) = P_1^{n_1} \cdots P_l^{n_l}$$

where l and the n_j may be finite or infinite and the n_j may be positive or negative. By the definition of G, the n_j must be finite for standard P_j, and only a finite number of such P_j appear in the product on the right side of 5.1. Hence, by deleting all such $P_j^{n_j}$ we obtain an *internal* ideal

$J = \gamma a$, which is an element of H, and we may verify immediately that γ is a homomorphism. The kernel of γ is just the multiplicative group of principal ideals (a) for $a \in F'$, which is isomorphic to the quotient group of F' by its group of units.

Finally, there is a canonical homomorphism from H onto $D = H/H_0$, which will be denoted by δ. Combining γ with δ, we obtain a homomorphism δ_γ from G into D. *We claim that δ_γ is an epimorphism into D.*

To see this, let $d \in D$ and $J \in H$ such that $d = \delta J$. Choose a standard ideal $^*J' \neq s$ (where J' is an ideal in F) such that $J \cdot {}^*J'$ is principal. The existence of such a J' follows immediately from the fact that the number of ideal classes in F is finite and hence does not increase on passing to $^*F$. Thus $J \cdot {}^*J' = (a')$ for some $a' \neq 0$ in $^*F$. Now choose an $a'' \in {}^*F$ that is positive in all real Archimedean valuations and is such that $\mathrm{ord}_{P_\nu}(a'' - 1)$ is positive infinite for all standard finite primes and $a = a'a'' \in G$. Equivalently, the last condition can be replaced by the requirement that, for all Archimedean valuations, a is finite but not infinitesimal. A suitable a'' may be found as follows.

Range all standard *finite* primes in a sequence $\{P(n)\}$ and let ω be an infinite natural number. $\{P(n)\}$ is continued automatically from F to $^*F$ and the set $^*\{P(n)\}_{n \leq \omega}$ contains all standard finite primes and is *star-finite*; that is, finite in the sense of the enlargement. Given a' as above, choose a'' so as to satisfy the conditions

5.2. $$\mathrm{ord}_{P(n)}(a'' - 1) > \omega \qquad \text{for } n \leq \omega$$

and

5.3. $$\left| a'' - \frac{e^{i\theta_\nu}}{a'} \right| < \frac{1}{\omega|a'|}$$

for all Archimedean valuations, where $\theta_\nu = \arg a'$ for the several valuations. Since their number is star-finite, conditions 5.2 and 5.3 can be satisfied simultaneously, by virtue of the approximation theorem. Also, from 5.3, and equivalent to it, we obtain for all Archimedean valuations,

5.4. $$\big|\, |a'|a'' - 1 \big| < \frac{1}{\omega}\cdot$$

This shows that a'' is positive for all real valuations. More generally, 5.4. shows that, for all Archimedean valuations, $a = a'a''$ must be infinitely close to the unit circle and so $a \in G$.

Now let $(a'') = Q_1^{k_1} \cdots Q_m^{k_m}$ be the prime power decomposition of the ideal (a''). Then none of the Q_i is standard and so $\gamma a = \gamma(a'a'') =$

$J \cdot (a'')$. Moreover, by the conditions imposed on a'', $(a'') \in H_0$ and so $\delta(a'') = 1$ and $\delta\gamma a = \delta J \delta(a'') = d$. This shows that $\delta\gamma$ is onto D.

We shall now show that for any two elements a and a' of G, $\beta\alpha a = \beta\alpha a'$ implies $\delta\gamma a = \delta\gamma a'$.

We know already that $\beta\alpha a = \beta\alpha a'$ implies the existence of $f \in F'$, $m \in \mu$, such that $a' = fa + m$. Accordingly, we only have to prove that, for any $a \in G$, $m \in \mu$,

$$\delta\gamma(fa + m) = \delta\gamma a.$$

But $$\delta\gamma(fa + m) = \delta\gamma\left(fa\left(1 + \frac{m}{\delta a}\right)\right) = \delta\gamma f \cdot \delta\gamma a \cdot \delta\gamma\left(1 + \frac{m}{fa}\right),$$

since $\gamma f = 1$ and $m' \in \mu$, taking into account that fa is neither infinite nor infinitesimal. Thus it only remains to be shown that $\delta\gamma(1 + m') = 1$ for any $m' \in \mu$, where we observe that $1 + m' \in b$ for such m'. But, for $m' \in \mu$, the ideal $(1 + m')$ belongs to H_0 and so $\delta\gamma(1 + m') = 1$, as required.

We now define a mapping φ from C onto D as follows. For any $c \in C$ choose $a \in G$ such that $c = \beta\alpha a$ and define $d = \varphi c$ by $d = \delta\gamma a$. As we have just seen, this definition is independent of the particular choice of a. The mapping φ is onto D, since $\delta\gamma$ is onto D and since any $a \in G$ belongs to the range of $\beta\alpha$. Moreover, φ is multiplicative and so *it represents the required epimorphism from C onto D.*

6. The Kernel of φ

The kernel C_0 of φ consists of the $c \in C$ for which there exists an $a \in G$ such that $c = \beta\alpha a$ and $\delta\gamma a = 1$; that is, $\gamma a \in H_0$. Thus γa is of the form $\gamma a = (g)$, where $g > 0$ for all real valuations and ord_{P_ν} $(g - 1)$ is positive infinite for all standard finite primes P_ν. It follows that only nonstandard prime ideals occur in the decomposition of g and so $(a) = (fg)$, where $f \neq 0$ is standard. We conclude that $a = f\epsilon g$, where ϵ is a unit in $^*F$ and $\epsilon g \in G$. Then $c = \beta\alpha(f\epsilon g) = \beta\alpha(\epsilon g)$. Conversely, if ϵ is any unit in $^*F$, $\epsilon g \in G$, $g > 0$, for all real valuations, and ord_{P_ν} $(g - 1)$ is positive infinite for all standard finite primes P_ν, then $c = \beta\alpha(\epsilon g)$ belongs to C_0.

Now suppose that F has r_1 real Archimedean primes and r_2 complex Archimedean primes, and let $r = r_1 + r_2 - 1$. Let $\epsilon_1, \cdots, \epsilon_r$ be a fundamental system of units in F. Then every unit ϵ *in* $^*F$ may be written

$$\epsilon_0 = \epsilon_1^{k_1} \cdots \epsilon_r^{k_r},$$

where the k_j are (rational) integers which may be either finite or infinite.

Now $\beta\alpha(\epsilon_j) = 1$ for $j = 1, \cdots, r$ and so the expression

$$6.1. \qquad \beta\alpha(\epsilon_1^{k_1} \cdots \epsilon_r^{k_r} g)$$

with g as above, does not change if we multiply by one or more ϵ_j. Accordingly, we obtain all elements of C_0 by considering the expressions 6.1 for even k_j only. Or, equivalently and varying our notation, we may take $\epsilon_1, \cdots, \epsilon_r$ as the squares of the units of a fundamental system. Then $\epsilon_1, \cdots, \epsilon_r$ are still an independent system of units and, moreover, are now totally positive, that is, positive in all real valuations. For g satisfying the same conditions as before, C_0 is obtained again from 6.1 by letting the k_j range over all integers, standard and nonstandard.

To continue, we write the group of idèles I as the direct product $\bar{I}\tilde{I}$ of the group of idèles that have component 1 at every Archimedean prime, $\bar{I}$, and the group of idèles that have component 1 at every finite prime, $\tilde{I}$. Let $\bar{\psi}$ and $\tilde{\psi}$ be the canonical maps from I to $\bar{I}$ and $\tilde{I}$, respectively, and let $\bar{\alpha} = \bar{\psi}\alpha$ and $\tilde{\alpha} = \tilde{\psi}\alpha$. For our last-mentioned choice of $\epsilon_1, \cdots, \epsilon_r$ and for g satisfying the conditions specified previously, consider the expressions

$$6.2. \qquad \tilde{\alpha}(\epsilon_1^{k_1} \cdots \epsilon_r^{k_r} g).$$

An application of the approximation theorem similar to that made earlier in this section to determine a'' shows that, for any fixed $\epsilon = \epsilon_1^{k_1} \cdots \epsilon_r^{k_r}$, we may still adjust g so as to obtain any given element of $\tilde{I}$ with positive components for the real primes and with nonzero components for the complex primes. Let this subset of $\tilde{I}$ be called $\tilde{E}$, and define $\bar{E}$ as the set of all idèles of $\bar{I}$ which are of the form $\bar{\alpha}(\epsilon_1^{k_1} \cdots \epsilon_r^{k_r} g)$. Since $\text{ord}_{P_\nu}(g - 1)$ is positive infinite for all finite primes,

$$\bar{\alpha}(\epsilon_1^{k_1} \cdots \epsilon_r^{k_r} g) = \bar{\alpha}(\epsilon_1^{k_1} \cdots \epsilon_r^{k_r})$$

and so $\bar{E}$ is also given by

$$6.3. \qquad \bar{\alpha}(\epsilon_1^{k_1}) \cdots \bar{\alpha}(\epsilon_r^{k_r})$$

where the k_j range over $^*Z$, Z being the ring of standard integers, as usual. Observe that $C_0 = \beta E$, where $E = \bar{E}\tilde{E}$.

To analyze E further, consider any expression $\bar{\alpha}(\epsilon^k)$, where $k \in Z$ and ϵ is a unit in F. As customary in algebraic number theory, we denote by $\bar{Z}$ the completion of Z as an additive group for the topology for which the nonzero ideals of Z form a fundamental system of neighborhoods of 0. $\bar{Z}$ is the direct sum of the p_ν-adic integers Z_{p_ν}, where p_ν ranges over the standard rational primes. Denoting by $\bar{\mu}$ the set of numbers of $^*Z$ which are divisible by all numbers of Z, we find that $\bar{Z}$ is isomorphic to, and may be identified with, $^*Z/\bar{\mu}$ (compare [8]). Let ζ be the canonical mapping from $^*Z$ to $\bar{Z}$.

Let F^i be the ring of integers of F as before and let μ' be the set of numbers of $^*F^i$ which are divisible by the numbers of Z. Then $\bar{F} = {}^*F^i$ is isomorphic to the direct sum (or product) $\Pi F_{p_\nu}{}^i$, where the $F_{p_\nu}{}^i$ are the completions of F^i for the standard finite primes P_ν of F [8]. The elements of $\bar{I}$ whose components are entire, for example, $\bar{\alpha}(\epsilon^k)$, may be identified with elements of $\bar{F}$, and $\bar{\alpha}$ then coincides with the canonical mapping from $^*F^i$ to $\bar{F}$. For any P_ν and for any finite natural number n, the theorem of Fermat–Euler shows that there exists a finite natural m such that

$$\epsilon^m \equiv 1 \bmod P_\nu{}^n.$$

We conclude that for all $k \in \bar{\mu}$, $\epsilon^k - 1$ is divisible by all finite powers of all P_ν and so $\epsilon^k - 1 \in \mu'$. Hence $\bar{\alpha}(\epsilon^k) = 1$ for $k \in \bar{\mu}$, and so $\bar{\alpha}(\epsilon^{k_1}) = \bar{\alpha}(\epsilon^{k_2})$ for $k_1 - k_2 \in \bar{\mu}$. This shows that, for any $Z \in \bar{Z}$, we may define ϵ uniquely and consistently with the old definition for $Z \in Z$—by putting $\epsilon^z = \bar{\alpha}(\epsilon^k)$ for any k such that $z = \zeta k$. With this definition, $\bar{E}$ consists of the totality of products

6.4. $$\epsilon_1{}^{z_1} \cdots \epsilon_r{}^{z_r}$$

as $z_1, \cdots, z_r$ range over $\bar{Z}$.

The function ϵ^z coincides with the exponential function used in [1] for the components at finite primes. Bearing in mind that exponentiation is defined there also for the Archimedean primes, so as to take care of the real components and of the moduli of the complex components, it is now not difficult to verify that $C_0 = \beta(\bar{E}\tilde{E})$ coincides with the connected component of the identity in the idèle class group C (see in particular eq. (1) of ref. [1]). We may sum up the conclusions reached in this and the preceding section in the following

Theorem 6.5. *There exists an epimorphism φ from the group $D = H/H_0$ to the idèle class group C of F such that the kernel of φ is the connected component of the identity in C.*

It is a fundamental classical result of Chevalley's [2] that C/C_0 is isomorphic to the Galois group Γ of the maximal Abelian extension of F over F. On the other hand, it has been shown ([9], sec. 6) that $D = H/H_0$ is isomorphic to Γ. Since the theory given there is independent of Chevalley's result, it actually provides a new proof of it when taken in conjunction with Theorem 6.5. However, as we have seen, the connection between D and C which is established by the analysis of the last two sections possesses some interest of its own.

References

1. E. ARTIN, Representatives of the Connected Component of the Idèle Class Group, *International Symposium on Algebraic Number Theory, Tokyo, 1955*, pp. 51–54, Collected papers, pp. 249–252.
2. C. CHEVALLEY, Généralisation de la théorie du corps de classes pour les extensiones infinis, *J. Math. Pure Appl.* (9)*15* (1936), 359–371.
3. J. FRAYNE, A. C. MOREL, AND D. S. SCOTT, Reduced Direct Products, *Fundamenta Math. 51* (1962), 195–227.
4. S. KOCHEN, Ultraproducts in the Theory of Models, *Ann. Math.* (2)*79* (1961), 221–261.
5. W. KRULL, Idealtheorie in unendlichen Zahlkörpern, II, *Math. Z. 31* (1930), 517–557.
6. A. ROBINSON, *Non-Standard Analysis* (Studies in Logic and the Foundations of Mathematics), Amsterdam: North-Holland, 1966.
7. A. ROBINSON, A New Approach to the Theory of Algebraic Numbers, *Atti. Accad. Nazl. Lincei, Rend.* (8)*40* (1966), 222–225, 770–774.
8. A. ROBINSON, Non-Standard Theory of Dedekind Rings, *Proc. Acad. Sci. Amsterdam A70* (1967), 444–452.
9. A. ROBINSON, Non-Standard Arithmetic (address before American Mathematical Society Meeting, San Jose, April 1967), *Bull. Am. Math. Soc. 73* (1967), 818–843.

A General Theory of Monads

by W. A. J. LUXEMBURG

Introduction

The notion of a monad of a standard real number was introduced for the first time by Abraham Robinson. The result that these monads are not internal sets became a basic tool in nonstandard analysis. In a more general context monads were introduced for the points of a topological space and it was shown in [13] that in a metric space a point is discrete or isolated if and only if its monad is internal. For general topological spaces which are not necessarily metrizable or which do not necessarily satisfy the first countability axiom (every neighborhood system has a countable subbasis) there are many interesting questions concerning the monads of its points which were left open in [13].

The purpose of the present paper is to develop a general theory of monads and to provide answers for these questions. The paper is divided into three chapters. Chapter I deals with the logical foundations of the theory and is except in a few places mainly expository. The theory of ultrapowers of formal structures is discussed. Enlargements and saturated models are also treated from the point of view of the theory of ultrapowers.

In Chapter II, the main chapter of the paper, we introduce essentially two types of monads for a family of sets: the union monad and the intersection monad. The basic result of this chapter is the theorem that in an enlargement the monad of a filter is internal if and only if it is a principal filter. This result provides all the answers for similar questions concerning the monads of the points in a topological space.

To probe deeper into the structure of the monads it became clear that more satisfactory results could only be obtained in saturated models. For instance, it is shown that in a saturated model a property that is shared by all the elements of the monad of a filter is already shared by the elements of a set of the given filter—a fact that is well known for the monad of infinitesimals and was already used intuitively by Cauchy.

In Chapter II we also take up the question of when an internal set is a standard set. In this context the notion of the discrete monad of an entity plays a fundamental role.

Chapter III was written primarily to illustrate in what fashion the general theory of monads affects general topology. Problems concerning the properties of near-standard points in relation to various notions of compactness and not dealt with in [13] are treated here in some detail. In particular, we give an affirmative answer to the following question raised by A. Robinson, and answered by Robinson affirmatively for spaces satisfying the first countability axiom. Is the standard part of an internal set closed? An example due to H. J. Keisler shows that in enlargements the answer may be no.

It is well known that uniformities are closely related to the theory of equivalence relations and the theory of partitions. This fact is reflected very nicely in the monad of a uniformity: It is shown that a monad is the monad of a uniformity if and only if it is the graph of an equivalence relation. Having shown that the standard part of an internal set is closed, we show further that in a uniform space the standard part of an internal set can be expressed very elegantly as an intersection. It is clear that near-standard points and convergent filters are intimately related. For uniform spaces we introduce the notion of pre-near-standard points, which of course are very closely related to Cauchy filters. Also the notion of precompactness can be expressed very neatly in terms of the properties of the set of all pre-near-standard points. Two sections are devoted to the completion of a uniform space. In particular, we introduce the notion of a nonstandard hull of a uniform space and show that it is complete. In the last two sections some applications to the theory of normed spaces are given.

Finally, I would like to state that any resemblance between the mathematical concept of a monad introduced in the present paper and the philosophical concept of a monad in the monadology of Leibniz is purely coincidental.

Chapter I Logical Foundations

1. Preliminaries

We shall use the following notation and terminology from set theory. The empty set will be denoted by $\varnothing$. Ordinals are considered to be defined so that each ordinal is equal to the set of all smaller ordinals. Cardinals are identified with initial ordinals and in general will be denoted by the small Greek letter κ with and without subscripts. The cardinal successor of κ will be denoted by κ^+. The cardinal of N, the set of natural numbers, will be denoted as usual by $\aleph_0$ and its successor by $\aleph_1$. The cardinal of a set X will be denoted by card(X) and also by $\kappa(X)$. Y^X will denote the set of all functions defined on X into Y. The power set of a set X will be denoted by $P(X)$; that is, $Y \in P(X)$ if and only if $Y \subset X$, and $P_f(X)$ denotes the set of all finite subsets of X.

By a *filter* over a set X we mean a nonempty set $\mathfrak{F}$ of subsets of X such that $\emptyset \notin \mathfrak{F}$, $\mathfrak{F}$ is closed under finite intersections, and any subset of X which includes a member of $\mathfrak{F}$ belongs to $\mathfrak{F}$. In particular, $X \in \mathfrak{F}$ for every filter $\mathfrak{F}$ over X. By an *ideal* over a set X we mean a nonempty set $\mathfrak{I}$ of subsets of X such that the set of the complements of the elements of $\mathfrak{I}$ is a filter. A filter $\mathfrak{F}$ is called *free* whenever $\bigcap\mathfrak{F} = \emptyset$; and $\mathfrak{F}$ is called a *principal filter* whenever there exists a subset $A \subset X$ such that $F \in \mathfrak{F}$ if and only if $A \subset F$. We say that a filter $\mathfrak{F}_1$ is *finer* than a filter $\mathfrak{F}_2$ whenever $F \in \mathfrak{F}_2$ implies $F \in \mathfrak{F}_1$ and in that case we write $\mathfrak{F}_2 \leq \mathfrak{F}_1$. This relation orders the set of all filters over a set X, the filter $\{X\}$ being the smallest element of the ordered set of filters over X.

The filter consisting of the complements of the finite subsets of an infinite set X is called the *Fréchet filter* of X and will be denoted by $\mathfrak{F}r(X)$. It is evident that the Fréchet filter over an infinite set is a free filter.

A filter $\mathfrak{F}$ over a set X is called an *ultrafilter* whenever for all $Y \subset X$ either $Y \in \mathfrak{F}$ or $X - Y \in \mathfrak{F}$. An ultrafilter $\mathfrak{U}$ is principal if and only if $\bigcap\mathfrak{U} \in \mathfrak{U}$, or equivalently, $\mathfrak{U}$ contains a set that consists of one element only. An ultrafilter $\mathfrak{U}$ over an infinite set X is free if and only if it is finer than $\mathfrak{F}r(X)$.

A nonempty family $\mathfrak{B}$ of subsets of a set X is said to have the *finite intersection property* whenever $\bigcap_{i=1}^n B_i \neq \emptyset$ for every finite subset $\{B_1, \cdots, B_n\} \subset \mathfrak{B}$. Dually, we say that a nonempty family $\mathfrak{B}$ of subsets of a set X has the *finite union property* whenever $\bigcup_{i=1}^n B_i \neq X$ for every finite subset $\{B_1, \cdots, B_n\} \subset \mathfrak{B}$. A nonempty family $\mathfrak{B}$ of subsets of a set X has the finite intersection (union property) if and only if it is a subset of a filter (ideal).

A subset $\mathfrak{B}$ of a filter $\mathfrak{F}$ is a *subbasis* of $\mathfrak{F}$ whenever $\mathfrak{F}$ is the filter generated by $\mathfrak{B}$, or equivalently, whenever for every $F \in \mathfrak{F}$ there exists a finite subset $\{F_1, \cdots, F_n\} \subset \mathfrak{B}$ such that $\bigcap_{i=1}^n F_i \subset F$.

2. Higher-order Nonstandard Models

The axiomatic systems of mathematical concepts can in most cases be formulated in a natural way within a first-order language. There are, however, many important cases where some of the axioms are outside the lower predicate calculus. To cope with these cases we shall, as in [13], consider higher-order structures and higher-order languages. Following A. Robinson, the following framework for higher-order structures seems to be adequate for our purposes.

To admit higher-order relations, as, for instance, relations between relations, and to exclude others we shall use the notion of a *type*.

The class of types is defined inductively as follows: (a) 0 is a type; (b) if $\sigma_1, \cdots, \sigma_k$ are types, then $(\sigma_1, \cdots, \sigma_k)$ is a type; (c) T is the smallest class satisfying (a) and (b).

Let X be an infinite set. To the elements of X we assign the type 0, and then we introduce the admissible relations in X and at the same time assign to them types by the following rule. If $\sigma = (\sigma_1, \cdots, \sigma_k)$ is an arbitrary but definite type, $k \geq 1$, and A is a set of k-tuples $(A_1, \cdots, A_k)$, where A_i is of the type σ_i $(i = 1, 2, \cdots, k)$, then A is a relation of type σ. For example, a subset of X is of type (0), the membership relation of set theory between the elements of $P(X)$ is of type ((0), (0)) and $P(X \times X)$ is of type ((0, 0)). Observe that in this way the empty set has all types $\neq 0$. Furthermore, the reader should observe that in this enumeration of types of relations we exclude relations such as sets that would contain as elements relations of a certain type and sets of relations of a certain type. For every $\sigma \in T$ we shall denote by X_σ the set of all relations of type σ based in X. Thus $X_0 = X$ and the set X_σ is itself a relation of type (σ).

We shall now introduce the notion of a *structure*.

A *higher-order structure* or simply a *structure* $\mathfrak{M} = \mathfrak{M}(M_\sigma\colon \sigma \in T)$ is a set indexed in T such that for some nonempty set X, every M_σ is a subset of X_σ but $M_0 = X_0 = X$, and for every $\sigma \neq 0$, $\sigma = (\sigma_1, \cdots, \sigma_n)$ $(n > 1)$, if $A \in M_\sigma$ and $(A_1, \cdots, A_n) \in A$, then $A_i \in M_{\sigma_i}$ $(i = 1, 2, \cdots, n)$. The elements of $\mathfrak{M}$ will be called the *entities* of $\mathfrak{M}$. The entities of $\mathfrak{M}$ of type 0 are called the *individuals* of $\mathfrak{M}$. The set of all entities of a structure $\mathfrak{M}$ will be denoted by M. Furthermore, $\mathfrak{M} = \mathfrak{M}(X, M)$ will denote the structure whose set of individuals is X and where M is its set of all entities of finite type based in X.

A structure $\mathfrak{M} = \mathfrak{M}(X, M)$ is said to be *full* whenever $M_\sigma = X_\sigma$ for all $\sigma \in T$.

The *formal language* L will now be introduced.

The atomic symbols of L are: (a) The *connectives*, "not," "and," "or," $\Rightarrow$ (read "implies"), $\Leftrightarrow$ (read "equivalent to"). (b) The *variables*, an infinite sequence of symbols, usually denoted by $x, y, z, \cdots$ with and without sub and superscripts. (c) The *type predicates*. For every $\sigma \in T$, a symbol $T_\sigma(\cdot)$. (d) The *basic predicates*, a sequence $\Phi_n(, \cdots ,)$, $n = 1, 2, \cdots$, Φ subscript n followed by round brackets enclosing $n + 1$ spaces, separated by commas. (e) The *quantifiers* $(\forall \cdot)$ (universal, "for all") and $(\exists \cdot)$ (existential, "there exists"). (f) *Brackets* for grouping formulas. (g) *Extralogical constants* or briefly *constants.* This is a set of symbols of which there are at least as many as to be put in one-to-one correspondence with the individuals and entities of a structure. When a basic predicate $\Phi_n(, \cdots ,)$ is filled with constants $a, a_1, \cdots, a_n$ we shall read $\Phi_n(a, a_1, \cdots, a_n)$ as "$a_1, \cdots, a_n$ satisfies a or "a holds for $a_1, \cdots, a_n$."

We recall that the set of well-formed formulas (wff) of L are obtained by means of the following rules. A basic predicate or type predicate whose empty places have been filled with variables and or constants is called an *atomic well-formed formula.* If W is a wff, then not (W) is a wff; if W_1 and W_2 are wff, then $(W_1$ and $W_2)$, $(W_1$ or $W_2)$, $W_1 \Rightarrow W_2$, and $W_1 \Leftrightarrow W_2$ are wff; if W is a wff and if W does not already contain a particular variable x under a quantifier, then $(\forall x)W$ and $(\exists x)W$ are wff. The class of wff is the smallest class that satisfies these rules; that is, any wff is obtained by applying these rules a *finite* number of times. A wff is called a *sentence* whenever every variable is under the scope of a quantifier; any other wff is called a *predicate.*

Let $\mathfrak{M} = \mathfrak{M}(X, M)$ be a structure. Suppose now that a subset of the set of extralogical constants of the language L has been put in one-to-one correspondence with the entities of $\mathfrak{M}$. A sentence of L is defined in $\mathfrak{M}$ whenever all the constants contained in it denote entities of $\mathfrak{M}$. A sentence of L defined in $\mathfrak{M}$ may be true or false in $\mathfrak{M}$ according to the following rules. (a) An atomic sentence $T_\sigma(a)$ defined in $\mathfrak{M}$ holds in $\mathfrak{M}$ if and only if the entity of $\mathfrak{M}$ denoted by a (under the given correspondence) is of type σ. (b) An atomic sentence of the form $\Phi(a, a_1, \cdots, a_n)$ defined in $\mathfrak{M}$ holds in $\mathfrak{M}$ if and only if the corresponding entity a in $\mathfrak{M}$ contains the n-tuple of entities denoted by $a_1, \cdots, a_n$ in that order. Observe that this can only be the case if and only if the type $\sigma = (\sigma_1, \cdots, \sigma_n)$ can be assigned to the entity a provided the entities $a_1, \cdots, a_n$ are of type $\sigma_1, \cdots, \sigma_n$, respectively. (c) If a sentence in $\mathfrak{M}$ is of the form not (W), then it holds in $\mathfrak{M}$ if and only if W does not hold in $\mathfrak{M}$. The sentence $(W_1$ or $W_2)$ holds in $\mathfrak{M}$ if and only if at least one of W_1 and W_2 holds in $\mathfrak{M}$, $(W_1$ and $W_2)$ holds in $\mathfrak{M}$ if and only if both W_1 and W_2 holds in $\mathfrak{M}$, $(W_1 \Rightarrow W_2)$ holds in $\mathfrak{M}$ if and only if (not (W_1) or $W_2)$ holds in $\mathfrak{M}$, $W_1 \Leftrightarrow W_2$ holds in $\mathfrak{M}$ if and only if $((W_1$ and $W_2)$ or (not (W_1) and not $(W_2)))$ holds in $\mathfrak{M}$. (d) $(\forall x)(W(x))$ holds in $\mathfrak{M}$ if and only if $W(a)$ holds in $\mathfrak{M}$ for all entities a of $\mathfrak{M}$, and $(\exists x)(W(x))$ holds in $\mathfrak{M}$ if and only if $W(a)$ holds in $\mathfrak{M}$ for at least one entity a of $\mathfrak{M}$.

If the entities of a structure $\mathfrak{M}$ are in one-to-one correspondence with a subset of the extralogical constants of L, then $\mathfrak{M}$ will be called an L-structure. In that case, we shall denote by $K = K(\mathfrak{M}, L)$ the set of all sentences of L which are defined in $\mathfrak{M}$ and by $K_0 = K_0(\mathfrak{M}, L)$ the subset of all sentences of K which hold in $\mathfrak{M}$.

We shall now introduce the notion of a *higher-order nonstandard model* of an L-structure, $\mathfrak{M}$.

An L-structure $^*\mathfrak{M} = {}^*\mathfrak{M}(^*X, {}^*M)$ is called a higher-order nonstandard model of an L-structure $\mathfrak{M} = \mathfrak{M}(X, M)$ whenever all the sentences of $K_0 = K_0(M, L)$ hold in $^*\mathfrak{M}$.

A higher-order nonstandard model $^*\mathfrak{M} = {}^*\mathfrak{M}(^*X, {}^*\mathfrak{M})$ may be regarded as an extension of $\mathfrak{M}$. Indeed, if the sentence $T_\sigma(a)$ belongs to K_0, then it also holds in $^*\mathfrak{M}$. Thus to a there corresponds an entity $^*a$ of type σ in $^*\mathfrak{M}$. The mapping $a \to {}^*a$ of the entities of $\mathfrak{M}$ into the entities of $^*\mathfrak{M}$ is easily seen to be one to one and defines an embedding of $\mathfrak{M}$ into $^*\mathfrak{M}$. In what is to follow we shall frequently identify the entities a of $\mathfrak{M}$ with the corresponding entities $^*a$ of $^*\mathfrak{M}$, and we shall write $X \subset {}^*X$ and $M_\sigma \subset {}^*M_\sigma (\sigma \in T)$, if no confusion is possible.

A nonstandard model $^*\mathfrak{M}$ of an L-structure $\mathfrak{M}$ need not be full even if $\mathfrak{M}$ is full. Thus we shall call the entities of $^*\mathfrak{M}$ *internal* and the relations of $(^*X)_\sigma - {}^*M_\sigma$ external. This terminology is only relevant for entities of type $\sigma \neq 0$, since there are obviously *no* external individuals. An entity a of $^*\mathfrak{M}$ which already belongs to $\mathfrak{M}$, that is, $a = {}^*b$ for some entity b of $\mathfrak{M}$, will be called a *standard entity* of $^*\mathfrak{M}$.

3. Higher-order Nonstandard Models That Are Ultrapowers

There are many ways in which new structures can be obtained from a given structure $\mathfrak{M}$.

We shall take up here the definition of structures that are *reduced powers* of a given structure.

Let $\mathfrak{M} = \mathfrak{M}(X, M)$ be an L-structure and let $\mathfrak{F}$ be a filter over a nonempty set I. A new structure can now be constructed as follows. The individuals of the new structure $\mathfrak{M}_0$ are the mappings of I into X, and the new entities of type σ, $\sigma \in T$, of $\mathfrak{M}_0$ are the mappings of I into M_σ. This structure extends $\mathfrak{M}$ in the sense that $\mathfrak{M}$ is embedded in $\mathfrak{M}_0$ by means of the constant mappings. To consider $\mathfrak{M}_0$ as an L-structure we have to define what it means to fill the basic predicates and type predicates with constants of L which denote the entities of $\mathfrak{M}_0$. This can be done in many ways. For instance, we could set $\Phi_n(a, a_1, \cdots, a_n)$ holds in $\mathfrak{M}_0$ if and only if $\Phi_n(a(i), a_1(i), \cdots, a_n(i))$ holds $\mathfrak{M}$ for all $i \in I$. We shall generalize this in the following sense as to become dependent on the given filter $\mathfrak{F}$. An atomic formula $\Phi_n(a, a_1, \cdots, a_n)$ holds in $\mathfrak{M}_0$ if and only if $\{i\colon \Phi_n(a(i), a_1(i), \cdots, a_n(i))$ holds in $\mathfrak{M}\} \in \mathfrak{F}$, and $T_\sigma(a)$ holds in $\mathfrak{M}_0$ if and only if $\{i\colon T_\sigma(a(i))$ holds in $\mathfrak{M}\} \in \mathfrak{F}$. The L-structure obtained in this way will be called a *reduced power* of $\mathfrak{M}$ with respect to $(I, \mathfrak{F})$ and will be denoted by $\mathfrak{F}$-prod $\mathfrak{M}$. If $\mathfrak{F}$ is an ultrafilter, then $\mathfrak{F}$-prod $\mathfrak{M}$ is called an *ultrapower* of $\mathfrak{M}$.

In general, $\mathfrak{F}$-prod $\mathfrak{M}$ is not a nonstandard model of $\mathfrak{M}$. However, the fundamental theorem about reduced powers, which is stated by Łos in [9], and which is proved in [3] and [13], is as follows.

Fundamental Theorem. *Let $\mathfrak{M} = \mathfrak{M}(X, M)$ be a higher-order L-structure. For every ultrafilter $\mathfrak{U}$, the L-structure $^*\mathfrak{M} = {}^*\mathfrak{M}(^*X, {}^*M) = \mathfrak{U}$-prod $\mathfrak{M}$ is a higher-order nonstandard model of $\mathfrak{M}$.*

In the remainder of the paper F.T. will mean the fundamental theorem.

From the definition of an ultrapower it follows immediately that F.T. holds for the atomic formulas by definition. The proof for a general sentence of $K_0(\mathfrak{M}, L)$ proceeds then by induction on its length or by means of the use of the Skolem–Herbrand functors to eliminate the quantifiers. In all cases it seems that the truth of F.T. depends on the axiom of choice.

Finally, we remark that in [7] and [8] the reader may find some interesting results concerning the question of which structures are ultrapowers.

4. Ultrapowers That Are Proper Extensions

Let $\mathfrak{M} = \mathfrak{M}(X, M)$ be an L-structure and let $\mathfrak{U}$ be an ultrafilter over a set I. If M is finite, then it is easy to see that $^*\mathfrak{M} = \mathfrak{U}$-prod $\mathfrak{M} = \mathfrak{M}$. If the set X of individuals is infinite, then the situation is quite different. If, for instance, in that case the ultrafilter is fixed, then it is obvious that $^*\mathfrak{M} = \mathfrak{U}$-prod $\mathfrak{M} = \mathfrak{M}$. This observation leads to the question: For which ultrafilters $\mathfrak{U}$ is $\mathfrak{U}$-prod $\mathfrak{M}$ a proper extension of $\mathfrak{M}$ in the case that X is infinite? For the answer to this question we need the following concept.

A filter $\mathfrak{F}$ is called *δ-incomplete* whenever there exists a sequence $F_n \in \mathfrak{F}(n = 1, 3, \cdots)$ such that $\bigcap F_n \notin \mathfrak{F}$. A filter that is not δ-incomplete will be called *δ-complete.*

It is obvious that every principal filter is δ-complete. It is not known whether δ-complete free ultrafilters exist. This existence problem in set theory is known as Ulam's measure problem. It was shown, however, that the assumption that every free ultrafilter is δ-incomplete is consistent with the other axioms of set theory (see [15]). It was shown by Ulam (see [18]) that if κ is less than the first inaccessible cardinal, then every free ultrafilter over κ is δ-incomplete. In particular, every free ultrafilter over $\aleph_0$ is δ-incomplete. More recently, Tarski showed (see [17]) that even many inaccessible cardinals have this property. Thus, except only on very exceptional sets, free ultrafilters may exist that are δ-complete.

It is easy to see that an ultrafilter $\mathfrak{U}$ over X is δ-incomplete if and only if there exists a decreasing sequence $F_n \in \mathfrak{U}(n = 1, 2, \cdots)$ such that $\bigcap F_n = \emptyset$ if and only if there exists a countable partition $\{X_n : n = 1, 2, \cdots\}$ of X such that $X_n \notin \mathfrak{U}$ for all n. This characterization of δ-incomplete ultrafilters implies immediately that plenty of δ-incomplete ultrafilters exist on every infinite set and that such ultrafilters are free.

For the following result we shall need the following bit of notation. Let $\mathfrak{M}$ be an L-structure and let $^*\mathfrak{M}$ be a nonstandard model of $\mathfrak{M}$. To every entity A of $\mathfrak{M}$ there corresponds an entity $^*A$ of $^*\mathfrak{M}$. If A is a set of elements of type σ, then by $^*A - A$ we shall denote that subset of $^*A$ of entities of $^*\mathfrak{M}$ which are *not* standard. In symbols, $^*A - A = {}^*A - \bigcup(\{^*a\} : a \in A)$.

The following characterization of δ-incomplete ultrafilters holds.

Theorem 1.4.1. *Let $\mathfrak{M} = \mathfrak{M}(X, M)$ be an L-structure whose set of individuals X is infinite and let $\mathfrak{U}$ be an ultrafilter over I. Then $\mathfrak{U}$ is δ-incomplete if and only if for every infinite subset A of $\mathfrak{M}$ of a certain type, the standard set $^*A$ of $^*\mathfrak{M} = \mathfrak{U}$-prod $\mathfrak{M}$ satisfies $^*A - A \neq \emptyset$, and in that case the set $^*A - A$ is an external set of entities of $^*\mathfrak{M}$.*

For a proof we refer to [10], Theorem 1.4.4, and Theorem 1.4.6.

5. Ultrapowers That Are Enlargements

Enlargements of L-structures were introduced by Robinson in [13]. We shall recall the definition.

Let $\mathfrak{M} = \mathfrak{M}(X, M)$ be an L-structure and let b be an entity of $\mathfrak{M}$, say of type $(\sigma_1, \sigma_2)(\sigma_1, \sigma_2 \in T)$; that is, b is a binary relation of $\mathfrak{M}$. Then b is called *concurrent* or *finitely satisfiable whenever for every finite set of entities* $x_1, \cdots, x_n \in \text{dom}(b)$ *there is an entity* $y \in \text{ran}(b)$ *such that* ($\Phi_3(b, x_1, y)$ and $\Phi_3(b, x_2, y)$ and $\cdots$ and $\Phi_3(b, x_n, y)$) *holds in* $\mathfrak{M}$.

A higher-order nonstandard model $^*\mathfrak{M}$ of an L-structure $\mathfrak{M}$ is called an *enlargement* of $\mathfrak{M}$ whenever *for every concurrent binary relation b of $\mathfrak{M}$ there exists an entity y in $^*\mathfrak{M}$ such that $\Phi_3(^*b, {}^*x, y)$ holds in $^*\mathfrak{M}$ for all $x \in$* dom(b).

Note that if the set of individuals of an L-structure $\mathfrak{M}$ is infinite, then every enlargement of $\mathfrak{M}$ is a proper extension of $\mathfrak{M}$. Indeed, the binary relation "$x \neq y$" in the set of individuals is *concurrent* if and only if it is *infinite,* and in that case the enlargement has an individual that is not equal to any of its original individuals.

The existence of enlargements follows immediately from the general compactness principle of model theory (see [13], p. 30). It was also observed by Robinson (see [14]), and by the author independently, that there also exist ultrapowers that are enlargements. To prove this result here we shall introduce the concept of an *adequate filter*. Adequate ultrafilters were also introduced by A. L. Stone in his thesis (see also [16]).

Let κ be an infinite cardinal. A filter $\mathfrak{F}$ over a set I is called *κ-adequate* whenever *for every nonempty family $\mathcal{B}$ of subsets of κ with the finite intersection property there exists a mapping f of I into κ such that for every $B \in \mathcal{B}$ there is an element $F \in \mathfrak{F}$ such that $f(F) \subset B$, or, in other words, the filter generated by $f(\mathfrak{F})$ contains $\mathcal{B}$.*

Every filter that is finer than a κ-adequate filter is κ-adequate. In particular, every ultrafilter that is finer than a κ-adequate filter is κ-adequate. If $\aleph_0 \leq \kappa' < \kappa$ and $\mathfrak{F}$ is κ-adequate, then $\mathfrak{F}$ is also κ'-adequate.

Concerning the existence of κ-adequate filters we have the following result.

Theorem 1.5.1. *Let κ be an infinite cardinal. Then there exists a filter $\mathfrak{F}$ which is κ-adequate.*

Proof. Let $I = P_f(P(\kappa))$ and let $\mathfrak{F}$ be the filter over I generated by the nonempty family of sets $\{F_A: A \subset \kappa\}$, where F_A is the subset of X consisting of all the elements of I of which A is an element. Assume now that $\mathcal{B}$ is a nonempty family of subsets of κ with the finite intersection property. For every $i \in I$ let $A_i = \bigcap \{B: B \in \mathcal{B}$ and $B \in i\}$. Then $\{A_i: i \in I\}$ is a nonempty family of nonempty sets. Let f be a choice function of this family. Then for every $B \in \mathcal{B}$ we have that $f(F_B) \subset B$, and so the filter $\mathfrak{F}$ is κ-adequate, and the proof is finished.

We shall now prove the following theorem.

Theorem 1.5.2. *Let $\mathfrak{M} = \mathfrak{M}(X, M)$ be an L-structure and let $\mathfrak{U}$ be an ultrafilter over I which is κ-adequate, where $\kappa >$* card(M). *Then the higher-order ultrapower $^*\mathfrak{M} = \mathfrak{U}$-prod $\mathfrak{M}$ is an enlargement of $\mathfrak{M}$.*

Proof. Let b be an entity of $\mathfrak{M}$ of type (σ_1, σ_2) which is concurrent. For every $x \in \text{dom}(b)$ we set $A_x = \{y: y \in M$ and $\Phi_2(b, x, y)$ holds in $\mathfrak{M}\}$. Since b is concurrent the nonempty family $\{A_x: x \in \text{dom}(b)\}$ has the finite intersection property. From the hypothesis $\mathfrak{U}$ is κ-adequate, it follows that there is a mapping f of I into M such that for every $x \in \text{dom}(b)$ there is a set $E_x \in \mathfrak{U}$ such that $f(E_x) \subset A_x$. Then f defines an entity of $^*\mathfrak{M}$ of type σ_2 with the following property: $\{i: \Phi_3(b, x, f(i))$ holds in $\mathfrak{M}\} \in \mathfrak{U}$ for all $x \in \text{dom}(b)$. Hence $\Phi_3({}^*b, {}^*x, f)$ holds in $^*\mathfrak{M}$ for all $x \in \text{dom}(b)$, and so $^*\mathfrak{M}$ is an enlargement. This completes the proof.

From Theorem 1.4.1 it follows, in particular, that for every infinite cardinal κ every κ-adequate ultrafilter is δ-incomplete.

Furthermore, note that if $^*\mathfrak{M} = \mathfrak{U}$-prod $\mathfrak{M}$ is an enlargement of an L-structure $\mathfrak{M} = \mathfrak{M}(X, M)$, then $\mathfrak{U}$ is κ-adequate for all $\kappa = \text{card}(M_\sigma)$, $\sigma \in T$.

By way of example we shall discuss briefly one important case of a concurrent binary relation of set theory.

Example 1.5.3. Let $\mathfrak{M} = \mathfrak{M}(X, M)$ be an L-structure whose set of individuals X is infinite. Let A be an entity of $\mathfrak{M}$ of type (σ); that is, A is a set of entities of type σ of $\mathfrak{M}$. Consider the following binary relation b in A. $\Phi_3(b, x, y)$ holds whenever $x \in y$ and y is a finite subset of A. It is obvious that b is concurrent in x. Hence, if $^*\mathfrak{M} = \mathfrak{U}$-prod $\mathfrak{M}$ is an enlargement of $\mathfrak{M}$, then there exists an entity F of type (σ) in $^*\mathfrak{M}$ such that F is finite holds in $^*\mathfrak{M}$ (we shall express this by saying that F is **-finite,* although its external cardinal may be infinite) and for every $x \in A$ we have $^*x \in F$ holds in $^*\mathfrak{M}$. In particular, *every entity of* $\mathfrak{M}$ *that is an infinite set can be embedded (externally) in a *-finite entity of* $^*\mathfrak{M}$ *of the same type.*

If b is an entity of $\mathfrak{M}$ of type (σ_1, σ_2) and if b is concurrent on its domain, then it follows from F.T. that $^*b$ has the following property in a higher-order nonstandard model $^*\mathfrak{M}$ of $\mathfrak{M}$. For every *-finite subset F of dom($^*b$) there exists an entity $y \in \text{ran}(^*b)$ such that $\Phi_3(^*b, x, y)$ holds in $^*\mathfrak{M}$ for all $x \in F$. In particular, if $^*\mathfrak{M}$ is an enlargement of $\mathfrak{M}$, then for every *-finite subset F of dom($^*b$) such that $^*x \in F$ for all $x \in \text{dom}(b)$, there exists an entity $y \in \text{ran}(^*b)$ such that $\Phi_3(^*b, x, y)$ holds for all $x \in F$, and so $\Phi_3(^*b, {^*x}, y)$ holds in $^*\mathfrak{M}$ for all $x \in \text{dom}(b)$.

Finally, we remark that if $^*\mathfrak{M}$ is a nonstandard model of $\mathfrak{M}$ with the property that every infinite entity A of $\mathfrak{M}$ of type σ, $\sigma \in T$, can be embedded in a *-finite entity of type (σ) of $^*\mathfrak{M}$, then $^*\mathfrak{M}$ is an enlargement of $\mathfrak{M}$.

For further details and applications of enlargements see [13] and [9], sec. 5 of chap. 1.

6. κ-saturated Models

In the introduction we indicated that for some applications enlargements are not comprehensive enough. We shall need an extension of the notion of an enlargement which is due to Morley and Vaught (see [11] and [5]): the so-called κ-saturated models.

We shall define it here for higher-order structures in a manner that will allow us to compare it easily with the notion of an enlargement.

Let κ be an infinite cardinal and let $\mathfrak{M} = \mathfrak{M}(X, M)$ be a higher-order L-structure. A higher-order nonstandard model $^*\mathfrak{M}$ of $\mathfrak{M}$ is called *κ-saturated* whenever $^*\mathfrak{M}$ has the following property. *If an internal binary relation b in $^*\mathfrak{M}$ is concurrent (finitely satisfiable) on a subset A of its domain, that is, for every finite set $x_1, \cdots, x_n \in A$ there exists an entity $y \in ran(b)$ such that* ($\Phi_3(b, x, y)$ and $\Phi_3(b, x_2, y)$ and $\cdots$ and $\Phi_3(b, x_n, y)$) *holds in $^*\mathfrak{M}$ and if $card(A) < \kappa$, then there exists an entity y in $^*\mathfrak{M}$ in the range of b such that $\Phi_3(b, x, y)$ holds in $^*\mathfrak{M}$ for all $x \in A$.*

In comparing the present definition with the definition of an enlargement we observe that it differs essentially in two places. First, the binary relation b is only required to be internal, that is, it is an entity of $^*\mathfrak{M}$, whereas in the case of the definition of an enlargement b is required to be a standard entity of $^*\mathfrak{M}$. Second, the set A on which b is to be satisfied simultaneously only has to satisfy a cardinality restriction; its elements need not be standard entities as in the case of the definition of an enlargement. In both definitions the set on which b is concurrent need not be an internal entity of $^*\mathfrak{M}$.

The reader should also note that the word finite used in the above definition refers to the word finite of the metalanguage; that is, n is equal to $1 + \cdots + 1$, n times.

If $\kappa >$ card(M), then every κ-saturated model is an enlargement in the sense of Robinson.

In [6] and [5], Keisler characterized the ultrafilters $\mathfrak{U}$ whose ultrapowers of L-structures are κ-saturated. Keisler calls such ultrafilters *κ-good ultrafilters.* The definition of a κ-good ultrafilter is as follows.

Let κ be an infinite cardinal. *An ultrafilter $\mathfrak{U}$ over I is called κ-good whenever $\mathfrak{U}$ satisfies the following conditions.*

(a) *$\mathfrak{U}$ is δ-incomplete.*

(b) *If* card $(X) < \kappa$ *and f is an increasing mapping of the Fréchet filter $\mathfrak{Fr}(X)$ of X into $\mathfrak{U}$, then there exists a mapping h of $\mathfrak{Fr}(X)$ into $\mathfrak{U}$ such that $h(F) \subset f(F)$ for all $F \in \mathfrak{Fr}(X)$ and h is multiplicative; that is, $h(F_1 \cap F_2) = h(F_1) \cap h(F_2)$ for all $F_1, F_2 \in \mathfrak{Fr}(X)$.*

Observe that if $\mathfrak{U}$ is a fixed ultrafilter, then (b) is always satisfied. The combination of (a) and (b), however, singles out a very interesting family of ultrafilters.

It follows immediately that if $\mathfrak{U}$ is κ-good, then $\mathfrak{U}$ is also κ'-good for all $\kappa' < \kappa$.

The following interesting theorem concerning the existence of κ-good ultrafilters is due to H. J. Keisler. For a proof we refer the reader to Keisler's paper [6].

Theorem 1.6.1 (***H. J. Keisler***). *Let κ be an infinite cardinal. If $\kappa^+ = 2^\kappa$, in particular, if the generalized continuum hypothesis holds, then for every filter subbasis $\mathfrak{B}$ of subsets of κ satisfying card $(\mathfrak{B}) \leq \kappa$ and card $(E) \leq \kappa$ for all $E \in \mathfrak{B}$ there exists 2^{2^κ} different ultrafilters $\mathfrak{U}$ on κ such that $\mathfrak{B} \subset \mathfrak{U}$ and $\mathfrak{U}$ is κ^+-good.*

We have already pointed out that the condition (b) in the definition of κ-goodness can always be satisfied for every κ in the case that the ultrafilter is fixed. In this connection it is not without interest to observe that any ultrafilter satisfies (b) for $\kappa = \aleph_1$. Thus we shall prove the following theorem, which is also due to H. J. Keisler (see [6]).

Theorem 1.6.2 (***H. J. Keisler***). *Every δ-incomplete ultrafilter is $\aleph_1$-good.*

Proof. Let $\mathfrak{Fr}(N)$ be the Fréchet filter over N, the set of natural numbers. To prove the required result we shall show that every increasing mapping of $\mathfrak{Fr}(N)$ in any ultrafilter $\mathfrak{U}$ dominates a multiplicative mapping. To this end, we shall first show that there exists a multiplicative mapping of $\mathfrak{Fr}(N)$ into $\mathfrak{Fr}(N)$. Indeed, if for every $F \in \mathfrak{Fr}(N)$ we define $g(F) = \{n: n \geq \max(N - F) + 1\}$, then it is easy to see that g is a multiplicative mapping of $\mathfrak{Fr}(N)$ into $\mathfrak{Fr}(N)$, which has the additional property $g(F) \subset F$ for all $F \in \mathfrak{Fr}(N)$. Assume now that f is an increasing mapping of $\mathfrak{Fr}(N)$ into $\mathfrak{U}$. Then we define for every $F \in \mathfrak{Fr}(N)$,

$$h(F) = \cap\ (f(E): g(F) \subset E).$$

Since there are only finitely many $E \in \mathfrak{Fr}(N)$ satisfying $E \supset g(F)$, we obtain that $h(F) \in \mathfrak{U}$ for all $F \in \mathfrak{Fr}(N)$. Furthermore, $g(F) \subset F$ implies that $h(F) \subset f(F)$ for all $F \in \mathfrak{Fr}(N)$. To complete the proof we have to show that h is multiplicative. To this end, let $F_1, F_2 \in \mathfrak{Fr}(N)$. Then $E_1 \supset g(F_1)$ and $E_2 \supset g(F_2)$ and g is multiplicative implies that $g(F_1 \cap F_2) \subset E_1 \cap E_2$, and so, using the fact that f is increasing, we obtain that $h(F_1 \cap F_2) \subset f(E_1 \cap E_2) \subset f(E_1) \cap f(E_2)$ for all such E_1 and E_2; that is, $h(F_1 \cap E_2) \subset h(F_1) \cap h(F_2)$. On the other hand, if $E \supset g(F_1 \cap F_2) = g(F_1) \cap g(F_2)$, then there exist sets E_1, E_2 such that $g(F_1) \subset E_1$, $g(F_2) \subset E_2$, and $E = E_1 \cap E_2$, and so $h(F_1) \cap h(F_2) \subset h(F_1 \cap F_2)$, which shows finally that h is multiplicative and the proof is complete.

The following theorem is the fundamental result about κ-good ultrafilters. It is a set-theoretic formulation of Keisler's result (see [5], Theorems 2.1 and 3.1) that an ultrapower is κ-saturated if and only if the ultrafilter is κ-good.

Theorem 1.6.3. *Let $\mathfrak{U}$ be an ultrafilter over an infinite set I and let $\kappa^+ > \aleph_0$. Then $\mathfrak{U}$ is κ^+-good if and only if $\mathfrak{U}$ has the following property. For any pair of nonempty sets Y_1, Y_2 and for any mapping $i \rightarrow b(i)$ of I*

into $P(Y_1 \times Y_2)$, *the power set of* $Y_1 \times Y_2$, *and for any subset* $A \subset Y_1{}^I$ *which satisfies the following conditions:* (a) *card*$(A) < \kappa^+$ *and* (b) *for every finite subset* $F \subset A$ *there is an element* $g \in Y_2{}^I$ *such that* $\cap (\{i: (f(i), g(i)) \in b(i)\} : f \in F) \in \mathfrak{U}$, *there exists an element* $f_0 \in Y_2{}^I$ *such that for all* $f \in A$ *we have* $\{i: (f(i), f_0(i)) \in b(i)\} \in \mathfrak{U}$.

Proof. We shall first assume that $\mathfrak{U}$ is κ^+-good, where κ is some infinite cardinal satisfying $\kappa^+ > \aleph_0$. Since $\mathfrak{U}$ is δ-incomplete, it follows from Section 4 that there exists a decreasing sequence $\{I_n : n \in N\}$ of subsets of I such that $I_1 = I$, $I_n \in \mathfrak{U}(n \in N)$ and $\cap I_n = \varnothing$. For every finite subset $F_k \subset A$, where $k = \text{card}(F_k) \in N$, define

$$A_k = \{i: i \in I \text{ and } (\exists y)(y \in Y_2 \text{ and } (f(i), y) \in b(i) \text{ for all } f \in F_k)\}.$$

Then $A_k \in \mathfrak{U}$ for all finite subsets $F_k \subset A$. Indeed, from the hypothesis it follows that there is an element $g \in Y_2{}^I$ such that

$$E = \cap (\{i: (f(i), g(i)) \in b(i)\} : f \in F_k) \in \mathfrak{U},$$

and so $E \subset A_k$ implies that $A_k \in \mathfrak{U}$. For every finite subset $F_k \subset A$ we define $p(A - F_k) = A_k \cap I_k$. Then p is an increasing mapping of $\mathfrak{Fr}(A)$ into $\mathfrak{U}$. Indeed, if $F_k \subset F_l(k \leq l)$, then $A_l \subset A_k$ implies that $p(A - F_l) = A_l \cap I_l \subset A_k \cap I_k = p(A - F_k)$. From card$(A) < \kappa^+$ and $\mathfrak{U}$ is κ^+-good, it follows that there exists a multiplicative mapping h of $\mathfrak{Fr}(A)$ into $\mathfrak{U}$ such that $h \subset p$. For every $i \in I$, we define $B_i = \{f: f \in A \text{ and } i \in h(A - \{f\})\}$. We shall prove that the sets $B_i \subset A$, $i \in I$ are finite. In fact, if we set $n(i) = \max(k: i \in I_k)$, then we shall prove that card$(B_i) \leq n(i)$ for all $i \in I$. If "not (card$(B_i) \leq n(i)$)" holds, then there is a subset $F_{n(i)+1} \subset B_i$. From $f \in F_{n(i)+1} \subset B(i)$ it follows that $i \in h(E - \{f\})$, and so, using h is multiplicative, we obtain

$$i \in \cap (h(A - \{f\}) : f \in F_{n(i)+1}) = h(A - F_{n(i)+1}) \subset p(A - F_{n(i)+1}) \subset I_{n(i)+1},$$

which contradicts the definition of $n(i)$, $i \in I$. We are now in a position to define the required mapping $f_0 \in Y_2{}^I$. To this end, we first define for every $i \in I$ the set $Y_i = \{y: y \in Y_2 \text{ and } (f(i), y) \in b(i) \text{ for all } f \in B_i\}$. Then $Y_i \neq \varnothing$ for all $i \in I$. Indeed, from the definition of B_i and h is multiplicative it follows that $i \in h(A - B_i) \subset p(A - B_i) = I_l \cap A_l$, where $l = \text{card}(B_i)(\leq n(i))$, and so i is an element of some A_l implies by its definition that there exists an element $y \in Y_2$ such that $(f(i), y) \in b(i)$ for all $f \in B_i$; that is, $y \in Y_i$. Thus the family $\{Y_i : i \in I\}$ I is a nonempty family of nonempty sets, and so from the axiom of choice it follows that there is a mapping f_0 of I into Y_2 such that $f_0(i) \in Y_i$ for all $i \in I$. We shall now show that the mapping f_0 has the required property. To this end, let $f \in A$ and let $i \in h(A - \{f\})$. Then $f \in B_i$, and so it follows from the definition of Y_i that $(f(i), f_0(i)) \in b(i)$. Thus the set $I_f = \{i\colon (f(i), f_0(i)) \in b(i)\}$ contains the set $h(A - \{f\})$, which is an element of $\mathfrak{U}$, and so $I_f \in \mathfrak{U}$, and the proof of the first half of the theorem is finished.

Assume now that conversely the condition of the theorem holds. Then from the results of Section 4 it follows immediately that $\mathfrak{U}$ is δ-incomplete. To complete the proof that $\mathfrak{U}$ is κ^+-good we shall show that every increasing mapping of $\mathfrak{Fr}(Z)$ into $\mathfrak{U}$, $\mathrm{card}(Z) < \kappa^+$ dominates a multiplicative mapping. If Z is finite, then there is nothing to prove. Assume that $\mathrm{card}(Z)$ is infinite and that d is an increasing mapping of $\mathfrak{Fr}(Z)$ into $\mathfrak{U}$. Then $\mathrm{card}(Z) = \mathrm{card}(\mathfrak{Fr}(Z))$ implies that there is a one-to-one mapping γ of $\mathfrak{Fr}(Z)$ onto Z. Then for every $i \in I$ and for every $p \in \mathfrak{Fr}(Z)$ we define

$$d_p(i) = \{\gamma(q)\colon q \in \mathfrak{Fr}(Z) \text{ and } q \subset p \text{ and } i \in d(q)\}.$$

Since d is increasing it follows that $d_p(i) \neq \emptyset$ if and only if $i \in d(p)$. Furthermore, it is easy to show that for every $i \in I$ and $p_1, p_2 \in \mathfrak{Fr}(Z)$, we have

$$(*) \qquad d_{p_1 \cap p_2}(i) = d_{p_1}(i) \cap d_{p_2}(i).$$

From the definition of $d_p(i)$ it follows that

$$(**) \qquad \{i\colon i \in I \text{ and } \gamma(p) \in d_p(i)\} = d(p) \in \mathfrak{U}.$$

The meaning of the properties (*) and (**) is the following. Let $Y = Y_1 = Y_2 = P(Z)$ and let $A = \{d_p\colon p \in \mathfrak{Fr}(Z)\}$, and let $(u, v) \in b(i)$ mean $v \subset u$ $v \neq \emptyset$ for all $i \in I$, v, $u \in P(Z)$. Then (*), (**), and $\mathrm{card}(A) < \kappa^+$ imply immediately that the conditions of the theorem are satisfied. To see this let $F \subset A$ be a finite subset of A. Then by (*) and (**) $\bigcap (\{i\colon d_p(i) \neq \emptyset\}\colon p \in F) \supset \{i\colon d_q(i) \neq \emptyset\} = d(q) \in \mathfrak{U}$, where $q = \bigcap (p\colon p \in F)$, and so $\{i\colon d_q(i) \subset d_p(i),\ d_q(i) \neq 0\} \in \mathfrak{U}$ for all $p \in F$. Hence the mapping $i \to g(i) = d_q(i)$ of I into $Y = P(Z)$ satisfies the required condition. Then it follows from the hypothesis that there is a mapping f_0 of I into $Y = P(Z)$ such that $\{i\colon \emptyset \neq f_0(i) \subset d_p(i)\} \in \mathfrak{U}$ for all $d_p \in A$. With f_0 we can now define the required multiplicative mapping of $\mathfrak{Fr}(Z)$ into $\mathfrak{U}$ as follows.

$$h(p) = \{i\colon i \in I \text{ and } \emptyset \neq f_0(i) \subset d_p(i)\},\ p \in \mathfrak{Fr}(Z).$$

It is evident that $h(p) \in \mathfrak{U}$ for all $p \in \mathfrak{Fr}(Z)$. From (*) it follows that h is multiplicative and from (**) it follows that if $j \in h(p)$, then

$d_p(j) \neq \emptyset$, and so $j \in d(p)$; that is, $h(p) \subset d(p)$ for all $p \in \mathfrak{F}r(Z)$. This completes the proof of the theorem.

From the definition of a κ-saturated model and Theorem 1.6.3 the following important theorem follows.

Theorem 1.6.4. *Let $\mathfrak{M} = \mathfrak{M}(X, M)$ be a higher-order L-structure and let κ be an infinite cardinal. If the ultrafilter $\mathfrak{U}$ over I is κ^+-good, then the higher-order nonstandard ultrapower $^*\mathfrak{M} = \mathfrak{U}$-prod $\mathfrak{M}$ is κ^+-saturated. In particular, any ultrapower of $\mathfrak{M}$ with respect to a δ-incomplete ultrafilter is $\aleph_1$-saturated, and so every enlargement of the form $\mathfrak{U}$-prod $\mathfrak{M}$ is $\aleph_1$-saturated.*

Proof. Let b be an internal binary relation of $^*\mathfrak{M} = \mathfrak{U}$-prod $\mathfrak{M}$ of type (σ_1, σ_2), and let $A \subset \text{dom}(b)$ such that b is concurrent on A and $\text{card}(A) < \kappa^+$. There is no loss in generality to assume that $b(i) \in M_{\sigma_1} \times M_{\sigma_2}$ for all $i \in I$. Since b is concurrent on A, it follows that for every finite set $F \subset A$ there is a mapping g of I into M_{σ_2} such that

$$\cap\ (\{i\colon (f(i), g(i)) \in b(i)\} : f \in F) \in \mathfrak{U}.$$

Thus Theorem 1.6.3 implies that there is a mapping f_0 of I into M_{σ_2} such that $\{i\colon (f(i)) \in b(i)\} \in \mathfrak{U}$ for all $f \in A$, or equivalently, $\Phi_3(b, f, f_0)$ holds in $^*\mathfrak{M}$ for all $f \in A$. This shows that $^*\mathfrak{M}$ is κ^+-saturated. The remainder of the theorem follows from Theorem 1.6.2.

Corollary 1.6.5. *Let κ be an infinite cardinal. If $\mathfrak{U}$ is an ultrafilter over κ such that $\mathfrak{U}$ is κ^+-good, then $\mathfrak{U}$ is κ'-adequate for all κ' such that $2^{\kappa'} < \kappa^+$.*

Remark. Let $^*\mathfrak{M} = \mathfrak{U}$-prod $\mathfrak{M}$ be κ^+-saturated, for some infinite cardinal κ. Then *every* set A of entities of a certain fixed type of $^*\mathfrak{M}$ which satisfies $\text{card}(A) < \kappa^+$ is contained in a *-finite entity of $^*\mathfrak{M}$. Indeed, the binary relation $x \in y$ and y is *-finite is internal and concurrent in x on A, and so $\text{card}(A) < \kappa^+$ implies that A is contained in a *-finite entity of $^*\mathfrak{M}$. From this fact it follows, in particular, that *if B is an infinite set of entities of $\mathfrak{M}$, then the external cardinal of the standard set $A = {}^*B$ of $^*\mathfrak{M}$ is at least equal to κ^+*. Indeed, $\text{card}(A) < \kappa^+$ would imply that $^*B \subset F$, where F is *-finite, and so F.T. implies that $B \subset F_0$ and F_0 is finite holds in $\mathfrak{M}$, contradicting that B is infinite. In particular, if A is an infinite entity of a structure $\mathfrak{M}$ and $\mathfrak{U}$ is δ-incomplete, then the *external cardinal of the standard set $^*A$ in $^*\mathfrak{M}$ is at least $\aleph_1$*.

7. Higher-order Ultralimits

In Section 6 we have shown that there are ultrapowers which are κ-saturated. The existence of such ultrapowers, however, seems to depend on the assumption that the generalized continuum hypothesis holds. There is another method to produce saturated models which does not depend on the G.C.H. These are the so-called ultralimits of a given L-structure.

For the sake of simplicity we shall first present the formation of an ultralimit of a well-ordered sequence of ultrapowers of an L-structure.

To this end, let $\mathfrak{M} = \mathfrak{M}(X, M)$ be an L-structure. We set $\mathfrak{M}_0 = \mathfrak{M}$ and $\mathfrak{M}_1 = \mathfrak{U}_1$-prod $\mathfrak{M}$, where $\mathfrak{U}_1$ is an ultrafilter over I_1 and $\mathfrak{M}_1$ is an enlargement of $\mathfrak{M}$. By j_1 we shall denote the embedding of $\mathfrak{M}$ into $\mathfrak{M}_1$ by means of the constant mappings. Next we consider $\mathfrak{M}_2 = \mathfrak{U}_2$-prod $\mathfrak{M}_1$, where $\mathfrak{U}_2$ is an ultrafilter over I_2 and $\mathfrak{M}_2$ is an enlargement of $\mathfrak{M}_1$; the embedding of $\mathfrak{M}_1$ into $\mathfrak{M}_2$ will be denoted by j_2. Then the composition method $j_2 \circ j_1$ embeds $\mathfrak{M}$ in $\mathfrak{M}_2$ and $\mathfrak{M}_2$ is a higher-order enlargement of $\mathfrak{M}$ which can still be shown to be an ultrapower of $\mathfrak{M}$. If we proceed in this way we define a sequence of L-structures $\mathfrak{M}_n (n = 0, 1, 2, \cdots)$ such that $\mathfrak{M}_{n+1} = \mathfrak{U}_n$-prod $\mathfrak{M}_n$ is an enlargement of $\mathfrak{M}_n$. We set $I_n = \bigcup \mathfrak{U}_n$ and j_n denotes the embedding of $\mathfrak{M}_n$ into $\mathfrak{M}_{n+1} (n = 0, 1, 2, \cdots)$. We say that the family $\{\mathfrak{M}_n : n \in N\}$ is a well-ordered family of L-structures produced by the ultrafilter sequence $\{I_n, \mathfrak{U}_n\}$, $n = 0, 1, 2, \cdots$. For such a family we can obtain in a well-known way a new L-structure $\mathfrak{M}_\infty$: the direct limit of $\{\mathfrak{M}_n\}$. We shall now take up the definitions of $\mathfrak{M}_\infty$.

To this end, we shall call the entities of the L-structure $\mathfrak{M}_n$ entities of rank n. The set of all entities of type σ and of rank n will be denoted by $M_{\sigma,n}$ and the set of all entities of rank n by M_n. We define now an equivalence relation between all the entities of all finite types and of all ranks as follows. $a_p \in M_p$ and $a_q \in M_q$ are called equivalent whenever for every $r \geq \max(p, q)$ we have

$$j_r \circ j_{r-1} \circ \cdots \circ j_p(a_p) = j_r \circ j_{r-1} \circ \cdots \circ j_q(a_q).$$

It is easy to see that this relation is indeed an equivalence relation and that equivalent elements are always of the same type. The set of sets of equivalent entities will be denoted by M_∞ and it will serve as the set of entities of the direct limit structure $\mathfrak{M}_\infty$. Then $\mathfrak{M}_\infty$ is an L-structure in the following sense. An entity $a \in M_\infty$ is of type $\sigma (\sigma \in T)$ if and only if $T_\sigma(a_p)$ holds in $\mathfrak{M}_p$ for all $a_p \in a$. If $b \in M_\infty$ is a relation of type $\sigma = (\sigma_1, \cdots, \sigma_n)$, then $\Phi_{n+1}(b, a_1, \cdots, a_n)$ holds in $\mathfrak{M}_\infty$ if and only if $\Phi_{n+1}(b_p, a_{1,p}, \cdots, a_{n,p})$ holds in $\mathfrak{M}_p$ for all $a_{i,p} \in a_i$ $(i = 1, 2, \cdots, n)$ and for all $b_p \in b$. With those definitions it is then readily verified that $\mathfrak{M}_\infty$ is a higher-order nonstandard model of $\mathfrak{M}$, and $\mathfrak{M}$ is identified in $\mathfrak{M}_\infty$ by the entities of $\mathfrak{M}_\infty$ which contain an entity of $\mathfrak{M}$. Of course, the entities of $\mathfrak{M}$ in $\mathfrak{M}_\infty$ are again called the standard entities of $\mathfrak{M}_\infty$.

We shall now show that $\mathfrak{M}_\infty$ is an enlargement of $\mathfrak{M}$ in the following strong sense.

Theorem 1.7.1. *Let $\mathfrak{M}$ be an L-structure and let $\mathfrak{M}_\infty$ be an ultralimit of $\mathfrak{M}$ with respect to a countable system $\{\mathfrak{M}_n\}$ of successive higher-order ultrapower enlargements of $\mathfrak{M}$. Then if b is an internal binary relation of $\mathfrak{M}_\infty$ of type $\sigma = (\sigma_1, \sigma_2)$ which is concurrent on a set A of entities in $\mathfrak{M}_\infty$ of type σ_1 such that A contains an at most finite number of nonstandard entities, then there exists an entity y of type σ_2 in $\mathfrak{M}_\infty$ such that $\Phi_3(b, x, y)$ holds in $\mathfrak{M}_\infty$ for all $x \in A$. In particular, $\mathfrak{M}_\infty$ is an enlargement of $\mathfrak{M}$.*

Proof. Let $b_n \in b$ be the binary relation of smallest rank which represents b. Since A contains an at most finite number of nonstandard elements there exists an index m such that A is a set of standard elements of $\mathfrak{M}_m$. There is no loss in generality to assume that $m \geq n$. Then $\mathfrak{M}_{m+1}$, being an enlargement of $\mathfrak{M}_m$, and b_n, being a standard binary relation of $\mathfrak{M}_{m+1}$ which is concurrent on the set of standard elements A, it follows that there is an entity y_{m+1} in $\mathfrak{M}_{m+1}$ of type σ_2 such that $\Phi_3({}^*b_n, {}^*x, y_{m+1})$ holds in $\mathfrak{M}_{m+1}$ for all $x \in A$. Hence, if y denotes the entity in $\mathfrak{M}_\infty$ determined by y_{m+1}, then we obtain that $\Phi_3(b, x, y)$ holds in $\mathfrak{M}_\infty$ for all $x \in A$, and the proof is finished.

Remark. Models that are saturated up to say $\kappa = \aleph_\alpha$-new additional constants can also be obtained as direct limits of suitable sequences of successive enlargements. Indeed, for that purpose it is sufficient to consider a direct limit of an ultrapower enlargement sequence with respect to an appropriate ultrafilter sequence $\{(I_i, \mathfrak{U}_i)\colon 0 \leq i < \omega_{\alpha+1}\}$ such that $\mathfrak{M}_{i+1} = \mathfrak{U}_i$-prod $\mathfrak{M}_i$ is an enlargement of $\mathfrak{M}_i$ and, if i is a limit ordinal, then $\mathfrak{M}_i$ is the direct limit of the sequence $\{\mathfrak{M}_j\colon 0 \leq j < i\}$. Then the direct limit $\mathfrak{M}_\infty$ of the sequence $\{\mathfrak{M}_i\colon 0 \leq i < \omega_{\alpha+1}\}$ is a higher-order nonstandard model of $\mathfrak{M} = \mathfrak{M}_0$ which is at least $\aleph_{\alpha+1}$-saturated. Of course $\mathfrak{M}_\infty$ is not an ultrapower of $\mathfrak{M}$.

8. Restrictions of Internal Mappings

Let $\mathfrak{M} = \mathfrak{M}(X, M)$ be an L-structure and let ${}^*\mathfrak{M}$ be a higher-order nonstandard model of $\mathfrak{M}$. In [14] Robinson considers the following question. Is any mapping from a set A of $\mathfrak{M}$ of entities say of type σ_1 into the extension ${}^*B$ in ${}^*\mathfrak{M}$ of a set B of $\mathfrak{M}$ of entities, say of type σ_2, the restriction of an internal mapping of ${}^*A$ into ${}^*B$? He showed that if ${}^*\mathfrak{M}$ is an ultrapower $\mathfrak{U}$-prod $\mathfrak{M}$ of $\mathfrak{M}$, then the answer is positive. Thus we have the following theorem.

Theorem 1.8.1. *If ${}^*\mathfrak{M} = \mathfrak{U}$-prod $\mathfrak{M}$, and if φ is a mapping of a set A of $\mathfrak{M}$ of entities of a certain type into the extension ${}^*B$ in ${}^*\mathfrak{M}$ of a set B of*

*$\mathfrak{M}$ of entities of a certain type, then φ is the restriction of an internal mapping of *A into *B.*

Proof. Let $\mathfrak{U}$ be an ultrafilter over I. The elements of the standard entity $^*B$ in $^*\mathfrak{M}$ are functions defined over I with values in B. The elements of A can be represented in $^*\mathfrak{M}$ by the constant mappings. Thus φ maps any $a \in A$ on a function f_a of I into B. By definition an internal mapping of $^*A$ into $^*B$ is determined by a mapping of I into the set of all mappings of $\mathfrak{M}$ of A into B. Let ψ be the internal mapping determined by the mapping $i \to f_a(i)$ of I into the set of $\mathfrak{M}$ of mappings of A into B. Then φ is a restriction of ψ. Indeed, if $a \in A$, then $\{i: \varphi(a)(i) = f_a(i)\} \in \mathfrak{U}$ by definition, and so $\varphi(a) = \psi(a)$, and the proof is finished.

Corollary 1.8.2. *Let $^*\mathfrak{M} = \mathfrak{U}$-prod $\mathfrak{M}$ and let D be an arbitrary nonempty set which is not necessarily an entity of $\mathfrak{M}$. If φ is a mapping of D into the extension $^*B$ of an entity B of $\mathfrak{M}$ of a certain type, then φ can be extended to $^*D = \mathfrak{U}$-prod D to an internal of mapping of $^*D$ into $^*B$.*

Proof. Add D to $\mathfrak{M}$ as a new set of individuals and apply Theorem 1.8.1.

For the truth of Theorem 1.8.1 it seems necessary that $^*\mathfrak{M}$ is an ultrapower of $\mathfrak{M}$. Even in the case that $^*\mathfrak{M}$ is an enlargement of $\mathfrak{M}$ but not necessarily an ultrapower, it seems that the required mapping cannot be determined by an appropriate concurrent standard binary relation. If, on the other hand, the model has a stronger saturation property than being an enlargement, a stronger result can be shown to hold.

Theorem 1.8.3. *Let $\mathfrak{M} = \mathfrak{M}(X, M)$ be an L-structure and let $^*\mathfrak{M} = {}^*\mathfrak{M}(^*X, {}^*M)$ be a higher-order nonstandard model of $\mathfrak{M}$ which is κ^+-saturated, where κ is some infinite cardinal. Then any mapping of a set A of entities of $^*\mathfrak{M}$ of say type σ_1 such that card$(A) < \kappa^+$ into an internal set B of $^*\mathfrak{M}$ of entities say of type σ_2 is the restriction of an internal mapping with values in B.*

Proof. Consider the following internal binary relation of $^*\mathfrak{M}$. "f_1 and f_2 are internal mappings with values in B and f_2 extends f_1." Let E be the set of all internal mappings $x \to f(x)$ of $\{x\}$, $x \in A$ into B. Then card $(E) < \kappa^+$ and the internal binary relation above is concurrent on E. Hence $^*\mathfrak{M}$ being κ^+-saturated implies that there exists an internal mapping f_0 in $^*\mathfrak{M}$ such that $f(x) = f_0(x)$ for all $x \in A$ and ran$(f) \subset B$, and the proof is complete.

Remarks (a) If $\kappa^+ >$ card(M), then Theorem 1.8.3 implies Theorem 1.8.1 and, in fact, is a stronger result than Theorem 1.8.1.

(b) It is easy to see that dom(f_0) can be any internal set containing A.

Chapter II A General Theory of Monads

1. The Monads of a Standard Entity of Type $((\sigma))$

Let X be an infinite set and let $\mathfrak{M} = \mathfrak{M}(X, M)$ denote the full L-structure determined by X; that is, M_σ is the set of all relations of type σ based in X for every $\sigma \in T$. By ${}^*\mathfrak{M} = \mathfrak{U}\text{-prod } \mathfrak{M}$ we shall denote a higher-order ultrapower L-structure of $\mathfrak{M}$ with respect to a δ-incomplete ultrafilter over an infinite set I. The structure ${}^*\mathfrak{M}$ is not a full structure on its set of individuals ${}^*X$, but it is according to Theorem 1.4.1 a proper extension of $\mathfrak{M}$.

We shall now introduce two types of monads for entities of $\mathfrak{M}$ of type $((\sigma))$, $\sigma \in T$.

Definition 2.1.1 (***The monads of entities of type*** $((\sigma))$). *Let Ω be a nonempty entity of $\mathfrak{M}$ of type $((\sigma))$, $\sigma \in T$. Then the set $\bigcap({}^*E\colon E \in \Omega)$ ($\bigcup({}^*E\colon E \in \Omega)$) of entities of type σ of ${}^*\mathfrak{M}$ is called the intersection (union) monad of Ω with respect to ${}^*\mathfrak{M}$ and will be denoted by $\mu(\Omega)(\nu(\Omega))$. If Ω is a filter (ideal) of type $((\sigma))$, then $\mu(\Omega)(\nu(\Omega))$ will be called the monad of the filter (ideal) Ω.*

Observe that in the terminology and notation of the concept of a monad we suppress the dependence on ${}^*\mathfrak{M}$.

The monad of the neighborhood filter of a point in a topological space is the monad of that point introduced by Robinson in [13], p. 90.

It is obvious that the intersection monad of a subbasis of a filter is equal to the monad of the filter and similarly for ideals.

If $\mathfrak{F}$ is a filter of type $((\sigma))$ and $\mathfrak{g}$ is the ideal of the complements of the elements of $\mathfrak{F}$, then $\mu(\mathfrak{F}) \cup \nu(\mathfrak{g}) = {}^*M_\sigma$ and $\mu(\mathfrak{F}) \cap \nu(\mathfrak{g}) = \emptyset$.

If $\mathfrak{F} = \mathfrak{F}(A)$ is a principal filter of $\mathfrak{M}$ of type $((\sigma))$, then $\mu(\mathfrak{F}) = {}^*A$. Futhermore, if A is an infinite set of $\mathfrak{M}$, then the monad of the Fréchet filter of A is equal to ${}^*A - A$ (see, for a definition, Section 4 of Chapter I).

We shall now characterize some properties of families of sets in terms of their monads.

Theorem 2.1.2. *Let ${}^*\mathfrak{M} = \mu\text{-prod } \mathfrak{M}$ be an enlargement of $\mathfrak{M}$ and let Ω be a nonempty entity of $\mathfrak{M}$ of type $((\sigma))$. Then Ω has the finite intersection (union) property if and only if $\mu(\Omega) \neq \emptyset(\nu(\Omega) \neq {}^*M_\sigma)$. In particular, $\mu(\mathfrak{F}) \neq \emptyset(\nu(\mathfrak{J}) \neq {}^*M_\sigma)$ for every filter $\mathfrak{F}$(ideal $\mathfrak{g}$) of type $((\sigma))$.*

Proof. We have only to prove Theorem 2.1.2 for the intersection monad. To this end, assume first that $\mu(\Omega) \neq \emptyset$. Then, if

$$E_1, \cdots, E_n \in \Omega, \text{ it follows from } \mu(\Omega) \subset \bigcap_{i=1}^{n} {}^*E_i \text{ that } \bigcap_{i=1}^{n} {}^*E_i \neq \emptyset$$

in $^*\mathfrak{M}$, and so by F.T. we obtain that $\bigcap_{i=1}^n E_i \neq \emptyset$. Thus Ω has the finite intersection property. Conversely, assume that Ω has the finite intersection property. Then the standard binary relation of type $(\sigma,(\sigma))$ defined by "$y \in x$ and $T_\sigma(y)$ and $T_{(\sigma)}(x)$" is concurrent in x on Ω. Since $^*\mathfrak{M}$ is an enlargement, it follows that there is an entity a in $^*\mathfrak{M}$ of type σ such that $a \in {}^*E$ holds in $^*\mathfrak{M}$ for all $E \in \Omega$. Thus $a \in \mu(\Omega)$ implies $\mu(\Omega) \neq \emptyset$ and the proof is finished.

Examples 2.1.3. The condition that $^*\mathfrak{M}$ is an enlargement of $\mathfrak{M}$ in Theorem 2.1.2 is in a sense essential, as the following example will show. Let X be such that $\operatorname{card}(X) > \aleph_0$, and let $\mathfrak{M} = \mathfrak{M}(X, M)$ be the full structure based in X. Let Ω be the family of all subsets of X whose complements are countable. Since $\operatorname{card}(X) > \aleph_0$ it follows that Ω has the finite intersection property. Let $\mathfrak{U}$ be a free ultrafilter over N, and let $^*\mathfrak{M} = \mathfrak{U}\text{-prod } \mathfrak{M}$. Then $\mu(\Omega) = \emptyset$. Indeed, if $a \in {}^*X$, then the complement A of the countable set $\{a(n)\colon n \in N\}$ in X satisfies $A \in \Omega$ and $a \notin {}^*A$; that is, $\mu(\Omega) = \emptyset$.

In fact, enlargements can be characterized as follows.

Theorem 2.1.4. *Let X be an infinite set, $\mathfrak{M} = \mathfrak{M}(X, M)$ be an L-structure based in X and let $^*\mathfrak{M} = {}^*\mathfrak{M}(^*X, {}^*M)$ be a higher-order nonstandard model of $\mathfrak{M}$. Then $^*\mathfrak{M}$ is an enlargement of $\mathfrak{M}$ if and only if $\mu(\Omega) \neq \emptyset$ for every nonempty entity Ω of $\mathfrak{M}$ of type $((\sigma))$, $\sigma \in T$, which has the finite intersection property.*

Proof. If $^*\mathfrak{M}$ is an enlargement, then the result is contained in Theorem 2.1.2. To prove the converse let b be a binary relation of $\mathfrak{M}$, say of type (σ_1, σ_2), which is concurrent on its domain. Then the family of sets $\Omega = \{E_x\colon y \in E_x \Leftrightarrow x \in \operatorname{dom}(b) \text{ and } \Phi_3(b, x, y) \text{ holds in } \mathfrak{M}\}$ is a nonempty entity of $\mathfrak{M}$ of type $((\sigma_2))$. Since b is concurrent, it follows that Ω has the finite intersection property. Hence, by hypothesis, $\mu(\Omega) \neq \emptyset$. Let $y \in \mu(\Omega)$. Then for every $x \in \operatorname{dom}(b)$ we have that $y \in {}^*(E_x)$ in $^*\mathfrak{M}$; that is, $\Phi_3(^*b, {}^*x, y)$ holds in $^*\mathfrak{M}$ for all standard entities $^*x$ of the $\operatorname{dom}(b)$. Thus $^*\mathfrak{M}$ is an enlargement of $\mathfrak{M}$ and the proof is finished.

In Example 1.5.3 we have shown that if $^*\mathfrak{M}$ is an enlargement of $\mathfrak{M}$, then to every infinite entity A of $\mathfrak{M}$ of type (σ) there corresponds a $*$-finite entity F in $^*\mathfrak{M}$ of type (σ) such that all the standard entities of the extension $^*A$ of A in $^*\mathfrak{M}$ are elements of F. If we apply this to an infinite set which is a filter or ideal, then we obtain the following property of the monad of a filter (ideal).

Theorem 2.1.5. *Let $^*\mathfrak{M}$ be an enlargement of the full structure $\mathfrak{M} = \mathfrak{M}(X, M)$.*

(a) *If $\mathfrak{F}$ is a filter in $\mathfrak{M}$ of type $((\sigma))$ and if A is a nonempty internal set of entities of type σ in $^*\mathfrak{M}$ such that $A \subset \mu(\mathfrak{F})$, then there exists a *-finite subset $\Omega \subset {}^*\mathfrak{F}$ in $^*\mathfrak{M}$ such that $^*E \in \Omega$ for all $E \in \mathfrak{F}$ and $\emptyset \neq A \subset A_0 = \bigcap (B: B \in \Omega) \subset \mu(\mathfrak{F})$ and $A_0 \in {}^*\mathfrak{F}$. In particular, $\mu(\mathfrak{F}) = \bigcup (E: E \in {}^*\mathfrak{F}$ and $E \subset \mu(\mathfrak{F}))$.*

(b) *If $\mathfrak{I}$ is an ideal in $\mathfrak{M}$ of type $((\sigma))$ and if A is an internal set of entities of type σ in $^*\mathfrak{M}$ such that $A \neq {}^*M_\sigma$ and $\nu(\mathfrak{I}) \subset A$, then there exists a *-finite subset $\Omega \subset {}^*\mathfrak{I}$ in $^*\mathfrak{M}$ such that $^*E \in \Omega$ for all $E \in \mathfrak{I}$ and $A_0 = \bigcup (B: B \in \Omega)$ satisfies $\nu(\mathfrak{I}) \subset B_0 \subset A$ and $B_0 \in {}^*\mathfrak{I}$. In particular, $\nu(\mathfrak{F}) = \bigcap (E: E \in {}^*\mathfrak{I}$ and $\nu(\mathfrak{F}) \subset E)$.*

Proof. We only need to prove (a). Let $\Lambda = \{E : E \in {}^*\mathfrak{F}$ and $A \subset E\}$. Then Λ is an internal subset of $^*\mathfrak{F}$ such that $^*F \in \Lambda$ for all $F \in \mathfrak{F}$. Then by Example 1.5.3 there exists a *-finite subset $\Lambda_0 \subset {}^*\mathfrak{F}$ in $^*\mathfrak{M}$ such that $^*F \in \Lambda_0$ for all $F \in \mathfrak{F}$. Let $\Omega = \Lambda \cap \Lambda_0$. Then Ω is *-finite, contains all the standard elements of $^*\mathfrak{F}$, and $A \subset E$ for all $E \in \Omega$. F.T. implies that $A_0 = \bigcap\Omega \in {}^*\mathfrak{F}$. Then from the properties of Ω we obtain that $A \subset A_0 \subset \mu(\mathfrak{F})$. To complete the proof apply the above result to the internal sets $\{a\}$, $a \in \mu(\mathfrak{F})$.

Corollary 2.1.6. *Let $^*\mathfrak{M}$ be an enlargement of M.*

(a) *If $\mathfrak{F}$ is a filter of $\mathfrak{M}$, say of type $((\sigma))$, and A is an internal set contained in $\mu(\mathfrak{F})$, then there exists an element $E \in {}^*\mathfrak{F}$ such that $A \subset E \subset \mu(\mathfrak{F})$. In particular, any internal set of type (σ) of $^*\mathfrak{M}$ which contains $\mu(\mathfrak{F})$ is an element of $^*\mathfrak{F}$. Similarly for ideals.*

(b) *Let Ω_1, Ω_2 be two nonempty entities of $\mathfrak{M}$ of type $((\sigma))$. Then $\mu(\Omega_1) = \mu(\Omega_2) \neq \emptyset$ $(\nu(\Omega_1) = \nu(\Omega_2) \neq {}^*M_\sigma)$ if and only if Ω_1 and Ω_2 are subbases of the same filter (ideal). In particular, every filter (ideal) is uniquely determined by its monad.*

(c) *If $\mathfrak{F}_1, \mathfrak{F}_2$ are filters, then $\mathfrak{F}_1$ is finer than $\mathfrak{F}_2$ if and only if $\mu(\mathfrak{F}_1) \subset \mu(\mathfrak{F}_2)$.*

The easy proof of Corollary 2.1.6 is left to the reader.

2. When Are Monads Internal?

Let X be an infinite set and let $\mathfrak{M} = \mathfrak{M}(X, M)$ denote the full L-structure based in X. If $^*\mathfrak{M} = \mathfrak{U}$-prod $\mathfrak{M}$ is an ultrapower of $\mathfrak{M}$ with respect to a δ-incomplete ultrafilter, then it follows from Theorem 1.4.1 that $^*\mathfrak{M}$ is not a full L-structure on its set of individuals $^*X$. It is therefore an interesting and also an important question whether certain formations of entities of $^*\mathfrak{M}$ result in entities of $^*\mathfrak{M}$ or, in other words, whether such formations define internal elements of $^*\mathfrak{M}$. We have already met with such a situation when we formed the monad of a filter (ideal). Indeed, if $\mathfrak{F}$ is a filter of $\mathfrak{M}$, say of type $((\sigma))$, then its monad $\mu(\mathfrak{F})$ is obtained by forming the intersection of all the standard elements in $^*\mathfrak{M}$ of the extension $^*F$ in $^*\mathfrak{M}$ of $F \in \mathfrak{F}$ and so $\mu(\mathfrak{F})$ is a set of entities of type σ of $^*\mathfrak{M}$. It is natural to inquire whether $\mu(\mathfrak{F})$ is an internal set of $^*\mathfrak{M}$. In some cases this question has been answered. For instance, from Theorem 1.4.1 it follows that the Fréchet filter $\mathfrak{Fr}(A)$ of an infinite set of entities of type σ of $\mathfrak{M}$, being equal to $^*A - A$, is *not* internal. On the other hand, if $\mathfrak{F}$ is the neighborhood filter of a point in a metric space, then it was shown by A. Robinson in [13], Theorem 4.3.5, that the monad of $\mathfrak{F}$ is internal if and only if the point is isolated; that is, if and only if $\mathfrak{F}$ is a principal filter. The more general question: When is the monad of a point in a topological space internal? was left open in [13].

These observations suggest the following conjecture. The monad of a filter (ideal) is internal if and only if the filter (ideal) is a principal filter (ideal). Of course, Example 2.1.3 shows that this conjecture only makes sense for models that are at least as strong as enlargements. In fact, we shall show below that the conjecture, indeed, holds for enlargements.

We shall begin with the following special case of the conjecture.

***Theorem* 2.2.1.** *Let $\mathfrak{F}(\mathfrak{I})$ be a filter (ideal) of $\mathfrak{M}$, say of type $((\sigma))$ and let $^*\mathfrak{M}$ be an enlargement of $\mathfrak{M}$. Then the monad $\mu(\mathfrak{F})(\nu(\mathfrak{I}))$ of $\mathfrak{F}(\mathfrak{I})$ in $^*\mathfrak{M}$ is a standard entity of $^*\mathfrak{M}$ if and only if $\mathfrak{F}(\mathfrak{I})$ is principal.*

Proof. We have already shown that if $\mathfrak{F}$ is principal, its monad is standard. Assume, conversely, that $\mu(\mathfrak{F})$ is standard; that is, $\mu(\mathfrak{F}) = {}^*A$ for some entity A of $\mathfrak{M}$ of type (σ). Then by (a) of Theorem 2.6.1 $\mu(\mathfrak{F}) = {}^*A \in {}^*\mathfrak{F}$, and so F.T. implies that $A \in \mathfrak{F}$. Hence $F \in \mathfrak{F}$ if and only if $A \subset F$; that is, $\mathfrak{F}$ is a principal filter, and the proof is finished.

If instead we assume the weaker hypothesis $\mu(\mathfrak{F})$ is internal, then the required result, $\mathfrak{F}$ is principal, is much harder to prove. Before we can turn to the proof of the conjecture we need first a number of results concerning the structure of a filter.

Let $\mathfrak{F}$ be a filter; a subbasis of $\mathfrak{F}$ of smallest cardinal will be called a *minimal subbasis* of $\mathfrak{F}$ and will be denoted by $\mathfrak{F}_m$. The cardinal of $\mathfrak{F}_m$ will be called the *dimension* of $\mathfrak{F}$ and will be denoted by $\dim(\mathfrak{F})$. In terms of the dimension of a filter, the principal filters can be characterized as follows.

***Lemma* 2.2.2.** *A filter $\mathfrak{F}$ is principal if and only if its dimension is finite, and in that case* $\dim(\mathfrak{F}) = 1$.

Proof. Let $\mathfrak{F}$ be a principal filter generated by the set A. Then $\{A\}$ is a subbasis of $\mathfrak{F}$ of minimal cardinal, and so $\dim(\mathfrak{F}) = 1$. If conversely, dim($\mathfrak{F}$) is finite, then $\mathfrak{F}$ has a finite subbasis $\{F_1, \cdots, F_n\}$. Hence $F \in \mathfrak{F}$ if and only if $\bigcap_{i=1}^n F_i \subset F$; that is, $\mathfrak{F}$ is a principal filter, and the proof is finished.

The above lemma shows that if a filter is not principal its dimension is infinite. The main idea used in the proof of the conjecture is to show that every filter of infinite dimension has a subbasis of minimal cardinal that satisfies additional properties. It is, of course, natural to look for independence-type properties. Now, in the propositional calculus in symbolic logic the following notion of *implicational independence* for sets of axioms plays a fundamental role. A set K of axioms is called implicational independent whenever for every finite set of axioms $\{A_1, \cdots, A_n\}$ of K it follows from $A \in K$ and (A_1 and $\cdots$ and A_n) $\Rightarrow A$ that $A = A_i$ for some $i = 1, 2, \cdots, n$. If we interpret this notion of independence in terms of the Boolean operations of the Boolean algebra of all subsets of a set E, we obtain the following notions of independence for families of sets.

A family Ω of subsets of a set E is called $\bigcap$*-independent* ($\bigcup$*-independent*) *whenever for every finite set* $\{E_1, \cdots, E_n\}$ *of elements of* Ω, $E_0 \in \Omega$ *and* $E_1 \cap \cdots \cap E_n \subset E_0 (E_0 \subset E_1 \cup \cdots \cup E_n)$ *implies* $E_0 = E_i$ *for some* $i = 1, 2, \cdots, n$.

For example, the family Ω of subsets of N, the set of natural numbers, of the form $\{k: k \neq n\}$, $n \in N$, is $\bigcap$-independent.

The reader should observe that every infinite family of sets which is $\bigcap$-independent ($\bigcup$-independent) has the finite intersection (union) property.

For independent families of sets the following result holds.

Theorem 2.2.3. *Let* $^*\mathfrak{M}$ *be an enlargement of the full L-structure* $\mathfrak{M}$ *and let* Ω *be a nonempty entity of* $\mathfrak{M}$ *of type* $((\sigma))$.

(a) *If* Ω *is* $\bigcap$*-independent, then* $\mu(\Omega)$ *is internal if and only if* Ω *is finite.*
(b) *If* Ω *is* $\bigcup$*-independent, then* $\nu(\Omega)$ *is internal if and only if* Ω *is finite.*

Proof. We shall only prove (a), since the proof of (b) is similar. If $\mu(\Omega)$ is internal, then, by F.T., the set Φ of all *-finite subsets Λ of $^*\Omega$ in $^*\mathfrak{M}$ satisfying $\bigcap (A: A \in \Lambda) \subset \mu(\Omega)$ is an *internal* set of $^*\mathfrak{M}$. Observe that $\Phi \neq \varnothing$, since as we pointed out in Example 1.5.3 there exists a *-finite subset Λ of $^*\Omega$ that contains all the standard elements of $^*\Omega$. We shall now prove that, in fact, all the elements of Φ have this property; that is, if $\Lambda \in \Phi$, then $^*A \in \Lambda$ for all $A \in \Omega$. Indeed, if $A \in \Omega$ and $\Lambda \in \Phi$, then $\bigcap (B: B \in \Lambda) \subset \mu(\Omega) \subset {}^*A$ and $^*\Omega$ being $\bigcap$-independent F.T. implies that $A \in \Lambda$. Since Φ is internal and each Λ is *-finite, it follows again from F.T. that there is an element $\Lambda_0 \in \Phi$ which has the smallest number of elements. Then every element of Λ_0 is standard. Indeed, if $A \in \Lambda_0$ is not standard, then $\Lambda_0 - \{A\} = \Lambda_1$ still contains all the standard elements of $^*\Omega$, and so $\bigcap \Lambda_1 \subset \mu(\Omega)$; that is, $\Lambda_1 \in \Phi$, contradicting the definition of Λ_0. Thus $^*\Omega - \Lambda_0$ is internal implies by Theorem 1.4.1 that Ω is finite, and the proof is finished.

From this result we obtain immediately a partial answer to our conjecture.

Theorem 2.2.4. *If a filter (ideal) has an $\bigcap$-independent ($\bigcup$-independent) subbasis, then its monad is internal if and only if it is a principal filter (ideal). In particular, the monad of every filter (ideal) whose dimension is $\aleph_0$ is not internal.*

Proof. The first part follows immediately from Theorem 2.2.3. To complete the proof we have to show that if a filter $\mathfrak{F}$ has a countable minimal basis $\{F_n: n \in N\}$, then it also has an $\bigcap$-independent basis. Indeed, the countable family of sets $\{F_n \cup F_1' \cup \cdots \cup F_{n-1}': n \in N\}$ is an $\bigcap$-independent basis of $\mathfrak{F}$, where, $'$ means complimentation in the set over which $\mathfrak{F}$ is defined.

In particular, Theorem 2.2.4 includes Robinson's result quoted above concerning the monads of the neighborhood systems of points in a metric space.

Unfortunately, it is not true that every filter has an $\bigcap$-independent subbasis, as the following example will show.

Let $\text{card}(X) > \aleph_0$ and let $\mathfrak{F}_0$ be the filter of all subsets of X whose complements are at most countable. It is easy to see that $\mathfrak{F}_0$ is not a principal filter; in fact, $\mathfrak{F}_0$ is finer than the $\mathfrak{F}r(X)$. Thus $\dim(\mathfrak{F}_0) \geq \aleph_0$. If $\mathfrak{B}$ is an $\bigcap$-independent subbasis of $\mathfrak{F}_0$, then $\dim(\mathfrak{F}_0) \geq \aleph_0$ implies that there exists a countably infinite subset $\{B_m: m \in N\}$ of $\mathfrak{B}$. Since X is uncountable and the union of countably many countable sets is countable, it follows that $B = \bigcap (B_m: m \in N) \in \mathfrak{F}$. Then $\mathfrak{B}$ being a subbasis of $\mathfrak{F}_0$ implies that there exists a finite set $\{E_1, \cdots, E_n\}$ of elements of $\mathfrak{B}$ such that $\bigcap_{i=1}^n E_i \subset B \subset B_m$ for all $m \in N$. Using the fact that $\mathfrak{B}$ is $\bigcap$-independent and the fact that $B_m \in \mathfrak{B}$ for all $m \in N$ we obtain from $\{E_1, \cdots, E_n\} \subset \mathfrak{B}$ and $E_1 \cap \cdots \cap E_n \subset B_m$ that $B_m \in \{E_1, \cdots, E_n\}$ for all $m \in N$, contradicting the fact that the set $\{B_m: m \in N\}$ is not finite.

The above proof shows that any δ-complete filter which is not principal does not possess an $\bigcap$-independent subbasis. It seems an interesting problem to characterize the filters that do have a $\bigcap$-independent minimal basis.

In this connection it is of interest to point out that in the case of the propositional calculus the situation is quite different. It was shown recently by Reznikoff (see [12]) that any system, not only countable systems of axioms, can always be replaced by an implicational independent system.

Although a filter may not possess an $\cap$-independent subbasis, the following theorem will show that there exists always a subbasis that enjoys a weaker $\cap$-independence property.

Theorem 2.2.5. *Let* $\mathfrak{F}$ *be a filter and let* $\dim(\mathfrak{F}) = \aleph_\alpha$ $(\alpha \geq 0)$. *Then there exists a minimal subbasis* $\mathfrak{B}_m$ *of* $\mathfrak{F}$ *which can be well ordered similar to the first initial ordinal* ω_α *in such a way that the well-ordered set* $\mathfrak{B}_m$ *has the following weak* $\cap$*-independence property. For every finite set* $\{E_{\gamma_1}, \cdots, E_{\gamma_n}\} \subset \mathfrak{B}_m$, $1 \leq \gamma_1 < \gamma_2 < \cdots \gamma_n < \omega_\alpha$, *if* $E_{\gamma_1} \cap \cdots \cap E_{\gamma_n} \subset E_\gamma$, *and* $E_\gamma \in \mathfrak{B}_m$ *then* $\gamma \leq \gamma_n$.

Proof. Let Ω be a subbasis of $\mathfrak{F}$ of minimal cardinal $\aleph_\alpha$ $(\alpha \geq 0)$ and let Ω be well ordered in the smallest possible way, that is, similar to the initial ordinal ω_α. We shall now define inductively a subset $\mathfrak{B}_m$ of Ω which has the required properties. Let $\Omega_1 = \{E_1\}$, where E_1 is the first element of Ω. Assume now that $1 < \gamma < \omega_\alpha$ and that Ω_β has been defined for all $1 \leq \beta < \gamma$. Then, if $\gamma = \delta + 1$, we define $\Omega_\gamma = \Omega_\delta$ whenever $E_\gamma \in \Omega$ is contained in the filter generated by Ω_δ and $\Omega_\gamma = \Omega_\delta \cup \{E_\gamma\}$ otherwise; if γ is a limit ordinal, then we define $\Omega_\gamma = \cup\ (\Omega_\beta\colon 1 \leq \beta < \gamma)$ whenever E_γ is contained in the filter generated by $\cup\ (\Omega_\beta\colon 1 \leq \beta < \gamma)$ and we define $\Omega_\gamma = \cup\ (\Omega_\beta\colon 1 \leq \beta < \gamma) \cup \{E_\gamma\}$ otherwise. It is obvious that the system of sets Ω_β is increasing in β. We define $\mathfrak{B}_m = \cup\ (\Omega_\gamma\colon 1 \leq \gamma < \omega_\alpha)$. Then $\mathfrak{B}_m \subset \Omega$, and we shall first show that $\mathfrak{B}_m$ is a subbasis of $\mathfrak{F}$. To this end, let $E \in \mathfrak{F}$. Then Ω being a subbasis of $\mathfrak{F}$, it follows that there exists a finite subset $\{F_{\gamma_1}, \cdots, F_{\gamma_p}\} \subset \Omega$, $1 \leq \gamma_1 < \gamma_2 < \cdots < \gamma_p < \omega_\alpha$ such that $F_{\gamma_1} \cap \cdots \cap F_{\gamma_p} \subset E$. If all the elements F_{γ_i} $(i = 1, 2, \cdots, p)$ are elements of $\mathfrak{B}_m$, then there is nothing to prove. Assume that F_{γ_i} is the first element such that $F_{\gamma_i} \notin \mathfrak{B}_m$. Then it follows from the definition of Ω_{γ_i} that F_{γ_i} is contained in the filter generated by Ω_{γ_i}. Thus there are elements $E_{\delta_1}, \cdots, E_{\delta_k}$ in $\Omega_{\gamma_i}(1 \leq \delta_1 < \cdots < \delta_k < \omega_\alpha)$ such that $E_{\delta_1} \cap \cdots \cap E_{\delta_k} \subset F_{\gamma_i}$. If we replace F_{γ_i} by the finite system $\{E_{\delta_1}, \cdots, E_{\delta_k}\}$, then the new system still has the property that its intersection is contained in E. By means of this process we can replace every element F_{γ_j} of $\{F_{\gamma_1}, \cdots, F_{\gamma_p}\} \subset \Omega$, which does not already belong to $\mathfrak{B}_m$, by finitely many elements of $\mathfrak{B}_m$ such that the resulting finite subset of $\mathfrak{B}_m$ generates a filter that contains E. This shows that $\mathfrak{B}_m$ is a subbasis of $\mathfrak{F}$, and so $\mathfrak{B}_m \subset \Omega$ and Ω has minimal cardinal implies $\operatorname{card}(\mathfrak{B}_m) = \aleph_\alpha$. We shall now turn to the proof that $\mathfrak{B}_m$ has the weak $\cap$-independence property. To this end, let $\{E_\gamma, E_{\gamma_1}, \cdots, E_{\gamma_n}\} \subset \mathfrak{B}_m$, $1 \leq \gamma_1 < \gamma_2 < \cdots < \gamma_n < \omega_\alpha$ and $1 \leq \gamma < \omega_\alpha$ and assume that $E_{\gamma_1} \cap \cdots \cap E_{\gamma_n} \subset E_\gamma$. If $\gamma > \gamma_n$, then the latter implies that $E_\gamma \notin \Omega_\tau$, and so $E_\gamma \notin \mathcal{B}_m$, contradicting its definition. Thus $\gamma \leq \gamma_n$. Finally, observe that $\mathcal{B}_m$ as a well-ordered subset of Ω is isomorphic to a segment of Ω. Since $\text{card}(\mathcal{B}_m) = \text{card}(\Omega)$ and Ω is similar to ω_α, it follows that $\mathcal{B}_m$ is isomorphic to ω_α as a well-ordered set. This completes the proof.

We are now in a position to prove the conjecture.

Theorem 2.2.6. *Let $^*\mathfrak{M}$ be an enlargement of the structure $\mathfrak{M}$ and let $\mathfrak{F}$ be a filter of $\mathfrak{M}$ of type $((\sigma))$. Then $\mu(\mathfrak{F})$ is internal if and only if $\mathfrak{F}$ is a principal filter. Similarly for ideals.*

Proof. We shall prove that the assumption $\mathfrak{F}$ is not principal and $\mu(\mathfrak{F})$ is internal leads to a contradiction. Since $\mathfrak{F}$ is not principal, Theorem 2.2.1 implies that $\dim(\mathfrak{F}) = \aleph_\alpha \geq \aleph_0$. Then, by Theorem 2.2.5, there exists a well-ordered subbasis $\mathcal{B}_m$ of $\mathfrak{F}$ of minimal cardinal $\aleph_\alpha$ which is isomorphic to ω_α as a well-ordered set and which has the weak $\cap$-independence property. Since $\mu(\mathfrak{F})$ is internal, it follows that the set $\Phi = \{\Lambda\colon \Lambda \subset {}^*\mathcal{B}_m$ and Λ is *-finite and $\cap\, \Lambda \subset \mu(\mathfrak{F})\}$ is internal. Observe that Φ is not empty. Indeed, $^*\mathfrak{M}$ being an enlargement, it follows from (a) of Theorem 2.1.5 that there exists a *-finite subset Λ of $^*\mathcal{B}_m$ which contains all the standard elements of $^*\mathcal{B}_m$, and so $\cap\, \Lambda \subset \mu(\mathfrak{F})$. Then from $\Phi \neq \emptyset$ it follows that there is an element $\Lambda_0 \in \Phi$ such that Λ_0 contains the element of smallest largest index, say β_0. Thus, if $\Lambda = \{A_{\gamma_1}, \cdots, A_{\gamma_n}\} \in \Phi$, $1 \leq \gamma_1 < \gamma_2 < \cdots < \gamma_n < \omega_\alpha$, $n \in {}^*N$, then $\beta_0 \leq \gamma_n$. We shall first show that $A_{\beta_0} \in \Lambda$ is *not* standard. Indeed, if $E_\gamma \in \mathcal{B}_m$, then $\cap \Lambda_0 \subset \mu(\mathfrak{F}) \subset {}^*(E_\gamma)$ implies by the weak $\cap$-independence property that $^*\gamma \leq \beta_0$ in $^*\mathfrak{M}$, and so, if β_0 is standard, then the set $\mathcal{B}_m$ would be isomorphic to a proper segment of ω_α, which contradicts the fact that $\mathcal{B}_m$ is isomorphic to ω_α. Since $^*\mathfrak{M}$ is an enlargement of $\mathfrak{M}$ there exists by (a) of Theorem 2.1.5 a *-finite subset $\{E_{\gamma_1}, \cdots, E_{\gamma_p}\} \subset {}^*\mathcal{B}_m$, $1 \leq \gamma_1 < \gamma_2 < \cdots < \gamma_p < \omega_\alpha$, $p \in {}^*N$, which contains all the standard elements of $^*\mathcal{B}_m$. Hence $E_{\gamma_1} \cap \cdots \cap E_{\gamma_p} \subset \mu(\mathfrak{F})$ implies $\{E_{\gamma_1}, \cdots, E_{\gamma_p}\} \in \Phi$. Let $\Lambda_1 = \{E_{\gamma_i}\colon \gamma_i < \beta_0\}$. Then the *-finite set Λ_1 still contains all the standard elements of $^*\mathcal{B}_m$. Indeed, it was shown above that every standard $E_\gamma \in \mathcal{B}_m$ satisfies $^*\gamma < \beta_0$. Thus $\cap \Lambda_1 \subset \mu(\mathfrak{F})$ implies $\Lambda_1 \in \Phi$. But the largest index of the elements of Λ_1 is less and *not* equal to β_0, which is a contradiction, and the proof is finished.

Corollary 2.2.7. *Let $^*\mathfrak{M}$ be an enlargement of $\mathfrak{M}$ and let Ω be a nonempty entity of $\mathfrak{M}$ of type $((\sigma))$. Then, if Ω has the finite intersection (union) property, its monad $\mu(\Omega)(\nu(\Omega))$ is internal if and only if the filter (ideal) generated by Ω of type $((\sigma))$ is principal.*

3. The Monad of the sup and inf of a Family of Filters

Since the intersection of a nonempty family of filters is again a filter it follows immediately that for every family $\{\mathfrak{F}_\lambda: \lambda \in \Lambda\}$, $\Lambda \neq \emptyset$, there exists a largest filter contained in all the filters $\mathfrak{F}_\lambda$. This filter is called the intersection filter or the inf of the family and will be denoted by $\wedge\ (\mathfrak{F}_\lambda: \lambda \in \Lambda)$, or simply $\wedge \mathfrak{F}_\lambda$. The intersection filter consists of the family of all sets of the form $\cup\ (F_\lambda: F_\lambda \in \mathfrak{F}_\lambda,\ \lambda \in \Lambda)$. Furthermore, there exists a smallest filter containing all the $\mathfrak{F}_\lambda$, $\lambda \in \Lambda$, whenever $F_{\lambda_1} \cap \cdots \cap F_{\lambda_n} \neq \emptyset$ for all finite systems $F_{\lambda_i} \in \mathfrak{F}_{\lambda_i}$ $(i = 1, 2, \cdots, n)$. This filter will then be denoted by $\vee\ (\mathfrak{F}_\lambda: \lambda \in \Lambda)$, or simply $\vee \mathfrak{F}_\lambda$.

We have the following result.

Theorem 2.3.1. *Let* $\{\mathfrak{F}_\lambda: \lambda \in \Lambda\}$ *be a nonempty family of filters of a certain type. Then* $\vee \mathfrak{F}_\lambda$ *exists if and only if* $\cap \mu(\mathfrak{F}_\lambda) \neq \emptyset$, *and in that case* $\mu(\vee \mathfrak{F}_\lambda) = \cap \mu(\mathfrak{F}_\lambda)$, *or, in other words, the intersection of a family of monads of filters is either empty or again a monad of a filter.*

Proof. If $\mathfrak{F} = \vee \mathfrak{F}_\lambda$ exists, then $\mathfrak{F}_\lambda \leq \mathfrak{F}$ implies by (c) of Corollary 2.1.6 that $\mu(\mathfrak{F}) \subset \mu(\mathfrak{F}_\lambda)$, and so $\mu(\mathfrak{F}) \subset \cap\, \mu(\mathfrak{F}_\lambda)$. On the other hand, if $E \in \mathfrak{F}$, then there exist elements $E_{\lambda_1} \in \mathfrak{F}_{\lambda_1}, \cdots, E_{\lambda_n} \in \mathfrak{F}_{\lambda_n}$, $n \in N$, such that $E_{\lambda_1} \cap \cdots \cap E_{\lambda_n} \subset E$, and so $\cap \mu(\mathfrak{F}_\lambda) \subset {}^*E_{\lambda_1} \cap \cdots \cap {}^*E_{\lambda_n} \subset {}^*E$ implies $\cap \mu(\mathfrak{F}_\lambda) \subset \mu(\mathfrak{F})$. Thus $\mu(\mathfrak{F}) = \cap \mu(\mathfrak{F}_\lambda)$. The remainder is easy.

Unfortunately the union of a family of monads of filters need not be a monad of a filter, as the following example will show.

Let $\{X_n: n \in N\}$ be a countable partition of X in finite subsets of X, and let $\mathfrak{F}_n$ be the principal filter generated by X_n $(n \in N)$. Then $\wedge \mathfrak{F}_n = \{X\}$, and so $\mu(\wedge \mathfrak{F}_n) = {}^*X$. But $\cup \mu(\mathfrak{F}_n) = \cup {}^*X_n \neq {}^*X$ by Theorem 2.1.2.

For finite families of filters the following result holds.

Theorem 2.3.2. *Let* $\{\mathfrak{F}_1, \cdots, \mathfrak{F}_n\}$ *be a finite family of filters. Then* $\mu(\wedge_{i=1}^n \mathfrak{F}_i) = \cup_{i=1}^n \mu(\mathfrak{F}_i)$, *or, in other words, a union of a finite set of filter monads is a filter monad.*

Proof. Let $\mathfrak{F} = \wedge_{i=1}^n \mathfrak{F}_i$. Then it is obvious that $\cup \mu(\mathfrak{F}_i) \subset \mu(\mathfrak{F})$. Let $a \in \mu(\mathfrak{F})$ and assume that $a \notin \mu(\mathfrak{F}_i) (i = 1, 2, \cdots, n)$. Then it follows from the definition of the monad of a filter that there exist elements $F_i \in \mathfrak{F}_i$ such that $a \notin {}^*F_i$ $(i = 1, 2, \cdots, n)$. Hence $a \notin \cup_{i=1}^n {}^*F_i = {}^*(\cup_{i=1}^n F_i)$, which contradicts $\mu(\mathfrak{F}) \subset {}^*(\cup_{i=1}^n F_i)$, and the proof is finished.

For the lattice of filters the following distributive laws hold.

Theorem 2.3.3. (a) *Let* $\{\mathfrak{F}_\lambda: \lambda \in \Lambda\}$ *be a nonempty family of filters of type* $((\sigma))$ *such that* $\vee \mathfrak{F}_\lambda$ *exists and let* $\mathfrak{F}$ *be a filter of the same type in* $\mathfrak{M}$. *Then* $\mathfrak{F} \wedge (\vee \mathfrak{F}_\lambda) = \vee\ (\mathfrak{F} \wedge \mathfrak{F}_\lambda)$.

(b) *Let* $\{\mathfrak{F}, \cdots, \mathfrak{F}_n\}$ *be a finite family of filters of type* $((\sigma))$ *and let* $\mathfrak{F}$ *be a filter of type* σ *such that* $\mathfrak{F} \vee (\wedge \mathfrak{F}_i)$ *exists. Then* $\mathfrak{F} \vee (\wedge \mathfrak{F}_i) = \wedge(\mathfrak{F} \vee \mathfrak{F}_i)$.

Proof. We shall only prove (a). To show that two filters are equal we have to show that they have the same monad. Using Theorems 2.3.1 and 2.3.2 we obtain $\mu(\mathfrak{F} \wedge (\vee \mathfrak{F}_\lambda)) = \mu(\mathfrak{F}) \cup \mu(\vee \mathfrak{F}_\lambda) = \mu(\mathfrak{F}) \cup (\bigcap \mu(\mathfrak{F}_\lambda)) = \bigcap (\mu(\mathfrak{F}) \cup \mu(\mathfrak{F}_\lambda)) = \bigcap \mu(\mathfrak{F} \wedge \mathfrak{F}_\lambda) = \mu(\vee(\mathfrak{F} \wedge \mathfrak{F}_\lambda))$.

It is well known that (b) does not hold in general for infinite families. Indeed, let $\mathfrak{F}_\lambda$ be the family of the principal filters over X generated by the sets whose complements are finite, and let $\mathfrak{F}$ be the Fréchet filter of X. Then $\mathfrak{F} \vee (\wedge \mathfrak{F}_\lambda) = \mathfrak{F}$ and $\wedge(\mathfrak{F} \wedge \mathfrak{F}_\lambda) = \{X\}$. We have always $\wedge(\mathfrak{F} \vee \mathfrak{F}_\lambda) \leq \mathfrak{F} \vee (\wedge \mathfrak{F}_\lambda)$.

4. The Monad of an Ultrafilter

As one may expect, the monad of an ultrafilter being in a sense the smallest filter monad has some interesting properties.

Theorem 2.4.1. *A filter* $\mathfrak{F}$ *of a certain type of* $\mathfrak{M}$ *is an ultrafilter if and only if for every filter* $\mathfrak{F}'$ *of the same type we have either* $\mu(\mathfrak{F}) \cap \mu(\mathfrak{F}') = \emptyset$ *or* $\mu(\mathfrak{F}) \subset \mu(\mathfrak{F}')$.

Proof. If $\mathfrak{F}$ is an ultrafilter and $\mathfrak{F}'$ is a filter such that $\mu(\mathfrak{F}) \cap \mu(\mathfrak{F}') \neq \emptyset$ and $\mu(\mathfrak{F}) \not\subset \mu(\mathfrak{F}')$, then $\mu(\mathfrak{F}) \cap \mu(\mathfrak{F}')$ is properly contained in $\mu(\mathfrak{F})$, and so by Theorem 2.3.1 and (b) of Corollary 2.1.6 $\mathfrak{F} \vee \mathfrak{F}'$ is strictly finer than $\mathfrak{F}$ and a contradiction is obtained. Conversely, if $\mathfrak{F}'$ is a filter such that $\mathfrak{F} \leq \mathfrak{F}'$, then $\mu(\mathfrak{F}') = \mu(\mathfrak{F})$, and so $\mathfrak{F} = \mathfrak{F}'$; that is, $\mathfrak{F}$ is an ultrafilter.

Corollary 2.4.2. *For every pair of ultrafillers* $\mathfrak{U}_1$, $\mathfrak{U}_2$ *we have either* $\mu(\mathfrak{U}_1) = \mu(\mathfrak{U}_2)$ *or* $\mu(\mathfrak{U}_1) \cap \mu(\mathfrak{U}_2) = \emptyset$.

Theorem 2.4.1 can be used to prove the following well-known criterion for a filter to be an ultrafilter. A filter $\mathfrak{F}$ is an ultrafilter if and only if for every finite set $\{A_1, \cdots, A_n\}$ such that $A_1 \cup \cdots \cup A_n \in \mathfrak{F}$ there exists an index i such that $A_i \in \mathfrak{F}$. Indeed, if $A_1 \cup \cdots \cup A_n \in \mathfrak{F}$, then $\mu(\mathfrak{F}) \subset \bigcup {}^*A_i$, and so for some i we have $\mu(\mathfrak{F}) \cap {}^*A_i \neq \emptyset$. Thus, if $\mathfrak{F}$ is an ultrafilter, then $\mu(\mathfrak{F}) \subset {}^*A_i$, and so $A_i \in \mathfrak{F}$. Conversely, if $\mathfrak{F}'$ is a filter such that $\mu(\mathfrak{F}) \cap \mu(\mathfrak{F}') \neq \emptyset$ and $\mu(\mathfrak{F}) \not\subset \mu(\mathfrak{F}')$, then there is an element $A \in \mathfrak{F}'$ such that ${}^*A \cap \mu(\mathfrak{F}) \neq \emptyset$ and $({}^*X - {}^*A) \cap \mu(\mathfrak{F}) \neq \emptyset$; that is, $A \notin \mathfrak{F}$ and $X - A \notin \mathfrak{F}$, contradicting the assumption.

We shall conclude with the following observation.

Theorem 2.4.3. *For every filter* $\mathfrak{F}$ *we have* $\mu(\mathfrak{F}) = \bigcup (\mu(\mathfrak{U})\colon \mathfrak{F} \leq \mathfrak{U}$ *and* $\mathfrak{U}$ *is an ultrafilter), or, in other words, every filter is the intersection of the family of ultrafilters finer than* $\mathfrak{F}$.

Proof. Of course, we have only to show that if $a \in \mu(\mathfrak{F})$, there is an ultrafilter $\mathfrak{U}$ finer than $\mathfrak{F}$ such that $a \in \mu(\mathfrak{U})$. To this end, let $\mathfrak{U}_a = \{E: a \in {}^*E\}$. Then $\mathfrak{U}_a$ is obviously an ultrafilter and $\mathfrak{F} \subset \mathfrak{U}_a$ and $a \in \mu(\mathfrak{U}_a)$, and the proof is finished.

5. The Monad of a Set of Entities

In Theorem 2.3.1 we have shown that if the intersection of an arbitrary family of monads of filters is nonempty, then it is a monad of a filter. Since for every $\sigma \in T$ the set ${}^*M_\sigma$ is the monad of the filter $\{M_\sigma\}$, it follows that for every set A internal or not of entities of ${}^*\mathfrak{M}$ of a certain type there exists the smallest filter monad containing A. This monad is called the *discrete monad* of A and will be denoted by $\mu_d(A)$. If $A = \{a\}$, where $a \in {}^*M_\sigma$, then we shall denote the discrete monad of $\{a\}$ by $\mu_d(a)$ rather than $\mu_d(\{a\})$ if no confusion can arise. Observe that $\mu_d(\emptyset) = \emptyset$.

The filter whose monad is equal to $\mu_d(A)$ can be characterized as follows.

***Theorem* 2.5.1.** *Let $\emptyset \neq A \subset {}^*M_\sigma$, $\sigma \in T$. Then $\mathfrak{D}_A = \{F: F \subset M_\sigma$ and $A \subset {}^*F\}$ is the unique filter of type $((\sigma))$ which satisfies $\mu_d(A) = \mu(\mathfrak{D}_A)$.*

Proof. From $A \subset \mu(\mathfrak{D}_A)$ it follows that $\mu_d(A) \subset \mu(\mathfrak{D}_A)$. If, on the other hand, $\mathfrak{F}$ is a filter such that $A \subset \mu(\mathfrak{F})$, then $F \in \mathfrak{F}$ implies $A \subset {}^*F$, and so $F \in \mathfrak{D}_A$; that is, $\mu(\mathfrak{D}_A) \subset \mu(\mathfrak{F})$. Hence $\mu_d(A) = \mu(\mathfrak{D}_A)$. The uniqueness of $\mathfrak{D}_A$ follows from (a) of Corollary 2.1.6.

From Theorem 2.5.1 it follows, in particular, that for every filter $\mathfrak{F}$, $\mu_d(\mu_d(\mu(\mathfrak{F}))) = \mu(\mathfrak{F})$.

For the case that $A = \{a\}$, $a \in {}^*M_\sigma$, Theorem 2.5.1 takes on the following form.

***Theorem* 2.5.2.** *If $A = \{a\}$, $a \in {}^*M_\sigma$, then $\mathfrak{D}_A = \mathfrak{D}_a$ is an ultrafilter, and so for all $a_1, a_2 \in {}^*M_\sigma$, $\sigma \in T$, either $\mu_d(a_1) = \mu_d(a_2)$ or $\mu_d(a_1) \cap \mu_d(a_2) = \emptyset$. Furthermore, $\mu_d(a) = \{a\}$ if and only if a is standard.*

Proof. If $a \in {}^*M_\sigma$, then obviously for every $E \subset M_\sigma$ we have either $a \in {}^*E$ or $a \in {}^*(M_\sigma - E)$, and so $\mathfrak{D}_a$ is an ultrafilter. Use Corollary 2.4.2 to prove the second part of the theorem. If $\mu_d(a) = \{a\}$, then $\mu_d(a) \in {}^*\mathfrak{D}_A$, and so $\{a\} \in {}^*\mathfrak{D}_A$. Hence, by F.T., $\mathfrak{D}_A$ has the same property, and the proof is finished.

From Theorem 2.5.2 it follows that the (external) binary relation "$a_1 \sim a_2$ if and only if $\mu_d(a_1) = \mu_d(a_2)$" between the elements of ${}^*M_\sigma$ is an equivalence relation whose sets of equivalent elements are the discrete monads of the entities of type σ. This suggests the following definition.

A set $A \subset {}^*M_\sigma$ (internal or not) is called *saturated* whenever $\mu_d(a) \subset A$ for all $a \in A$.

Observe that if $A \subset M_\sigma$, then ${}^*A$ is saturated, or, in other words, every standard set of entities of ${}^*\mathfrak{M}$ is saturated. Also the monads $\mu(\Omega)$ and $\nu(\Omega)$ of entities of type $((\sigma))$ of $\mathfrak{M}$ are saturated. Thus, if $A \subset {}^*M_\sigma$, then $\mu_d(A)$ is the smallest filter monad containing A. Observe, however, that an internal set need not be saturated. Indeed, if $a \in {}^*M_\sigma$ and a is not standard, then, by Theorem 2.5.2, the internal set $\{a\}$ is not saturated.

Since the monad of a filter is saturated, it follows once more that every filter is the intersection of all the ultrafilters containing it.

In the following theorem we will show that for all $\sigma \in T$ the mapping μ_d of $P({}^*M_\sigma)$ into $P({}^*M_\sigma)$ is a *closure* operator.

Theorem 2.5.3. *Let $\sigma \in T$; then the discrete monad operator μ_d on $P({}^*M_\sigma)$ is a closure operator; that is, μ_d is inclusive, monotone, idempotent, and distributive with respect to finite unions.*

Proof. The statements $\mu_d(\emptyset) = 0$, $\mu_d({}^*M_\sigma) = {}^*M_\sigma$, $A \subset \mu_d(A)$, and $A_1 \subset A_2$ implies $\mu_d(A_1) \subset \mu_d(A_2)$ follow immediately from Theorem 2.5.1. If $A \subset {}^*M_\sigma$, then $\mu_d(\mu_d(A)) = \mu_d(\mu(\mathfrak{D}_A)) = \mu(\mathfrak{D}_A) = \mu_d(A)$ shows that μ_d is idempotent. Finally, $\mu_d(A_1 \cup A_2) = \mu_d(A_1) \cup \mu_d(A_2)$ follows by observing that $A_i \subset A_1 \cup A_2$, $i = 1, 2$, implies that $\mu_d(A_1) \cup \mu_d(A_2) \subset \mu_d(A_1 \cup A_2)$, and that $A_1 \cup A_2 \subset \mu_d(A_1) \cup \mu_d(A_2) = \mu(\mathfrak{D}_{A_1} \wedge \mathfrak{D}_{A_2})$ (by Theorem 2.3.2) implies that $\mu_d(A_1 \cup A_2) \subset \mu_d(A_1) \cup \mu_d(A_2)$, and so the proof is finished.

The topology induced by the closure operator μ_d on ${}^*M_\sigma$ will be called the *discrete S-topology*, or simply the S-topology. The S-topology, although it does not have the Hausdorff separation property, is compact.

Theorem 2.5.4. *For every σ, ${}^*M_\sigma$ is compact in its S-topology.*

Proof. Let Ω be a nonempty family of S-closed subsets of ${}^*M_\sigma$ with the finite intersection property. Then every $E \in \Omega$ is the monad of a unique filter $\mathcal{E}$ of $\mathfrak{M}$. From the finite intersection property of Ω it follows that the family of filters $\{\mathcal{E}\colon \mu(\mathcal{E}) \in \Omega\}$ has a supremum, and so by Theorem 2.3.1 we obtain that $\bigcap\, (E\colon E \in \Omega) \neq \emptyset$, and the proof is finished.

The following result is now evident.

Theorem 2.5.5. *For every $\sigma \in T$, the quotient space of the space ${}^*M_\sigma$ in its S-topology with respect to the equivalence relation "$a_1 \sim a_2$ if and only if $\mu_d(a_1) = \mu_d(a_2)$" is homeomorphic to the Stone–Čech compactification of the discrete space M_σ.*

From the important result that a filter monad is internal if and only if the filter is principal, it follows using the notation of Theorem 2.5.1 that $\mu_d(A)$ is internal, $\emptyset \neq A \subset {}^*M_\sigma$, if and only if $\mathfrak{D}_A$ is principal. A more precise result is possible. For its formulation we shall need the following additional bit of notation.

Notation 2.5.6. Let A be an arbitrary set of entities, say of type σ in ${}^*\mathfrak{M}$, which need not be internal. Then by ${}^0A$ we shall denote the set of all entities a of $\mathfrak{M}$ of type σ such that ${}^*a \in A$, or, in other words, ${}^0A$ is the set of entities of type σ of $\mathfrak{M}$ whose extensions in ${}^*\mathfrak{M}$ are elements of A. In particular, if A is a standard entity of ${}^*\mathfrak{M}$ of type (σ); that is, there exists a set E in $\mathfrak{M}$ of entities of type σ of $\mathfrak{M}$ such that $A = {}^*E$, then ${}^0A = E$.

Theorem 2.5.7. *Let $\emptyset \neq A \subset {}^*M_\sigma$, $\sigma \in T$. Then $\mu_d(A)$ is internal if and only if $\mu_d(A) = {}^*({}^0A)$ if and only if $\mathfrak{D}_A = \mathfrak{D}_{{}^0A}$ if and only if $A \subset {}^*({}^0A)$.*

Proof. Assume first that $A \subset {}^*({}^0A)$; then by Theorem 2.5.1, ${}^0A \in \mathfrak{D}_A$, and so $\mu_d(A) \subset {}^*({}^0A)$. On the other hand, if $A \subset {}^*E$, $E \subset M_\sigma$, then ${}^0A \subset E$ implies ${}^*({}^0A) \subset {}^*E$, and so ${}^*({}^0A) \subset \mu_d(A)$; that is, $\mu_d(A) = {}^*({}^0A)$. If, conversely, $\mu_d(A)$ is internal, then, by Theorem 2.2.6, $\mu_d(A) = {}^*E$, for some $\emptyset \neq E \subset M_\sigma$. From $A \subset \mu_d(A) \subset {}^*E$ it follows that ${}^0A \subset E$. If ${}^0A \neq E$, then there is an element $x \in E$ such that $x \notin {}^0A$. Hence $A \subset {}^*E - \{x\}$, contradicting $\mu_d(A) = {}^*E$, and so ${}^0A = E$, which finishes the proof.

Since a closure operator is not necessarily distributive relative to finite intersections, the formula $\mu_d(A_1) \cap \mu_d(A_2) = \mu_d(A_1 \cap A_2)$ does not necessarily hold either. Of course, we always have that $\mu_d(A_1 \cap A_2) \subset \mu_d(A_1) \cap \mu_d(A_2)$. On the other hand, it is well known that in a general topological space $A_1 \cap \bar{A}_2 \subset \overline{A_1 \cap A_2}$ whenever A_1 is open (see [1], proposition 5 of sec. 1 of chap. 1). Hence the intersection of the closure of two sets is equal to the closure of their intersection provided one of the sets is both open and closed. Since a standard subset $A \subset {}^*M_\sigma$ is S-open and S-closed we obtain that $\mu_d(A \cap E) = \mu_d(A) \cap \mu_d(E)$ for all $E \subset {}^*M_\sigma$ provided A is a standard set entities of type σ. The following theorem shows that the converse also holds.

Theorem 2.5.8. *Let $\emptyset \neq A \subset {}^*M_\sigma$, $\sigma \in T$. Then A is standard if and only if A is S-open and S-closed if and only if $\mu_d(A \cap E) = \mu_d(A) \cap \mu_d(E)$ for all $E \subset {}^*M_\sigma$.*

Proof. If A is standard, then $A = {}^*E$, $E \subset M_\sigma$ implies that A is S-closed. From ${}^*M_\sigma - A = {}^*(M_\sigma - E)$ it then follows that A is also S-open. Thus as shown above we have also $\mu_d(A \cap E) = \mu_d(A) \cap \mu_d(E)$

for all $E \subset {}^*M_\sigma$. To complete the proof we have to show that conversely the latter statement implies that A is standard. Now for $E = {}^*M_\sigma - A$ we have that $\mu_d(A) \cap \mu_d(E) = \emptyset$, and so there are sets $G,F \subset M_\sigma$ such that $A \subset {}^*G$, ${}^*M_\sigma - A \subset {}^*F$, and ${}^*G \cap {}^*F = \emptyset$, and so $A = {}^*G$, and the proof is finished.

We can supplement Theorem 2.5.7 as follows.

Theorem 2.5.9. *Let* $\emptyset \neq A \subset {}^*M_\sigma$, $\sigma \in T$. *Then* $\mu_d(A \cap F) = \mu_d(A) \cap \mu_d(F)$ *for all saturated sets* $F \subset {}^*M_\sigma$ *if and only if* $A \subset \mu_d(A) = {}^*({}^0A)$ *and* $A \cap \mu_d(a) \neq \emptyset$ *for all* $a \in {}^*({}^0A)$.

Proof. If $A \cap \mu_d(a) \neq \emptyset$ for all $a \in {}^*({}^0A)$, then $A \subset {}^*({}^0A)$, and so $\mu_d(A) = {}^*({}^0A)$. Furthermore, if F is saturated, then ${}^*({}^0A) \cap F = \bigcup (\mu_d(a)\colon a \in A \cap F)$, and so $\mu_d(A \cap F) = \mu_d({}^*({}^0A) \cap F)$ and the proof of half of the theorem is finished. Conversely, if $\mu_d(A \cap F) = \mu_d(A) \cap \mu_d(F)$ for all saturated sets $F \subset {}^*M_\sigma$, then by taking $F = {}^*M_\sigma - \mu_d(A)$ we obtain that $\mu_d(F) = F$; that is, $\mu_d(A)$ is both S-closed and S-open, and so $\mu_d(A)$ is standard by Theorem 2.5.8 and $A \subset {}^*({}^0A) = \mu_d(A)$ by Theorem 2.5.7. Now let $a \in {}^*({}^0A)$ and $\mu_d(a) \cap A = \emptyset$; then by taking $F = \mu_d(a)$ we see that $\mu_d(A \cap F) = \mu_d(\emptyset) = \emptyset = {}^*({}^0A) \cap F = \mu_d(a)$, which is a contradiction, and the proof is finished.

We shall conclude this section with an application concerning the dual distributive law for the lattice of filters over a given set. We shall begin with the following simple observation:

Theorem 2.5.10. *Let* $\{\mathfrak{F}_\lambda\}$ *be a nonempty family of filters of* $\mathfrak{M}$ *of a certain type. Then* $\mu(\wedge \mathfrak{F}_\lambda) = \mu_d(\bigcup (\mu(\mathfrak{J}_\lambda))$.

Proof. It is obvious that $\mu_d(\bigcup(\mu(\mathfrak{F}_\lambda)) \subset \mu(\wedge \mathfrak{F}_\lambda)$. To prove the converse inclusion, observe that if $\mathcal{E}$ is a filter such that $\mu_d(\bigcup(\mu(\mathfrak{F}_\lambda))) \subset \mu(\mathcal{E})$, then $\mathcal{E} \leq \mathfrak{F}_\lambda$ for all λ, and so $\mu(\wedge \mathfrak{F}_\lambda) \subset \mu(\mathcal{E})$. Hence $\mu(\wedge \mathfrak{F}_\lambda) \subset \mu_d(\bigcup \mu(\mathfrak{F}_\lambda))$, and the proof is finished.

In general the distributive law of the sum $\mathfrak{F} \vee (\wedge \mathfrak{F}_\lambda) = \wedge (\mathfrak{F} \vee \mathfrak{F}_\lambda)$ does not hold, as we indicated in Section 3. In the following theorem we shall characterize the filters $\mathfrak{F}$ for which it holds unrestrictedly.

Theorem 2.5.11. *Let* $\mathfrak{F}$ *be a filter of a certain type of* $\mathfrak{M}$. *Then* $\mathfrak{F} \vee (\wedge \mathfrak{F}_\lambda) = \wedge (\mathfrak{F} \vee \mathfrak{F}_\lambda)$ *holds for every system of filters* $\{\mathfrak{F}_\lambda\}$ *of the same type of* $\mathfrak{M}$ *whenever both sides make sense if and only if* $\mathfrak{F}$ *is principal.*

Proof. Assume that $\mathfrak{F}$ is principal. Then $\mu(\mathfrak{F} \vee (\wedge \mathfrak{F}_\lambda)) = \mu(\mathfrak{F}) \cap (\mu_d(\bigcup \mu(\mathfrak{F}_\lambda))) =$ (Theorem 2.5.8) $= \mu_d(\mu(\mathfrak{F}) \cap ((\bigcup \mu(\mathfrak{F}_\lambda))) = \mu_d(\bigcup (\mu(\mathfrak{F}) \cap \mu(\mathfrak{F}_\lambda)) = \mu_d(\bigcup \mu(\mathfrak{F} \vee \mathfrak{F}_\lambda)) = \mu(\wedge (\mathfrak{F} \vee \mathfrak{F}_\lambda))$, and so the distributive law holds. If conversely the distributive law holds, then $\mu(\mathfrak{F})$ satisfies $\mu(\mathfrak{F}) \cap (\mu_d(\bigcup \mu(\mathfrak{F}_\lambda))) = \mu_d(\mu(\mathfrak{F}) \cap (\bigcup \mu(\mathfrak{F}_\lambda)))$, which is equivalent to $\mu(\mathfrak{F})$

$\cap \mu_d(E) = \mu_d(\mu(\mathfrak{F}) \cap E)$ for all saturated sets, and so by Theorem 2.5.9 we obtain that $\mu(\mathfrak{F})$ is standard. Hence $\mathfrak{F}$ is principal, and the proof is finished.

6. The Discrete Monad of an Entity

In this section we shall prove a few theorems about the discrete monad of an internal set of entities.

If a is a nonstandard entity of $^*\mathfrak{M}$, an interesting question is: Which entities belong to its discrete monad $\mu_d(a)$? From the definition of $\mu_d(a)$ it follows that, roughly speaking, $a' \in \mu_d(a)$ if and only if a and a' satisfy the same standard sentences. In other words, if an element of a discrete monad has a certain property which refers only to standard statements, then all the other entities of that monad have that same property. In the following results we shall make use of this principal.

Theorem 2.6.1. *Let b be an entity of $^*\mathfrak{M}$ of type $\sigma = (\sigma_1, \cdots, \sigma_n)$. If there exist standard entities $a_1, \cdots, a_n$ in $^*\mathfrak{M}$ of type $\sigma_1, \cdots, \sigma_n$, respectively, such that $\Phi_{n+1}(b, a_1, \cdots, a_n)$ holds in $^*\mathfrak{M}$, then $\Phi_{n+1}(b', a_1, \cdots, a_n)$ holds in $^*\mathfrak{M}$ for at least all $b' \in \mu_d(b)$.*

Proof. The set E of all $x \in {}^*M_\sigma$ such that $\Phi_{n+1}(x, a_1, \cdots, a_n)$ holds in $^*\mathfrak{M}$ is a standard nonempty subset of $^*\mathfrak{M}_\sigma$ such that $b \in E$. Since E is standard it is saturated, and so $\mu_d(b) \subset E$, that is, $\Phi_{n+1}(b', a_1, \cdots, a_n)$ holds for all $b' \in \mu_d(b)$, and the proof is finished.

We shall use this simple result to solve the following problem. If A is a nonempty *internal* set of type (σ), then its discrete monad $\mu_d(A)$ is a set of entities of type σ. Since A is internal and $\mathfrak{M}$ is full, it follows that $\{A\}$, the set that consists of the element A only, is an entity of $^*\mathfrak{M}$ of type $((\sigma))$, and so its discrete monad $\mu_d(\{A\})$ is defined and is a set of entities of type (σ). The question that arises is: What is the connection if any between $\mu_d(A)$ and $\mu_d(\{A\})$? An answer is contained in the following theorem.

Theorem 2.6.2. *Let A be an entity of $^*\mathfrak{M}$ of type $((\sigma))$, $\sigma \in T$. Then $\mu_d(A) = \mu_d(\cup \mu_d(\{A\}))$.*

Proof. If $\cup \mu_d(\{A\}) \subset {}^*E$, where E is a set of entities of type σ of $\mathfrak{M}$, then $\{A\} \in \mu_d(\{A\})$ implies that $A \subset {}^*E$, and so $\mu_d(A) \subset {}^*E$. Thus $\mu_d(A) \subset \mu_d(\cup \mu_d(\{A\}))$. If, on the other hand, $A \subset {}^*E$, where $^*E$ is the extension of some set E of $\mathfrak{M}$ of type (σ), then the internal relation b defined as follows: $\Phi(b, x) \Leftrightarrow A \subset x$ is satisfied by $^*E$; hence by Theorem 2.6.1 we have that $B \subset {}^*E$ for all $B \in \mu_d(\{A\})$, and so $\cup \mu_d(\{A\}) \subset {}^*E$. Finally, from the definition of $^*E$ it follows now that $\mu_d(\cup(\mu_d(\{A\}))) \subset \mu_d(A)$, which proves the theorem.

Another question that is intimately related to the principle expressed in Theorem 2.6.1 is the following question. When is a nonempty internal set A of entities of $^*\mathfrak{M}$ an element of a standard filter of $^*\mathfrak{M}$? In general, the answer to this question is that *not* every internal set has this property, as the following example will show.

Let N denote as usual the set of natural numbers and let $^*N$ denote the set of individuals of an enlargement of arithmetic based in N. For an infinitely large natural number $\omega \in {}^*N - N$ we may define the following internal subset A of $^*N \times {}^*N$, $A = \{p, q\colon p \in {}^*N, q \in {}^*N$ and $p = \omega q\}$. Assume now that there exists a filter $\mathfrak{F}$ of subsets of $N \times N$ such that $A \in {}^*\mathfrak{F}$. Then it follows from F.T. that $\mathfrak{F}$ has an element E with the following property: $(\exists n)(n \in N$ and $\forall((p, q))(p, q \in E \Rightarrow p = nq))$. Thus again by F.T. for all $p, q \in {}^*E$ we have also $p = nq$. Since ω is infinitely large we see that $^*E \cap A = \emptyset$, and so $A \notin {}^*\mathfrak{F}$.

In the following theorem we shall give a necessary and sufficient condition for an internal set to be an element of a standard filter.

Theorem 2.6.3. *Let A be a nonempty internal set of $^*\mathfrak{M}$ of type (σ). Then there exists a filter $\mathfrak{F}$ in $\mathfrak{M}$ of type $((\sigma))$ such that $A \in {}^*\mathfrak{F}$ holds in $^*\mathfrak{M}$ if and only if for every *-finite subset $\Lambda \subset \mu_d(\{A\})$ we have $\bigcap (B\colon B \in \Lambda) \neq \emptyset$.*

Proof. The condition is necessary. Indeed, A is internal and $A \in {}^*\mathfrak{F}$ implies that $\mu_d(\{A\}) \subset {}^*\mathfrak{F}$, and so $^*\mathfrak{F}$ having the *-finite intersection property in $^*\mathfrak{M}$ the required condition follows. To prove that the condition is sufficient we consider the ultrafilter $\mathfrak{D}_{\{A\}}$ of type $(((\sigma)))$ whose monad is $\mu_d(\{A\})$. From (a) of Theorem 2.1.5 it follows that there is an element $E \in {}^*\mathfrak{D}_{\{A\}}$ in $^*\mathfrak{M}$ such that $E \subset \mu_d(\{A\})$. By hypothesis, the family E of internal sets of $^*\mathfrak{M}$ has the *-finite intersection property. Thus in $^*\mathfrak{M}$ the following result holds.

(*) $(\exists E)(E \in {}^*\mathfrak{D}_{\{A\}}$ and E has the *-finite intersection property).

Since $^*\mathfrak{D}_{\{A\}}$ is standard, we obtain from F.T. that (*) holds in $\mathfrak{M}$ also. Thus there exists an element $\Omega \in \mathfrak{D}_{\{A\}}$ such that Ω has the finite intersection property. From $\Omega \in \mathfrak{D}_{\{A\}}$ it follows that $A \in {}^*\Omega$, and so A is an element of the extension in $^*\mathfrak{M}$ of the filter $\mathfrak{F}$ generated by Ω in $\mathfrak{M}$. This completes the proof of the theorem.

7. On the Saturation of Monads

As in the preceding sections, $\mathfrak{M}$ is a full L-structure based in an infinite set X, and $^*\mathfrak{M}$ is an ultrapower enlargement of $\mathfrak{M}$. In the present section we are interested in the following question concerning the monads of filters.

Let $\mathfrak{F}$ be a filter of $\mathfrak{M}$, say of type $((\sigma))$, and let A be a nonempty subset of $^*M_\sigma$. If $A \cap {}^*F \neq \emptyset$ for all $F \in \mathfrak{F}$, does it follow that $A \cap \mu(\mathfrak{F}) \neq \emptyset$? Of course, in this generality, the answer to the question is negative. Indeed, if $A = {}^*M_\sigma - \mu(\mathfrak{F})$, then ${}^*F \cap A \neq \emptyset$ for all $F \in \mathfrak{F}$ and $A \cap \mu(\mathfrak{F}) = \emptyset$ provided $\mathfrak{F}$ is not principal. This leads to the problem of finding sufficient conditions for A which will imply that the answer to the above question is affirmative for all filters $\mathfrak{F}$. From the example it follows that the condition A is saturated is not such a sufficient condition. If, on the other hand, A is a monad of a filter, that is, S-closed, then we will show in the following theorem that the answer is affirmative.

Theorem 2.7.1. *If A is S-closed, that is, A is the monad of a filter, and ${}^*F \cap A \neq \emptyset$ for all $F \in \mathfrak{F}$, then $A \cap \mu(\mathfrak{F}) \neq \emptyset$. In particular, if A is standard, then the result holds.*

Proof. Let $\mathfrak{F}_1$ be the filter of $\mathfrak{M}$ whose monad is A. Then the condition ${}^*F \cap A \neq \emptyset$ for all $F \in \mathfrak{F}$ implies that $\mathfrak{F} \vee \mathfrak{F}_1$ exists, and so by Theorem 2.3.1 we have $\emptyset \neq \mu(\mathfrak{F} \vee \mathfrak{F}_1) = \mu(\mathfrak{F}) \cap \mu(\mathfrak{F}_1) = \mu(\mathfrak{F}) \cap A$, and the proof is finished.

For the following special case see also the proof of Theorem 4.3.12 in [13].

Theorem 2.7.2. *If A is internal and $\mathfrak{F}$ has a countable subbasis, then $A \cap {}^*F \neq \emptyset$ for all $F \in \mathfrak{F}$ implies $A \cap \mu(\mathfrak{F}) \neq \emptyset$.*

Proof. Let $\{F_n: n \in N\}$ be a decreasing countable subbasis of $\mathfrak{F}$. Since A is internal, it follows that the set $D = \{m: m \in {}^*N, E_m \cap A \neq \emptyset$ and $E_m \in {}^*\{F_n: n \in N\}\}$ is internal. Since by hypothesis $N = {}^0D$, we obtain that D contains an infinitely large natural number, which we shall denote by n_0. Then $\{F_n: n \in N\}$ decreasing implies that $E_{n_0} \subset {}^*F_n$ for all $n \in N$, and so $E_{n_0} \subset \mu(\mathfrak{F})$. Then $A \cap \mu(\mathfrak{F}) \neq \emptyset$, since by definition of n_0 we have $E_{n_0} \cap A \neq \emptyset$, and the proof is finished.

If $\mathfrak{F}$ does not have a countable subbasis and A is internal, the answer is not so easy to give. We shall first establish that the question whether $A \cap \mu(\mathfrak{F}) \neq \emptyset$ whenever ${}^*F \cap A \neq \emptyset$ for all $F \in \mathfrak{F}$ is related to another question concerning filters.

Let $\mathfrak{F}$ be a filter of $\mathfrak{M}$ of a certain type. If $\Lambda \subset {}^*\mathfrak{F}$ is an *internal* subset of the extension ${}^*\mathfrak{F}$ of $\mathfrak{F}$ in ${}^*\mathfrak{M}$ such that $\mathfrak{F} = {}^0\Lambda$, does it follow that there exists an element $E \in \Lambda$ such that $E \subset \mu(\mathfrak{F})$, or, dually, if Λ is an *internal* subset of ${}^*\mathfrak{F}$ such that $E \subset \mu(\mathfrak{F})$ and $E \in {}^*\mathfrak{F}$ implies $E \in \Lambda$, does it follow that there is an element $F \in \mathfrak{F}$ such that its extension ${}^*F \in \Lambda$?

Concerning these questions we shall first establish the following result.

Theorem 2.7.3. *Let $\mathfrak{M}$ be a full L-structure based in the infinite set X and let $^*\mathfrak{M}$ be an enlargement of $\mathfrak{M}$. Then the following statements are mutually equivalent.*

(a) *For every $\sigma \in T$ and for every filter $\mathfrak{F}$ of $\mathfrak{M}$ of type $((\sigma))$ and for every internal subset A of $^*M_\sigma$, if $^*F \cap A \neq \emptyset$ for all $F \in \mathfrak{F}$, then $\mu(\mathfrak{F}) \cap A \neq \emptyset$.*

(b) *For every $\sigma \in T$ and for every filter $\mathfrak{F}$ of $\mathfrak{M}$ of type $((\sigma))$, if Λ is an internal subset of $^*\mathfrak{F}$ such that $\mathfrak{F} = {}^0\Lambda$, then there exists an element $E \in \Lambda$ such that $E \subset \mu(\mathfrak{F})$.*

(c) *For every $\sigma \in T$ and for every filter $\mathfrak{F}$ of $\mathfrak{M}$ of type $((\sigma))$, if Λ is an internal subset of $^*\mathfrak{F}$ such that $E \in {}^*\mathfrak{F}$ and $E \subset \mu(\mathfrak{F})$ implies $E \in \Lambda$, then there exists an element $F \in \mathfrak{F}$ such that $^*F \in \Lambda$.*

Proof. (a) $\Rightarrow$ (b). Let $\mathfrak{F}$ be a filter of $\mathfrak{M}$ of type $((\sigma))$. For every $E \in \mathfrak{F}$ we set $\mathcal{E} = \{F: F \in \mathfrak{F}$ and $F \subset E\}$. Then the family $\{\mathcal{E}: E \in \mathfrak{F}\}$ is a basis of a filter $\mathfrak{F}_s$ of type $(((\sigma)))$, the filter of the sections of $\mathfrak{F}$. It is easy to see that $\mu(\mathfrak{F}_s) = \{D: D \in {}^*\mathfrak{F}$ and $D \subset \mu(\mathfrak{F})\}$. From the definition of Λ it follows that for all $\mathcal{E} \in \mathfrak{F}_s$ $\Lambda \cap {}^*\mathcal{E} \neq \emptyset$. Thus, Λ being internal, it follows from (a) that $\Lambda \cap \mu(\mathfrak{F}_s) \neq \emptyset$; that is, there is an element $E \in {}^*\mathfrak{F}$ such that $E \subset \mu(\mathfrak{F})$ and $E \in \Lambda$; that is, (b) holds.

(b) $\Rightarrow$ (c). If Λ does not contain any standard element of $^*\mathfrak{F}$, then $\Lambda_0 = {}^*\mathfrak{F} - \Lambda$ satisfies the conditions of (b), and so contains an element $E \in {}^*\mathfrak{F}$ with $E \subset \mu(\mathfrak{F})$ contradicting $E \in \Lambda$. Thus (c) holds.

(c) $\Rightarrow$ (a). If $A \cap \mu(\mathfrak{F}) = \emptyset$, then the set $\Lambda = \{E: E \in {}^*\mathfrak{F}$ and $E \cap A = \emptyset\}$ is internal and satisfies the conditions of (c). Hence there is an element $F \in \mathfrak{F}$ such that $^*F \in \Lambda$, and so $^*F \cap A = \emptyset$, contradicting the assumptions, and the proof is finished.

We shall now show by means of an example, the idea of which is due to H. J. Keisler, that (a), and so (b) and (c), may be false for even an ultrapower enlargement of $\mathfrak{M}$.

Example 2.7.4. We shall need the following preliminary results.

Theorem 2.7.5. *Let $\mathfrak{M}$ be an L-structure based in an infinite set X and let $\mathfrak{U}$ be an ultrafilter over a set I. If A is a *-finite set of $^*\mathfrak{M} = \mathfrak{U}$-prod $\mathfrak{M}$ of type (σ), then* $\operatorname{card}({}^0A) \leq \operatorname{card}(I)$.

Proof. If A is *-finite, then $\{i: A(i)$ is finite$\} \in \mathfrak{U}$. If $a \in A$ is standard, that is, $a = {}^*a_0$ for entity a_0 of $\mathfrak{M}$, then $\{i: a_0 \in A(i)\} \in \mathfrak{U}$. Hence ${}^0A \subset \bigcup(A(i), A(i)$ is finite$)$, and so $\operatorname{card}({}^0A) \leq \operatorname{card}(I)$.

The next theorem states that an iteration of ultrapowers is an ultrapower. Suppose that $\mathfrak{U}_0$ and $\mathfrak{U}_1$ are ultrafilters over I_0 and I_1, respectively.

Then by $\mathfrak{U}_0 \times \mathfrak{U}_1$ we shall denote all sets $E \subset I_0 \times I_1$ which satisfy $\{j: \{i: (i, j) \in E\} \in \mathfrak{U}_0\} \in \mathfrak{U}_1$. It is easy to verify that $\mathfrak{U}_0 \times \mathfrak{U}_1$ is an ultrafilter over $I_0 \times I_i$.

Theorem 2.7.6. *The L-structure* $\mathfrak{U}_1$-prod ($\mathfrak{U}_0$-prod $\mathfrak{M}$) *is isomorphic to the L-structure* ($\mathfrak{U}_0 \times \mathfrak{U}_1$)-prod $\mathfrak{M}$.

Proof. The required isomorphism is defined as follows. Let a be an entity of $\mathfrak{U}_1$-prod ($\mathfrak{U}_0$-prod $\mathfrak{M}$) of type σ; then $a(j)$ is an entity of $\mathfrak{U}_0$-prod $\mathfrak{M}$ of type σ for all j on a set E of $\mathfrak{U}$. Thus setting $a(i, j) = a(j)(i)$, we see that $a(i, j)$, $(i, j) \in I_0 \times I_1$, is an entity a' of $\mathfrak{U}_0 \times \mathfrak{U}_1$-prod $\mathfrak{M}$ of type σ. The mapping $a \rightarrow a'$ is easily seen to be the required isomorphism.

The easy proof of the following result is left to the reader.

Lemma 2.7.7. *Let* $\mathfrak{U}_0$-prod $\mathfrak{M}$ *be an enlargement of* $\mathfrak{M}$ *and let* $\mathfrak{U}_1$ *be an ultrafilter. Then* ($\mathfrak{U}_0 \times \mathfrak{U}_1$)-prod $\mathfrak{M} \cong \mathfrak{U}_1$-prod ($\mathfrak{U}_0$-prod $\mathfrak{M}$) *is also an ultrapower enlargement of* $\mathfrak{M}$.

Let n_0 be an infinitely large natural number of $\mathfrak{U}_1$-prod($\mathfrak{U}_0$-prod $\mathfrak{M}$), where $\mathfrak{M}$ is a full L-structure based in an infinite set X. Then n_0 will be called $\mathfrak{U}_1$-*infinitely* large whenever $\{j: n_0(j) \in N\} \in \mathfrak{U}_1$. Of course, if m_0 is an infinitely large natural number of $\mathfrak{U}_0$-prod $\mathfrak{M}$, then $n < m_0$.

Lemma 2.7.8. *Let* n_0 *be a* $\mathfrak{U}_1$*-infinitely large natural number. Then for every *-finite set* A *of* $\mathfrak{U}_1$-prod ($\mathfrak{U}_0$-prod $\mathfrak{M}$) $\cong$ ($\mathfrak{U}_0 \times \mathfrak{U}_1$)-prod $\mathfrak{M}$ *with fewer than* n_0*-elements we have* $\text{card}({}^0A) \leq \text{card}(I_1)$, *where* $I_1 = \bigcup \mathfrak{U}_1$.

Proof. Observe that $\{j: \text{card}\,(A(j)) \in N\} \in \mathfrak{U}_1$ and apply Theorem 2.7.5.

We shall now turn to a description of the proposed example.

Let $\text{card}(x) > \aleph_0$, let $\mathfrak{M}$ be the full L-structure based in X and $\mathfrak{M}_0 = \mathfrak{U}_0$-prod $\mathfrak{M}$ be an ultrapower enlargement of $\mathfrak{M}$, and let $I_0 = \bigcup \mathfrak{U}_0$. Assume now that $\mathfrak{U}_1$ is a free ultrafilter over a *countable* set I_1. Then, by Lemma 2.7.8, ${}^*\mathfrak{M} = \mathfrak{U}_1$-prod $\mathfrak{M}_0 = \mathfrak{U}_1$-prod($\mathfrak{U}_0$-prod $\mathfrak{M}$) $\cong$ ($\mathfrak{U}_0 \times \mathfrak{U}_1$)-prod $\mathfrak{M}$ is an ultrapower enlargement of $\mathfrak{M}$.

Consider the set $X_0 = P_f(X)$, that is, the set of all finite subsets of X. For every element $a \in X_0 = P_f(X)$ we shall denote by F_a the set of all $a' \in X_0$ such that $a \subset a'$. The family $\{F_a: a \in X_0\}$ generates a filter $\mathfrak{F}$ of $\mathfrak{M}$ of type (((0))) based in X_0. We can easily determine the monad of $\mathfrak{F}$ in ${}^*\mathfrak{M}$. Indeed, $e \in \mu(\mathfrak{F})$ if and only if e is a *-finite subset of ${}^*X$ and $X = {}^0e$. Let n_0 be a $\mathfrak{U}_1$-infinitely large natural number of ${}^*\mathfrak{M}$ and let $A = \{a: a$ is a *-finite subset of ${}^*X$ with at most n_0 elements$\}$. Then A is internal, and $A \cap {}^*d \neq \emptyset$ for all $d \in \mathfrak{F}$; the latter follows from the fact that ${}^0A = P_f(X) = X_0$. From Lemma 2.7.8 it follows that $a \in A$ implies that $\text{card}({}^0a) \leq \text{card}(I_1) = \aleph_0$. On the other hand, $a \in \mu(\mathfrak{F})$ implies that

$X = {}^0a$, and since $\operatorname{card}(X) > \aleph_0$, we obtain that $A \cap \mu(\mathfrak{F}) = \varnothing$, and the required result is obtained.

Having shown that Theorem 2.7.3 may be false for enlargements, the following result may not be without interest.

***Theorem* 2.7.9.** *Let $^*\mathfrak{M}$ be an enlargement of $\mathfrak{M}$. If $\mathfrak{F}$ is a filter of subsets of M_σ and if $A \subset {}^*M_\sigma$ is internal such that $A \cap {}^*F \neq \varnothing$ for all $F \in \mathfrak{F}$, then there exists an element $A' \in \mu_d(\{A\})$ such that $A' \cap \mu(\mathfrak{F}) \neq \varnothing$.*

Proof. Let $\mathfrak{D}_{\{A\}}$ be the ultrafilter of type $((((\sigma))))$ whose monad is equal to $\mu_d(\{A\})$. If $^*F \in {}^*\mathfrak{F}$ is a standard element of $^*\mathfrak{F}$ and $^*E \in \mathfrak{D}_{\{A\}}$ is a standard element of $\mathfrak{D}_{\{A\}}$, then it follows from the hypothesis that the following sentence holds in $^*\mathfrak{M}$. $(\exists A)(A \in {}^*E$ and $^*F \cap A \neq \varnothing)$. Since this is a sentence of $\mathfrak{M}$ it follows from F.T. that there exists a set $B \in E$ in $\mathfrak{M}$ such that $F \cap B \neq \varnothing$. Thus in $\mathfrak{M}$ the following statement holds. $(\forall F)(\forall E)(F \in \mathfrak{F}$ and $E \in \mathfrak{D}_{\{A\}} \Rightarrow (\exists B)(B \in E$ and $F \cap B \neq \varnothing)$. This statement holds in $^*\mathfrak{M}$ also. Thus if $E \in {}^*\mathfrak{D}_{\{A\}}$ such that $E \subset \mu_d(\{A\})$ and if $G \in {}^*\mathfrak{F}$ such that $G \subset \mu(\mathfrak{F})$, then there is an element $A' \in E$ such that $A' \cap G \neq \varnothing$, and so $\mu(\mathfrak{F}) \cap A' \neq \varnothing$. Since $A' \in E$ and $E \subset \mu_d(\{A\})$, it follows that $A' \in \mu_d(\{A\})$, and the proof is finished.

The reason Theorem 2.7.3 may be false for enlargements can be traced to the fact that certain concurrent internal relations are not satisfiable. For instance, consider in Example 2.7.4 the following binary relation b (we use the same notation):

(*) $\Phi_3(b, x, y)$ holds in $^*\mathfrak{M} \Leftrightarrow {}^*\mathfrak{F} \ni y \subset x$ and $y \cap A \neq \varnothing$ and $T_{((0))}(y)$ and $T_{((0))}(x)$.

Then since A is internal, it follows that b is internal. Furthermore, from the definition of A it follows that b is concurrent on the subset of standard elements of $^*\mathfrak{F}$. If b could be satisfied simultaneously, then there would exist a set $y \in {}^*\mathfrak{F}$ such that $y \subset {}^*F$ for all $F \in \mathfrak{F}$, and $y \cap A \neq \varnothing$. The former condition implies that $y \subset \mu(\mathfrak{F})$, and so $\mu(\mathfrak{F}) \cap A \neq \varnothing$. Thus the internal binary relation b cannot be simultaneously satisfied in $^*\mathfrak{M}$ on the set of standard elements of $^*\mathfrak{F}$. This argument thus shows that the following result holds for saturated models.

***Theorem* 2.7.10.** *If $^*\mathfrak{M}$ is a countable ultralimit sequence of successive ultrapower enlargements of $\mathfrak{M}$ or if $^*\mathfrak{M}$ is κ-saturated, where $\kappa >$ card(M), then Theorem* 2.7.3 *holds in $^*\mathfrak{M}$.*

Proof. If $^*\mathfrak{M}$ is an ultralimit, then use the above binary relation and Theorem 1.7.1. In the case that $^*\mathfrak{M}$ is κ-saturated, use again (*) and the fact that $\kappa > \operatorname{card}(M)$.

Remark. We shall now present a simpler proof of Theorem 2.2.6 for the case that $^*\mathfrak{M}$ is κ-saturated, $\kappa > \text{card}(M)$, or $^*\mathfrak{M}$ is an ultralimit satisfying Theorem 1.7.1. We have to show that $\mathfrak{F}$ is principal if and only if $\mu(\mathfrak{F})$ is internal. If $\mu(\mathfrak{F})$ is internal, then $\Lambda = \{E: E \in {}^*\mathfrak{F}$ and $\mu(\mathfrak{F}) \subset E\}$ is an internal subset of $^*\mathfrak{F}$ such that $^0\Lambda = \mathfrak{F}$. Thus $\mu(\mathfrak{F})$ is not standard; then the internal set $\Lambda_0 = \Lambda - \{\mu(\mathfrak{F})\}$ also satisfies $^0\Lambda_0 = \mathfrak{F}$, and so by (b) of Theorem 2.7.3 there is an element $E \in \Lambda_0$ such that $E \subset \mu(\mathfrak{F})$. This contradicts the definition of Λ_0, and so $\mu(\mathfrak{F})$ is standard; that is, $\mu(\mathfrak{F}) = {}^*A$ for some entity A of $\mathfrak{M}$, and $\mathfrak{F}$ is the principal filter generated by A.

In saturated models Theorem 2.7.3 has some interesting consequences. For future reference we shall list a number of them in the following theorem.

Theorem 2.7.11. *Let $^*\mathfrak{M}$ be an ultralimit of a sequence of ultrapower enlargements of $\mathfrak{M} = \mathfrak{M}(X, M)$, or let $^*\mathfrak{M}$ be κ-saturated with $\kappa >$* card(M).

(a) *Let A be an infinite subset of M_σ, $\sigma \in T$. If $\Lambda \subset {}^*(P_f(A))$ is internal such that $E \in \Lambda$ for every *-finite subset of $^*A$ satisfying $A = {}^0E$, then there exists a finite subset $\{a_1, \cdots, a_n\} \subset A$ such that $\{^*a_1, \cdots, {}^*a_n\} \in \Lambda$.*

(b) *Let A be an internal set of entities of type σ, $\sigma \in T$, and let $\{A_\lambda\}$ be a family of subsets of M_σ in $\mathfrak{M}$ such that $A \subset \bigcup {}^*A_\lambda$. Then there is a finite set $\{\lambda_1, \cdots, \lambda_n\}$ such that $A \subset {}^*A_{\lambda_1} \cup \cdots \cup {}^*A_{\lambda_n}$.*

(c) *If $A \subset {}^*M_\sigma$ is internal, then $\mu_d(A)$ is the smallest saturated set containing A; that is, $\mu_d(A) = \bigcup(\mu_d(a): a \in A)$,*

(d) *Let $A \subset {}^*M_\sigma$ be internal and let $A' \in \mu_d(\{A\})$. Then $a' \in A'$ implies that there exists an element $a \in A$ such that $a' \in \mu_d(a)$.*

Proof. (a) Apply Theorem 2.7.3(c) to the Fréchet filter of A.

(b) Apply (a) to the set of all *-finite subsets of $^*\{A_\lambda\}$ which cover A.

(c) It is clear that $\mu_d(A)$ is saturated and $A \subset \mu_d(A)$. If $a \in \mu_d(A)$ and $a \notin \bigcup(\mu_d(a'): a' \in A)$, then for every $a' \in A$ there is a standard set $A_{a'} \subset M_\sigma$ such that $a \notin {}^*A_{a'}$ and $a' \in {}^*A_{a'}$. Then $A \subset \bigcup ({}^*A_{a'}: a' \in A)$ implies by (b) that there is a *finite* set $\{^*A_{a'_1}, \cdots, {}^*A_{a'_n}\}$ such that $A \subset {}^*A_{a'_1} \cup \cdots \cup {}^*A_{a'_n} = {}^*(A_{a'_1} \cup \cdots \cup A_{a'_n})$. Then $a \in \mu_d(A) \subset {}^*(A_{a'_1} \cup \cdots \cup A_{a'_n})$ is a contradiction, and so $\mu_d(A) = \bigcup(\mu_d(a): a \in A)$.

(d) Let $A' \in \mu_d(\{A\})$ and let $a' \in A'$. Now $A' \in \mu_d(\{A\})$ implies, by Theorem 2.6.2, that $A' \subset \mu_d(A) = \bigcup(\mu_d(a): a \in A)$ by the preceding result, and so there is an element $a \in A$ such that $a' \in \mu_d(a)$. This completes the proof of the theorem.

Remark. It may not be without interest to point out once more that for some results the hypothesis that $^*\mathfrak{M}$ is saturated at least to the point that Theorem 1.7.1 holds in $\mathfrak{M}$ is essential. For instance, (a) of Theorem 2.7.11 does not necessarily hold in enlargements. To show this we can again use Example 2.7.4. Indeed, if n_0 is the $\mathfrak{U}_1$-infinitely large natural number, then the set Λ consisting of all *-finite subsets of $*X$ with at least n_0 elements satisfies all the hypotheses of (a) of Theorem 2.7.11, but Λ does not contain any standard finite set.

We shall conclude this section with a characterization of K-saturated models analogously to the characterization of enlargements given in Theorem 2.1.4.

Theorem 2.7.12. *Let $*\mathfrak{M}$ be a higher-order nonstandard model of the higher-order L-structure $\mathfrak{M}$ and let $\kappa > \aleph_0$. Then $*\mathfrak{M}$ is κ-saturated if and only if for all $\sigma \in T$ and for every family Ω of internal sets of $*\mathfrak{M}$ of type (σ) with the finite intersection property and* card$(\Omega) < \kappa$ *we have $\bigcap (E\colon E \in \Omega) \neq \varnothing$.*

Proof. Assume that $*\mathfrak{M}$ is κ-saturated. Then the binary relation $\varnothing \neq y \subset x$ and $T_{(\sigma)}(x)$ and $T_{(\sigma)}(y)$ is concurrent in x on Ω, and so by definition $\bigcap (E\colon E \in \Omega) \neq \varnothing$. Conversely, assume that b is an internal binary relation in $*\mathfrak{M}$ of type $\sigma = (\sigma_1, \sigma_2)$, and assume that b is concurrent on some subset A of its domain with external cardinal $<\kappa$. Then the family $\Omega = \{E_x\colon x \in A \text{ and } y \in E_x \Leftrightarrow \Phi_3(b, x, y) \text{ holds in } *\mathfrak{M}\}$ is a nonempty family of internal sets such that card$(\Omega) < \kappa$ (card$(A) < \kappa$) and Ω has the finite intersection property (b is concurrent on A). Then from the hypothesis of the theorem, there is an entity $y \in *M_{\sigma_2}$ such that $y \in E_x$ for all $x \in A$; that is, $\Phi_3(b, x, y)$ holds in $*\mathfrak{M}$ for all $x \in A$, and the proof is finished.

8. When Is an Internal Set a Standard Set?

Let $\mathfrak{M} = \mathfrak{M}(X, M)$ denote the full L-structure based in the infinite set X, and let $*\mathfrak{M}$ be either a higher-order ultralimit power of $\mathfrak{M}$ with respect to a sequence of successive ultrapower enlargements of $\mathfrak{M}$ or a κ-saturated model where card$(M) < \kappa$.

If A is an internal subset of $*M_\sigma$, then it is natural to ask for necessary and sufficient conditions in order that A contains a standard set or is equal to a standard set. The answers are contained in the following theorem.

Theorem 2.8.1. (a) *An internal set $A \subset *M_\sigma$, $\sigma \in T$, contains a standard set if and only if $\mu_d(a) \subset A$ for some $a \in A$.*

(b) *An internal set is standard if and only if it is saturated.*

Proof. (a) We have only to show that if $\mu_d(a) \subset A$ and A is internal, then A contains a standard set. To this end, let $\Omega = \{E: E \in {}^*\mathfrak{D}_a$ and $E \subset A\}$. Then Ω is internal, and by (b) of Theorem 2.7.3, Ω contains a standard element.

(b) Assume that A is internal and saturated. Then, by (a), ${}^0A$ is not empty. We shall show that ${}^*({}^0A) = A$. For every $a \in A$, there is a standard set ${}^*E \in {}^*\mathfrak{D}_a$ such that $a \in {}^*E \subset A$, and so ${}^*E \subset {}^*({}^0A)$ implies $A \subset {}^*({}^0A)$. If, on the other hand, $a \in {}^*({}^0A)$, then for every $E \in \mathfrak{D}_a$ we have ${}^*E \cap A \neq \varnothing$, and so, by (a) of Theorem 2.7.3, $\mu_d(a) \cap A \neq \varnothing$. Hence A being saturated implies that $\mu_d(a) \subset A$, and so $A = {}^*({}^0A)$. This completes the proof.

9. The $\cup$-Monad of a Covering

A nonempty family $\gamma = \{X_\lambda: \lambda \in \Lambda\}$ of subsets of a set X is called a covering of X whenever $X = \cup X_\lambda$. The following question is often of importance. When does a covering contain a finite subcover? An answer is contained in the following theorem.

Theorem 2.9.1. *Let* $\gamma = \{A_\lambda: \lambda \in \Lambda\}$ *be a covering of a set* $A \subset M_\sigma$, $\sigma \in T$. *Then the following conditions are equivalent.*

(a) *There exists a finite subset* $\Gamma \subset \Lambda$ *such that* $\{A_\lambda: \lambda \in \Gamma\}$ *covers* A.
(b) $\nu(\gamma) = {}^*A$.
(c) $\nu(\gamma)$ *is standard.*
(d) $\nu(\gamma)$ *is internal.*
(e) *For every ultrafilter* $\mathfrak{U}$ *over* A *there exists an element* $\lambda \in \Lambda$ *such that* $A_\lambda \in \mathfrak{U}$.

Proof. (a) $\Rightarrow$ (b) $\Rightarrow$ (c) $\Rightarrow$ (d) is obvious. If (d) holds, then $\nu(\gamma)$ is standard, by Theorem 2.2.6, and so $\nu(\gamma) = {}^*A$. If $\mathfrak{U}$ is an ultrafilter over A, then for some λ $\mu(\mathfrak{U}) \subset {}^*A_\lambda$, and so $A_\lambda \in \mathfrak{U}$; that is, (e) holds. We shall now prove that (e) implies (a). From (e) it follows that $\mu_d(a) \subset \nu(\gamma)$ for all $a \in {}^*A$, and so $\nu(\gamma) = {}^*A$. The result then follows from (b) of Theorem 2.7.11.

A cover γ_1 of A is called finer than a cover γ_2 of A whenever for every $A_1 \in \gamma_1$ there is an element $A_2 \in \gamma_2$ such that $A_1 \subset A_2$. If γ is a cover, then by $\bar{\gamma}$ we shall denote the ideal generated by γ. Then $\bar{\gamma}$ is a cover and $\bar{\gamma}$ is finer than γ. Using Corollary 2.1.6 the following result is evident.

Theorem 2.9.2. *If* γ_1, γ_2 *are covers of* $A \subset M_\sigma$, $\sigma \in T$, *then* γ_1 *is finer than* γ_2 *implies* $\nu(\gamma_1) \subset \nu(\gamma_2)$. *Conversely,* $\nu(\gamma_1) \subset \nu(\gamma_2)$ *implies that* $\bar{\gamma}_1$ *is finer than* $\bar{\gamma}_2$.

Chapter III General Topology

1. The Monad of a Point in a Topological Space

Let (X, τ) be a topological space. Thus X is a nonempty set whose elements are called points and τ denotes the set of open subsets of the topological space. We shall denote by τ' the set of the complements of the elements of τ. Thus τ' is the set of all closed subsets of (X, τ).

Let L be a higher-order language which has sufficiently many constants to denote the set of all entities of all finite types starting from the set of individuals X. By $^*(X, \tau)$ we shall denote a higher-order nonstandard model of (X, τ) which at least is an enlargement. On a number of occasions we shall have to assume that $^*(X, \tau)$ is saturated at least up to finitely many new constants. For this purpose, the ultralimits described in Section 7 of Chapter I will be sufficient for our purpose.

For every $x \in X$ we shall denote by $\mathfrak{N}_\tau(x)$ the τ-neighborhood system of x and by $\mu_\tau(x)$ we shall denote the monad of the filter $\mathfrak{N}_\tau(x)$. Thus $x \in \mu_\tau(x)$ for all $x \in X$; and if τ is the discrete topology, then $\{x\} = \mu_\tau(x)$ for all $x \in X$. We shall also introduce a τ-monad for the nonstandard points of $^*X$. If $a \in {}^*X$, then by $\mathfrak{N}_\tau(a)$ we shall denote the set of all subsets E of X for which there exists an open set $\mathcal{O}$ such that $a \in {}^*\mathcal{O} \subset {}^*E$. It is easy to see that $\mathfrak{N}_\tau(a)$ is a proper filter. Its monad will be denoted by $\mu_\tau(a)$. If a is standard, then $\mu_\tau(a)$ is of course the τ-monad of the standard point a. Observe that $\mu_d(a) \subset \mu_\tau(a)$ for all $a \in {}^*X$.

As was shown in [13], the separation axioms can easily be described in terms of the monads of the standard points. For the sake of completeness we shall recall those results here.

First, observe that if x and y are standard points, then $x \in \mu_\tau(y)$ if and only if $\mu_\tau(x) \subset \mu_\tau(y)$.

(a) (X, τ) is a T_0-space if and only if either $x \notin \mu_\tau(y)$ or $y \notin \mu_\tau(x)$ for any pair of standard points x, y such that $x \neq y$.

(b) (X, τ) is a T_1-space if and only if $x \notin \mu_\tau(y)$ and $y \notin \mu_\tau(x)$ for any pair of standard points x, y such that $x \neq y$; that is, equivalently, $^0(\mu_\tau(x)) = \{x\}$ for all standard points x, where $^0(\mu_\tau(x))$ denotes the set of standard points of $\mu_\tau(x)$ (see Notation 2.5.6).

(c) (X, τ) is a T_2-space (Hausdorff space) if and only if $\mu_\tau(x) \cap \mu_\tau(y) = \emptyset$ for any pair of standard points x, y such that $x \neq y$.

Furthermore, a subset $A \subset X$ is open if and only if $\mu_\tau(x) \subset {}^*A$ for all standard points $x \in A$; a subset $A \subset X$ is closed if and only if $\mu_\tau(x) \cap {}^*A \neq \emptyset$ and x is standard implies $x \in A$; and $x \in A^{-\tau}$ if and only if $\mu_\tau(x) \cap {}^*A \neq \emptyset$.

If τ_1 and τ_1 define topological structures on X, then we say that τ_1 is *finer* than τ_2 whenever $\tau_2 \subset \tau_1$. Thus τ_1 is finer than τ_2 if and only if $\mu_{\tau_1}(x) \subset \mu_{\tau_2}(x)$ for all standard points $x \in X$ if and only if $\mu_{\tau_1}(a) \subset \mu_{\tau_2}(a)$ for all $a \in {}^*X$.

Let S be *any* nonempty subset of ${}^*X$. Then the family of all subsets E of X for which there exists an open set $\mathcal{O}$ such that $S \subset {}^*\mathcal{O} \subset {}^*E$ is a *proper filter* of subsets of X; its monad will be denoted by $\mu_\tau(S)$ and will be called the τ-*monad* of S. It is obvious that $\mu_d(S) \subset \mu_\tau(S)$ for all nonempty subsets S of ${}^*X$.

In terms of the monad of a set, the notion of regularity and normality can be easily expressed.

(d) τ is *regular* if and only if for every closed set $A \subset X$ and $x \notin A$ we have $\mu_\tau(x) \cap \mu_\tau(A) = \varnothing$.

(e) τ is *normal* if and only if for every pair of closed sets $A,B \in \tau'$ such that $A \cap B$ we have $\mu_\tau(A) \cap \mu_\tau(B) = \varnothing$.

Finally, we observe that a filter $\mathfrak{F}$ of subsets of X is τ-*convergent* if and only if $\mu(\mathfrak{F}) \subset \mu_\tau(x)$ for some standard point $x \in X$.

2. τ-saturated Sets

A subset S of ${}^*X$ whether it is internal or not is called τ-*saturated* whenever $\mu_\tau(a) \subset S$ for all $a \in S$. It is obvious that if τ_1 is finer than τ_2, then every τ_2-saturated set is also τ_1-saturated. In particular, every τ-saturated set is saturated in the sense of Section 5 of Chapter 2.

Theorem 3.2.1. (a) *If $A \subset X$, then A is open, that is, $A \in \tau$, if and only if ${}^*A$ is τ-saturated.*

(b) *For any subset $S \subset {}^*X$ its τ-monad $\mu_\tau(S)$ is τ-saturated.*

(c) *A filter has an open basis if and only if its monad is τ-saturated.*

Proof. (a) If ${}^*A$ is τ-saturated, then it is obvious that A is τ-open, and conversely

(b) $\mu_\tau(S)$ is the intersection of τ-saturated sets.

(c) If $\mu(\mathfrak{F})$ is τ-saturated, then $\mu(\mathfrak{F}) = \cup\ (\mu_\tau(a){:}\ a \in \mu(\mathfrak{F}))$, and so by Theorem 2.3.1 we have that $\mathfrak{F} = \vee\ \mathfrak{N}_\tau(A)$; that is, $\mathfrak{F}$ has an open basis.

It is obvious from the definition that $\mu_\tau(S)$ is the smallest τ-saturated monad containing S. If S is internal, however, the following stronger result holds.

Theorem 3.2.2. *For every internal set $S \subset {}^*X$ its τ-monad is the smallest τ-saturated set containing S; that is, $\mu_\tau(S) = \cup\ (\mu_\tau(a){:}\ a \in S)$.*

Proof. We have already shown that $\mu_\tau(S)$ is τ-saturated, and so $\mu_\tau(S)$ contains the τ-saturated set $T = \bigcup (\mu_\tau(a): a \in S)$. If $S \neq T$, then there exists an element $b \in S$ such that $b \notin T$. Hence for every $a \in S$ there exists an open set $\mathcal{O}_a \in \tau$ such that $b \notin {}^*\mathcal{O}_a$. Since S is internal and since $S \subset \bigcup ({}^*\mathcal{O}_a: a \in S)$, it follows from (b) of Theorem 2.7.11 that there is a standard finite subset $({}^*\mathcal{O}_{a_1}, \cdots, {}^*\mathcal{O}_{a_n})$ such that

$$S \subset {}^*\mathcal{O}_{a_1} \cup \cdots \cup {}^*\mathcal{O}_{a_1} = {}^*(\mathcal{O}_{a_1} \cup \cdots \cup \mathcal{O}_{a_n}).$$

Then

$$\mathcal{O}_{a_1} \cup \cdots \cup \mathcal{O}_{a_n} \in \tau,\ b \notin {}^*\mathcal{O}_{a_1} \cup \cdots \cup {}^*\mathcal{O}_{a_n} \text{ and } b \in \mu_\tau(S)$$

contradicts the definition of $\mu_\tau(S)$, and so $\mu_\tau(S) = \bigcup (\mu_\tau(a): a \in S)$ is the smallest τ-saturated set containing S.

***Theorem* 3.2.3.** (a) *Let $S \subset {}^*X$ be internal. Then there exists an open set $\mathcal{O} \in \tau$ such that ${}^*\mathcal{O} \subset S$ if and only if $\mu_\tau(a) \subset S$ for some $a \in S$.*

(b) *An internal subset of ${}^*X$ is a standard open set if and only if it is τ-saturated.*

Proof. (a) The condition is obviously necessary. To show that it is sufficient observe that the set $\mathcal{B}$ of all elements $E \in {}^*\mathfrak{N}_\tau(a)$ such that $E \subset S$ is internal. Hence $\mu_\tau(a) \subset S$ implies that every element of $\mathfrak{N}(a)$ which is a subset of $\mu_\tau(a)$ is an element of $\mathcal{B}$. Thus, by (c) of Theorem 2.7.3, there exists an open set $\mathcal{O} \in \mathfrak{N}_\tau(a)$ such that ${}^*\mathcal{O} \in \mathcal{B}$. From the definition of $\mathcal{B}$ it follows then that the standard open set ${}^*\mathcal{O}$ is a subset of S.

(b) If an internal set S is τ-saturated, then it is saturated and so by (b) of Theorem 2.8.1 S is standard; that is, $S = {}^*({}^0S)$. Then S is τ-saturated implies that ${}^0S \in \tau$. This completes the proof.

3. Near-standard Points

From a model-theoretic point of view the notion of a near-standard point plays a fundamental role in the theory of topological spaces. We shall recall the definition.

A point $a \in {}^*X$ is called a *τ-near-standard point* whenever there exists a *standard* point $x \in X$ such that $a \in \mu_\tau(x)$. In that case, $\mu_\tau(a) \subset \mu_\tau(x)$. The set of all τ-near-standard points will be denoted by $\mathrm{ns}_\tau({}^*(X, \tau))$, or simply $\mathrm{ns}_\tau({}^*X)$. Of course, every standard point is near-standard; that is $X \subset \mathrm{ns}_\tau({}^*X)$. The set of all standard points $x \in X$ such that $a \in \mu_\tau(x)$ will be denoted by $\mathrm{st}_\tau(a)$ and will be called the *standard part set* of a. The elements of $\mathrm{st}_\tau(a)$ will be called the standard parts of a.

If τ_1 is finer than τ_2, then every τ_1-near-standard point is τ_2-near-standard and conversely. Furthermore, if $a \in {}^*X$ is near-standard, then $\mu_d(a) \subset \mu_\tau(x)$ for all $x \in \mathrm{st}_\tau(a)$. Indeed, if $x \in \mathrm{st}_\tau(a)$, then $a \in \mu_d(a) \cap \mu_\tau(x)$ implies, by Theorem 2.4.1, that $\mu_d(a) \subset \mu_\tau(x)$. Thus if a is τ-near-standard, then b is τ-near-standard for all $b \in \mu_d(a)$.

In the following theorem we shall present a characterization of a near-standard point.

Theorem 3.3.1. *A point $a \in {}^*X$ is τ-near-standard if and only if for every τ-open covering γ of X we have $a \in \nu(\gamma)$.*

Proof. Assume that $a \in \mathrm{ns}_\tau({}^*X)$ and that γ is an open covering of X. Then, for every $x \in \mathrm{st}_\tau(a)$ there exists an element $A \in \gamma$ such that $x \in A$. Since A is open we have that $a \in {}^*A$, and so it follows from the definition of ν that $a \in \nu(\gamma)$. Conversely, assume that a is not near-standard, then for every $x \in X$ we have that $a \notin \mu_\tau(x)$, and so there is a standard open set $\mathcal{O}_x \in \tau$ such that $a \notin {}^*\mathcal{O}_x$. Then $a \notin \nu(\gamma)$, where $\gamma = \{\mathcal{O}_x \colon x \in X\}$ is an open covering of X. This finishes the proof.

Corollary 3.3.2. $\mathrm{ns}_\tau({}^*(X, \tau)) = \bigcup (\mu_\tau(x) \colon x \in X) = \bigcap (\nu(\gamma) \colon \gamma$ *is an open covering of* $X)$.

The Hausdorff separation axiom can be characterized as follows.

Theorem 3.3.3. *τ is Hausdorff if and only if $\mathrm{st}_\tau(a)$ is a singleton set for all $a \in \mathrm{ns}_\tau({}^*X)$.*

Proof. If $x,y \in \mathrm{st}_\tau(a)$, $a \in \mathrm{ns}_\tau({}^*X)$ and $x \neq y$, then $a \in \mu_\tau(x) \cap \mu_\tau(y)$ implies that τ is not Hausdorff. If $\mu_\tau(a)$ is a singleton for all $a \in \mathrm{ns}_\tau({}^*X)$, then $x,y \in X$ and $x \neq y$ implies that $\mu_\tau(x) \cap \mu_\tau(y) = \varnothing$; that is, τ is Hausdorff.

Theorem 3.3.4. *A point $a \in {}^*X$ is not near-standard if and only if $\mu_d(a) \cap \mathrm{ns}_\tau({}^*X) = \varnothing$.*

4. The τ-standard Part of a Set

Let A be any subset of ${}^*X$ internal or not. Then by $\mathrm{st}_\tau(A)$ we shall denote the set $\{x \colon x \in X \text{ and } \mu_\tau(x) \cap A \neq \varnothing\}$, and we shall call $\mathrm{st}_\tau(A)$, *the τ-standard part of A*. If $A = \{a\}$, then $\mathrm{st}_\tau(A)$ is the standard part set of a. For the case that τ is the discrete topology it follows from Notation 2.5.6 that $\mathrm{st}_\tau(A) = {}^0A$ for all $A \subset {}^*X$. It is evident that for all topologies τ we have ${}^0A \subset \mathrm{st}_\tau(A)$. More generally, if τ_1 is finer than τ_2, then $\mathrm{st}_{\tau_1}(A) \subset \mathrm{st}_{\tau_2}(A)$ for all $A \subset {}^*X$.

Theorem 3.4.1. *If $A \subset {}^*X$ is S-closed, that is, A is the monad of a filter, then* $\mathrm{st}_\tau(A)$ *is τ-closed. In particular, if $A \subset X$, then* $\bar{A} = \mathrm{st}_\tau({}^*A)$.

Proof. Let $x \in \overline{\mathrm{st}_\tau(A)}$. Then for every open neighborhood V of x we have that ${}^*V \cap A \neq \varnothing$. Indeed, x being an adherent point of $\mathrm{st}_\tau(A)$ it follows that there is an element $y \in X$ such that $y \in V \cap \mathrm{st}_\tau(A)$, and so $a \in \mu_\tau(y)$ for some $a \in A$ implies that $a \in {}^*V$ since V is open at y. Then, by Theorem 2.7.1 we have $A \cap \mu_\tau(x) \neq \varnothing$, that is, $x \in \mathrm{st}_\tau(A)$, and the proof is finished.

Remark. If A is the monad of a filter $\mathfrak{F}$, then $\mathrm{st}_\tau(A)$ is the set of τ-adherent points of $\mathfrak{F}$, that is, $\mathrm{st}_\tau(A) = \bigcap (\bar{F}^\tau, F \in \mathfrak{F})$.

Furthermore, observe that Theorem 3.4.1 also holds in an enlargement of (X, τ).

From Theorem 3.4.1 it follows, in particular, that $\mathrm{st}_\tau({}^*(\mathrm{st}_\tau(A))) = \mathrm{st}_\tau(A)$ for all $A \subset {}^*X$.

It is easy to see that the standard part of an arbitrary subset of ${}^*X$ need not be a closed subset of X. Indeed, if $A \subset X$ is not τ-closed and if B denotes the subset of ${}^*X$ of standard elements which are elements of B, then $\mathrm{st}_\tau(B) = A$.

For internal sets the following result holds.

Theorem 3.4.2. *Let $A \subset {}^*X$ be internal. Then for all $B \in \mu_d(\{A\})$ we have that* $\mathrm{st}_\tau(B) = \mathrm{st}_\tau(A)$ *and* $\mathrm{st}_\tau(A)$ *is a closed subset of X.*

Proof. From (d) of Theorem 2.7.11 and from the fact that a is near-standard if and only if $\mu_d(a) \subset \mathrm{ns}_\tau({}^*X)$, it follows that $\mathrm{st}_\tau(B) = \mathrm{st}_\tau(A)$ for all $B \in \mu_d(A)$. To show that $\mathrm{st}_\tau(A)$ is τ-closed we shall assume that $x \in \overline{\mathrm{st}_\tau(A)}$. Then for every open $V \in \mathfrak{N}_\tau(x)$ we have ${}^*V \cap A \neq \varnothing$, and so, by Theorem 2.7.10, $\mu_\tau(x) \cap A \neq \varnothing$; that is, $x \in \mathrm{st}_\tau(A)$, and the proof is finished.

We shall now show by means of Example 2.7.4 that Theorem 3.4.2 may be false for an enlargement.

Example 3.4.3 (H. J. Keisler). We shall use the notation of Example 2.7.4. Let $X = X_0 \cup \{p_0\}$, where $p_0 \neq X_0$. The topology τ will be defined as follows: $\{a\} \in \tau$ for all $a \in X_0$ and $F_a \cup \{p_0\} \in \tau$ for all $a \in X_0$. Then (X, τ) is a topological space which is a Hausdorff space. Let ${}^*(X, \tau)$ be the same ultrapower enlargement as defined in Example 2.7.4 and let $A = \{a\colon a$ is *-finite subset of ${}^*X$ with at most n_0-elements$\}$. Then $p_0 \notin \mathrm{st}_\tau(A)$. Indeed, the only nonstandard near-standard points are the *-finite subsets containing all the standard elements. On the other hand, $p_0 \in \overline{\mathrm{st}_\tau(A)}$. Thus $\mathrm{st}_\tau(A) = X_0$ is not closed.

Remark. For the case that τ has a countable fundamental neighborhood system at each of its points, that is, (X, τ) satisfies the first axiom of countability, the above result (Theorem 3.4.2) is due to A. Robinson (see Theorem 4.3.12 in [13]).

5. Compactness

We recall that a topological space (X, τ) is *compact* if and only if every open covering has a finite subcovering. The following theorem extends Theorem 2.9.1. The equivalence of (a) and (b) is due to Robinson (see Theorem 4.1.13 of [13]).

Theorem 3.5.1. *Let (X, τ) be a topological space. Then the following conditions are equivalent.*

(a) *(X, τ) is compact.*
(b) $\mathrm{ns}_\tau({}^*X) = {}^*X$.
(c) *$\mathrm{ns}_\tau({}^*X)$ is internal.*

Proof. (a) $\Rightarrow$ (b). Since (X, τ) is compact, it follows immediately that for every open covering γ of X we have ${}^*X = \nu(\gamma)$, and so by Corollary 3.3.2 we have ${}^*X = \mathrm{ns}_\tau({}^*X)$.

(b) $\Rightarrow$ (c) is trivial.

(c) $\Rightarrow$ (a). Let γ be an open covering of X. Then $\mathrm{ns}_\tau({}^*X) \subset \nu(\gamma)$ implies by (b) of Theorem 2.7.11 that there exists a finite subset $\{\mathcal{O}_1, \cdots, \mathcal{O}_n\}$ of γ such that $\mathrm{ns}_\tau({}^*X) \subset {}^*\mathcal{O}_1 \cup \cdots \cup {}^*\mathcal{O}_n = {}^*(\mathcal{O}_1 \cup \cdots \cup \mathcal{O}_n)$. Hence $X \subset \mathrm{ns}_\tau({}^*X)$ implies that $X \subset \mathcal{O}_1 \cup \cdots \cup \mathcal{O}_n$. We conclude that (a) holds and the proof is finished.

For subsets of a topological space the following result holds.

Theorem 3.5.2. *Let A be a subset of a topological space (X, τ). Then the following conditions are equivalent.*

(a) *A is compact in the relative topology.*
(b) *$A \cap \mathrm{st}_\tau(a) \neq \emptyset$ for all $a \in {}^*A$.*
(c) $\mu_\tau(A) = \bigcup(\mu_\tau(x) \colon x \in A)$.

Proof. (a) $\Rightarrow$ (b). If there is an element $a \in {}^*A$ such that $A \cap \mathrm{st}_\tau(a) = \emptyset$, then for every $x \in A$ there is an open set $\mathcal{O}_x \in \tau$ such that $a \notin {}^*\mathcal{O}_x$. The family $\gamma = \{\mathcal{O}_x \colon x \in A\}$ of open sets covers A, and so since A is compact ${}^*A \subset \nu(\gamma)$, contradicting $A \cap \mathrm{st}_\tau(a) = \emptyset$.

(b) $\Rightarrow$ (c). Since by Theorem 3.2.2 $\mu_\tau(A)$ is the smallest τ-saturated set containing ${}^*A$, we have that $\bigcup\, (\mu_\tau(x) \colon x \in A) \subset \mu_\tau(A)$. Furthermore, it follows from the hypothesis that for every $a \in {}^*A$ there is an element $x \in A \cap \mathrm{st}_\tau(a)$, and so $\mu_\tau(a) \subset \mu_\tau(x)$ implies by (Theorem 3.2.3) that $\mu_\tau(A) = \bigcup\, (\mu_\tau(a) \colon a \in {}^*A) = \bigcup\, (\mu_\tau(x) \colon x \in A)$.

(c) $\Rightarrow$ (a). Assume that $\mu_\tau(A) = \bigcup (\mu_\tau(x): x \in A)$ and assume that γ is an open cover of A. Then ${}^*A \subset \mu_\tau(A) = \bigcup (\mu_\tau(x): x \in A)$ implies that ${}^*A \subset \nu(\gamma)$. Hence, by Theorem 2.9.1, there exists a finite subset of γ which covers A. This completes the proof of the theorem.

Let (X_i, τ_i) $(i = 1, 2)$ be two topological spaces. We recall that a mapping f of X_1 into X_2 is continuous at $x \in X_1$ if and only if

$$f(\mu_{\tau_1}(x)) \subset \mu_{\tau_2}(f(x))$$

(see [13], Theorem 4.2.7). The following result is then evident.

Theorem 3.5.3. *A continuous mapping maps every near-standard point in a near-standard point, and so the continuous image of a compact set is compact.*

We shall conclude this section with a few applications.

1. If (X, τ) is compact and if A is a closed subset of X, then A is compact. Indeed, ${}^*A$ consists of near-standard points only and, since $\mathrm{st}_\tau({}^*A) = \bar{A} = A$, it follows from Theorem 3.5.2 that A is compact.

2. Every compact subset of a Hausdorff space is closed. Indeed, if A is compact, then ${}^*A \subset \mathrm{ns}_\tau({}^*X)$ and τ is Hausdorff and using Theorem 3.5.2 we see $\bar{A} = \mathrm{st}_\tau({}^*A) = A$.

3. Every compact Hausdorff space is normal. Let A and B be two closed subsets such that $A \cap B = \varnothing$. Then τ is Hausdorff implies $\mu_\tau(x) \cap \mu_\tau(y) = 0$ for all $x \in A$ and $y \in B$. Furthermore, A is compact and B is compact implies by Theorem 3.5.2 that $\mu_\tau(A) \cap \mu_\tau(B) = \varnothing$; that is, the space is normal.

4. If (X, τ) is compact and Hausdorff and τ is a Hausdorff topology on X, then $\tau_1 \leq \tau$ implies $\tau_1 = \tau$.

Let $A \subset X$. Then ${}^*A \subset \mathrm{ns}_\tau({}^*X) \subset \mathrm{ns}_{\tau_1}({}^*X)$ and τ is Hausdorff and τ_1 is Hausdorff imply that $\mathrm{st}_\tau({}^*A) = \mathrm{st}_{\tau_1}({}^*A)$. Hence, if A is τ-closed, then A is also τ_1-closed.

6. Relative Compactness

We recall that a subset A of a topological space (X, τ) is called *relatively compact* whenever $\bar{A}$ is compact. It is well known that in a topological space which is not Hausdorff a compact subset need not be relatively compact. Thus the condition: the elements of ${}^*A$ are near-standard, need not imply that A is relatively compact. We do have, however, the following two results.

Theorem 3.6.1. *Let (X, τ) be a regular topological space and let A be an internal subset of* $\mathrm{ns}_\tau({}^*X)$. *Then* $\mathrm{st}_\tau(A)$ *is compact. In particular, a sub-*

set A of a regular topological space is relatively compact if and only if $^*A \subset \mathrm{ns}_\tau(^*X)$.

Proof. Let A be an internal subset of $\mathrm{ns}_\tau(^*X)$ and let γ be an open covering of the closed set $\mathrm{st}_\tau(A)$. Since τ is regular there exists an open covering γ' of $\mathrm{st}_\tau(A)$ such that for every $E \in \gamma'$ there is an element $F \in \gamma$ such that $\bar{E} \subset F$. From $A \subset \mathrm{ns}_\tau(^*X)$ it follows that $A \subset \nu(\gamma')$, and so by (b) of Theorem 2.7.11 there is a finite subset $\{E_1, \cdots, E_n\} \in \gamma'$ such that $A \subset {}^*E_1 \cup \cdots \cup {}^*E_n$. Hence $\mathrm{st}_\tau(A) \subset \bar{E}_1 \cup \cdots \cup \bar{E}_n \subset F_1 \cup \cdots \cup F_n$ for suitable elements $F_1, \cdots, F_n$ of γ. This shows that every open cover of $\mathrm{st}_\tau(A)$ has a finite subcover, and so $\mathrm{st}_\tau(A)$ is compact. To prove the second part of the theorem we first observe that if A is relatively compact, then $^*A \subset \mathrm{ns}_\tau(^*X)$. Conversely, if $^*A \subset \mathrm{ns}_\tau(^*X)$, then from the first part of the theorem it follows that $\bar{A} = \mathrm{st}_\tau(^*A)$ is compact, and the proof is finished.

It is an interesting question whether in Theorem 3.6.1 the condition that the topological space is regular can be replaced by other conditions. The following example will show that for T_1-spaces the theorem may be false. Let $X_1 \cup X_2 = X$ be a partition of X in two infinite subsets. Then $\mathcal{O} \in \tau$ whenever either $\mathcal{O} = \emptyset$ or there exists a nonempty subset $\mathcal{O}_1 \subset X_1$ and a nonempty subset $\mathcal{O}_2 \subset X_2$ such that $X_2 - \mathcal{O}_2$ is finite and $\mathcal{O} = \mathcal{O}_1 \cup \mathcal{O}_2$. It is easy to see that (X, τ) is a T_1-space, $^*X_2 \subset \mathrm{ns}_\tau(^*X_2)$ but $X = \mathrm{st}_\tau(^*X_2)$ is not compact. For this reason the following result is not without interest.

Theorem 3.6.2. *Let (X, τ) be a Hausdorff space and let A be an internal subset of* $\mathrm{ns}_\tau(^*X)$. *Then* $\mathrm{st}_\tau(A)$ *is compact. In particular, a subset A of a Hausdorff space is relatively compact if and only if* $^*A \subset \mathrm{ns}_\tau(^*X)$.

Proof. We have only to prove the first part of the theorem. Let A be an internal subset of $\mathrm{ns}_\tau(^*X)$. Assume that $\mathrm{st}_\tau(A)$ is not compact. Then we shall prove that the following statement holds.

(*) For every compact subset $C \subset \mathrm{st}_\tau(A)$ there is a closed neighborhood V_c of C such that $A - {}^*V_c \neq \emptyset$.

Indeed, if (*) does not hold, then there exists a compact subset $C \subset \mathrm{st}_\tau(A)$ such that for every closed neighborhood V of C we have $A \subset {}^*V$, and so $\mathrm{st}_\tau(A) \subset \bar{V} = V$ implies that $\mathrm{st}_\tau(A) = \cap\ (V\colon V$ is a closed neighborhood of $C)$ which is equal to C, since C is compact and τ is Hausdorff, contradicting the assumption that $\mathrm{st}_\tau(A)$ is not compact. This proves (*). Consider now the following *internal* binary relation b.

"$\Phi_3(b, x, y) \Leftrightarrow x \subset {}^*(\mathrm{st}_\tau(A))$ and y is a closed neighborhood of x and $A - y \neq \emptyset$." Since a finite union of compact sets is compact, it follows that b is concurrent on the set of all compact subsets of $\mathrm{st}_\tau(A)$. Then by the saturation it follows that there is an element $a \in A$ such that $a \in A - {}^*V_c$ for all compact subsets $C \subset \mathrm{st}_\tau(A)$. Now $\mathrm{st}_\tau(a)$ is a compact subset of $\mathrm{st}_\tau(A)$ since $A \subset \mathrm{ns}_\tau({}^*X)$. But every closed neighborhood of $\mathrm{st}_\tau(a)$ contains a as an element, and a contradiction is obtained. This completes the proof of the theorem.

Remark. The reader can easily check that the same result could have been shown to hold whenever the following conditions are satisfied: (a) For every $a \in \mathrm{ns}_\tau({}^*X)$ the set $\mathrm{st}_\tau(a)$ is compact and (b) for every compact subset $C \subset X$ and $x \in X$ with $x \notin C$ there exists a closed neighborhood V of C such that $x \in V$.

Of course, if a topological space is Hausdorff or regular, then (a) and (b) are fulfilled.

7. Local Compactness

In this section we shall attempt to characterize the notion of local compactness and discuss the Alexandroff compactification of a topological space.

Let (X, τ) be a topological space. The *compact Fréchet filter* of X is the filter generated by the complements of the compact subsets of X. We shall denote this filter by $\mathfrak{F}c(X)$. Thus X is compact if and only if $\mathfrak{F}c(X)$ is trivial. The monad $\mu(\mathfrak{F}c)$ of $\mathfrak{F}c$ satisfies $\mu(\mathfrak{F}c) \cap {}^*C = \varnothing$ for all compact subsets C of X. This suggests the following definition.

A near-standard point $a \in \mathrm{ns}_\tau({}^*X)$ will be called τ-compact whenever there exists a compact subset $C \subset X$ such that $a \in {}^*C$. The set of all τ-compact near-standard points will be denoted by $\mathrm{cns}_\tau({}^*X)$.

It is easy to see that $X \subset \mathrm{cns}_\tau({}^*X) \subset \mathrm{ns}_\tau({}^*X)$ and $\mu(\mathfrak{F}c) \cap \mathrm{cns}_\tau({}^*X) = \varnothing$.

If C is compact and $a \in {}^*C$, then also $\mu_d(a) \subset {}^*C$. Hence, if a is τ-cns, then b is τ-cns for all $b \in \mu_d(a)$. Thus $\mathrm{cns}_\tau({}^*X)$ is *saturated.*

The importance of the concept of τ-compact near-standard point can be derived from the following theorem.

Theorem 3.7.1. *A topological space is locally compact if and only if every near-standard point is compact.*

Proof. If a is near-standard, then $x \in \mathrm{st}_\tau(a)$ implies that $a \in \mu_\tau(x)$. Thus, if the space is locally compact, then there exists a compact neighborhood V of x, and so $a \in \mu_\tau(x) \subset {}^*V$ is compact near-standard. Conversely, assume that every near-standard point is compact. Then $\mu(\mathfrak{F}c) \cap \mathrm{ns}_\tau({}^*X) = \varnothing$, and so, in particular, $\mu_\tau(x) \cap \mu(\mathfrak{F}c) = \varnothing$ for all standard points x. Hence for every $x \in X$ there exists a neighborhood $V \in \mathfrak{N}(x)$

and an element $E \in \mathfrak{F}c$ such that $V \cap E = \emptyset$; that is, $X - E$ is a compact neighborhood of x. This completes the proof.

Compactness can also be described in terms of $\text{cns}_\tau(^*X)$ as follows.

Theorem 3.7.2. *A topological space is compact if and only if its set of compact near-standard points is internal.*

Proof. If X is compact, then $^*X = \text{ns}_\tau(^*X) = \text{cns}_\tau(^*X)$. Conversely, if $\text{cns}_\tau(^*X)$ is internal, then being saturated it follows from Theorem 2.8.1 and $X \subset \text{cns}_\tau(^*X)$ that $\text{cns}_\tau(^*X) = {}^*X$, and so X is compact by Theorem 3.5.1, and the proof is finished.

Having singled out the elements a of $^*X$ for which there is a compact set C with $a \in {}^*C$, it seems also of interest to characterize all internal sets with this property. The following theorem is in this direction.

Theorem 3.7.3. *Let A be an internal subset of $^*X$. Then there exists a compact subset C of X such that $A \subset {}^*C$ if and only if $A \subset \text{cns}_\tau(^*X)$.*

Proof. We have only to show that the condition is necessary. To this end, observe that $A \cap \mu(\mathfrak{F}c) = \emptyset$, and so by Theorem 2.7.10 there exists an element $E \in \mathfrak{F}c$ such that $A \cap {}^*E = \emptyset$. Hence $A \subset {}^*X - {}^*E = {}^*(X - E)$ and $X - E$ is compact, and the proof is finished.

Remark. If a topological space is regular or Hausdorff, then $A \subset X$ and $^*A \subset \text{ns}_\tau(^*X)$ implies $^*A \subset \text{cns}_\tau(^*X)$. In this direction, local compactness can also be characterized as follows.

Theorem 3.7.4. *A topological space (X, τ) is locally compact if and only if for every internal set A the condition $A \subset \text{ns}_\tau(^*X)$ implies that there exists a compact subset C of X such that $A \subset {}^*C$.*

Proof. If the condition holds, then it follows immediately by applying it to the sets $A = \{a\}$, where $a \in \text{ns}_\tau(^*X)$ that $\text{ns}_\tau(^*X) = \text{cns}_\tau(^*(X))$, and so, by Theorem 3.7.1, (X, τ) is locally compact. Conversely, if (X, τ) is locally compact, then by Theorem 3.7.1 we have that $\text{ns}_\tau(^*X) = \text{cns}_\tau(^*X)$, and so, by Theorem 3.7.3, $A \subset \text{ns}_\tau(^*X) = \text{cns}_\tau(^*X)$ and A is internal implies $A \subset {}^*C$ for some compact subset $C \subset X$, and the proof is finished.

Remark. The notion of relative compactness introduced in Section 6 can be extended in the following way. A subset A of a topological space (X, τ) is called τ-relatively compact whenever there exists a compact subset $C \subset X$ such that $A \subset C$. From Theorem 3.7.3 it follows then immediately that a subset A of (X, τ) is τ-relatively compact if and only if $^*A \subset \text{cns}_\tau(^*X)$. Thus using Theorems 3.6.1 and 3.6.2 we obtain immediately the following result.

For the class of Hausdorff topological spaces and the class of regular topological spaces, the above notion of relative compactness coincides with the notion of relative compactness defined in Section 6.

For the class of regular topological spaces the above result seems to be new.

Theorem 3.7.5. *Let* (X_i, τ_i) $(i = 1, 2)$ *be two topological spaces and let* f *be a continuous mapping of* X_1 *into* X_2. *Then* $f(\mathrm{cns}_{\tau_1}(^*X_1)) \subset \mathrm{cns}_{\tau_2}(^*X_2)$.

Proof. If $a \in \mathrm{cns}_\tau(^*X)$, then there is a compact set $C_a \subset X_1$ such that $a \in {}^*C_a$. Hence $^*f(a) \in {}^*f(^*C_a) = {}^*(f(C_a)) \subset \mathrm{cns}_{\tau_2}(^*X_2)$ since $f(C_a)$ is compact.

Let $\{(X_\lambda, \tau_\lambda): \lambda \in \Lambda\}$ be a nonempty family of nonempty topological spaces and let $(X, \tau) = (\Pi X_\lambda, \Pi\tau_\lambda)$ be the product space with the product topology. We recall that if $x \in {}^*(X, \tau)$ is standard, then $a \in \mu_\tau(x)$ if and only if $a(\lambda) \in \mu_{\tau_\lambda}(x(\lambda))$ for all *standard* $\lambda \in {}^*\Lambda$ (see [13], Theorem 4.11.7). More generally, we have that if $a, b \in {}^*X$, then $b \in \mu_\tau(a)$ if and only if $b(\lambda) \in \mu_{\tau_\lambda}(a(\lambda))$ for all *standard* $\lambda \in {}^*\Lambda$.

We shall now prove the following theorem, which supplements Tychonoff's theorem (see [13], Theorem 4.1.19, for a nonstandard proof of Tychonoff's theorem).

Theorem 3.7.6. *Let* $(X, \tau) = (\Pi X_\lambda, \Pi\tau_\lambda)$, *where* $\{(X_\lambda, \tau_\lambda): \lambda \in \Lambda\}$ *is a nonempty family of nonempty topological spaces. Then* (X, τ) *is locally compact if and only if the set* Γ *of all* $\lambda \in \Lambda$ *such that* X_λ *is not compact is finite and* X_λ *is locally compact for all* $\lambda \in \Gamma$.

Proof. The condition is sufficient. Assume that $a \in {}^*X$ is near-standard. Then for all $\lambda \in \Lambda$, we have that $a(\lambda)$ is compact near-standard. For every $\lambda \in \Gamma$, let C_λ be a compact subset of X_λ such that $a(\lambda) \in {}^*C_\lambda$. Since Γ is finite we have that $a \in {}^*(\Pi Y_\lambda)$, where $Y_\lambda = X_\lambda$ for all $\lambda \notin \Gamma$ and $Y_\lambda = C_\lambda$ for all $\lambda \in \Gamma$. Observe that ΠY_λ is a compact subset of X, and so a is compact near-standard. Thus, by Theorem 3.7.1, (X, τ) is locally compact. The converse is much simpler. Let $x \in X$ be an arbitrary element and let V be a compact neighborhood of x. Then $\mathrm{pr}_\lambda(V) = V_\lambda$ is compact for all $\lambda \in \Lambda$. Since $\Lambda_\lambda = X_\lambda$ except for finitely many λ, the result follows.

8. An Example of a Near-Standard Point That Is Not Compact

For our purpose we need the famous theorem of Ascoli concerning compact families of continuous functions. For the sake of completeness we shall include a new proof of this result.

Let (X, τ) be a compact Hausdorff space and let (Y, d) be a metric space. By $C(X, Y)$ we shall denote the metric space of all continuous mappings of X into Y, where the distance $\rho(f, g)$ between two functions is given by $\max(d(f(x), g(x)): x \in X)$. We shall first characterize the near-standard elements of $C(X, Y)$.

Theorem 3.8.1. *An element $f \in {}^*C(X, Y)$ is near-standard if and only if $f(x)$ is near-standard for all $x \in X$ and ${}^*d(f(a), f(b)) =_1 0$ for all a, $b \in {}^*X$ satisfying* $\mathrm{st}_\tau(a) = \mathrm{st}_\tau(b)$.

Proof. If f is near-standard, then there exists a standard continuous g of X into Y such that ${}^*d(f(a), {}^*g(a)) =_1 0$ for all $a \in {}^*X$. Thus for every $x \in X$, we have $f(x)$ is near-standard. Furthermore, from g is continuous and X is compact it follows that ${}^*d({}^*g(a), {}^*g(b)) =_1 0$ for all a, $b \in {}^*X$ satisfying $\mathrm{st}_\tau(a) = \mathrm{st}_\tau(b)$, and so ${}^*d(f(a), f(b)) \leq {}^*d(f(a), {}^*g(a)) + {}^*d({}^*g(a), {}^*g(b)) + {}^*d(g(b), f(b)) =_1 0$ shows that the other condition is also necessary. Conversely, assume that the conditions are satisfied. First we shall show that the function $g(x) = \mathrm{st}_d(f(x))$, $x \in X$, is a continuous mapping of X into Y. From $\mathrm{st}_\tau(a) = \mathrm{st}_\tau(b) \Rightarrow {}^*d(f(a), f(b)) =_1 0$, it follows immediately that for every standard point $s \in X$ and every standard $\epsilon > 0$ there exists a standard neighborhood V of x such that $y \in V$ implies ${}^*d(f(y), f(x)) < \epsilon$. Hence $d(g(x), g(y)) \leq {}^*d({}^*g(x), f(x)) + {}^*d(f(x), f(y)) + {}^*d(f(y), {}^*g(y)) < \epsilon$ shows that g is continuous. Finally, observe that if $a \in {}^*X$, then $0 =_1 d(f(a), f(st_\tau(a))) =_1 {}^*d(f(a), {}^*g(\mathrm{st}_\tau(a))) =_1 {}^*d(f(a), g(a))$, and so $\rho(f, {}^*g) =_1 0$. This completes the proof.

From the above result the following theorem of Ascoli is an immediate consequence.

Theorem 3.8.2 (*Ascoli*). *Let (X, τ) be a compact Hausdorff space and let (Y, d) be a metric space. Then a subset H of $C(X, Y)$ is relatively compact if and only if H is equicontinuous and for every $x \in X$, the set $H(x) = \{h(x): h \in H\}$ is a relatively compact subset of Y.*

Proof. Assume that H is relatively compact. Then the elements of ${}^*H$ are near-standard. Then, by Theorem 3.8.1, we have that for every $x \in X$, the elements of ${}^*H(x) = {}^*\{h(x): h \in H\}$ are near-standard, and so $H(x)$ is relatively compact by Theorem 3.5.2. Furthermore, if $\epsilon > 0$ and $x \in X$, then there is a standard neighborhood V of x such that $a \in {}^*V$ implies ${}^*d(g(a), g(x)) < \epsilon$ for all $g \in {}^*H$. Hence the family H is equicontinuous. Conversely, the conditions immediately imply that every $g \in {}^*H$ is near-standard, and so by Theorem 3.5.1 we have that $\bar{H}$ is compact, and the proof is finished.

To present a near-standard point that is not compact we need the following preliminary discussion.

A subset $A \subset N \times N$, where N is the set of natural numbers is called *finite in the second coordinate* or simply *p_2-finite* whenever for every $k \in N$ the set $A_k = \{l: (k, l) \in A\}$ is finite. It is clear that every finite subset of $N \times N$ is p_2-finite. Furthermore, the family $\mathfrak{A}$ of all two projection finite sets is a proper ideal of subsets of $N \times N$. Thus the family $\mathfrak{A}'$ of the complements of the elements of $\mathfrak{A}$ is a *proper* filter, and so its monad $\mu(\mathfrak{A}')$ is not empty. It is obvious that $\mathfrak{A}$ is finer than the Fréchet filter of $N \times N$, and so $\mu(\mathfrak{A}') \subset {}^*N \times {}^*N - N \times N$. The elements of $\mu(\mathfrak{A}')$ can be characterized as follows.

Lemma 3.8.3. *$\omega_1, \omega_2 \in \mu(\mathfrak{A}')$ if and only if for every subset $E \subset N \times N$ such that $\omega_1, \omega_2 \in {}^*E$ there is an element $k \in N$ such that $\{l: (k, l) \in E\}$ is infinite.*

Proof. If $\omega_1, \omega_2 \in \mu(\mathfrak{A}')$ and $\omega_1, \omega_2 \in {}^*E$, then E is not two projection finite. Thus there exists an element $k \in N$ such that $\{l: (k, l) \in E\}$ is infinite. Conversely, assume that (ω_1, ω_2) satisfies the condition but $\omega_1, \omega_2 \notin \mu(\mathfrak{A}')$. Then the latter implies that there exists a subset $E \subset N \times N$ such that $E \in \mathfrak{A}'$ and $\omega_1, \omega_2 \notin {}^*E$, and so $\omega_1, \omega_2 \in {}^*A$, where $A = N \times N - E$. Hence $A \in \mathfrak{A}$ contradicts the assumption, and the proof is finished.

For the sake of convenience we shall call a pair $\omega_1, \omega_2 \in \mu(\mathfrak{A}')$ *a random pair*.

Theorem 3.8.4. *Let f be a continuous function of a real variable which is periodic mod 1 and not equal to a constant. If (ω_1, ω_2) is a random pair of infinitely large natural numbers, then the mapping $x \to (1/\omega_1){}^*f(\omega_2 x)$ of $0 \leq x \leq 1$ into ${}^*R$, where R denotes the real number system, is a near-standard element of ${}^*C([0, 1])$ but it is not compact.*

Proof. Let us denote the function $(1/\omega_1){}^*f(\omega_2\cdot)$ by (f, ω_1, ω_2). From $\|(f, \omega_1, \omega_2)\| =_1 0$ it follows immediately that (f, ω_1, ω_2) is near-standard to zero. Assume now that there exists a compact subset A of C ([0, 1]) such that $(f, \omega_1, \omega_2) \in {}^*A$. Observe that the set D of all $(k, l) \in N \times N$ such that $f, k, l \in A$ is not empty. Furthermore, $\omega_1, \omega_2 \in {}^*D$, and so (ω_1, ω_2) is a random pair implies, by Lemma 3.8.3, that there exists a standard natural number k such that the set $N_k = \{l: (k, l) \in D\}$ is infinite. From Ascoli's theorem we conclude that A is equicontinuous. But it is easy to see that the set of functions $f, k, l, l \in N_k$ is not equicontinuous. Thus A is not compact, and so (f, ω_1, ω_2) is not compact, and the proof is finished.

Remark. If $\{e_n: n = 1, 2, \cdots\}$ denote a complete orthonormal system of elements of a separable Hilbert space H, then it follows immediately that for every random pair (ω_1, ω_2), the near-standard element $(1/\omega_1)e_{\omega_2} \in {}^*H$ is not a compact near-standard point of ${}^*H$. Conversely, if $\omega_1, \omega_2 \in {}^*N - N$ such that $(1/\omega_1)e_{\omega_2}$ is not compact near-standard, then (ω_1, ω_2) is a random pair.

9. The Monad of a Uniformity

Let X be a nonempty set and let u be a filter of subsets of $X \times X$ which defines a uniform structure on X; that is, u satisfies the following conditions: (a) Every element of u contains the diagonal $\Delta = \{(x, x): x \in X\}$ of $X \times X$. (b) $V \in u$ implies $V^{-1} = \{(x, y): y, x \in V\} \in u$. (c) For every $V \in u$ there exists an element $W \in u$ such that $W \circ W = \{(x, y): (\exists z)(x, z) \in W \text{ and } (z, y) \in W\} \subset V$. The conditions (b) and (c) can be combined in one condition (d). For every $V \in u$ there exists an element $W \in u$ such that $W \circ W^{-1} \subset V$.

We recall that if u_1 and u_2 are two uniform structures on X, then u_1 is said to be *finer* than u_2 whenever the filter u_1 is finer than the filter u_2. The largest element of the set of all uniform structures on X is the *discrete uniform structure* which consists of the principal filter generated by the diagonal Δ; the smallest element is the uniform structure defined by the principal filter $\{X \times X\}$.

A uniform structure can be characterized in terms of its monad in the following way.

Theorem 3.9.1. *A filter $\mathfrak{F}$ of subsets of $X \times X$ defines a uniform structure on X if and only if its monad $\mu(\mathfrak{F})$ has the following properties:* (a) ${}^*\Delta \subset \mu(\mathfrak{F})$; *that is, $\mu(\mathfrak{F})$ is reflexive.* (b) $(\mu(\mathfrak{F}))^{-1} = \mu(\mathfrak{F})$; *that is, $\mu(\mathfrak{F})$ is symmetric.* (c) $\mu(\mathfrak{F}) \circ \mu(\mathfrak{F}) = \mu(\mathfrak{F})$; *that is, $\mu(\mathfrak{F})$ is transitive.*

Proof. Assume that the filter $\mathfrak{F} = u$ defines a uniform structure on X. Then $\Delta \subset V \in u$ implies that ${}^*\Delta \subset \mu(u)$. From property (b) of u it follows that $(\mu(u))^{-1} = \mu(u)$. Property (c) of u implies immediately that $\mu(u) \circ \mu(u) \subset \mu(u)$. If, on the other hand, $a, b \in \mu(u)$, then $a, a \in \mu(u)$ implies that $a, b \in \mu(u) \circ \mu(u)$; that is, $\mu(u) = \mu(u) \circ \mu(u)$. To prove the converse, we shall show that for every standard element $V \in \mathfrak{F}$, $\Delta \subset V$ and that there exists an element $W \in \mathfrak{F}$ such that $W \circ W^{-1} \subset V$. The former follows immediately from the fact that ${}^*\Delta \subset \mu(\mathfrak{F})$. For the latter property, we observe that if $U \in {}^*\mathfrak{F}$ and $U \subset \mu(\mathfrak{F})$, then $U \circ U^{-1} \subset {}^*V$. Since ${}^*\mathfrak{F}$ and ${}^*V$ are standard it follows from the fundamental theorem that there exists an element $W \in \mathfrak{F}$ such that $W \circ W^{-1} \subset V$. This completes the proof.

The above result shows the interesting fact that *a filter of subsets of $X \times X$ is a uniformity if and only if its monad is the graph of an* (*external*) *equivalence relation on ${}^*X$*. We shall draw some conclusions from this fact. But first we shall introduce some additional notation.

If A is a subset of $X \times X$ and Y is a subset of X, then we shall denote as usual by $A(Y)$ the set $\{x: (\exists y)(y \in Y \text{ and } (x, y) \in A)\}$. If $Y = \{y\}$, then we shall write $A(y)$ rather than $A(\{y\})$. It is easy to see that $A(Y) = \bigcup(A(y): y \in Y)$. Furthermore, we recall that if A, B are subsets of $X \times X$, then $A(B)(Y) = A \circ B(Y)$ for all $Y \subset X$.

Now let u be a uniformity on X. Then for every subset S of $^*X$ we set $\mu_u(S) = \mu(u)(S)$ and, if $S = \{a\}$, then $\mu_u(a) = \mu(u)(\{a\})$. In this way, we define an (external) operator μ_u on the set of all subsets of $^*X$, which will turn out to be of fundamental importance in the theory of uniform structures.

It is easy to see that the operator μ_u is *increasing*, that is, $S_1 \subset S_2 \Rightarrow \mu_u(S_1) \subset \mu_u(S_2)$; idempotent, that is, $\mu_u(S) = \mu_u(\mu_u(S))$; and *inclusive*, that is, $S \subset \mu_u(S)$.

If u_1 is finer than u_2, then $\mu_{u_1}(S) \subset \mu_{u_2}(S)$ for all $S \subset {}^*X$.

Theorem 3.9.2. *Let u define a uniform structure on X.*

(a) *For every $a \in {}^*X$, $\mu_u(a) = \bigcap\, ({}^*V(a): V \in u)$.*
(b) *For all $a,b \in {}^*X$ we have either $\mu_u(a) = \mu_u(b)$ or $\mu_u(a) \cap \mu_u(b) = \varnothing$, that is, the family $\{\mu_u(a): a \in {}^*X\}$ in a partition of $^*X$.*
(c) $\mu(u) = \bigcup\, (\mu_u(a) \times \mu_u(a): a \in {}^*X)$.

Proof. (b) and (c) follow immediately from the fact that the monad of u is the graph of an equivalence relation on X. To prove (a) let $b \in \mu_u(a)$. Then $b, a \in \mu(u) \subset {}^*V$ for all $V \in u$ implies that $b \in \bigcap\, ({}^*V(a): a \in {}^*X)$. If, on the other hand, $b \in \bigcap\, ({}^*V(a): a \in {}^*X)$, then $b, a \in {}^*V$ for all $V \in u$, and so $b, a \in \bigcap\, ({}^*V: V \in u) = \mu(u)$; that is, $b \in \mu_u(a)$, and the proof is finished.

For thc case that u is *discrete*, the reader should observe that $\mu_u(a) = \{a\}$ for all $a \in {}^*X$, and so $\mu_d \neq \mu_u$.

It is well known that a uniform structure u on a set X induces a topology on X, which we shall denote by τ_u. For every $x \in X$ the fundamental neighborhood system $\mathfrak{N}_{\tau_u}(x)$ of this topology consists of all sets of the form $V(x)$, $V \in u$. Thus for every (standard) element $x \in X$, it follows from (a) of Theorem 3.8.2 that $\mu_u(x)$ is the *monad* of the τ_u-neighborhood filter $\mathfrak{N}_{\tau_u}(x)$ of x. Observe, however, that for $a \in {}^*X$ which is nonstandard, $\mu_{\tau_u}(a) \neq \mu_u(a)$ may hold, as in the case of the discrete uniform structure.

Theorem 3.9.3. *If u is a uniform structure on X, then τ_u is regular.*

Proof. Let $V \in \mathfrak{N}_{\tau_u}(x)$ and let $U \in {}^*u$ be such that $U \subset \mu(u)$. Then $\overline{U(x)} \subset \mu_u(x)$. Now $a \in \bar{U}(x)$ implies $U(a) \cap U(x) \neq \varnothing$, and so there exists an element $b \in U(x)$ such that $b, a \in U \subset \mu(u)$, from which we conclude $a \in \mu_u(b)$. Then $b \in U(x)$ and (b) of Theorem 3.9.3 implies $\mu_u(b) = \mu_u(x)$, and so $a \in \mu_u(x)$ implies $\bar{U}(x) \subset \mu_u(x) \subset {}^*V$. Then the result follows from F.T. since ${}^*V$ is standard.

Corollary 3.9.4. *A subset A of a uniform space X is relatively compact if and only if ${}^*A \subset ns_{\tau_u}({}^*X)$.*

Proof. This result follows immediately from Theorems 3.6.1 and 3.9.3.

Another conclusion that can be drawn from Theorem 3.9.2 is the following:

Theorem 3.9.5. *Let u be a uniform structure on X. Then τ_u is Hausdorff if and only if $\bigcap (V\colon V \in u) = \Delta$; that is, the subset of standard elements of $\mu(u)$ is the diagonal Δ of X. In particular, if τ_u is a T_0-space, then τ_u is Hausdorff.*

Proof. This follows easily from the observation that if $x,y \in X$, then $\mu_u(x) = \mu_u(y)$ if and only if $\mu_u(x) \cap \mu_u(y) \neq \emptyset$.

We conclude this section with the following observation.

Theorem 3.9.6. *Let (X, u) be a uniform space, and let $a \in {}^*X$. Then $\mu_u(a)$ is internal if and only if there exists an element $V \in u$ such that $\mu_u(a) = {}^*V(a)$.*

Proof. If $\mu_u(a) = {}^*V(a)$, then $\mu_u(a)$ is obviously internal. If $\mu_u(a)$ is internal, then the set $\mathcal{B} = \{U\colon U \in {}^*u \text{ and } U(a) \subset \mu_u(a)\}$ is internal. Furthermore, $\mathcal{B}$ contains all the elements of ${}^*u$ that are subsets of the monad of u. Thus by Theorem 2.7.10 there exists a standard element ${}^*V \in {}^*u$ such that ${}^*V \in \mathcal{B}$, and so ${}^*V(a) \subset \mu_u(a)$. Then $\mu_u(a) \subset {}^*V(a)$ implies $\mu_u(a) = {}^*V(a)$, and the proof is complete.

Remark. The reader should observe that $\mu_u(a) = {}^*V(a)$ that for all $W \in u^*$, $W(a)$ contains $\mu_u(a)$, and so for all $U \in {}^*u$ we have $\mu_u(a) \subset U(a)$, or, in other words, *$\mu_u(a)$ is internal if and only if the filter $\{U(a)\colon U \in {}^*u\}$ is a principal filter generated by an element ${}^*V(a)$ with $V \in u$.*

10. An Expression for the τ_u-standard Part of an Internal Set

We recall from Notation 2.5.6 that if S is any subset of ${}^*X$, then ${}^0S$ denotes the set of all standard elements a of X such that ${}^*a \in S$.

The τ_u-standard part of a set can be expressed as follows.

Theorem 3.10.1. *Let u be a uniform structure on X and let A be an internal subset of ${}^*X$. Then $st_{\tau_u}(A) = {}^0(\bigcap ({}^*V(A)\colon V \in u))$. In particular, if $A = {}^*B$ is a standard subset of ${}^*X$, then $\bar{B} = st_{\tau_u}({}^*B) = {}^0(\bigcap ({}^*V({}^*B)\colon V \in u)) = \bigcap (V(B)\colon V \in u)$.*

Proof. Assume that $x \in \mathrm{st}_\tau(A)$. Then there exists an element $a \in A$ such that $a \in \mu_{\tau_u}(x)$, and so $x \in {}^*V(a)$ for all $V \in u$ implies $x \in \bigcap ({}^*V(A)\colon V \in u)$. Assume that x is standard and that $x \in \bigcap ({}^*V(A)\colon V \in u)$. Then ${}^*V(x) \cap A \neq \varnothing$ for all $V \in u$, and so by Theorem 2.7.10 we obtain that $\mu_{\tau_u}(x) \cap A \neq \varnothing$; that is, $x \in \mathrm{st}_{\tau_u}(A)$. Using Theorem 3.4.1 and the formula ${}^0({}^*V({}^*B)) = {}^0({}^*(V(B))) = V(B)$ the second part of the theorem follows readily.

Corollary 3.10.2. *If A is an internal subset of ${}^*X$, then ${}^0(\bigcap ({}^*V(A)\colon V \in u))$ is τ_u-closed.*

Proof. Combine Theorem 3.10.1 with Corollary 3.9.4.

11. The Monad of a Cauchy Filter

Let (X, u) be a uniform space. We recall that a proper filter $\mathfrak{F}$ is said to be a *u-Cauchy filter* or, shortly, a *Cauchy filter*, if no confusion can arise, whenever for every $V \in u$ there exists an element $F \in \mathfrak{F}$ such that $F \times F \subset V$. It is obvious that a filter which is finer than a Cauchy filter is a Cauchy filter. If a uniform structure u_1 is finer than a uniform structure u_2, then every u_2-Cauchy filter is a u_1-Cauchy filter.

It follows immediately from the definition that a filter $\mathfrak{F}$ is a Cauchy filter if and only if $\mu(\mathfrak{F}) \times \mu(\mathfrak{F}) \subset \mu(u)$. From this observation it follows immediately that if a filter $\mathfrak{F}$ is convergent, then it is a Cauchy filter. Indeed, if $\mathfrak{F}$ converges to x, then $\mu(\mathfrak{F}) \subset \mu_u(x)$, and so $\mu(\mathfrak{F}) \times \mu(\mathfrak{F}) \subset \mu(u)$.

Cauchy filters can also be characterized as follows.

Theorem 3.11.1. *Let (X, u) be a uniform space and let $\mathfrak{F}$ be a proper filter of subsets of X. Then the following statements are mutually equivalent.*

(a) *$\mathfrak{F}$ is a Cauchy filter.*
(b) *$\mu(\mathfrak{F}) \subset \mu_u(a)$ for all $a \in \mu(\mathfrak{F})$.*
(c) *$\mu_u(a) \cap \mu_u(b) \neq \varnothing$ for all $a, b \in \mu(\mathfrak{F})$.*

Proof. (a) $\Rightarrow$ (b). If $\mathfrak{F}$ is a Cauchy filter, then $\mu(\mathfrak{F}) \times \mu(\mathfrak{F}) \subset \mu(u)$ implies that for all $a \in \mu(\mathfrak{F})$, $\mu(\mathfrak{F}) = (\mu(\mathfrak{F}) \times \mu(\mathfrak{F}))(a) \subset \mu_u(a)$, which proves (b).

(b) $\Rightarrow$ (c) is obvious.

(c) $\Rightarrow$ (a). From (b) of Theorem 3.9.2 we obtain that $\mu_u(a) = \mu_u(b)$ for all $a, b \in \mu(\mathfrak{F})$, and so $\mu(\mathfrak{F}) \subset \mu_u(a)$. The latter implies, however, that $\mu(\mathfrak{F}) \times \mu(\mathfrak{F}) \subset \mu(u)$, and the proof is finished.

The following characterization of Cauchy filters is in a somewhat different direction.

Theorem 3.11.2. *A proper filter* $\mathfrak{F}$ *is a u-Cauchy filter if and only if for every* $V \in u$ *there is an element* $x \in X$ *such that* $\mu(\mathfrak{F}) \subset {}^*V(x)$.

Proof. If $\mathfrak{F}$ is a Cauchy filter and $V \in u$, then by definition there is an element $F \in \mathfrak{F}$ such that $F \times F \subset V$, and so $\mu(\mathfrak{F}) \subset {}^*F \subset {}^*V(x)$ for all $x \in F$. Conversely, if for every $V \in u$ there is an element $x \in X$ such that $\mu(\mathfrak{F}) \subset {}^*V(x)$, then the set $\mathfrak{B} = \{E: E \in {}^*\mathfrak{F} \text{ and } E \subset {}^*V(x)\}$ is internal. Since $\mathfrak{B}$ contains all the elements of ${}^*\mathfrak{F}$ which are subsets of $\mu(\mathfrak{F})$ it follows from Theorem 2.7.3 that there is a standard element ${}^*F \in {}^*\mathfrak{F}$ such that $F \subset V(x)$, and so $F \times F \subset V \circ V \in u$ shows that $\mu(\mathfrak{F}) \times \mu(\mathfrak{F}) \subset \mu(u)$; that is, $\mathfrak{F}$ is a Cauchy filter.

Corollary 3.11.3. *A filter* $\mathfrak{F}$ *is a u-Cauchy filter if and only if for every* $V \in u$ *the set* $\{x: x \in X \text{ and } \mu(\mathfrak{F}) \subset {}^*V(x)\} \in \mathfrak{F}$.

Proof. Apply the preceding result.

12. Pre-near-standard Points and Minimal Cauchy Filters

Let (X, u) be a uniform space. An element $a \in {}^*X$ is called a *pre-near-standard* point whenever there exists a Cauchy filter $\mathfrak{F}$ of subsets of X such that $\mu(\mathfrak{F}) \subset \mu_u(a)$. The set of pre-near-standard points will be denoted by $\text{pns}_u({}^*X)$. It is obvious that every near-standard point is pre-near-standard. Thus $\text{ns}_{\tau_u}({}^*X) \subset \text{pns}_u({}^*X)$.

A Cauchy filter $\mathfrak{F}$ is called *minimal* when it does not properly contain a Cauchy filter. It is well known and easy to see that for every Cauchy filter $\mathfrak{F}$ there exists a minimal Cauchy filter $\mathfrak{F}_m$ contained in $\mathfrak{F}$. Indeed, $\mathfrak{F}_m$ is generated by the family of sets $\{V(F): F \in \mathfrak{F} \text{ and } V \in u\}$. The following theorem gives a characterization of pre-near-standard points.

Theorem 3.12.1. *A point* $a \in {}^*X$ *is pre-near-standard if and only if there exists a minimal Cauchy filter* $\mathfrak{F}_m$ *such that* $\mu(\mathfrak{F}_m) = \mu_u(a)$.

Proof. We have only to show that if a is pre-near-standard, then $\mu_u(a)$ is the monad of a minimal Cauchy filter. From the definition of a pre-near-standard point it follows that there is a Cauchy filter $\mathfrak{F}$ such that $\mu(\mathfrak{F}) \subset \mu_u(a)$. From Theorem 3.9.2 it follows that for every Cauchy filter $\mathfrak{F}' \subset \mathfrak{F}$ we have $\mu(\mathfrak{F}) \subset \mu(\mathfrak{F}') \subset \mu_u(a)$. Now the filter $\mathfrak{F}_m$ generated by the family of sets $\{V(F): F \in \mathfrak{F} \text{ and } V \in u\}$ satisfies $\mu(\mathfrak{F}) \subset \mu(\mathfrak{F}_m) \subset \mu_u(a)$. But it is obvious that $\mu_u(\mu(\mathfrak{F})) \subset {}^*V({}^*F)$ for all $V \in u$ and all $F \in \mathfrak{F}$, and so $\mu_u(\mu(\mathfrak{F})) \subset \mu(\mathfrak{F}_m)$. But if $b \in \mu(\mathfrak{F})$, then $\mu_u(b) \subset \mu_u(\mu(\mathfrak{F}))$, and so $\mu_u(b) = \mu_u(a)$ implies that $\mu(\mathfrak{F}_m) = \mu_u(a)$. This completes the proof and shows at the same time that $\mathfrak{F}_m$ is a minimal Cauchy filter.

For every standard $x \in X$, $\mu_u(x)$ is the monad of the τ_u-neighborhood filter of x which is itself obviously a minimal Cauchy filter. One may raise the question for which $a \in {}^*X$ is $\mu_u(a)$ the monad of some filter of subsets of X. The answer is contained in the following theorem.

Theorem 3.12.2. *A point $a \in {}^*X$ is pre-near-standard if and only if $\mu_u(a)$ is the monad of some filter $\mathfrak{F}$ of subsets of X and in that case, $\mu_{\tau_u}(a) \subset \mu_u(a)$.*

Proof. If a is pre-near-standard, then, by Theorem 3.12.1, $\mu_u(a)$ is the monad of a minimal Cauchy filter. Conversely, assume that $\mu_u(a) = \mu(\mathfrak{F})$ for some filter $\mathfrak{F}$ of subsets of X. Then $a \in \mu(\mathfrak{F})$ implies that $\mu(\mathfrak{F}) \times \mu(\mathfrak{F}) \subset \mu_u \circ \mu_u$, and so $\mathfrak{F}$ is a Cauchy filter, and the proof is finished.

Theorem 3.12.3. *We have* $\text{pns}_u({}^*X) = \bigcup(\mu(\mathfrak{F})\colon \mathfrak{F}$ *is a Cauchy filter of subsets of X). Consequently,* $\text{pns}_u({}^*X)$ *is saturated.*

Proof. This result follows immediately from the preceding result. Since $\mu(\mathfrak{F})$ is saturated, the second result follows.

We shall say that a subset $S \subset {}^*X$ is u-saturated whenever for every $a \in S$ we have $\mu_u(a) \subset S$. Minimal Cauchy filters can be characterized as follows.

Theorem 3.12.4. *A Cauchy filter $\mathfrak{F}$ is minimal if and only if it has a basis of u-saturated sets. In particular,* $\text{pns}_u({}^*X)$ *is also u-saturated.*

Proof. If the condition is satisfied, then $\mu(\mathfrak{F})$ is u-saturated and so $\mu(\mathfrak{F}) = \mu_u(a)$ for all $a \in \mu(\mathfrak{F})$. The converse is obvious, since all sets of the type ${}^*((V \circ V)(F))$, $V \in u$ and $F \in \mathfrak{F}$, are u-saturated.

Remark. If (X, u) is a uniform space such that τ_u is Hausdorff and a is pre-near-standard, then a is a discrete standard point if and only if $\mu_u(a)$ is internal.

13. Precompactness

A uniform space (X, u) is called *precompact* or *totally bounded* whenever for every $V \in u$ there exists *finitely* many points $x_1, \cdots, x_n \in X$ such that $X = \bigcup_{i=1}^{n} V(x_i)$.

Analogously to Theorem 3.5.1 we have the following result.

Theorem 3.13.1. *Let (X, u) be a uniform space. Then the following conditions are equivalent.*

(a) *(X, u) is precompact.*
(b) *Every element of ${}^*X$ is pre-near-standard.*
(c) *Every ultrafilter of subsets of X is a Cauchy filter.*
(d) $\text{pns}_u({}^*X)$ *is internal.*

Proof. (a) $\Rightarrow$ (b). If X is precompact, and if $a \in {}^*X$, then for every $V \in u$ there is an element $x_v \in X$ such that $a \in {}^*V(x_v)$. Let $\mathfrak{F} = \{V(x_v): V \in u\}$. Then $\mathfrak{F}$ is a proper filter and according to Theorem 3.11.2 $\mathfrak{F}$ is a Cauchy filter. Hence $a \in \mu(\mathfrak{F})$ implies a is pre-near-standard.

(b) $\Rightarrow$ (c). Let $\mathfrak{U}$ be an ultrafilter and let $a \in \mu(\mathfrak{U})$. Then a being pre-near-standard, $\mu_u(a)$ is the monad of a Cauchy filter (Theorem 3.12.1), and so $\mu(\mathfrak{U}) \subset \mu_u(a)$ shows that $\mathfrak{U}$ is a Cauchy filter.

(c) $\Rightarrow$ (d) is obvious, since (c) implies that $\text{pns}_u({}^*X) = {}^*X$.

(d) $\Rightarrow$ (a). Let $V \in u$. Then by Theorem 3.12.3 and Corollary 3.10.2 we have that $\text{pns}_u({}^*X) \subset \bigcup\,({}^*V(x): x \in X)$. Hence from (b) of Theorem 2.7.11 it follows that there exists a finite set $\{x_1, \cdots, x_n\} \subset X$ such that $X \subset \text{pns}_u({}^*X) \subset \bigcup_{i=1}^n V(x_i)$, and the proof is finished.

A subset A of a uniform space (X, u) is called precompact whenever for every $V \in u$ there exists finitely many points $x_1, \cdots, x_n$ in A such that $A \subset \bigcup_{i=1}^n V(x_i)$.

Then analogously to Theorem 3.5.2 the following theorem holds.

Theorem 3.13.2. *Let A be a subset of a uniform space (X, u). Then the following conditions are mutually equivalent.*

(a) *A is precompact.*
(b) *For every $a \in {}^*A$ there exists a Cauchy filter $\mathfrak{F}$ such that $a \in \mu(\mathfrak{F})$.*

Proof. (b) $\Rightarrow$ (a). From (b) it follows that ${}^*A \subset \bigcup\,({}^*V(x): x \in A)$, and so there are finitely many points $x_1, \cdots, x_n \in A$ such that $A = \bigcup_{i=1}^n V(x_i)$, and the proof is finished.

14. Completeness

We recall that a uniform (X, u) is called *complete* whenever every Cauchy filter is convergent. The following theorem is evident.

Theorem 3.14.1. *A uniform space (X, u) is complete if and only if every pre-near-standard point is near-standard.*

Proof. Assume that (X, u) is complete and that $a \in \text{pns}_u({}^*X)$. Then $\mu_u(a)$ is the monad of a Cauchy filter, and so (X, u) being complete there is a standard point $x \in X$ such that $\mu_u(x) = \mu_u(a)$. Hence a is near-standard. If every pre-near-standard point is near-standard, then for every Cauchy filter $\mathfrak{F}$ there is a standard point $x \in X$ such that $\mu(\mathfrak{F}) \subset \mu_u(x)$; that is, $\mathfrak{F}$ is convergent, and the proof is finished.

Combining Theorems 3.13.1, 3.14.1, and 3.5.1 we obtain the following well-known criteria for compactness.

Theorem 3.14.2. *A uniform space* (X, u) *is compact if and only if it is complete and precompact.*

Remark. If (X, τ) is a compact Hausdorff space, then there exists a unique uniform structure u on X such that $\tau_u = \tau$. Indeed, if u is a uniform structure such that $\tau_u = \tau$, then $\mu(u) = \bigcup (\mu_u(a) \times \mu_u(a) \colon a \in {}^*X) = \bigcup (\mu_\tau(x) \times \mu_\tau(x) \colon x \in X)$, since X is compact and Hausdorff. Conversely, $\bigcup (\mu_\tau(x) \times \mu_\tau(x) \colon x \in X)$ is the monad of a filter containing the diagonal provided the space is compact and Hausdorff, and it is obviously the graph of an equivalence relation.

15. The Completion and the Nonstandard Hull of a Uniform Space

Let (X, u) be a uniform space. It is well known that a uniformity u on X can be equivalently defined by means of a family $\{\rho_\gamma \colon \gamma \in \Gamma\}$ of semimetrics on X. In terms of the semimetrics the monad of u can be expressed as follows. $a, b \in \mu(u)$ if and only if ${}^*\rho_\gamma(a, b) =_1 0$ (= infinitesimal) for all $\gamma \in \Gamma$. In particular, $\mu_u(a) = \{b \colon b \in {}^*X$ and ${}^*d_\gamma(a, b) =_1 0$ for all $\gamma \in \Gamma\}$.

For the case of a metric space, that is, when u has a countable subbasis, u is determined by a single metric ρ, and so $\mu(u)$ consists of all pairs (a, b) such that ${}^*\rho(a, b) =_1 0$. Furthermore, $\mu_u(a) = \{x \colon x \in {}^*X$ and ${}^*\rho(a, x) =_1 0\}$ for all $a \in {}^*X$. The sets $\mu_u(a)$ for the case of a metric space were also introduced in [13]. Unfortunately, they are called monads in [13], which conflicts with our terminology. Indeed, in Theorem 3.12.2 we have shown that $\mu_u(a)$ is a genuine filter monad if and only if a is pre-near-standard, and so if the metric space is complete and not compact, then $\mu_u(a)$ is not a filter monad whenever a is not near-standard.

As in the case of a metric space (see [13]) we shall introduce the *galaxies* for uniform spaces by means of the following definition. We shall say that two points $x, y \in {}^*X$ are in the same *galaxy* whenever ${}^*\rho_\gamma(x, y)$ is *finite* for all $\gamma \in \Gamma$. This binary relation is obviously an equivalence relation, and the sets of equivalent points will be called *galaxies* of ${}^*X$. Since any two points of X are in the same galaxy, the standard points of ${}^*X$ belong to one and the same galaxy, which will be called the *principal galaxy* of ${}^*X$ and will be denoted by ${}^*X_0$. The elements of ${}^*X_0$ can also be characterized as follows. A point $a \in {}^*X$ is called a *finite point* whenever for every $\gamma \in \Gamma$ there is a point $x \in X$ such that ${}^*\rho_\gamma(a, x)$ is finite. It is then easy to see that $a \in {}^*X_0$ if and only if a is *finite*. In particular, every pre-near-standard point, and so also all the near-standard points, are *finite*. Furthermore, observe that if $a \in {}^*X$ is finite, then ${}^*\rho_\gamma(a, x)$ is finite for all $\gamma \in \Gamma$ and all $x \in X$.

In Theorem 3.11.1 we have shown that for all $a, b \in {}^*X$ either $\mu_u(a) = \mu_u(b)$ or $\mu_u(a) \cap \mu_u(b) = \emptyset$, or equivalently that $\mu(u)$ is the graph of an equivalence relation. Since a_1 and a_2 are in the same galaxy implies that a_1' and a_2' are in the same galaxy as a_1 and a_2 for all $a_1' \in \mu_u(a_1)$ and $a_2' \in \mu_u(a_2)$, it follows that the galaxies are $\mu(u)$-saturated. Thus, in particular, $a \in {}^*X_0$ implies $\mu_u(a) \in {}^*X_0$. This justifies us to consider the set $X_0 = \{\mu_u(a) : a \in {}^*X_0\}$. Furthermore, ${}^*\rho_\gamma(a, b)$ being finite for all $a, b \in {}^*X_0$, the following definition is justified. For all $x, y \in X_0$ and $\gamma \in \Gamma$ we set $\rho_\gamma(x, y) = st({}^*\rho_\gamma(a, b))$, where $x = \mu_u(a)$ and $y = \mu_u(b)$. It is obvious that if $a' \in \mu_u(a)$ and $b' \in \mu_u(b)$, then ${}^*\rho_\gamma(a, b) =_1 {}^*\rho_\gamma(a', b')$, and so ρ_γ is well defined. The family $\{\rho_\gamma : \gamma \in \Gamma\}$ defines a uniform structure on X_0. The mapping $x \to \mu_u(x)$ of X into X_0 is one to one and embeds X into X_0 and preserves its uniform structure. That is why the notation of the semimetrics was not changed.

The uniform space $(X_0, \{\rho_\gamma : \gamma \in \Gamma\})$ is called the *nonstandard hull* of $(X, \{\rho_\gamma : \gamma \in \Gamma\})$, and its topology is sometimes referred to as the S_τ-topology. If X is discrete and u denotes the uniform structure defined by the finite partitions of X, then its u-nonstandard hull is the quotient space introduced in Theorem 2.5.5, and the S_τ-topology is the S-topology.

Concerning the nonstandard hull we have the following result.

Theorem 3.15.1. *Let* $(X, \{\rho_\gamma : \gamma \in \Gamma\})$ *be a uniform space and let* ${}^*(X, \{\rho_\gamma : \gamma \in \Gamma\})$ *be a* κ*-saturated ultrapower model of* $(X, \{\rho_\gamma : \gamma \in \Gamma\})$. *If* $\kappa > \max(\mathrm{card}(\Gamma), \aleph_0)$, *then the nonstandard hull* $(X_0, \{\rho_\gamma : \gamma \in \Gamma\})$ *of* X *is a complete uniform space. In particular, the nonstandard hull of a metric space in an ultrapower of the metric space with respect to a* δ*-incomplete ultrafilter is always complete.*

Proof. Let $\{\mu_u(a_p) : p \in D\}$ be a Cauchy net in X_0. Then for every $\gamma \in \Gamma$ and $\epsilon > 0$ there is an index $n_0(\epsilon) \in D$ such that $\rho_\gamma(\mu_u(a_p), \mu_u(a_q)) < \epsilon$ for all $p,q > n_0$, and so also ${}^*\rho_\gamma(a_p, a_q) < \epsilon$ for all $p,q > n_0(\epsilon)$. According to Corollary 1.8.2 the mapping $p \to a_p$ of D into ${}^*X$ can be extended to an internal mapping $p \to a_p$ of ${}^*D$ into ${}^*X$. Now for every $k \in N$ and $\gamma \in \Gamma$ there is an index $n_0(\gamma, k) \in D$ such that ${}^*\rho_\gamma(a_p, a_q) < 1/k$ for all $p,q \in D$ and $p,q > n_0(\gamma, k)$. There is no loss of generality to assume that the set $\{n_0(\gamma, k) : \gamma \in \Gamma, k \in N\}$ is unbounded in D, or, in other words, $\bigcap_{\gamma,k}(\{p : p > n_0(\gamma, k) \text{ and } p \in D\}) = \emptyset$. Since the mapping $p \to a_p$ of ${}^*D$ into ${}^*X$ is internal, it follows that for every $\gamma \in \Gamma$ and $k \in N$, the set $E(\gamma, k)$ of all $m \in {}^*D$ such that ${}^*\rho_\gamma(a_r, a_s) < 1/k$ for all $r,s \in {}^*D$ satisfying $n_0(\gamma, k) < r,s \leq m$ is an internal nonempty set of indices of ${}^*D$. Furthermore, the family $\{E(\gamma, k) : \gamma \in \Gamma \text{ and } k \in N\}$ has the finite intersection property. From $\kappa > \mathrm{card}(\Gamma \times N)$, Theorem

2.7.13, and $^*(X, \{\rho_\gamma: \gamma \in \Gamma\})$ is κ-saturated it follows that $E = \bigcap (E(\gamma, k): \gamma \in \Gamma \text{ and } k \in N) \neq \varnothing$. Let $m_0 \in E$. Then $m_0 \in {}^*D - D$, and so $^*\rho_\gamma(a_p, a_{m_0}) < 1/k$ for all $p \in D$ and $p > n_0(\gamma, k)$. Hence a_{m_0} is finite and $\rho_\gamma(\mu_u(a_p), \mu_u(a_{m_0})) < 1/k$ for all $p \in D$ such that $p > n_0(\gamma, k)$; that is, the Cauchy net $\{\mu_u(a_p): p \in D\}$ converges to $\mu_u(a_{m_0})$ in X_0.

In the case of a metric space we have that $\operatorname{card}(\Gamma \times N) = \aleph_0$, and since by Theorem 1.6.2 every δ-incomplete ultrafilter is $\aleph_1$-good, the result follows. This completes the proof.

From Theorem 3.15.1 it follows then that the closure of X in its nonstandard hull X_0 is the completion of X—a fact that was observed in [13] for metric spaces, although it was not shown there that the space X_0 is complete. We shall now answer the question of which elements of X_0 are in the closure of X.

Theorem 3.15.2. *An element $\mu_u(a)$ of X_0 is in the closure of X if and only if a is pre-near-standard.*

Proof. If a is pre-near-standard, then for every $\gamma \in \Gamma$ and $k \in N$ there is a point $x_{\gamma,k} \in X$ such that $^*\rho_\gamma(a, x_{\gamma,k}) < 1/k$ (Theorem 3.11.2). Then the Cauchy net $\{\mu_u(x_{\gamma,k})\}$ converges to $\mu_u(a)$ in X_0. Conversely, assume that $\mu_u(a) \in \bar{X}$; then there is a net $\{\mu_u(x_p): p \in D\}$ with $x_p \in X$ such that $\mu_u(x_p)$ converges to $\mu_u(a)$ in X_0. Thus for every $\epsilon > 0$ and $\gamma \in \Gamma$ there is an index $p \in D$ such that $\rho_\gamma(\mu_u(x_p), \mu_u(a)) < \epsilon$, and so $^*\rho_\gamma(x_p, a) < \epsilon$; that is, a is pre-near-standard by Theorem 3.11.2.

Let us now examine a few examples. Assume that (X, τ) is a completely regular Hausdorff space. By $C(X)$ we shall denote the ring of all real τ-continuous functions and by $C_b(X)$ the subring of the bounded elements. Then $C(X)(C_b(X))$ induces a uniform structure $C(C_b)$ by means of the family of semimetrics $\{\rho_f(x, y) = |f(x) - f(y)|,\ x,y \in X$ and $f \in C(C_b)\}$. They both induce the topology τ on X. Furthermore, C is finer than C_b.

Theorem 3.15.3. *Every point $a \in {}^*X$ is a C_b-pre-near-standard point.*

Proof. Let $a \in {}^*X$ and let $f \in C_b$ and $0 < \epsilon \in R$ be given. To show that a is C_b-pre-near-standard we have to show that there is a point $x \in X$ such that $|{}^*f(x) - {}^*f(a)| < \epsilon$ (Theorem 3.11.2). Observe that since f is bounded, $^*f(a)$ is finite for all $a \in {}^*X$. Furthermore, $b \in \mu_d(a)$ implies that $^*f(b) \in \mu_d({}^*f(a))$, and so the internal set $F_a = \{b: |{}^*f(b) - {}^*f(a)| < \epsilon\}$ is saturated. Hence, by (b) of Theorem 2.8.1, F_a is standard. Thus there is a point $x \in X$ such that $|{}^*f(x) - {}^*f(a)| < \epsilon$, and the proof is finished.

We can draw now immediately the following conclusion.

Theorem 3.15.4. (a) *(X, τ) is compact if and only if (X, τ) is C_b-complete.*

(b) *The C_b-nonstandard hull of (X, τ) is its Stone-Čech compactification.*

Proof. (a) If (X, τ) is compact, then every $a \in {}^*X$ is near-standard (Theorem 3.5.1), and so, by Theorem 3.15.3, every C_b-pre-near-standard point is near-standard. Hence, by Theorem 3.14.2, X is C_b-complete. Conversely, if (X, τ) is C_b-complete, then by Theorems 3.15.2 and 3.15.3 we obtain that every $a \in {}^*X$ is near-standard, and so, by Theorem 3.5.1, (X, τ) is compact.

(b) From Theorems 3.15.3 and 3.15.2 it follows that X is dense in X_0. Furthermore, it is obvious that the elements of C_b extend to X_0 uniquely by taking the standard part. To show that X_0 is compact, let $\{F\}$ be a nonempty family of nonempty closed subsets of X_0 with the finite intersection property. Since F is closed it is the monad of a filter $\mathfrak{F}$, and so it follows from the finite intersection property that $\sup\{\mathfrak{F}\}$ exists; that is, $\bigcap F \neq \emptyset$. This completes the proof.

For the C-uniformity the situation is quite different.

Theorem 3.15.5. *A point $a \in {}^*X$ is C-pre-near-standard if and only if ${}^*f(a)$ is finite for all $f \in C(X)$.*

Proof. Follows immediately from the proof of Theorem 3.15.3.

A space (X, τ) is called *pseudocompact* if and only if every real continuous function is bounded; and it is called *realcompact* if and only if it is C-complete.

Thus we have immediately the following result.

Theorem 3.15.6. *A completely regular Hausdorff space is compact if and only if it is pseudocompact and realcompact.*

16. The Nonstandard Hull of a Normed Space

Let $(E, \|\cdot\|)$ be a real normed space and let E' be its Banach dual space of all continuous linear functionals on E. We shall denote the elements of E by $x, y, z, \cdots$ and the elements of E' by $x', y', z', \cdots$. The bilinear functional determined by the duality will be denoted by (x, x'), $x \in E$, $x' \in E'$.

Let ${}^*(E, \|\cdot\|)$ be a higher-order ultrapower of $(E, \|\cdot\|)$ with respect to some δ-incomplete ultrafilter.

An element $a \in {}^*E$ is called *norm-finite* whenever $\|a\|$ is a finite number. The set of all finite elements will be denoted by ${}^*E_0$. An element $h \in {}^*E$ is called a *strong infinitesimal* or *norm-infinitesimal* whenever $\|h\| =_1 0$. The set of norm-infinitesimals will be denoted by E_1. It is obvious that ${}^*E_0$ is the principal galaxy of the metric space ${}^*(E, \|\cdot\|)$.

Observe that $^*E_0$ is a normed linear space over R and that E_1 is a linear subspace. Thus in this case the nonstandard hull appears as the quotient space $^*E_0/E_1 = \mathbf{E}_0$. Furthermore, $E \subset \mathbf{E}_0$ and $\mathbf{E}_0$ is a normed space with norm $\mathrm{st}(\|\cdot\|)$ of which E is a subspace. The reader should note that E_1 is the monad of zero of the neighborhood system of zero.

From Theorem 3.15.1 we obtain the following result.

Theorem 3.16.1. *If $\mathbf{E}_0$ is the nonstandard hull of E with respect to an ultrapower $\mathcal{U}$-prod E of E, then $\mathbf{E}_0$ is complete; that is, $\mathbf{E}_0$ is a Banach space, provided $\mathcal{U}$ is δ-incomplete.*

A proof of Theorem 3.16.1 was first given by R. F. Taylor.

If E is finite-dimensional, then every finite point in $^*E$ is near-standard and, conversely, if every finite point in $^*E$ is near-standard, then the unit ball of E is compact, and so E is finite-dimensional. Thus we have shown that the following result holds.

Theorem 3.16.2. *A normed linear space E is finite-dimensional if it coincides with its nonstandard hull.*

Remark. The nonstandard hull of a Hilbert space appeared, although in a somewhat different form, for the first time in a very interesting paper by S. K. Berberian (see [1]). Using the notation of this paper it appears now that if the generalized Banach limit used in [1] in addition satisfies $\mathrm{glim}(\lambda_n\mu_n) = \mathrm{glim}\ \lambda_n\ \mathrm{glim}\ \mu_n$, then the space $\mathcal{P}$ introduced in Section 3 of [1] is a Hilbert space; that is, it is complete.

We hope to return to the theory of the nonstandard hull of a normed space in another paper.

17. A Characterization of the Pre-near-standard Points of a Normed Space

Let $(E, \|\cdot\|)$ be a normed space over R, the real number system, and let E' be its Banach conjugate space. The weak topologies on E and E' will be denoted by $\sigma(E, E')$ and $\sigma(E', E)$, respectively. Then $\mu_{\sigma(E,E')}(0) = \{z\colon (z, x') =_1 0$ (is infinitesimal) for all $x' \in E'\}$ and $\mu_{\sigma(E',E)}(0) = \{z'\colon (x, z') =_1 0$ for all $x \in E\}$, where $(\cdot, \cdot)$ denote the bilinear form determining the duality between E and E'.

If $z \in {}^*E$ and $\|z\|$ is finite, then $\mathrm{st}(z, x')$, $x' \in E'$, defines a bounded linear functional on E' such that $(z, x') - \mathrm{st}(z, x') =_1 0$ for all $x' \in E'$, which we shall denote by $\mathrm{st}_w(z)$.

Since a norm Cauchy filter contains a set that is norm-bounded it follows immediately that *every norm pre-near-standard point has a finite norm.*

We begin with the following simple result.

Theorem 3.17.1. *An element $z \in {}^*E$ is norm pre-near-standard if and only if for every standard number $\epsilon > 0$ there exists a standard element $x \in E$ such that $\|z - x\| < \epsilon$.*

Proof. If z is norm pre-near-standard, then by Theorem 3.11.1 the set $\{z' : \|z - z'\| =_1 0 \text{ and } z' \in {}^*E\}$ is the monad of a minimal Cauchy filter (sequence). Hence, by Corollary 3.10.2, for every standard $\epsilon > 0$ there is a standard element $x \in E$ such that $\|z - x\| < \epsilon$. Conversely, if the condition holds, then for every $n = 1, 2, \cdots$ there exists an element $x_n \in E$ such that $\|z - x_n\| \leq 1/n$. The sequence $\{x_n\}$ is a Cauchy sequence and its monad $\mu(\{x_n : n \in N\}) = \{x_p : p \in {}^*N - N\}$ is contained in $\{z' : \|z - z'\| =_1 0\}$ and so z is norm pre-near-standard by definition.

In the following theorem we shall give a more useful characterization.

Theorem 3.17.2. *Let $z \in {}^*E$ be an element of finite norm. Then the following conditions are mutually equivalent.*

(a) *z is norm pre-near-standard.*

(b) *$\|z - \mathrm{st}_w(z)\|_1 = 0$ and $\mathrm{st}_w(z)$ is continuous on the unit ball of E' with respect to the $\sigma(E', E)$-topology.*

(c) *$(z, z') =_1 0$ for all $z' \in {}^*(E')$ such that $\|z'\| \leq 1$ and $z' \in \mu_{\sigma(E,E')}(0)$.*

Proof. (a) $\Rightarrow$ (b). From Theorem 3.14.1 it follows that there exists a sequence $\{x_n\}$ of standard elements of ${}^*E$ such that $\|z - x_n\| < 1/n$. It is easy to check that $(\mathrm{st}_w(z), x') = \lim(x_n, x')$, $x' \in E'$, and so $\|z - \mathrm{st}_w(z)\| =_1 0$ and the second part follows from the uniform convergence of $\{x_n\}$ to $\mathrm{st}_w(z)$ on the unit ball of E'.

(b) $\Rightarrow$ (c). From the second part of (b) and the fact that every point of the unit ball of ${}^*(E')$ is $\sigma(E', E)$-near-standard, it follows immediately that $\mathrm{st}_w(z)$ satisfies the condition of (c). Then $\|z - \mathrm{st}_w(z)\| =_1 0$ shows that (c) holds.

(c) $\Rightarrow$ (a). Let $\epsilon > 0$ be a positive standard number and let $\mathcal{B}$ be the set of all weak neighborhoods U of 0 in E' such that $\|z'\| \leq 1$ and $z \in U$ implies $|(z, z')| < \epsilon$. Then from the hypothesis it follows that every weak neighborhood U which is a subset of $\mu_{\sigma(E',E)}(0)$ is an element of $\mathcal{B}$, and so, by Theorems 2.7.11 and 2.7.3, $\mathcal{B}$ has an element that is a standard neighborhood. Thus we have shown that for every standard positive number $\epsilon > 0$ there exist elements $x_1, \cdots, x_n \in E$ such that

$$\max(|(x_i, z')| : i = 1, 2, \cdots, n) \leq 1 \text{ and } \|z'\| \leq 1 \Rightarrow |(z, z')| < \epsilon.$$

Let $H = \{z' : (x_i, z') = 0,\ i = 1, 2, \cdots, n\}$. Then $z' \in H \Rightarrow |(z, z')| < \epsilon$. Since H is an internal linear subspace of ${}^*(E')$, the restriction z_H of z to H can be extended to a bounded linear functional φ on E' such that $|\varphi(z')| \leq$

$\epsilon\|z'\|$ for all $z' \in {}^*(E')$. Then $(\varphi - z, z') = 0$ for all $z' \in H$ implies, by a well-known theorem of linear algebra, that there are constants $c_1, \cdots, c_n$ such that $\varphi - z = \Sigma_{i=1}^n c_i x_i$. Hence $\|\varphi\| < \epsilon$ implies $\|z - \Sigma_{i=1}^n c_i x_i\| \leq \epsilon$. Since z has finite norm it follows that $c_1, \cdots, c_n$ are finite numbers. Then $x_0 = \Sigma_{i=1}^n \operatorname{st}(c_i) x_i$ satisfies $\|z - x_0\| < \epsilon$. Thus z is norm pre-near-standard, and the proof is complete.

We shall make a few applications of the preceding theorem.

1. If E is a Banach space, then a well-known theorem of Mazur states that the closed convex hull of a compact set $A \subset E$ is compact. Let $c(A)$ denote the convex hull of A. Then ${}^*(c(A)) = c({}^*A)$ implies that $z = \Sigma_{i=1}^n c_i z_i$, where $z_i \in {}^*A$ and $0 \leq c_i$ $(i = 1, 2, \cdots, n)$, $\Sigma c_i = 1$ for all $z \in {}^*(c(A))$. Since A is compact, all the elements $z_1, \cdots, z_n$ are near-standard. Let $\|z'\| \leq 1$ and $z' \in \mu_{\sigma(E',E)}(0)$. Then $(z, z') = \Sigma c_i(z_i, z') =_1 0$, and so, by Theorem 3.14.2, z is near-standard (E is complete).

2. A theorem of Grothendieck states that a bounded linear functional φ on the dual E' of a normed space E is in the completion of E if and only if φ is $\sigma(E', E)$-continuous on the unit ball of E'. This result follows immediately from Theorem 3.14.2 by observing that $\varphi \in E''$ is in the completion of E if and only if there is a norm pre-near-standard point $z \in {}^*E$ such that $\|z - \varphi\| =_1 0$.

3. The Gelfand–Phillips compactness criterion. Let A be a subspace of a Banach space E. Then A is relatively compact if and only if A is bounded and for every bounded filter $\mathfrak{F}$ of subsets of E' which is $\sigma(E, E')$-convergent to zero converges uniformly to zero on A. This result follows immediately by observing that the conditions of the Gelfand–Phillips theorem are equivalent to the statement every $a \in {}^*A$ is norm pre-near-standard. Then E being complete, the result follows.

References

1. S. K. BERBERIAN, Approximate Proper Vectors, *Proc. Am. Math. Soc. 13* (1962), 111–114.
2. N. BOURBAKI, *Éléments de mathématique, topologie générale.* Paris: 3rd ed., 1961, Chaps. 1 and 2.
3. T. FRAYNE, A. MOREL, and D. SCOTT, Reduced Direct Products, *Fundamenta Math. 51* (1962), 195–228.
4. H. J. KEISLER, Ultraproducts and Elementary Classes, *Proc. Acad. Sci. Amsterdam A64* (1961), 477–495.
5. H. J. KEISLER, Ultraproducts and Saturated Models, *Proc. Acad. Sci. Amsterdam A67* (1964), 178–186.
6. H. J. KEISLER, Good Ideals in Fields of Sets, *Ann. Math. 79* (1964), 338–359.
7. H. J. KEISLER, A Survey of Ultraproducts, in Y. Bar-Hillel (ed.), *Logic,*

Methodology and Philosophy of Science, Proc. 1964 Intern. Conf. Amsterdam: North-Holland, 1964, pp. 112–126.

8. H. J. KEISLER, Ultraproducts Which Are Not Saturated, *J. Symbolic Logic, 32* (1967), 23–46.
9. J. ŁOŚ, Quelques remarques, théorèmes, et problèmes sur les classes definissables d'algèbres, in Skolem et al., *Mathematical Interpretations of Formal Systems* (Studies in Logic and the Foundations of Mathematics). Amsterdam: North-Holland, 1955, pp. 98–113.
10. W. A. J. LUXEMBURG, A New Approach to the Theory of Monads, *ONR Tech. Rept. 1* (1967).
11. M. MORLEY and R. VAUGHT, Homogeneous Universal Models, *Math. Scand., 11* (1962), 37–57.
12. I. REZNIKOFF, Tout ensemble de formules de la logique classique est équivalent à un ensemble indépendent, *Compt. Rend. 260* (1965), 2385–2388.
13. A. ROBINSON, *Non-Standard Analysis* (Studies in Logic and the Foundations of Mathematics). Amsterdam: North-Holland, 1966.
14. A. ROBINSON, Non-Standard Theory of Dedekind Rings, *Proc. Acad. Sci. Amsterdam A70* (1967), 444–452.
15. D. SCOTT, Measurable Cardinals and Constructible Sets, *Bull. Acad. Polon. Sci. Ser. Math. Astron. Phys. 9* (1961), 521–524.
16. A. L. STONE, Nonstandard Analysis in Topological Algebra (this volume).
17. A. TARSKI, *Some Problems Relevant to the Foundations of Set Theory, Logic, Methodology and Philosophy of Science.* Stanford: Stanford Univ. Press, 1962, pp. 125–135.
18. S. ULAM, Zur Mass Theorie der allgemeinen Mengenlehre, *Fundamenta Math. 16* (1930), 140–150.

Boolean Models and Nonstandard Analysis

by DANA SCOTT[1]

It is certainly debatable whether the crisis over the set-theoretical paradoxes was really a crisis or not. For a long time there was really no impact on the working (or should one say *proving*) mathematician. Only in the last few years have the people in abstract category theory found anything to complain about. It seems to the author that the situation with the continuum hypothesis is much worse. The Russell paradox can be easily dismissed by saying that such all inclusive sets were not intended, but not so with the question of the cardinality of the continuum. Everyone who does modern abstract mathematics uses the continuum as a well-determined set. Only the strict constructivist questions this "obvious" fact. But as Gödel and Cohen have shown us, the cardinality of this continuum is not at all well determined by the current axioms. What to do? Maybe we have to face the fact that there are many distinct theories of the continuum. It is hard to swallow the idea, but, as will be shown below, it is easy to cook up those exotic models out of everyday ingredients.

The Construction of Models for Analysis

We shall employ the Boolean algebraic method presented in my expository paper [4]. As is done there, we shall construct models for analysis (a portion of the higher-order theory of real numbers). For details of checking the logical properties of the models we shall refer to [4] and be content here with descriptive remarks. A thorough exposition of the models for full set theory will be found in the joint paper with Solovay [5].

The idea of constructing Boolean-valued models could have been

[1] Preparation of this manuscript was partially supported by National Science Foundation Grant 7655.

(but was not) discovered as a generalization of the ultraproduct method used now so often to obtain nonstandard models for ordinary analysis. Roughly, we can say that ultraproducts use the *standard* Boolean algebras (the power-set algebras) to obtain models elementarily equivalent to the standard model, whereas the Boolean method allows the nonstandard complete algebras (such as the *Lebesgue algebra* of measurable sets modulo sets of measure zero or the *Baire algebra* of Borel sets modulo sets of the first category). Thus the Boolean method leads to *nonstandard* nonstandard models that are not only not isomorphic to the standard model but are not even equivalent. Nevertheless, they do satisfy all the usual axioms and deserve to be called models of analysis.

To make this comparison clear, let us consider the ultraproduct construction in general. So as not to complicate notation, let us use structures

$$\mathfrak{A} = \langle A, R \rangle,$$

where $R \subseteq A \times A$ is a binary relation. Suppose that for i in an index set I we have corresponding structures

$$\mathfrak{A}_i = \langle A_i, R_i \rangle.$$

We then form the product

$$\underset{i \in I}{X} \mathfrak{A}_i = \langle \underset{i \in I}{X} A_i, S \rangle = \langle B, S \rangle,$$

where S is *not* a binary relation in the ordinary sense. Instead we make S a *Boolean-valued relation*. We define

$$S \colon B \times B \to PI$$

(where P is the power-set operator), so that for $a, b \in B$ we have

$$S(a, b) = \{i \in I \colon a_i R_i b_i\}.$$

Extension of the Definition of Boolean Values

In regard to PI as a complete Boolean algebra, the mapping S defined above allows us to extend the definition of Boolean values from atomic formulas to all logical formulas by means of the following obvious rules (for more detail see [3] and [4]):

$$\begin{aligned}
[\![aSb]\!] &= S(a, b) = \{i \in I \colon a_i R_i b_i\}, \\
[\![a = b]\!] &= \{i \in I \colon a_i = b_i\}, \\
[\![\Phi]\!] &= I - [\![\Phi]\!], \\
[\![\Phi \vee \Psi]\!] &= [\![\Phi]\!] \cup [\![\Psi]\!], \\
[\![\exists x \Phi(x)]\!] &= \bigcup_{a \in B} [\![\Phi(a)]\!].
\end{aligned}$$

Thus every formula $\Phi(a, b, \cdots)$ with constants $a, b, \cdots \in B$ (and without free variables) has a uniquely determined Boolean value

$$[\![\Phi(a, b, \cdots)]\!] \in PI.$$

We call such a formula *valid* (Boolean valid) iff

$$[\![\Phi(a, b, \cdots)]\!] = I.$$

We note that

$$[\![\Phi(a, b, \cdots)]\!] = \{i \in I : \mathcal{A}_i \vdash \Phi(a_i, b_i, \cdots)\};$$

hence it is valid iff it is *true* in *all* the $\mathcal{A}_i$.

The basic lemma about ultraproducts shows (see [1], Theorem 2.2): Given $\exists x\Phi(x, b, \cdots)$, there exists an element $a \in B$ such that

$$[\![\exists x\Phi(x, b, \cdots)]\!] = [\![\Phi(a, b, \cdots)]\!].$$

That is, even though the value of the existentially quantified formula was defined as a *union* (supremum), it is actually a *maximum*. That is interesting. There are very few homomorphisms of PI (into $\{\mathbf{0}, \mathbf{1}\}$, say) that preserve *all* sups; but it is obvious that any homomorphism of one Boolean algebra into another preserves a max. Therefore, if we regard an ultrafilter D as really being a homomorphism,

$$D: PI \to \{\mathbf{0}, \mathbf{1}\},$$

then we can form in the obvious way the *quotient structure*

$$\underset{i \in I}{X} \mathcal{A}_i / D.$$

This structure in view of the above *maximum principle* is such that any sentence *valid* in $X\mathcal{A}_i$ is *true* in $X\mathcal{A}_i/D$. (Of course, this can be sharpened, but the point is to see the conclusion as a consequence of general facts about quotients of Boolean-valued models.) In short, we have divided the ultraproduct construction into two stages: *product* followed by *ultra*. It is the generalization of the product part we wish to emphasize.

Let $\mathcal{B}$ be an arbitrary complete Boolean algebra. Since $\mathcal{B}$ is in particular a Boolean σ-algebra, we know that $\mathcal{B}$ can be represented

$$\mathcal{B} = \mathcal{A}/\mathfrak{N}$$

where $\mathcal{A}$ is a σ-algebra of subsets of a set I and $\mathfrak{N}$ is a σ-ideal of $\mathcal{A}$. (In [4] the set I was called Ω because it was a measure space. We also change another convention of [4] by using the notation $+$, $\cdot$, Σ, Π for the Boolean operations of $\mathcal{B}$, saving $\cup$, $\cap$, $\bigcup$, $\bigcap$ for use with their ordinary set-theoretical meanings.)

Now since we are interested in the theory of the real numbers (the set of which is denoted by $\mathbf{R}$) we will form a special product structure. We do not use the full Cartesian power $\mathbf{R}^I$ but only the *subset* $\mathcal{R} \subseteq \mathbf{R}^I$, consisting of the $\mathcal{A}$-*measurable* functions $a\colon I \to \mathbf{R}$. This makes it possible to define the $\mathcal{B}$-values of formulas:

$$[\![a = b]\!] = \{i \in I\colon a_i = b_i\}/\mathfrak{N},$$

$$[\![a > b]\!] = \{i \in I\colon a_i < b_i\}/\mathfrak{N},$$

$$[\![a + b = c]\!] = \{i \in I\colon a_i + b_i = c_i\}/\mathfrak{N}.$$

Indeed, if $R \subseteq \mathbf{R}^n$ is any n-ary relation with a *Borel* graph, then we can be sure that

$$\{i \in I\colon R(a_i, b_i, \cdots)\} \in \mathcal{A},$$

so that we can define

$$[\![R(a, b, \cdots)]\!] = \{i \in I\colon R(a_i, b_i, \cdots)\}/\mathfrak{N}.$$

Thus any ordinary Borel relation on $\mathbf{R}$ becomes a $\mathcal{B}$-valued relation on $\mathcal{R}$. This makes $\mathcal{R}$ into quite an interesting structure. (Quantified formulas get values just as above. So far $\mathcal{R}$ is only a *first-order* structure having to do with Borel relations. By the same token we extend Borel *functions* $\varphi\colon \mathbf{R}^2 \to \mathbf{R}$ to functions $\varphi\colon \mathcal{R}^n \to \mathcal{R}$, as we already indicated with $+\colon \mathbf{R}^2 \to \mathbf{R}$.)

Well, just how interesting a structure is $\mathcal{R}$? First, it is fairly easy to see that $\mathcal{R}$ *is a* ($\mathcal{B}$-*valued*) *real-closed field*. For example, it is clear that

$$a < b \lor a = b \lor a > b$$

is $\mathcal{B}$-valid, and similarly for all the other axioms for ordered fields. Using the extensions of Borel functions to $\mathcal{R}$ we get the roots needed for the axioms of real-closure (see [4] for more details). By quite a different method (see [2]) it can be shown that if $R \subseteq \mathbf{R}^3$ is a Borel relation such that

$$\exists x\, \forall y\, \exists z\, R(x, y, z)$$

is *true* in $\mathbf{R}$, then this formula is *valid* in $\mathcal{R}$. [We can replace x, y, z here each by a string of variables and $R(x, y, z)$ by any quantifier-free combination of Borel relations.] This goes quite a way. Many facts about analytic sets can be expressed in this elementary form. Note, however, that we have only claimed an *implication:* from truth to validity. The converse is *not* correct. There are choices of (nonstandard) algebras $\mathcal{B}$ where the converse fails. (This has to do with Gödel's axiom of constructibility; see [5].)

Of course, analysis wants to have results about arbitrary real functions, and our theory of $\mathcal{R}$ so far has only to do with formulas involving real variables. To bring in the functions we define the set $\mathcal{R}^{\mathcal{R}}$ of allowed functions to be those mappings

$$f: \mathcal{R} \to \mathcal{R}$$

such that
$$[\![a = b]\!] \leq [\![f(a) = f(b)]\!]$$

for all $a,b \in \mathcal{R}$. (Here $\leq$ is Boolean inclusion in $\mathcal{B}$.) All formulas involving function values $f(x)$ and real variables can now be given $\mathcal{B}$-values for any $f \in \mathcal{R}$. We can also evaluate equations between functions using the definition

$$[\![f = g]\!] = \prod_{a \in \mathcal{R}} [\![f(a) = g(a)]\!].$$

The next step is to give $\mathcal{B}$-values to formulas involving *quantifiers* over functions. And then we can go on to the higher orders. As is shown in [4] (and more fully in [5]) all *axioms* of higher-order real number theory are $\mathcal{B}$-valid. But for a suitable choice of $\mathcal{B}$ the continuum hypothesis fails to be valid. The form of this sentence is very simple:

$$\forall h[\exists f\, \forall y[h(y) = 0 \to \exists x[N(x) \wedge y = f(x)]] \vee \exists g\, \forall y\, \exists x[h(x) = 0 \wedge y = g(x)]].$$

Why is it that this fails when the axiom of choice holds?

We remark that this $\mathcal{B}$-valued model for analysis satisfies the maximum principle. Hence quotients can be taken by ultrafilters forming *really* nonstandard models for analysis in the usual sense of model (see [5] for the proof of the maximum principle and remarks on the Löwenheim–Skolem theorem). We must ask whether there is any interest in these nonstandard models aside from the independence proof; that is, do they have any mathematical interest?

The answer must be yes, but we cannot yet give a really good argument. Certainly there is *intrinsic* interest in certain of the models. Take the case where $\mathcal{B}$ is a measure algebra, I is a measure space, $\mathcal{A}$ is the σ-field of measurable sets, and $\mathfrak{N}$ is the σ-ideal of sets of measure 0. Then $\mathcal{R}$ is the space of *random variables*, a very well-known space. That it forms a model for real number theory in a precise (although $\mathcal{B}$-valued) sense must mean something.

Here is one remark that may be useful. In general, one wants to know how various notions familiar from ordinary analysis look in the model. Take the concept of a Borel function; there is a certain formula,

Borel (f),

that expresses this in higher-order logic. What can be shown is that if Borel (f) is valid for some $f \in \mathcal{R}^{\mathcal{R}}$, then there exists an ordinary Borel function $\varphi: \mathbf{R}^2 \to \mathbf{R}$ and a particular $a \in \mathfrak{R}$ such that

$$f(x) = \varphi(a, x)$$

for all $x \in \mathfrak{R}$. In words, we can say that all the nonstandard Borel functions are *quasi-standard* in the sense that they result from standard Borel functions by specializing certain parameters to nonstandard reals. (The details of this theorem were worked out in [2].) There must be other such results.

Of course, the Boolean-valued models have been remarkably successful in solving problems about the existence of certain kinds of unpleasant, complete Boolean algebras (see [5]). But this is a different kind of application from what we usually want nonstandard analysis to do. But maybe there is some hope. Note that in the usual nonstandard models certain standard sets are made subsets of *finite* sets (finite in the model, that is). Then, some fact about finite sets gives us the desired conclusion. The unpleasant Boolean algebras mentioned above can be chosen to make a given standard set *countable* in the Boolean model (see [5]).

In many ways these Boolean models are more like the standard model than the usual nonstandard models (witness the remark about Borel functions). In fact, *countability* behaves very well in the Boolean sense, so that perhaps an argument that uses some formal property of countable sets may reveal something.

References

1. T. FRAYNE, A. MOREL, AND D. SCOTT, Reduced Direct Products, *Fundamenta Math. 51* (1962), 195–228.
2. P. KRAUSS, Probability Logic, Ph.D. dissertation, Berkeley: Univ. of Calif., 1966.
3. H. RASIOWA AND R. SIKORSKI, *The Mathematics of Metamathematics*. Warsaw: 1963.
4. D. SCOTT, A Proof of the Independence of the Continuum Hypothesis, *Math. Systems Theory 1* (1967), 89–111.
5. D. SCOTT AND R. SOLOVAY, Boolean-Valued Models for Set Theory, *Proc. AMS Summer Institute on Set Theory*, Los Angeles: Univ. Calif., 1967. In preparation.

Axiomatizations of Nonstandard Analysis That Are Conservative Extensions of Formal Systems for Classical Standard Analysis

by G. KREISEL[1]

1. Introduction

The present paper is concerned with two questions:

1. Is there a simple formal system (in the usual sense, that is, with a recursive, preferably finite, list of rules and axiom schemata) in which existing practice of nonstandard analysis can be codified? And if the answer is positive:

2. Is this formal system a conservative extension of the current systems of analysis (in which existing practice of standard analysis has been codified)?

The empirical character of these questions is quite evident because they refer to *existing* practice. So whatever interest the answers may have, this must be expected to involve a case study of existing practice.

Independently of such a case study, that is, from a purely mathematical point of view, we have the following results relevant to (2).

(a) The answer *does* depend on what formal system of standard analysis one uses, for example, on whether or not the axiom of choice is included.[2]

This is to be expected quite naïvely, because the usual proof of the existence of nonstandard models uses the so-called extended completeness theorem, which, by Vaught's observation [11], implies the axiom of choice. Both R. J. Parikh and Dana Scott have pointed out that non-standard analysis without principles of choice or well ordering, that is,

[1] The preparation of this paper was supported by Grant DA-ARO (D)-31-124-G-655 of the United States Army Research Office.

[2] It is well known that the axiom of choice is conservative for a fairly wide class of statements, for example, Σ_3^1-sentences. But this is, so to speak, an internal affair of standard analysis.

the natural modification of the axiomatization below, is in fact a *non-conservative* extension of standard analysis because one can explicitly define ultrafilters in terms of nonstandard elements.

(b) Once the means for defining nonstandard models (more precisely of elementary nonstandard extensions) and for establishing their basic properties are included in the system **S** of standard analysis used, we get a positive result to question 2. We shall not need such nonstandard models for the whole system **S** but only for each formal *derivation;* and, *a fortiori*, it will be enough to have such models for each finite subsystem of **S**. This is provided by the method of (partial) *truth definitions for formulas of bounded complexity* in [6]; for an agreeable exposition, particularly for the theory of real numbers, see Montague's [7]. Technically, different measures of complexity have to be used for "full" analysis, that is, the theory of sets of *all finite types* over the natural numbers, and for the theory of bounded types, for example, for arithmetic itself; in the first case, "complexity" can be measured by the highest type of the variables occurring in a formula; in the latter the number of nested quantifiers also has to be counted. For a systematic exposition of such matters see [5].

The practical conclusion to be drawn from the mathematical facts (a) and (b) is this. On the positive side, one must analyze the role of the axiom of choice in existing analysis, particularly in view of the conflict between the "theory" of many mathematicians on this subject and their practice. Of course, nobody particularly wants a conservative extension of standard analysis: one would like evident principles that imply new analytic theorems. So one must ask oneself what properties of non-standard models, besides the "basic" ones mentioned in (b), could be exploited. We shall return to this point at the end [which may well be the only useful contribution contained in this note since the proofs of (a) and (b) are quite standard[3]].

The results reported grew out of casual conversations with A. Robinson, and an observation of H. Friedman in connection with nonstandard arithmetic. In particular, A. Robinson posed a question on nonstandard arithmetic related to (2) at a meeting in London, 1965 (which is solved in app. B of [3] by a crude model-theoretic method[4]), and others later. As

[3] And essentially unrewarding. For, if one asks oneself question (2) at all and overlooks these simple points, one will feel frustrated; but seeing them does not get one much satisfaction.

[4] In the sense that (a) one started with any model M of one system (and not with the collection of models of arbitrary finite subsystems) and, more important, (b) defined explicitly from M a particular model M' of the other system, in particular an *end* model. One can, so to speak, "visualize" these algebraic constructions; this element

to (1), the question posed itself as soon as Robinson published [8] (and granted a few simple assumptions about the immortality of Leibniz's monad and his continued interest in logic, one can be *sure* that Leibniz, or at least the trustee of his monad, asked himself this question). The real problem was only to know when the time was ripe for an answer. Relying on Robinson's judgment, the author thought that the publication of Robinson's book [9] made it worthwhile to codify existing practice.

2. Sketches of a Formal System S for Standard Analysis (Theory of Finite Types)

To define the language, we consider, in the first place: finite types (of individuals and relations, not functions) and a partial ordering, the least class T and the least relation on $T \times T$ such that $0 \in T$, if $\tau_1, \cdots, \tau_n$ all $\in T$, then $(\tau_1, \cdots, \tau_n) \in T$ and $\tau_i < \tau$ for each i, $1 \leq i \leq n$.

The *language* is a many-sorted predicate calculus, with one sort of variable ($x^\tau, y^\tau, \cdots$) for each $\tau \in T$, containing two binary relation symbols $=$ and $\in$ (with arguments of arbitrary type), formation of n-tuples, a function symbol $'$ (for successor) whose arguments and values are of type 0. For a description of such languages and their realizations, see, for example, [4], pp. 88–90.

Remark. For a convenient formulation of actual practice one also needs function *variables* and the primitive operation of *application* or function *evaluation*. Also the statement of some axioms becomes simpler if one uses certain normal forms for functions of several variables, namely: If f has arguments of type $\tau_1, \cdots, \tau_n$ and values of type τ, we consider g whose arguments are of type τ_l and values are of the type of functions with arguments of type $\tau_2, \cdots, \tau_n$ and values of type τ such that

$$(gx_1^{\tau_1})(x_2^{\tau_2}, \cdots, x_n^{\tau_n}) = f(x_1^{\tau_1}, \cdots, x_n^{\tau_n}).$$

Clearly the reduction in the number of variables is at the cost of an increase in the type of the values. The appropriate-type structure for functions is the least class T' such that $0 \in T'$, and if σ' and $\tau' \in T'$, then $(\sigma' \to \tau') \in T'$. But for the present *metamathematical* purposes it is best to replace a function f of type $\sigma \to \tau$ by the relation x_f of type (σ, τ), which is its graph and hence satisfies the usual functionality condition, the operation of function evaluation: the value of f at the argument g (of type σ) if h (of type τ) is replaced by $(x_g, x_h) \in x_f$.

---

gets lost once one has to consider models of *all* finite subsystems, as in the present text; and it makes little difference from this point of view whether one defines the models by means of old-fashioned completeness arguments or by ultraproducts.

Besides the elementary axioms (successor, existence of n-tuples, domain operation, extensionality) one uses the following schemata and axioms (they will be stated first; some logical relationships will be noted in the remarks below):

Induction Schema. For each formula Ax whose only free variable is $\mathbf{x}$: If $\mathbf{x}$ is of type 0, derive $\forall x\, Ax$ from $\forall x(Ax \rightarrow Ax')$.

Remark. The schema implies the corresponding axiom: $\forall x_1^{\tau_1} \cdots \forall x_n^{\tau_n}([B0 \wedge \forall x(Bx \rightarrow Bx')] \rightarrow \forall x\, Bx)$, where Bx contains the free variables $x_1^{\tau_1}, \cdots, x_n^{\tau_n}$ besides x; apply the rule to the formula Ax: $\forall x_1^{\tau_1} \cdots \forall x_n^{\tau_n}([B0 \wedge \forall y(By \rightarrow By')] \rightarrow Bx)$.

Well Ordering. For each type σ and $\tau = (\sigma, \sigma)$, there exists a well ordering of all objects of type σ; that is, if $0(x^\tau)$ expresses that x is a linear ordering of all objects of type σ,

$$\exists x^\tau\, \forall y^{(\sigma)}([\exists z^\sigma(z \in y) \rightarrow \exists z^\sigma(z \in y) \wedge \forall u^\sigma[u \in y \rightarrow \neg(u, y) \in x])] \wedge 0x$$

Choice Schemata. For each formula $A(x, y)$, x of type σ, y of type τ, A possibly containing free variables other than x and y, derive $\exists f\, \forall x A(x, fx)$ from $\forall x\, \exists y A(x, y)$. The function quantifier $\exists f$ is of course short for

$$\exists u^{(\sigma,\tau)}\{\forall x^\sigma\, \exists y^\tau[(x, y) \in u] \wedge \forall x^\sigma\, \forall y^\tau\, \forall^\tau([(x, y) \in u \wedge (x, z) \in u] \rightarrow y = z)\}.$$

Dependent Choices. For each formula $A(x, y)$, where x and y have the same type τ, and f of type $0 \rightarrow \tau$,

$$\forall x^\tau\, \exists y^\tau A(x, y) \rightarrow \forall z^\tau\, \exists f(f0 = z \wedge \forall n A[f(n), f(n+1)]),$$

where n is of type 0.

Remarks

(a) The axiom of choice: $\forall x\, \exists y B(x, y) \rightarrow \exists f\, \forall x B(x, fx)$ follows from the rule by putting $A(x, y)$: $\forall u\, \exists v B(u, v) \rightarrow B(x, y)$, where, of course, $\mathbf{u}$ has the same type as $\mathbf{x}$, $\mathbf{v}$ as y.

(b) The choice schema for type $(\sigma, 0)$ (together with the domain operation) implies the comprehension axiom for type σ; that is, for any Bx (not containing the variable y), $\exists y^{(\sigma)}\, \forall x^\sigma(x \in y \leftrightarrow Bx)$ follows by applying the schema to $A(x, y)$:

$$(n = 0 \wedge Bx) \vee (n \neq 0 \wedge \neg Bx),$$

where $\mathbf{n}$ is of type 0.

(c) The author does not know the latest news on the logical relationships between (for example) axioms of choice and axioms of dependent choices, or between the postulate of a well ordering and axioms of choice, relative to comprehension axioms. [As S. Feferman pointed out, it is not immediate that the axiom of choice in *analysis*, particularly when restricted to fixed rank as below, implies the existence of well orderings, nor (for example) Zorn's lemma.] For the present purpose (see Section 6), all the schemata are included because they are widely used.

Analysis $\mathbf{S}_n$ *of rank* n, where the rank $n(0)r(10)$ of the type 0 is 0, and $r(\tau) = 1 + \max[r(\tau_1), \cdots, r(\tau_n)]$ for $\tau = (\tau_1, \cdots, \tau_n)$ follows.

For $n > 0$, $\mathbf{S}_n$ is obtained from the system $\mathbf{S}$ by restricting the language to (terms and formulas built up from variables of) types of rank $\leq n$.

For $n = 0$ we have to add symbols and axioms for some additional operations besides the successor, for example, addition and multiplication. It is well known that these cannot be defined from the successor in $\mathbf{S}$ restricted to rank 0 (in contrast to the situation at higher rank). So $\mathbf{S}$ restricted to rank 0 would be quite inadequate for formulating mathematical practice of arithmetic.

Remark. The restriction to types τ' of *rank* $\leq n$, and not, for example, to $\tau' \leq \tau$ (for the partial ordering defined above) avoids certain artificial features, for example, if $\tau = (\sigma_1, \cdots, \sigma_k)$, where $\sigma_i = \sigma(1 \leq i \leq k + 1)$, the (graphs of) functions with k variables of type σ are $\leq \tau$ but not those with $(k + 1)$ variables. However, although the restriction by *rank* avoids this artificial feature, for example, the choice schema cannot be stated for all formulas $A(x, y)$ in a language restricted by rank, since, if x and y are of rank $= n$, z may have rank $> n$. It may well be that only the restriction to rank $= 0$ is formally satisfactory. (In fact, also foundationally it is not particularly clear why one should stop at any finite rank once one goes beyond 0. But see Section 6 concerning the formulation of existing practice.)

3. Sketch of a Formal System NS for Nonstandard Analysis

The system *includes* the system $\mathbf{S}$ for standard analysis given in Section 2, in particular the axioms asserting the existence of well orderings.

In addition, for each type $\tau \in T$ we have a type $^*\tau$, and variables $x^{*\tau}, y^{*\tau}, \cdots$; the use of the relation symbols $=$ and $\in$ is extended to allow arguments of arbitrary types, and so is formation of n-tuples; the function symbol $'$ is permitted to have also arguments and values of type ^{*0}. There is a *new* monadic function symbol, also denoted by $*$ (on the suggestion of Dana Scott) whose arguments are of type τ for $\tau \in T$, and whose values are those of type $^*\tau$.

The intended realization of the extended language is this: The variables of the old language are to range over the standard (principal) model, that is, the finite-type structure over the natural numbers, that is, the set ω, with the successor operation, and those of the new language over a nonstandard model. If t denotes an object of the standard model, $*t$ is its canonical image in the nonstandard model. For comparison with Robinson's exposition, recall that he introduces a symbol, say a, for each object $\bar{a}$ of the standard model; then $*a$ denotes the realization of a in the nonstandard model. Note that we can regard the domain of type $*0$ without loss of generality as an extension of the domain of type 0, where all the nonstandard elements come after the standard ones, in symbols, $\forall x^0 \exists y^{*0} (x = y)$, but not, for example, at type $*(0)$, that is, of sets of individuals. For, no *infinite* subset of ω, that is, no infinite object of type (0) in the standard model, is also an element of $*(0)$.[5]

Embedding Axioms. For each formula A *of the old language* whose free variables are among $x_1, \cdots, x_n$ of types $\tau_1, \cdots, \tau_n$, respectively, let $*A$ be obtained from A by replacing x_i by $*x_i$, and bound variables x^τ (assumed distinct from x_i, $1 \leq i \leq n$) by $x^{*\tau}$.

Schema for elementary extensions. $\forall x_1^{\tau_1} \cdots \forall x_n^{\tau_n}(A \leftrightarrow *A)$.

Remark. This schema implies, for example, the successor axioms: $\forall y(*0 \neq y')$, and $\forall x\, \forall y(x' = y' \rightarrow x = y)$ for x and y of type $*0$, from the corresponding axioms in Section 2.

*Two new axioms for types 0 and *0:*

$$\forall x[*(x') = (*x)'] \qquad \text{and} \qquad \exists y\, \forall x(y \neq *x)$$

for x of type 0, and y of type $*0$; the second axiom asserts that the model is properly nonstandard.

Axioms for Transcendental Elements[6] (or "confluence" or "concurrence" in Robinson's terminology, [9], p. 31).

Since we have types for n-tuples we may consider formulas $A(y^\tau, z^\sigma)$ instead of $A(x_1^{\tau_1}, \cdots, x_n^{\tau_n}, z^\sigma)$. We assume some coding of n-tuples of elements of the *same* type τ by type-τ elements, obtained, for example, by extending some coding of n-tuples of natural numbers by natural numbers. Then for each $\tau (\tau \in T)$ we have a formula $C_\tau(n, i, x^\tau, y^\tau)$, where **n** and **i** are of type 0, expressing that y^τ is the ith element of the n-tuple of type-τ objects coded by x^τ.

$$\forall x^\tau\, \forall n\, \exists z^\sigma\, \forall i\, \forall y^\tau[C_\tau(n, i, x^\tau, y^\tau) \rightarrow A(y^\tau, z^\sigma)] \rightarrow \exists z^{*\sigma}\, \forall y^\tau\, A'(*y^\tau, z^{*\sigma}),$$

[5] Instead of Robinson's terminology of "internal" and "external" sets, we simply speak of elements of type τ or type $*\tau$, respectively. In the author's (limited) experience of the matter, it is convenient to reserve "finite" and "infinite" for the standard model, and use "bounded" and "unbounded" for the corresponding notions in the nonstandard model.

[6] For choice of terminology, see, for example, [4], p. 150, lines 21–24.

where A' is obtained from A by replacing y^τ, z^σ by $^*y^\tau$, $z^{*\sigma}$, respectively, and changing the bound variables of type τ' ($\tau' \in T$) to type $^*\tau'$. [Note: A' is "nearly" $^*A$ defined above, except that we have $z^{*\sigma}$ instead of $^*z^\sigma$; in fact, in general, a nonstandard element $z^{*\sigma}$ satisfying $\forall y^\tau\, A'(^*y^\tau, z^{*\sigma})$ will *not* be the image of a standard element.]

***Strengthening of the Principal Schemata of* S.** Recall the properties of the natural numbers and of the type structure over them which justify the principles of induction and choice (in Section 2). These properties do not only justify the schemata given in Section 2, that is, for monadic and binary relations *definable* in the language of Section 2 (denoted by A), but for *all* relations. The restriction to definable relations is made only because, in the framework of **S**, we cannot make effective use of other relations. But once the language is extended we have stronger schemata.

Induction Schema. For an arbitrary formula Ax of the extended language (in which variables of types τ and $^*\tau'$, any $\tau, \tau' \in T$, may occur) whose only free variable is x of type 0:

derive $\forall x\, Ax$ from $A0$ and $\forall x(\mathrm{A}x \rightarrow \mathrm{A}x')$.

Remark. The corresponding schema for type *0 (that is, with *0 in place of 0 and x of type *0) would simply be false; in other words, induction in the full sense does *not* hold in the nonstandard model. Take, for example, for Ay, with y of type *0: $\exists x(y = {}^*x)$:

Choice Schemata. For an *arbitrary* formula $A(x, y)$, where x and y are of (standard) types but the other free variables may be of any type, derive $\exists f\, \forall x A(x, fx)$ from $\forall x\, \exists y A(x, y)$. Similarly for the schema of dependent choices.

Note the *asymmetry* between the schemata for standard and nonstandard types. A different way of putting it is this: In the standard model one can define a nonstandard model (to be used in the next two sections), but not conversely; for foundational implications of this fact see app. B of [3].

4. Conservative Extension Results: Full Analysis

As usual, we call the system **NS** for nonstandard analysis in Section 3 a *conservative* extension of the system **S** for standard analysis (in Section 2) provided exactly the same formulas of **S** can be proved in the two systems. Clearly, **NS** is an extension of **S** because it includes **S**.

To prove the *conservative character* of the extension, consider any derivation in nonstandard analysis **NS** of a formula A of **S**. Note that the types of the variables occurring in the derivation are bounded, say $\leq \tau$ and $\leq {}^*\tau$. It is clearly sufficient to *define* in **S** a realization of the language of **NS** restricted to types $\leq \tau$ such that (a) all true sentences of standard analysis $\leq \tau$ with constants for each object of type $\leq \tau$, and (b) the axioms of **NS** for all types $\leq (\tau, {}^*\tau)$ can be proved in **S** to be satisfied in this realization. For, by (b), all formulas occurring in the given derivation are then true in the realization, in particular A; and, by (a), A is true for the standard model. The definition of the realization goes in two steps, the second taking care of the "strengthened" schemata.

First we follow simply the usual proof, for example, in [9], pp. 30–32, of the existence of "enlargements." Specifically, to be able to *describe* the set of true sentences of analysis of type $\leq \tau$ we define formally the *satisfaction relation* for formulas of type $\leq \tau$; the definition of this relation uses variables of type (τ); note that the satisfaction relation is needed, and not merely a truth definition for closed formulas in the language of **S**, in order to express truth for formulas with symbols for all objects of type $\leq \tau$. Next, to prove the existence of a nonstandard model, satisfying the embedding axioms, that is, an enlargement, we have to formalize in **S** a proof of, for example, the (extended) completeness theorem, applied to the present set of axioms. But granted a well ordering of the formulas built up from symbols for objects of type $\leq \tau$ (which is implied by a well ordering of these objects if, for example, these objects are themselves used as symbols), the definition of an enlargement from the satisfaction relation is classical.

The second step is to extract from the model so defined a submodel which is (probably) isomorphic to the standard model of type $\leq \tau$. Note if say $D_\tau(x)$, $E(x, y)$ are the formal definitions of the domain of type τ, and of the membership relation, then there is no guarantee that the structure defined is isomorphic to the standard model (for example, the type of the argument x of D must not be less than τ but may be bigger!). However, because of the occurrence of symbols a for each standard element, the model defined will *contain* the standard model, namely, as denotations of ${}^*a$. We take this submodel. Now consider the strengthened schemata, for example, induction. Since the realization is defined in **S**, the property defined in the realization by the formula A (of the induction schema) is also defined in **S**, and so the validity of

$$[A0 \wedge \forall x(Ax \rightarrow Ax')] \rightarrow \forall x\, Ax$$

in the realization reduces to an instance of induction in **S** itself, say $[B0 \wedge \forall x(Bx \rightarrow Bx')] \rightarrow \forall x\, Bx$, since in the submodel considered the domain of type 0 (with successor) is isomorphic to the natural numbers. The only difference is that, while the variables in A are of type $\leq \tau$, $\leq {}^*\tau$, those of B are at least of type (τ): This formal fact corresponds to the intended meaning that induction holds for *all* properties. The verification of the choice schemata is similar.

Remark. In the case of full analysis $\mathbf{S}$, two distinct notions of model (of $\mathbf{NS}$) in $\mathbf{S}$, coincide: the "strict" notion, which requires that the domain of the model be a set or an "object," and the "generalized" notion, which allows the domain to be given by a property of such objects ("D" above; for the case of set theory, see [4], p. 162). We have chosen the latter notion because it can also be used for systems $\mathbf{S}_n$ in the next section.

5. Sketch of Conservative Extension Results for Analysis $\mathbf{S}_n$ of Fixed Rank

The first obstacle to an immediate application of the little argument in Section 4 is that a derivation of a formula A may contain variables of highest rank, say n, and then we do not have a definition of the satisfaction relation for *all* formulas with variables of this rank, in the fragment of analysis considered. The second obstacle, for $n > 0$, is that we cannot even express the existence of a well ordering of all objects of rank $\leq n$.

Arithmetic $(n = 0)$.[7] To apply Section 4 it is *not* necessary to have a nonstandard model that satisfies *all* axioms of $\mathbf{NS}$ (in Section 3) of the rank considered but only those that actually occur in a given derivation. By [6], given a (finite set of) formula(s) there is a definition in first-order arithmetic of the satisfaction relation for all subformulas ($A0$, $A0'$, $A0''$, and so on, being counted as subformulas of $\forall x\, Ax$ and of $\exists x\, Ax$). The required well ordering for the definition of a nonstandard model is provided by the order of magnitude of the natural numbers. (For an explicit definition of a nonstandard model from an explicitly defined set of axioms see, for example, [2].) The argument is then completed as in Section 4.

Remark. Note that the argument proves rather more than stated. It applies even if we add to $\mathbf{S}_0$ additional and, for example, not necessarily ω-consistent, axioms. In other words, we do not use the fact that the system $\mathbf{S}_0$ for standard arithmetic has the structure of the natural numbers (with addition and multiplication) as a model.

[7] This case is due to H. Friedman.

Analysis of Fixed Finite Rank n: $n > 0$. The following refinements of the ideas of Section 4 are needed. First, as discussed above, one defines the satisfaction relation not for the whole language of rank n but only for subformulas of a given formula; details of the definition in the case $n = 1$ are to be found in [7], pp. 65–68, and the extension to other n is straightforward. Second, one introduces a binary relation symbol R and axioms asserting that R defines a well ordering of the universe, that is, of all objects of rank n. Note that the *existence* of such an R cannot be expressed in the fragment of analysis here considered, and that there is no *definable* well ordering (without additional assumptions such as $V = L$). But a well ordering is needed to define a nonstandard model.

Consider then a derivation of the formula A of standard analysis; define a nonstandard model M in standard analysis $\mathbf{S}_n$ extended by the relation symbol R, such that the following statements can be formally proved in $\mathbf{S}_n$: (a) all formulas in the given derivation are satisfied in M, and (b) A itself holds in M if and only if A is true. Then we have a derivation of A in $\mathbf{S}_n$ together with the axioms for $\mathbf{R}$, where A, of course, does not contain R. To eliminate the use of R, extend the language to rank $(n + 1)$, restricting, however, the comprehension axiom for sets of rank $(n + 1)$: $\exists x^{(\tau)}\, \forall y^{\tau}(y \in x \leftrightarrow Cy)$, for τ of rank n, to formulas C of rank n (as Gödel–Bernays' theory of classes is related to set theory); C may contain the symbol R. This restricted form is sufficient for the definition of our nonstandard model.

To eliminate the axioms for R, that is, to show that A is a theorem of $\mathbf{S}_n$ itself, one adapts the method of Easton [1] for proving that the "global" class axiom of choice is a conservative extension of set theory (of course, *with* the axiom of choice for sets, corresponding to our axiom of choice restricted to analysis of rank n).

NOTE: This elimination has not been carried out in full detail; for example, the author has not checked carefully whether the forms of the axiom of choice and well orderings stated are sufficient, but it seems plausible. Also it may be that the newer method of Boolean-valued models [10] would simplify matters.

It is clear that in this elimination something more elaborate than the usual trick of relativizing to constructible sets is needed: For if that trick worked one would eliminate the axiom of choice at rank $<n$, too!, contrary to the introduction. Since the problem of conservative extensions is a formal (axiomatic) problem, it is not surprising that it requires attention to axiomatic details of analysis of fixed rank. Whether this case is worthwhile depends on the significance of the formal system, a point that will be taken up in the next section.

Remark. In answer to a question of Robinson, it was observed in [3], app. B, that *any* model M of (first-order standard) arithmetic can be so extended to a model M' of a certain, weak axiom system of nonstandard arithmetic that M *itself* is the standard part of M'. It seems to be open whether this (model-theoretic) result holds also for models M of $\mathbf{S}$ and $\mathbf{S}_n$ and M' of $\mathbf{NS}$ and $\mathbf{NS}_n$, respectively. Although principally of technical interest, the question is connected with an interesting *distinction:* (a) the existence of a "generalized" model M' of a system S' in a system S, and (b) the existence in S of a truth definition for the formula A holds in M' (which provides one way of proving the consistency of S' *in* S, not only its consistency relative to that of S). It is well known that (a) does not presuppose (b) for infinite systems of axioms (in predicate calculus). We cannot expect a positive answer to (b) when $S = \mathbf{S}$, and $S' = \mathbf{NS}$; but a positive answer to (a) implies a positive answer to our model-theoretic question above.

6. Discussion of the Systems Considered

Note first that the systems are not of interest for *logic* in the strict sense, which is concerned with validity. For, either they are too weak, for example, they are incomplete with respect to truth in the intended model; or too strong, for example, they cannot be predicatively justified. (For a discussion of the foundational interest of nonstandard analysis, see [3], app. B.)

We shall consider instead another possibility: that they are of *descriptive* interest, as an approximation to existing mathematical practice; in particular, as a theory of what mathematicians are *likely* to prove when they think in terms of standard and nonstandard analysis, respectively (see [9], p. 4). (In the light of such a theory one may then decide in which terms one ought to think!) From this empirical point of view the mathematical results are only an auxiliary: one needs a case study to see how good the approximation is. Note also that, as always, in realistic applications, approximations may be quite conclusive if they imply a particular conclusion but not for the opposite conclusion.

Example. Suppose it had turned out that some specific, evidently interesting, result A in the language of standard analysis $\mathbf{S}$ of Section 2 is a theorem of nonstandard analysis $\mathbf{NS}$, but not a formal consequence of the axioms $\mathbf{S}$ at all. Since there is good evidence that $\mathbf{S}$ covers comfortably the reasoning of analysts who think in "standard terms," the effectiveness of thinking in nonstandard terms would be conclusively established. In contrast, a conservative extension result leaves open whether proofs formulated in nonstandard analysis can be (a) significantly *shorter*, and (b) more *intelligible* than in **S**, and therefore not only easier to find but easier to check.[8]

It may be of interest to say a word about the *inclusion* of the principles of choice and well ordering (in **S**) and the interest of systems restricted to a *fixed* rank.

Axiom of Choice. If, as a matter of fact, the use of Zorn's lemma in practical analysis had been rare, the practice of nonstandard analysis would be a nonconservative extension of practical analysis. (Formally: **NS** without principles of choice or well ordering is a nonconservative extension of the corresponding fragment of **S**.) But the uses of Zorn's lemma are not rare, for good reasons.[9] (Of course, from an axiomatic point of view, there is a proper objection to using it without stating it. The issue is merely whether, in informal proofs, one should emphasize its use; after all, one does not single out the pairing axiom for emphasis.) Almost certainly the *only* reason for singling out this axiom depended on the following, quite interesting oversight: The other existential axioms assert the existence of *explicitly definable* or "namable" sets (and at the turn of the century, where there was most discussion about the axiom of choice, there was also a great deal of emphasis on *ensemble nommable*); and the axiom of choice is different in this respect. What is overlooked, or simply not considered, is that *there are purely logical existential assertions about sets which certainly cannot be proved to be satisfied by explicitly definable sets,* at least not by means of principles accepted at the turn of the century!

Example. Consider the property $C(X)$: X is nonconstructible or all sets of natural numbers are constructible. Clearly $\exists X\ C(X)$ is logically valid.

In short, not only is the inclusion of the choice schema dictated by actual practice, but this practice is quite coherent.

Incidentally there is a formal question here which, as far as the author knows, is open: Does the full comprehension schema for nonstandard analysis imply *all* instances of the choice schema for standard analysis?

[8] Whereas (a) can be made precise quite easily and fairly unambiguously, a tractable formulation of (b) obviously presents a major problem. The importance of (b) can hardly be exaggerated, not only from a pedagogic point of view, but logically. For instance, the widespread opinion that mathematical reliability is connected with (and, some would say, consists in) the *formal,* that is, *mechanical* character of (the usual) inference rules completely disregards the fact that *actual checking* is done by making arguments more intelligible.

[9] The popular reason that it is "needed" could do with a little elaboration; for instance, one doesn't accept the principle: $a \cdot 0 = b \cdot 0 \to a = b$ even if somebody happens to need it (for his particular proof).

Restriction on Types. This concerns principally the restriction to *fixed* finite rank, but the restriction to all finite ranks, thus excluding infinite ones, also needs examination from the present descriptive point of view. The main interest of the restriction depends on the curious empirical fact that in mathematics, in contrast to logic (for example, consistency proofs) [4], pp. 181–182, in proofs of theorems in the language of rank n one may indeed use the language of higher rank, *but rarely uses strong axioms for variables of higher rank.* So to speak, mathematicians have not yet learned how to exploit these axioms effectively. As long as this is so, it would be of evident interest from the present point of view if nonstandard analysis $\mathbf{NS}_n$ of fixed rank were *not* a conservative extension of $\mathbf{S}_n$. For this reason one has to look at such systems.

The tendency of current mathematical practice not to use axioms about higher types than those occurring in the problem considered holds out, the present author thinks, a certain hope for a more effective use of the ideas of nonstandard analysis. Roughly speaking, Section 4 shows that as long as one only uses the existence of *some* nonstandard model (enlargement), that is, of properties that follow evidently from its existence (axioms of Section 3), one only gets conservative extensions. The matter would be different if one had *specific constructions* of nonstandard models (which automatically would use higher types in an essential way) and used detailed properties of them. True, in *principle* this would be nothing else than using the perfectly well-known possibility, mentioned above, of exploiting comprehension axioms of higher type, but *in practice* this might be most important as being the first place where one is actually led to an effective use of such axioms.[10]

References

1. W. B. EASTON, Ph.D. dissertation, Princeton, N.J.: Princeton Univ., 1964.
2. G. HASENJAEGER, Eine Bemerkung zu Henkin's Beweis für die Vollständigkeit des Prädikatenkalkuls, *J. Symbolic Logic 18* (1953), 42–48.

[10] The results of Sections 4 and 5 would certainly not justify as extensive a discussion as given in Section 6. Naturally this discussion applies generally to any *empiricist* or purely *descriptive* treatment of foundations. But the concrete case considered here seems to be particularly convenient. *Some* analysis of the kinds of questions that have to be faced in such an empirical approach is very much needed: It might fairly be said that the difficulties in the classical foundational schemes are so well known because these have been intensively studied. In contrast, most people who look for a pragmatist or empirical "methodology" of mathematics have hardly considered what problems arise when one takes such a program seriously at all. Of course Frege, Russell, and others gave such an analysis; but this leaves open the question whether their *criticisms* are valid in the light of recent work. The present author believes they are.

3. G. KREISEL, Informal Rigour and Completeness Proofs, *Proc. Intern. Coll. Philosophy of Science, London, 1965*, Vol. I. Amsterdam: North-Holland, 1967.
4. G. KREISEL AND J. L. KRIVINE, *Éléments de logique mathématique; théorie des modèles*. Paris: 1966.
5. G. KREISEL AND A. LEVY, Reflection Principles and Their Use for Establishing the Complexity of Axiom Systems, *Z. Math. Logik Grundlagen Math.*, *14* (1968). To appear.
6. G. KREISEL AND HAO WANG, Some Applications of Formalized Consistency Proofs, *Fundamenta Math.* *42* (1955), 101–110; *45* (1958), 334–335.
7. R. M. MONTAGUE, Semantical Closure and Non-Finite Axiomatizability. I. Infinitistic Methods, *Proc. Symposium on Foundations of Mathematics, Warsaw, 1959*. Warsaw: 1961, pp. 45–69.
8. A. ROBINSON, Non-Standard Analysis, *Indagationes Math.* *23* (1961), 432–440.
9. A. ROBINSON, *Non-Standard Analysis* (Studies in Logic and the Foundations of Mathematics). Amsterdam: North-Holland, 1966.
10. DANA SCOTT, Boolean Models and Nonstandard Analysis (this volume).
11. R. L. VAUGHT, On the Axiom of Choice and Some Metamathematical Theorems, *Bull. Am. Math. Soc.* *62* (1956), 262–263.

A Conservation Result[1]

Given some definitions, corrections a useful note.

by ROHIT PARIKH

In this note we point out two related conservation results that hold when a theory T in the first-order predicate calculus with equality is expanded to include some nonstandard apparatus. Roughly the theory of a proper extension of a model of T and the theory of an enlargement (in Robinson's sense) of a model of T are conservative extensions of T.

Specifically, let T be a theory in a first-order language L and let A be some set of axioms for T (perhaps $A = T$). Expand L to L' by adding a new unary predicate symbol S (S for standard). If φ is a formula of L ($\varphi \in \mathrm{Fm}(L)$), let φ_1 denote the formula of L' obtained by relativizing all quantifiers to S and, if $x_1, \cdots, x_n$ are all the free variables of φ, let φ' be the formula $(x_1)(x_2) \cdots (x_n)(Sx_1 \wedge \cdots \wedge Sx_n \rightarrow (\varphi \leftrightarrow \varphi_1))$.

***Theorem* 1.** *Let T_1 be the L'-theory whose axioms are (a) A; (b) for every $\varphi \in \mathrm{Fm}(L)$, the formula φ'; (c) the formula $(\exists x) \neg Sx$. Then T_1 is a conservative extension of T iff all models of T are infinite.*

Proof. Let T_2 be an L-extension of T. Then $T_1 \cup T_2$ is consistent. For suppose $\mathfrak{A} = \langle X, \cdots \rangle$ is a model of T_2. Let $\mathfrak{L} = \langle X, \cdots, \{a_i\} \rangle$, where $\{a_i\}$ is an enumeration of X and let $T_3 = \mathrm{Th}(\mathfrak{L})$. Clearly $T_3 \supseteq T_2$. Add a new constant c to the language of T_3 and for each $a \in X$, the axiom $a \neq c$. Then T_3 with these axioms is finitely satisfiable and hence has a model $\mathfrak{L}_1$ which is a proper elementary extension of $\mathfrak{L}$. By interpreting Sx to mean $x \in X$, and throwing away the structure not belonging to L', we get a model of $T_1 \cup T_2$ from $\mathfrak{L}_1$.

2 But now suppose $\psi \in T$. Then there is an extension T_2 of T such that $\neg\psi \in T_2$. Since $T_1 \cup T_2$ is consistent, we cannot have $\psi \in T_1$. Thus T_1 is a conservative extension of T.

[1] This note is the result of a conversation with John Myhill.

2 Note: "$\psi \notin T$" is intended: If $\psi \in T$ then there is no (consistent) extension T_2 of T (much less T_1) such that $(\neg\psi) \in T_2$ (by way of making sense of nonsense)

To show the converse, suppose T had a finite model, of power n. Then the formula $(x_1) \cdots (x_n)(\exists y)(y \neq x_1 \wedge \cdots \wedge y \neq x_n)$ is a theorem of T_1 but not of T. (All models of T_1 are infinite.)

Definition. Let $\varphi(x, y) \in \mathrm{Fm}(L)$. ($\varphi$ may have other free variables also.) φ defines a concurrent relation relative to T if for all n, the formula

$$(x_1) \cdots (x_n)(\exists y)(\varphi(x_1, y) \wedge \cdots \wedge \phi(x_n, y))$$

is a theorem of T.

Theorem 2. *Let T be as before. Let T_1 be the L'-theory whose axioms are* (*a*) A; (*b*) *for every formula φ, concurrent relative to T, the formula* $(\exists y)(x)(Sx \rightarrow \varphi(x, y))$; (*c*) *the formulas φ' as in Theorem* 1. *Then T_1 is a conservative extension of T.*

Proof. Entirely similar.

Remark. These theorems do not apply if axiom schemata are used in formalizing T. The reason is that the expansion from L to L' may introduce new axioms under the old schemata and lead to a real strengthening of the formal system. In other cases the new system may still be a conservative extension, but proof-theoretic arguments are needed to show this (see Kreisel's paper in this volume).

A Set-Theoretical Characterization of Enlargements

by ABRAHAM ROBINSON and ELIAS ZAKON

Introduction

Nonstandard analysis was developed in [4] within a type-theoretical version of higher-order logic. In the present paper we shall describe a purely set-theoretical approach to the subject. In particular, we shall show that the basic notions of nonstandard analysis, such as the concept of enlargement and the concepts of standard and internal entities, can all be defined in terms of certain injections (or monomorphisms) of one model of set theory into another. Even the ultrapower construction, which, in other respects, is helpful in giving a concrete picture of the situation, does not reveal some of the characteristics of internal elements as they will appear from our present approach. In conformity with the spirit of axiomatic set theory, the type-theoretical restrictions of [4] will be replaced by a simpler and less restrictive condition imposed on quantifiers (see Section 3). The equivalence of our present approach with that of [4] follows directly from set-theoretical relations between a full structure, as defined in [4], and a model of set theory (called "superstructure" below).

We are pleased to acknowledge that there are certain points of contact between the theory presented here and the formulation outlined by Kreisel during this symposium.

1. Preliminaries. Terminology and Notation

An *ordered pair* and *n-tuple* are defined, as usual, by $(a, b) = \{\{a, b\}, \{b\}\}$ and $(x_1, \cdots, x_n) = ((x_1, \cdots, x_{n-1}), x_n)$, $(x_1) = x_1$. An *n-ary relation* is any set of ordered n-tuples for a fixed n. For any set R, we define its *domain* $D_R = D(R) = \{x \mid (\exists y)(x, y) \in R\}$, and its *range*

$D'_R = D'(R) = \{y \mid (\exists x)(x, y) \in R\}$. The *image* of a set X under R (briefly, "the R-image of X") is defined by $R[X] = \{y \mid (\exists x \in X)(x, y) \in R\}$. Here the quantifier "$(\exists x \in X)$" means "there is an $x \in X$ such that . . . ." Equivalently, $R[X]$ is the range D'_S of the relation $S = R \cap (X \times D'_R)$. The set X in this definition may, but need not, be a subset of D_R. The *inverse image*, $R^{-1}[X]$, is the image of X under the *inverse relation* $R^{-1} = \{(y, x) \mid (x, y) \in R\}$. A binary relation R is called a *mapping* (*function*) if, for each $x \in D_R$, $R[\{x\}]$ has only one element, denoted by $R(x)$ and called the *function value* at x. In all cases, and especially if x is a set, $R(x)$ must be distinguished from $R[x]$. The *composition* $R \circ S$ of two binary relations R and S is the relation $\{(x, y) \mid (\exists z)(x, z) \in S, (z, y) \in R\}$. For n-ary relations R, we also define the operations of *grouping* and *permuting* the arguments. If $\mathcal{P}$ is a permutation on n elements, we denote by $\mathcal{P}R$ the relation obtained from R by applying the permutation $\mathcal{P}$ to each n-tuple $(x_1, \cdots, x_n) \in R$. Instead, we can *group* the n-tuples in various manners; say, split a quintuple $(a, b, c, d, e) \in R$ into a triple (a, b, c) and a pair (d, e): $((a, b, c), (d, e))$. Then the quintary relation R becomes a binary one, with D_R a set of triples and D'_R a set of ordered pairs. If the same grouping $\mathcal{G}$ is applied to all n-tuples in R, the resulting relation is denoted by $\mathcal{G}R$.

Given a set A, we define inductively the sets $A_0 = A$ and $A_{n+1} = P(\bigcup_{k=0}^{n} A_k)$, $n = 0, 1, \cdots$, where $P(X)$ is the set of all subsets of X. This construction can be continued transfinitely, but we shall not need it. The union of all A_n, $\bigcup_{n=0}^{\infty} A_n$, is called the *superstructure* on A, denoted $\hat{A}$. Clearly, $A_n \in A_{n+1}$ for $n = 0, 1, \cdots$, and also $A_n \subset A_{n+1}$ for $n \geq 1$. Elements of $A_n - A_{n-1}$ $(n \geq 1)$ are said to be *of type n* (in $\hat{A}$); those *of type 0*, that is, elements of A_0, are also called "individuals." For convenience we shall assume that "individuals" are objects other than the empty set $\emptyset$ but possessing no elements (so called "Urelements"), although the theory can also be developed under other assumptions. Thus, if $a \in A_0$, then $x \notin a$ for all $x \in \hat{A}$ (but the formula $x \notin a$ or $x \in a$ is always meaningful). No entities other than sets and individuals exist inside $\hat{A}$. Under these assumptions, A_0 is disjoint from other A_n. The latter increase with n, so that $\bigcup_{k=0}^{n} A_k = A_n \cup A_0$; hence $x \in y \in A_{n+1}$ implies $x \in A_n \cup A_0$. If $a,b \in A_n$ then $(a, b) = \{\{a, b\}, \{b\}\} \in A_{n+2}$; thus (a, b) is in $\hat{A}$ when $a, b \in \hat{A}$. Similarly for n-tuples, by induction, hence for n-ary relations of *bounded type* (that is, such that all n-tuples are in *one* A_n for some n).[1] We have $\varphi \in A_n$ for $n \geq 1$. As $A_n \in A_{n+1} \subset \hat{A}$,

[1] Equivalently, a set R is an n-ary relation in $\hat{A}$ iff $R \subseteq (A_0 \cup A_m)^n$ for some m, where X^n is the Cartesian product of n factors equal to X.

each A_n is an element of $\hat{A}$. We write C^n for $C \times C \times \cdots \times C$ (n times), and $x \in y \in c$ for $(x \in y,\ y \in c)$.

Although we use the language of naïve set theory, it is clear that, with small adjustments (such as replacing individuals by nonempty sets with no elements in $\hat{A}$), all can be formalized in any existing axiomatic theory.

2. Monomorphisms

Let A, B be two sets with superstructures $\hat{A}$, $\hat{B}$, respectively. A one-to-one map $\Phi: \hat{A} \to \hat{B}$ is called a *monomorphism* of $\hat{A}$ into $\hat{B}$ if, writing $^*x$ for $\Phi(x)$, we have:

2.1. *For any* $x \in \hat{A}$, $^*\{x\} = \{^*x\}$.

2.2. *If* $X, Y \in \hat{A}$, *then* $^*(X - Y) = {}^*X - {}^*Y$ *and* $^*(X \times Y) = {}^*X \times {}^*Y$.

2.3. *If* $\mathcal{P}$ *is a grouping or permutation on* n *elements, then* $^*(\mathcal{P}R) = \mathcal{P}(^*R)$ *for any* n*-ary relation* $R \in \hat{A}$*; hence* $^*(R^{-1}) = (^*R)^{-1}$.

2.4. *For any binary relation* $R \in \hat{A}$, $^*D_R = D(^*R)$*; hence* $^*D'_R = D'(^*R)$.

2.5. *If* $C \in \hat{A}$ *and* $R = \{(x, y) \mid x \in y \in C\}$, *then* $^*R = \{(x, y) \mid x \in y \in {}^*C\}$.

A monomorphism Φ is said to be *normal* if it also preserves all identity relations; that is, we have:

2.5′. *If* $C \in \hat{A}$ *and* $R = \{(x, x) \mid x \in C\}$, *then* $^*R = \{(x, x) \mid x \in {}^*C\}$.[2]

Postulate 2.3 could be split into a few "simpler" ones, dealing with ordered pairs and triples only. We often identify $^*x$ with x *if* x *is an individual* ($x \in A_0$); then we have:

2.6. *For any* $x \in A_0$, $^*x = x$*; hence* $X \subseteq {}^*X$ *for* $X \subseteq A_0{}^n$ $(n \geq 1)$.

Note that, except for individuals, Φ is a set function; so it is imperative to distinguish $^*X = \Phi(X)$ from $\Phi[X] = \{^*x \mid x \in X\}$. We now derive a few simple consequences of Postulates 2.1–2.5.

[2] Postulates 2.5 and 2.5′ may be limited to the case where C is one of the sets A_n. The general case then follows by Corollary 2.7(d), proved below.

Corollaries 2.7. *Under any monomorphism* $\Phi: \hat{A} \to \hat{B}$, *we have:*

(a) $*\emptyset = \emptyset$.
(b) $X \subseteq Y$ *iff* $*X \subseteq *Y$.
(c) $x \in Y$ *iff* $*x \in *Y$.
(d) $*(X \cap Y) = *X \cap *Y$.
(e) $*(X \cup Y) = *X \cup *Y$.
(f) $*\{x_1, \cdots, x_n\} = \{*x_1, \cdots, *x_n\}$.
(g) $*(x_1, \cdots, x_n) = (*x_1, \cdots, *x_n)$.
(h) $(x_1, \cdots, x_n) \in R$ *iff* $(*x_1, \cdots, *x_n) \in *R$.
(i) *If* $R \in \hat{A}$ *is an* n*-ary relation, so is* $*R$.
(j) *For any binary relation* $R \in \hat{A}$ *and any* $X \in \hat{A}$, $*(R[X]) = (*R)[*X]$.
(k) *If* $x \in Q \in *A_n$, *then* $x \in *A_0 \cup *A_{n-1}$.
(l) *If* $(x_1, \cdots, x_m) \in Q \in *A_n$, *then* $x_k \in *A_0 \cup *A_{n-1}$, $k = 1, \cdots, m$.

Proof. (a) By Postulate 2.2, $*\emptyset = *(X - X) = *X - *X = \emptyset$. As $X \subseteq Y$ is equivalent to $X - Y = \emptyset$, also (b) follows. Hence replacing $x \in Y$ by $\{x\} \subseteq Y$, we obtain (c). To obtain (d), we note that $X \cap Y = X - (X - Y)$ and apply Postulate 2.2. Similarly, $X \cup Y = Z - [Z - (X \cap Y)]$, with $Z = X \cup Y \in \hat{A}$, yields (e). This, combined with Postulate 2.1, yields (f): $*\{x_1, \cdots, x_n\} = \bigcup_1^n\{*x_k\} = \{*x_1, \cdots, *x_n\}$; and hence also (g) easily follows, by the definition of an ordered pair and ordered n-tuple. Combining (g) with (c), we obtain (h). For the proof of (i), we note that R is an n-ary relation in $\hat{A}$ iff $R \subseteq (A_0 \cup A_m)^n$ for some m; but then, by (b), (e), and Postulate 2.2, we have $*R \subseteq (*A_0 \cup *A_m)^n$, so that $*R$, too, is a set of n-tuples. To prove (j), let $S = R \cap (X \times D'_R)$. Then (see Section 1) $R[X] = D'_S$. Hence, by Postulates 2.4, 2.2, and 2.7 (d), $*(R[X]) = *D'_S = D'(*S) = D'(*R \cap (*X \times D'_{*R})) = (*R)[*X]$, as required. Next, for (k), let $R = \{(x, y) \mid x \in y \in A_n\}$. By Postulate 2.5, $*R = \{(x, y) \mid x \in y \in *A_n\}$. As $x \in y \in A_n$ implies $x \in A_0 \cup A_{n-1}$ (see Section 1), the definition of R yields $D_R \subseteq A_0 \cup A_{n-1}$. Hence, by (b), (e), and Postulate 2.4, $D(*R) = *A_0 \cup *A_{n-1}$. Now, if $x \in Q \in *A_n$, we have $(x, Q) \in *R$ by the formula for $*R$ obtained above, and hence $x \in D(*R) \subseteq *A_{n-1} \cup *A_0$. Thus (k) is proved. Finally, (l) easily follows from (k) by the definition of an ordered pair and n-tuple. This completes the proof.

NOTE 1. By (f), we have $*X = \Phi(X) = \Phi[X]$ if X is *finite*.
We now extend Postulate 2.5 to $(n + 1)$-ary relations.

2.8. *If* $C \in \hat{A}$ *and* $R = \{(x_1, \cdots, x_n, y) \mid (x_1, \cdots, x_n) \in y \in C\}$, *then, under any monomorphism* Φ *on* $\hat{A}$, $*R = \{(x_1, \cdots, x_n, y) \mid (x_1, \cdots, x_n) \in y \in *C\}$.

Proof. As $C \in \hat{A}$, we have $C \in A_m$ for some m, and so the defining condition of R, $(x_1, \cdots, x_n) \in y \in C$, implies that all x_k and y in the $(n+1)$-tuples belonging to R are in the set $D = A_0 \cup A_m$. Hence $R = \{(x, y) \mid x \in y \in C\} \cap D^{n+1}$, where $x = (x_1, \cdots, x_n)$; indeed, the added term D^{n+1} ensures that $(x, y) \in R$ is an $(n+1)$-*tuple* also in the new formula for R, as it is in the original one; thus the two formulas coincide. Now, by Postulates 2.5, 2.2, and 2.7(d), we have $*R = \{(x, y) \mid x \in y \in *C\} \cap *D^{n+1} = \{(x_1, \cdots, x_n, y) \mid (x_1, \cdots, x_n) \in y \in *C\} \cap *D^{n+1}$. But $*D^{n+1}$ is redundant here because the condition $(x_1, \cdots, x_n) \in y \in *C$, combined with $*C \in *A_m$ and $*D = *A_m \cup *A_0$, *implies* that each x_k and y is in $*D$, as follows from Corollary 2.7(l). Thus, dropping $*D^{n+1}$, we obtain the result.

NOTE 2. If Φ is normal (but not otherwise), Postulate 2.8 holds also with *repeating* variables, such as in $R = \{(x, x, y) \mid (x, x) \in y \in C\}$. In this particular case, we put $R = T \cap (S \times C)$, where $S = \{(u, u) \mid u \in A_0 \cup A_m\}$, $T = \{(x, u, y) \mid (x, u) \in y \in C\}$, and the result follows by Postulates 2.8 and 2.5′.

In more complicated cases, we use *several* identity maps S.

The following example illustrates a typical procedure to be used later.

2.9. *Let* $E = \{(x, y, z) \mid (x, a, b, y, z, c) \in d\}$ *where* $a, b, c, d \in \hat{A}$ *are fixed. Then* $*E = \{(x, y, z) \mid (x, *a, *b, y, z, *c) \in *d\}$.[3]

Proof. Replacing a, b, c, d by variables s, t, u, v, consider the *binary* relation $R = \{((s, t, u, v), (x, y, z)) \mid (x, s, t, y, z, u) \in v \in C\}$ choosing $C \in \hat{A}$ such that $d \in C$, $*d \in *C$. By Postulates 2.8 and 2.3, we easily obtain $*R = \{((s, t, u, v), (x, y, z)) \mid (x, s, t, y, z, u) \in v \in *C\}$. Let $X = \{(a, b, c, d)\}$. Then $R[X]$ consists of all triples (x, y, z) such that the pair $((a, b, c, d), (x, y, z))$ is in R, that is, satisfies $(x, a, b, y, z, c) \in d$. In other words, $R[X] = R[\{(a, b, c, d)\}]$ is exactly the set E given above. Similarly, by definition, $*R[*X] = *R[\{(*a, *b, *c, *d)\}] = \{(x, y, z) \mid (x, *a, *b, y, z, *x) \in *d\}$. Thus, by Corollary 2.7(j), this set equals $*E$, as asserted.

Obviously, this proof does not depend on the number of the variables x, y, z and the constants a, b, c, d, and on their arrangement.[4] By Note 2, we may admit repeating variables if Φ is normal.

[3] Observe that, when passing from E to $*E$, we replace each *constant* c by $*c$, leaving the variables and the rest unchanged.

[4] Moreover, with slight modifications, the proof also works if E has the form $\{(x, y, z) \mid (x, a, b, y, d, c) \in z\} \cap C$, $C \in \hat{A}$.

3. Internal and Standard Elements. The Metatheorem

Given a monomorphism $\Phi: \hat{A} \to \hat{B}$ as in Section 2, we define $*\hat{A} = \bigcup_{n=0}^{\infty} *A_n = \bigcup_{n=0}^{\infty} \Phi(A_n)$, and call all elements of $*\hat{A}$ the Φ-*internal* (briefly, *internal*) elements (of $\hat{B}$). As previously noted, $\Phi(A_n) \neq \Phi[A_n]$ in general. Thus $*\hat{A}$ is different from $\Phi[\hat{A}] = \bigcup_{n=0}^{\infty} \Phi[A_n] = \{*x \mid x \in \hat{A}\}$. Elements of the form $*x$ $(x \in \hat{A})$, that is, those of $\Phi[\hat{A}]$, are called Φ-*standard* (briefly, *standard*) elements. As $x \in A_n$ implies $*x \in *A_n$ [Corollary 2.7(c)], *all standard elements are internal,* that is, $\Phi[\hat{A}] \subset *\hat{A}$, but the converse is not true.[5] If Postulate 2.6 is assumed, all elements of A_0 (individuals of $\hat{A}$) are standard, hence internal. They belong to $*A_0$, called the set of *individuals in* $*\hat{A}$[6]; however, $*A_0$ may also have other (internal) elements. From Corollary 2.7(k) we immediately obtain:

3.1. *If a set* $Q \in \hat{B}$ *is internal, so are all its elements.*

The converse fails, as follows from well-known examples.

To shorten further proofs we shall now adopt a first-order logical language L, using the connectives $\wedge$, $\vee$, $\supset$, $\cdot\!\equiv\!\cdot$, and $\neg$ for "and," "or," "implies," "iff," and "not," respectively, with other details as in [4, p. 6ff.]. For simplicity, we assume that all constants of L are in one-to-one correspondence with all elements of $\hat{A}$, and identify such constants with the corresponding elements, so that these become a part of L and denote themselves. Atomic formulas in L are those of the form $(x_1, \cdots, x_n) \in y$, where y and the x_k are constants or *distinct* variables (constants need not be distinct); if, however, the monomorphism Φ is normal, then also repeating variables are allowed in atomic formulas. Well-formed formulas (wff) and well-formed sentences (wfs) then are defined inductively, as in [4, p. 7]. We use the abbreviations "$(\forall x \in C)$" and "$(\exists x \in C)$" for "$(\forall x)[[x \in C] \supset \cdots]$" and "$(\exists x)[[x \in C] \wedge \cdots]$," respectively (read: "*for every* x *in* C, $\cdots$" and "*there is an* x *in* C *such that* $\cdots$"); here C is supposed to be an element of $\hat{A}$, that is, a *constant* of L (not a variable). We single out those wff in which all quantifiers (if any) are of that particular *form; that is, each quantifier specifies the domain of its variable in the manner described above, with* $C \in \hat{A}$. Henceforth *only such formulas will be admitted and called "wff" or "wfs."* This is tantamount to singling out a certain set of wff in L, without changing

[5] This, combined with Postulate 3.1, implies that internal elements are exactly all elements of standard elements; that is, $x \in *\hat{A}$ iff $x \in *X$ for some $X \in \hat{A}$. This extremely simple characterization of internal elements has been made possible by our present set-theoretical approach based on monomorphisms.

[6] Members of $*A_1$ need not be genuine "Urelements," but they have no *internal* elements (see Postulate 3.3). Thus, *inside* $*\hat{A}$, they behave like individuals.

the nature of L as a *first-order* language. Note that it suffices to use quantifiers with $C = A_n \cup A_0$; for if $C \in A_{n+1}$, the quantifiers $(\forall x \in C)$ and $(\exists x \in C)$ can be written $(\forall x \in A_n \cup A_0)[[x \in C] \supset \cdots]$ and $(\exists x \in A_n \cup A_0)[[x \in C] \wedge \cdots]$, respectively.

By the *Φ-transform* of such a wff α, denoted $^*\alpha$, we mean the formula (not necessarily in L) obtained from α by replacing in it every constant c by $^*c$, but leaving the variables and the rest of the formula unchanged (see the footnote to Postulate 2.9); $^*\alpha$ has a self-evident interpretation in $^*\hat{A}$ (not in $\hat{A}$). For example, the Φ-transform of the formula $(\forall x \in C)[[x \in a] \vee [y \in b]]$, where a, b, C are constants, is $(\forall x \in {}^*C)[[x \in {}^*a] \vee [x \in {}^*b]]$. The symbol $\{x \in C \mid \alpha(x)\}$, where $\alpha(x)$ is a wff containing x as a free variable, means "the set of all elements x of C, satisfying $\alpha(x)$." Similarly, for sets of n-tuples, $\{(x_1, \cdots, x_n) \in C \mid \alpha(x_1, \cdots, x_n)\}$, and for sets in $^*\hat{A}$ such as $\{x \in {}^*C \mid {}^*\alpha(x)\}$. We shall sometimes use semiformal abbreviations of wff such as $a \subseteq b$ for $(\forall x \in a)[x \in b]$, $a \notin b$, for $\neg[a \in b]$, $x \in a \cup b$, for $[x \in a] \vee [x \in b]$, and so on. (Note that these expressions are also defined if a and b are individuals; then, by our conventions, $a \cup b = a \cap b = \emptyset$.) We shall now prove jointly two metamathematical propositions:

Meta-theorem 3.2. (a) *A well-formed sentence α is true in $\hat{A}$ iff its Φ-transform $^*\alpha$ is true in $^*\hat{A}$.* (b) *If $\alpha(x_1, \cdots, x_m)$ is a wff, with $x_1, \cdots, x_m$ its only free variables, and if, for some $C \in \hat{A}$, $E = \{(x_1, \cdots, x_m) \in C \mid \alpha(x_1, \cdots, x_m)\}$, then $^*E = \{(x_1, \cdots, x_m) \in {}^*C \mid {}^*\alpha(x_1, \cdots, x_m)\}$.*

Proof. If α is an atomic sentence, it has the form $(a_1, \cdots, a_n) \in b$ $(a_k, b \in \hat{A})$. By Corollaries 2.7 it is equivalent to $({}^*a_1, \cdots, {}^*a_n) \in {}^*b$. Thus (a) is true for atomic sentences. A simple induction process (over the number of brackets $[\cdots]$ that show how α is built from atomic formulas) extends (a) to all wfs *containing no quantifiers*. Next, take an atomic wff $\alpha(x_1, \cdots, x_p, a_1, \cdots, a_q)$, with $x_1, \cdots, x_p$ its variables, and a_k its constants. Then it has the form $(x_1, \cdots, x_p, a_1, \cdots, a_{q-1}) \in a_q$, or $(x_1, \cdots, x_{p-1}, a_1, \cdots, a_q) \in x_p$, with the x_k and a_i possibly permuted. In all such cases, (b) follows in the manner exemplified in Postulate 2.9, that is, by regrouping the relation $R = \{(x_1, \cdots, x_p, y_1, \cdots, y_q) \mid \alpha(x_1, \cdots, x_p, y_1, \cdots, y_k)\}$, and computing $R[\{(a_1, \cdots, a_q)\}]$. This proves (b) for atomic formulas.

Next we show that, if (b) holds for two wff α and β, then it also holds for $\alpha \wedge \beta$ and $\neg\alpha$ (this takes care of *all* logical connectives). Let $\alpha = \alpha(x_1, \cdots, x_m, y_1, \cdots, y_n)$, $\beta = \beta(x_1, \cdots, x_m, z_1, \cdots, z_p)$, $m \geq 0$, where the x_k are the *common* free variables of α and β (if any). For brevity, we put $x = (x_1, \cdots, x_m)$, $y = (y_1, \cdots, y_n)$, $z = (z_1, \cdots, z_p)$. With x, y, z so defined, let $R = \{(x, y) \in D^2 \mid \alpha\}$ and $S = \{(x, z) \in D^2 \mid \beta\}$, where $D \in \hat{A}$ is to be fixed later; we treat R and S as *binary* relations.[7] Even so, using Postulate 2.3 and our assumptions as to α and β, we easily obtain [since (b) holds for α and β]

3.2.1. $\quad {}^*R = \{(x, y) \in {}^*D^2 \mid {}^*\alpha\}, \qquad {}^*S = \{(x, z) \in {}^*D^2 \mid {}^*\beta\}.$

Now let $E = \{(x, y, z) \in C \mid \alpha \wedge \beta\}$, $C \in \hat{A}$. Again, by Postulate 2.3, it does not matter whether E is treated as an $(m + n + p)$-ary or ternary relation. For, if E is $(m + n + p)$-ary ,we may safely assume that the set C, too, consists of $(m + n + p)$-tuples only (otherwise, drop the redundant other elements of C!). Then we can regroup *both* E and C as ternary relations, and by Postulate 2.3 it suffices to show that ${}^*E = \{(x, y, z) \in {}^*C \mid {}^*\alpha \wedge {}^*\beta\}$, as a set of *triples*.[8] This is what we shall prove now.

As $C \in \hat{A}$, we have $C \in A_r$ for some r. Hence, for any $(x, y, z) \in E$, the assumed condition $(x, y, z) \in C$ implies $x,y,z \in A_r \cup A_0 = D$ (*we thus fix D in Postulate* 3.2.1). Noting this, we obtain at once: $E = \{(x, y, z) \in C \mid \alpha \wedge \beta\} = \{(x, y, z) \in C \mid (x, y) \in R,\ (x, z) \in S\} = C \cap \{(x, y, z) \mid (x, y) \in R, z \in D\} \cap \{(x, y, z) \mid (x, z) \in S, y \in D\} = C \cap (R \times D) \cap \mathcal{P}(S \times D)$, where $\mathcal{P}$ is the permutation $(x, z, y) \rightarrow (x, y, z)$. Hence, by Postulates 2.2, 2.7(d), and 2.3, we have ${}^*E = {}^*C \cap ({}^*R \times {}^*D) \cap \mathcal{P}({}^*S \times {}^*D)$ or, by Postulate 3.2.1, after simplifications, ${}^*E = \{(x, y, z) \in {}^*C \mid {}^*\alpha \wedge {}^*\beta\}$, as required. Thus, indeed, if (b) holds for α and β, it also holds for $\alpha \wedge \beta$.

Now let $E = \{(x, y, z) \in C \mid \neg\alpha(x, y, z)\} = C - \{(x, y, z) \in C \mid \alpha\}$. Then, by Postulate 2.2, ${}^*E = {}^*C - \{(x, y, z) \in {}^*C \mid {}^*\alpha\} = \{(x, y, z) \in {}^*C \mid \neg{}^*\alpha\}$. Thus, again using induction over the number of brackets, we can complete the proof of both (a) and (b) *for wff without quantifiers.*

If there are quantifiers, we use induction over their number. Suppose that both (a) and (b) hold for formulas with n quantifiers ($n \geq 0$), and let α be a wfs with $n + 1$ quantifiers in prenex form: $\alpha = \alpha(qx_{n+1})(qx_n) \cdots (qx_1)\ \beta(x_1, \cdots, x_{n+1})$, where the (qx_k) are quantifiers and $\beta = \beta(x_1, \cdots, x_{n+1})$ is a wff without quantifiers. We may assume that (qx_{n+1}) is an *existential* quantifier, $(\exists x_{n+1} \in Q)$, $Q \in \hat{A}$; otherwise, we achieve this by replacing α by $\neg\alpha$. Thus, writing y for x_{n+1}, we have $\alpha = (\exists y \in Q)(qx_n) \cdots (qx_1)\ \beta(x_1, \cdots, x_n, y)$. In other words, α states that the set

$$D = \{y \in Q \mid (qx_n) \cdots (qx_1)\ \beta(x_1, \cdots, x_n, y)\} \qquad (Q \in \hat{A})$$

[7] If α and β have no free variables in common ($m = 0$), then R and S become *unary* relations, and the proof is trivial. We omit this trivial case and assume henceforth that $m > 0$.

[8] Owing to Postulate 2.3, no generality is lost by assuming this particular arrangement of the variables: $(x_1, \cdots, x_m, y_1, \cdots, y_n, z_1, \cdots, z_p)$.

is not empty. As the right-hand expression contains only n quantifiers, our inductive assumption yields [by Corollary 2.7(a)]

3.2.2. $\quad {}^*D = \{y \in {}^*Q \mid ({}^*qx_n) \cdots ({}^*qx_1) \qquad {}^*\beta(x_1, \cdots, x_n, y)\} \neq \emptyset,$

where $({}^*qx_k)$ stands for $(\exists x_k \in {}^*Q_k)$ or $(\forall x_k \in {}^*Q_k)$, $Q_k \in \hat{A}$. But Formula 3.2.2 means exactly that ${}^*\alpha$ holds in ${}^*\hat{A}$. Conversely, if ${}^*\alpha$ holds, then ${}^*D \neq \emptyset$ implies that $D \neq \emptyset$, hence that α is true. This completes the inductive process as far as (a) is concerned.

For (b), consider a set $E = \{(x_1, \cdots, x_m) \in C \mid \alpha(x_1, \cdots, x_m)\}$ and suppose that $\alpha = \alpha(x_1, \cdots, x_m) = (qy_{n+1}) \cdots (qy_1)\ \beta(x_1, \cdots, x_m, y_1, \cdots, y_{n+1})$, that is, α contains $n + 1$ quantifiers. We may again assume that (qy_{n+1}) is an existential quantifier, $(\exists y \in Q)$, $Q \in \hat{A}$. Thus, with $y = y_{n+1}$,

3.2.3. $\quad E = \{(x_1, \cdots, x_m) \in C \mid (\exists y \in Q)(qy_n) \cdots (qy_1)\beta\}, \qquad Q \in \hat{A},$

where $\beta = \beta(x_1, \cdots, x_m, y_1, \cdots, y_n, y)$ has no quantifiers.

Now consider also the set $R = \{((x_1, \cdots, x_m), y) \in C \times Q \mid (qy_n) \cdots (qy_1)\beta\}$, treating it as a *binary* relation. Our inductive assumption again yields ${}^*R = \{((x_1, \cdots, x_m), y) \in {}^*C \times {}^*Q \mid ({}^*qy_n) \cdots ({}^*qy_1){}^*\beta\}$. The domain of ${}^*R$ is, by definition, $D_{*R} = \{(x_1, \cdots, x_m) \in {}^*C \mid (\exists y \in {}^*Q)({}^*qy_n) \cdots ({}^*qy){}^*\beta\}$. Similarly, D_R is exactly the set E in Formula 3.2.3. Hence, by Postulate 2.4, ${}^*E = {}^*D_R = D({}^*R) = \{(x_1, \cdots, x_m) \in {}^*C \mid {}^*\alpha\}$, and the proof is complete.

We shall denote by K_A or K the set of all sentences that are true in $\hat{A}$ and can be written as *wfs* (in the restricted sense). All such sentences will be called *K-sentences.* In a wider sense, we apply the name "K-sentence" also to any Φ-transform of a K-sentence, under any monomorphism Φ. We shall now give a few examples of applications of Meta-theorem 3.2.[9]

3.3. *No internal elements* $x \in {}^*\hat{A}$ *can belong to any* $y \in {}^*A_0$.

Proof. As A_0 consists of individuals, we have for every n the K-sentence: $(\forall y \in A_0)(\forall x \in A_n)$, $x \notin y$. By Meta-theorem 3.2, then, $(\forall y \in {}^*A_0)(\forall x \in {}^*A_n)$, $x \notin y$; hence $x \notin y$ for every $x \in {}^*\hat{A}$, as asserted.

3.4. *The union, difference, and intersection of any finite number of members of* ${}^*\hat{A}$ *is an internal set. So also is the union or intersection of any internal set family* $U \in {}^*\hat{A}$, *even if* U *is infinite.*

[9] The propositions to be proved are known for "internal relations" as defined in [4, p. 42]. We prove them for "*φ-internal elements*" defined by monomorphisms, mainly to demonstrate the economy gained by the use of Theorem 3.2 and the set-theoretical approach.

Proof. For any n, we have the K-sentence $(\forall X, Y \in A_n \cup A_0)$ $(\exists Z \in A_{n+1})(\forall x \in A_n \cup A_0)[x \in Z] \cdot\equiv\cdot [x \in X \cup Y]$. Hence, by Theorem 3.2, for any $X, Y \in {}^*A_n \cup {}^*A_0$, there is a $Z \in {}^*A_{n+1}$ (hence $Z \in {}^*\hat{A}$) containing the same elements $x \in {}^*A_n \cup {}^*A_0$ as does $X \cup Y$. But, by Corollary 2.7(k), *all* elements of Z, X, and Y are in ${}^*A_n \cup {}^*A_0$. Thus $Z = X \cup Y \in {}^*\hat{A}$; similarly for $X - Y$ and $X \cap Y$. Since every $X, Y \in {}^*\hat{A}$ are in *one* ${}^*A_n \cup {}^*A_0$ for a large n, all is proved for *two* sets, hence for finitely many sets. Next, if $U \in {}^*A_{n+2}$, we use the K-sentence $(\forall U \in A_{n+2})(\exists Z \in A_{n+1})(\forall x \in A_n \cup A_0)[x \in Z] \cdot\equiv\cdot [(\exists Y \in A_{n+1}), x \in Y \in U]$. The rest is obvious.

Similarly we obtain: If two binary relations R and S are internal, so is their composition $R \circ S$.

3.5. *For any binary relations $R,S \in \hat{A}$, we have ${}^*(R \circ S) = {}^*R \circ {}^*S$.*

Proof. Choose n such that $R,S \in A_n$ and put $D = A_0 \cup A_n$. Then $(x, y) \in R \cup S$ implies $x,y \in D$; $(x, y) \in {}^*R \cup {}^*S$ implies $x,y \in {}^*D$; and so the definitions of $R \circ S$ and ${}^*R \circ {}^*S$ can be formally written as $R \circ S = \{(x, y) \in D^2 \mid (\exists z \in D)[(x, z) \in S] \wedge [(z, y) \in R]\}$, and similarly for ${}^*R \circ {}^*S$. By applying Theorem 3.2(b) to $R \circ S$, we immediately obtain ${}^*(R \circ S) = {}^*R \circ {}^*S$, as required.

3.6. *If the monomorphism Φ is normal and if $f \in \hat{A}$ is a mapping, so also is ${}^*f$.*

Proof. By Corollary 2.7(i), ${}^*f$ is certainly a binary relation. The requirement that it be a mapping is equivalent to ${}^*f \circ {}^*f^{-1} = {}^*R$, where ${}^*R = \{(x, x) \mid x \in D'_{*f}\}$ is the identity map on D'_{*f}. This, however, follows from $f \circ f^{-1} = R = \{(x, x) \mid x \in D'_f\}$ by Theorem 3.5 and Postulates 2.4 and 2.5′ (2.5′ applies since Φ is normal).

3.7. *A monomorphism Φ on $\hat{A}$ is normal iff $x \in {}^*\hat{A}$ implies $\{x\} \in {}^*\hat{A}$; more precisely, $x \in {}^*A_n$ implies $\{x\} \in A_{n+1}$.*

Proof. The identity map I_n on A_n coincides with the relation $\{(x, y) \in A_n{}^2 \mid (\forall Z \in A_{n+1})\ x \in Z \cdot\equiv\cdot y \in Z\}$. By Theorem 3.2(b), we have ${}^*I_n = \{(x, y) \in {}^*A_n{}^2 \mid (\forall Z \in {}^*A_{n+1})\ x \in Z \cdot\equiv\cdot y \in Z\}$. If Φ is normal, ${}^*I_n$ must be the identity map on ${}^*A_n$ (by Postulate 2.5′) and so, for each $x \in {}^*A_n$, ${}^*I_n(x) = x$ and ${}^*I_n[\{x\}] = \{x\} = \{y \in {}^*A_n \mid (x, y) \in {}^*I_n\}$. We can now use the K-sentence $(\forall x \in A_n)(\exists Z \in A_{n+1})(\forall y \in A_n)[y \in Z \cdot\equiv\cdot (x, y) \in I_n]$ to obtain that for each $x \in {}^*A_n$ there is $Z \in {}^*A_{n+1}$ such that $Z = {}^*I_n[\{x\}] = \{x\}$, whence $\{x\} \in {}^*A_{n+1}$, as asserted. Conversely, if $x \in {}^*A_n$ implies $\{x\} \in {}^*A_{n+1}$, then ${}^*I_n$ must be the identity relation on ${}^*A_n$; indeed, if $x \neq y$ $(x, y \in {}^*A_n)$, then $Z = \{x\} \in {}^*A_{n+1}$, $x \in Z$, $y \notin Z$, whence $(x, y) \notin {}^*I_n$; thus ${}^*I_n$ can only contain pairs (x, y) with $x = y$.

4. Concurrent Relations. Enlargements

A binary relation $R \in \hat{A}$ is said to be *concurrent* (see [4], pp. 41–42) if, for any finite number of elements $a_1, \cdots, a_m$ of its domain D_R, there is some $b \in \hat{A}$ such that $(a_k, b) \in R$, $k = 1, \cdots, m$. A monomorphism $\Phi: \hat{A} \to \hat{B}$ is referred to as *enlarging* if, for every concurrent relation $R \in \hat{A}$, there is some $b \in {}^*\hat{A}$ such that $({}^*x, b) \in {}^*R$ for all $x \in D_R$ simultaneously; we then also say that Φ *"bounds"* all concurrent relations. In this case ${}^*\hat{A}$ is called an *enlargement* of $\hat{A}$ (a *normal enlargement* if Φ is normal). The enlargement ${}^*\hat{A}$ (and the monomorphism Φ) are said to be *comprehensive* (see [6]) if, for any sets $C, D \in \hat{A}$ and any mapping $f: C \to {}^*D$, there is an *internal* map $g: {}^*C \to {}^*D$ ($g \in {}^*\hat{A}$) such that $f(x) = g({}^*x)$ for every $x \in C$. The existence of enlargements can be proved in various ways (see [4], p. 30ff., for higher-order structures). We shall use a construction based on ultrapowers; this will also lead to a construction of a set-theoretical monomorphism as defined in Section 2.

For this purpose (although not for the later work) it is convenient to replace the language L of Section 3 by a language L' as follows. The constants of L' are again all elements of $\hat{A}$, which thus denote themselves. The logical connectives are as before. The atomic formulas in L' are those of the form $x \dot{\in} y$ or $x \doteq y$, where x and y are variables or constants (possibly, constant n-tuples, treated as *single* elements of $\hat{A}$). The symbols $\dot{\in}$ and $\doteq$ are interpreted in $\hat{A}$ as the ordinary membership $\in$ and equality $=$, respectively; in other structures they may have a different meaning. Well-formed formulas (wff) and sentences (wfs) are defined as usual for first-order logic (see [4], p. 7), *without the restriction imposed on quantifiers in L*. We denote by K' the set of all wfs in L' which hold in $\hat{A}$, and call them *K'-sentences*. Two important K'-sentences are $(\forall x)(\forall y)[x \doteq y] \cdot\!\equiv\!\cdot (\forall z)[x \dot{\in} z \cdot\!\equiv\!\cdot y \dot{\in} z]$ and $(\forall x)(\forall y)(\forall z)(\forall u)[[x \dot{\in} y] \wedge [x \doteq z] \wedge [y \doteq u]] \supset [z \dot{\in} u]$. They show that $\doteq$ is an equivalence relation with substitutivity property (with respect to $\dot{\in}$) in $\hat{A}$, hence in any other model M of K'.[10] Thus, replacing each element $x \in M$ by its equivalence class $[x] = \{y \mid y \doteq x\}$ and setting $[x] \dot{\in} [z]$ iff $x \dot{\in} z$, we can obtain a new model of K' in which $\doteq$ is the ordinary identity relation. We shall henceforth always assume that this is the case. Another K'-sentence states that, for any X, Y, there is Z such that Z is the "union" of X and Y, that is, $(\forall x)[[x \dot{\in} X \vee x \dot{\in} Y] \cdot\!\equiv\!\cdot x \dot{\in} Z]$; so we define $Z = X \dot{\cup} Y$ in M; the "dot" is to

[10] For brevity, we denote by M both the *structure* and the *set of its objects;* "$x \in M$" means that x is one of such objects.

distinguish $X \dot{\cup} Y$ from ordinary set-theoretical unions; similarly for other set-theoretical concepts.

Moreover, if M is a model of K', there is a one-to-one correspondence $\psi: \hat{A} \to M$ between the constants of K' and some elements of M, with the property that K'-sentences containing constants hold in M when each constant c is replaced by $\psi(c)$; we call ψ the *interpretation map* for M. Setting $\psi(A_n) = {}^*A_n$, $n = 0, 1, \cdots$ (where $\hat{A} = \bigcup_{n=0}^{\infty} A_n$), we call an element $x \in M$ *internal* if $x \dot{\in} {}^*A_n$ for some n. Using suitable K'-sentences, one can easily show that Corollary 2.7(k) and Postulate 3.3 hold in M with $\in$ replaced by $\dot{\in}$[11] (we say that x is an "element" of X if $x \dot{\in} X$); also $X \dot{\in} {}^*A_1$ iff $X \dot{\subseteq} {}^*A_0$; that is, $(\forall x)[[x \dot{\in} X] \supset [x \dot{\in} {}^*A_0]]$. Thus we can replace each $X \dot{\in} {}^*A_1$ by the genuine *set* $\{x \mid x \dot{\in} X\}$; then we do the same with each $X \dot{\in} {}^*A_2$, and so on. Proceeding inductively, we can achieve that, for *internal* members of M, $\dot{\in}$ becomes the ordinary $\in$. We call M so modified a *collapsed* model of K'. In such models we use the ordinary set-theoretical notation. We now obtain:

***Theorem* 4.1.** *For every collapsed model M of K', there is a normal monomorphism Φ on $\hat{A}$ into a superstructure $\hat{B}$ such that the Φ-internal members of $\hat{B}$ are exactly the internal members of M.*

Proof. Let $\Phi: \hat{A} \to M$ be the interpretation map of M. As noted above, members of $\Phi(A_0)$ have no elements in M; so we may treat them as a set of individuals B and replace M by the superstructure $\hat{B}$ (this does not affect the map Φ and the *internal* members of M because they have internal elements only). We shall now verify that $\Phi: \hat{A} \to \hat{B}$ satisfies the Postulates 2.1–2.5′.

1. Fix $a \in \hat{A}$ and let $P = \{a\}$. Then we have the K'-sentence $[a \in P] \wedge (\forall x)[[x \in P] \cdot\!\equiv\!\cdot [x = a]]$. Hence, writing again ${}^*a$ for $\Phi(a)$, $[{}^*a \in {}^*P] \wedge (\forall x)[[x \in {}^*P] \cdot\!\equiv\!\cdot [x = {}^*a]]$, by the properties of interpretation maps. This means that $\{{}^*a\} = {}^*P = {}^*\{a\}$, proving Postulate 2.1.

2. Fix $C, D \in \hat{A}$ and let $P = C - D$. Then we easily obtain ${}^*P = {}^*C - {}^*D$ from the K'-sentence: $(\forall x)[[x \in P] \cdot\!\equiv\!\cdot [x \in C \wedge \neg [x \in D]]$. A similar proof yields ${}^*C \times {}^*D = {}^*(C \times D)$ on noting that $(x, y) \in P$ can be written as a wff.[12] This proves Postulate 2.2.

3. For Postulate 2.3 it suffices to consider groupings and permutations on two and three elements. Let $\mathcal{P}: (x, y) \to (y, x)$, and fix a binary relation $R \in \hat{A}$. Then, by the already proved property 2.2, ${}^*R$ is a binary

[11] More precisely: If $x \dot{\in} Q$ and $Q \dot{\in} {}^*A_n$, then $x \dot{\in} {}^*A_0$ or $x \dot{\in} {}^*A_{n-1}$. If $x \dot{\in} {}^*A_0$, then $y \dot{\notin} x$ for all y.

[12] Indeed, we have $(x, y) \in$ P iff $(\exists z)(\exists u)(\exists v)[[z \in P] \wedge [z = \{u, v\}] \wedge [u = \{x, y\}] \wedge [v = \{y\}]]$, where "$z = \{u, v\}$" stands for "$[u \in z] \wedge [v \in z] \wedge (Vw)[[w \in z] \supset [w = u] \vee [w = v]]$"; similarly for "$u = \{x, y\}$ and "$v = \{y\}$."

relation, too [indeed, Corollary 2.7(i) is proved from Postulate 2.2 alone]. Now we easily obtain $*(R^{-1}) = (*R)^{-1}$ from the K'-sentence $(\forall x)(\forall y)[(x, y) \in R^{-1} \cdot\equiv\cdot (y, x) \in R]$; similarly for the other cases involved. Thus Φ satisfies Postulate 2.3.

4. Postulate 2.4 follows from the K'-sentence $(\forall x)[[(\exists y)(x, y) \in R] \cdot\equiv\cdot [x \in P]]$, where $P = D_R$.

5. If R is the identity map on $C \in \hat{A}$, the K'-sentence $(\forall x)(\forall y)[[x \in C \wedge y \in C \wedge x = y] \cdot\equiv\cdot (x, y) \in R]$ shows that $*R$ is the identity map on $*C$. This proves Postulate 2.5′. Similarly for Postulate 2.5.

Thus Φ is, indeed, a normal monomorphism. As it is also the interpretation map of M, the Φ-internal elements are, by definition, the internal elements of M. Thus all is proved.

NOTE 1. From Theorem 3.2(a) it now follows that the internal elements of $\hat{B}$ (hence of M) form a model $*\hat{A}$ of K as defined in Section 3. On the other hand, given a monomorphism $\Phi\colon \hat{A} \to \hat{B}$, the Φ-internal elements *do not, in general, constitute a model of* K', even if we define in $*\hat{A}$ an equality relation by setting $x \doteq y$ iff $[x \in Z \cdot\equiv\cdot y \in Z]$ for all $Z \in *\hat{A}$. This is the main reason why the language L and the set K of Section 3 are more useful in applications than L' and K'.

NOTE 2. It also follows that every monomorphism $\Phi\colon \hat{A} \to \hat{B}$ can be transformed into a normal one by defining the equivalence relation as in Note 1 and replacing each element of $*\hat{A}$ by its equivalence class.

NOTE 3. If the model M in Theorem 4.1 is not organized, the same proof shows that Φ still satisfies Postulates 2.1–2.5, but with ordinary set-theoretical concepts replaced by their "dotted" counterparts. Theorem 4.1, combined with known results, now yields:

Theorem 4.2. *For every superstructure $\hat{A}$, there is a superstructure $\hat{B}$ and a monomorphism $\Phi\colon \hat{A} \to \hat{B}$ which is normal, enlarging, and comprehensive. Thus $\hat{A}$ always has a normal comprehensive enlargement, $*\hat{A}$, generated by a monomorphism Φ.*

Proof. Let I be an infinite index set and let F be an ultrafilter of subsets of I. Let M be the family of all maps $f\colon I \to \hat{A}$. Given $f, g \in M$, we write $f \doteq g$ iff the set $\{i \in I \mid f(i) = g(i)\}$ is a member of F; similarly, we put $f \mathrel{\dot{\in}} g$ iff $\{i \in I \mid f(i) \in g(i)\} \in F$. Then M, with $\doteq$ and $\dot{\in}$ so defined, is the F-ultrapower of $\hat{A}$ (as a model of K'). As is well known (see [1], [2], [3], or [5], p. 242), such an ultrapower must itself be a model of K'.[13] Passing to equivalence classes and collapsing, we can transform

[13] The interpretation map $\varphi\colon \hat{A} \to M$ is given by setting, for each $a \in \hat{A}$, $\varphi(a) = *a$, where $*a$ is the constant function $*a\colon I \to M$, with $*a(i) = a$ for all $i \in I$.

M into a structure to which Theorem 4.1 applies. Thus we obtain a normal monomorphism $\Phi: \hat{A} \to \hat{B}$, and the corresponding set $^*\hat{A}$. Finally, as is shown in [6], the index set I and the ultrafilter F can be so chosen that all concurrent relations $R \in \hat{A}$ are "bounded" in M, and also the comprehensiveness condition is satisfied. (Although "internal" elements are defined in [6] in terms of higher-order logic, the argument carries over, almost verbally, to our case as well.) Thus the monomorphism $\Phi: \hat{A} \to \hat{B}$ becomes comprehensive and enlarging, and the proof is complete.

References

1. T. FRAYNE, D. C. MORE, AND D. S. SCOTT, Reduced Direct Products, *Fundamenta Math. 51* (1962), 195–227.
2. H. J. KEISLER, A Survey of Ultraproducts, *Logic, Methodology and Philosophy of Science, Proc. 1964 Intern. Conf.* Amsterdam: North-Holland, 1965, pp. 112–124.
3. S. KOCHEN, *Ultraproducts in the Theory of Models, Ann. Math.* (2)*79* (1961), 221–261.
4. A. ROBINSON, *Non-Standard Analysis* (Studies in Logic and the Foundations of Mathematics). Amsterdam: North-Holland, 1966.
5. A. ROBINSON, *Introduction to Model Theory and to the Metamathematics of Algebra.* Amsterdam: North-Holland, 1965.
6. A. ROBINSON, Non-Standard Theory of Dedekind Rings, *Proc. Acad. Sci. Amsterdam A70* (1967), 444–452.

Reduced Powers of the Real Number System and Equivalents of the Hahn–Banach Extension Theorem

by W. A. J. LUXEMBURG

1. Introduction

There are a number of axioms in set theory such as the axiom of choice (AC), the continuum hypothesis (CH), and the prime ideal theorem for Boolean algebras (PI) which have been studied extensively from various points of view. In particular, there exist detailed studies concerning the question of which other axioms of set theory are effectively equivalent to these axioms. For such results the reader is referred to the book of Sierpinski on the continuum hypothesis (see [1]) and Rubin and Rubin's book on the axiom of choice (see [2]).

One of the main principles of functional analysis is the so-called Hahn–Banach extension theorem (HB). It was shown in [3] and [4] by different methods that (PI) implies (HB). The earlier proofs of (HB) were based on (AC). Thus we have (AC) $\Rightarrow$ (PI) $\Rightarrow$ (HB). It is known that the former implication cannot be reversed (see [5]); whether the same holds for the latter implication seems to be an open question. In the present paper we are mainly interested in the problem of which other statements in mathematics can be shown to be effectively equivalent to (HB). A number of such results are given below which culminate in the result that (HB) is effectively equivalent to the statement that every Boolean algebra admits a nontrivial real measure. We do not include the well-known equivalent forms of (HB), which deal with results concerning separation of convex sets in locally convex spaces.

Many of the proofs given below are based on the basic properties of reduced powers, so that Sections 2, 3, and 4 are devoted to this concept.

For the present paper it is of importance to state explicitly which axioms of set theory we shall assume to hold. These are the axiom groups A, B, C, and D of Gödel (see [6]). We shall not make any additional assumption if not otherwise stated. Thus the (AC) (axiom E in [6]) or any of its weaker forms are not assumed to hold. For the sake of simplicity we shall denote the system of axioms of groups A, B, C, and D of [6] by Σ. If a theorem in this paper is stated without further specification it means that it holds in Σ. Furthermore, we shall say (see above) that two statements are effectively equivalent whenever their logical equivalence can be shown in Σ.

2. Reduced Powers of Mathematical Structures

For terminology and notation not explained below we refer the reader to Chapter 1 of [7].

Let $\mathfrak{M}$ be an L-structure and let L denote a higher-order language with type structure T. By $K(K_0)$ we shall denote all sentences of L which are defined (hold) in $\mathfrak{M}$ with respect to some correspondence between the constants of L and the entities of all finite types of $\mathfrak{M}$.

Let $\mathfrak{D}$ be a proper filter of subsets of an infinite set I. We shall now describe a new structure $'\mathfrak{M}$ which in some weak sense has the same properties as $\mathfrak{M}$. As in chapter 1 of [7], we shall denote by M_σ the set of all entities of type σ of $\mathfrak{M}$ and by $M = \bigcup (M_\sigma : \sigma \in \mathfrak{J})$ the set of all entities of all finite types of $\mathfrak{M}$. Thus M_0 denotes here the set of individuals of $\mathfrak{M}$.

For the sake of convenience we shall denote by $'M$ the set of all mappings of I into M. An element $a \in {'M}$ will be called an *admissible entity* of $'\mathfrak{M}$ whenever there exists a type $\sigma \in T$ such that $\{i : T_\sigma(a(i))$ holds in $\mathfrak{M}\} \in \mathfrak{D}$, and in that case a will be called an *admissible entity of type* σ. As usual we shall say that an admissible entity a of type σ of $'\mathfrak{M}$ is *standard* whenever there exists an entity b of type σ of $\mathfrak{M}$ such that $\{i : a(i) = b\} \in \mathfrak{D}$. With this definition a one-to-one embedding of $\mathfrak{M}$ into $'\mathfrak{M}$ is obtained. An entity a of $\mathfrak{M}$ of type $\sigma \neq 0$ is usually denoted by $'a$ in $'\mathfrak{M}$ under this embedding. Individuals, that is, entities of type 0, of $\mathfrak{M}$ are usually denoted in $'\mathfrak{M}$ by the same symbol. The reader should observe that if A is a set of entities of type σ of $\mathfrak{M}$, then $a \in {'A}$ holds in $'\mathfrak{M}$ if and only if $\{i : a(i) \in A \text{ in } \mathfrak{M}\} \in \mathfrak{D}$. In a similar fashion the atomic formulas are extended. For instance, if β is a relation of type $(\sigma_1, \cdots, \sigma_n)$ in $\mathfrak{M}$, then $\Phi_{n+1}('\beta, a_1, \cdots, a_n)$ holds in $'\mathfrak{M}$ if and only if $\{i : \Phi_{n+1}(\beta, a_1(i), \cdots, a_n(i))$ holds in $\mathfrak{M}\} \in \mathfrak{D}$.

It is obvious that all the individuals of $'\mathfrak{M}$ are admissible entities of type 0. A set A whose elements are admissible entities of type σ of $'\mathfrak{M}$ need not be itself admissible. It is admissible if and only if there exists an admissible entity B of type (σ) in $'\mathfrak{M}$ such that $a \in A \Leftrightarrow \{i : a(i) \in B(i) \text{ in } \mathfrak{M}\} \in \mathfrak{D}$.

Since $\mathfrak{D}$ is not necessarily an ultrafilter all the sentences of K_0 do not necessarily hold in $'\mathfrak{M}$. It can be shown, however, that the fundamental theorem holds in the following restricted sense (see [8], Lemma 2.1). A sentence Φ of K is called a *Horn sentence* whenever written in its prenex normal form (see sec. 4 of Chap. 2 of [9]) has a matrix which is a conjunction of (quantifier free) wff which are disjunctions of atomic formulas or negation of atomic formulas, but where at least one atomic formula occurs unnegated.

A Horn sentence of K holds in $\mathfrak{M}$ if and only if it holds in $'\mathfrak{M}$. Unfortunately, the proof of this result requires the axiom of choice. Since we shall be studying equivalents of (HB) in a set theory without (AC), the above result cannot be used. We shall, in fact, only make use of the fact that the atomic formulas of K hold in $\mathfrak{M}$ if and only if they hold in $'\mathfrak{M}$—a statement which holds by definition.

3. Concurrent Binary Relations and Reduced Powers

Let $\mathfrak{M}$ be an L-structure. We recall (see [7], sec. 3 of chap. 1) that a binary relation β of $\mathfrak{M}$ of a certain type is said to be *concurrent* whenever for every finite set of entities $a_1, \cdots, a_n \in \operatorname{dom}(\beta)$ there is an entity $b \in \operatorname{ran}(\beta)$ such that $(\Phi_3(\beta, a_1, b)$ and $\cdots$ and $\Phi_3(\beta, a_n, b))$ holds in $\mathfrak{M}$.

We continue with the following definition.

Let $\mathfrak{M}$ be an L-structure and let β be a concurrent binary relation of say type (σ_1, σ_2) of $\mathfrak{M}$. A higher-order reduced power $'\mathfrak{M} = \mathfrak{M}(I, \mathfrak{D})$ of $\mathfrak{M}$ is said to satisfy β whenever there exists an admissible entity b of type σ_2 of $'\mathfrak{M}$ such that $\Phi_3('\beta, 'a, b)$ holds in $'\mathfrak{M}$ for all standard elements $'a$ of the domain of $'\beta$; that is, $\{i: \Phi_3(\beta, a, b(i))$ holds in $\mathfrak{M}\} \in \mathfrak{D}$ for all standard a in the domain of β.

We shall now prove the following simple theorem.

***Theorem* 3.1.** *Let $\mathfrak{M}$ be an L-structure and let β be a concurrent binary relation of $\mathfrak{M}$ of type (σ_1, σ_2). Then the family of sets $(B_a = \{b: \Phi_3(\beta, a, b)$ holds in $\mathfrak{M}\}: a \in \operatorname{dom} \beta)$ has the finite intersection property. Furthermore, the higher-order reduced power $'\mathfrak{M} = \mathfrak{M}(I, \mathfrak{D})$, where $I = M_{\sigma_2}$ and $\mathfrak{D}$ is the filter generated by the family of sets $\{B_a: a \in \operatorname{dom} \beta\}$, satisfies β.*

Proof. Let $a_1, \cdots, a_n \in \operatorname{dom} \beta$. Then, β being concurrent, there is an element $b \in M_{\sigma_2}$ such that $\Phi_3(\beta, a_i, b)$ holds in $\mathfrak{M}$ for $i = 1, 2, \cdots, n$, and so $b \in \bigcap_{i=1}^n B_{a_i}$. This shows that the family $(B_a: a \in \operatorname{dom} \beta)$ has the finite intersection property. To prove the second part of the theorem consider the identity map e of $I = M_{\sigma_2}$ onto itself. Then e is an admissible entity of type σ_2 of $'\mathfrak{M}$. Furthermore, if $a \in \operatorname{dom} \beta$, then $\{i: \Phi_3(\beta, a, e(i))$ holds in $\mathfrak{M}\} = B_a \in \mathfrak{D}$. Thus $'\mathfrak{M}$ satisfies $'\beta$ on the standard elements of its domain, and the proof is complete.

It is easy to derive from the above theorem that *if* $\beta_1, \cdots, \beta_p$ *are a finite number of concurrent relations of a certain type, then there exists a reduced power* $'\mathfrak{M}$ *with the property that* $'\mathfrak{M}$ *satisfies* $\beta_1, \cdots, \beta_p$ *simultaneously in the sense defined.* For this purpose consider the binary relation $\beta = \beta_1 \times \cdots \times \beta_p$ with domain dom $\beta_1 \times \cdots \times$ dom β_n. It is obvious that β is concurrent. Furthermore, any reduced power which satisfies β on its domain also satisfies $\beta_1, \beta_2, \cdots,$ and β_p. Without the axiom of choice it does not seem possible to show that there are reduced powers which satisfy the elements of an infinite set of concurrent binary relations. If the axiom of choice holds, then the adequate filters introduced in section 5 of Chapter 1 of [7] can be used to satisfy all the concurrent binary relations in a reduced power. Fortunately, in the proofs which will follow we shall only use one concurrent binary relation at a time.

Remark. If the set of individuals of a mathematical structure $\mathfrak{M}$ is infinite, then the binary relation "not $(x = y)$" restricted to the set of individuals is concurrent, and conversely. Thus a reduced power which satisfies "not $(x = y)$" is a proper extension of the given mathematical structure. In that case, the filter $\mathfrak{D}$ is δ-incomplete (see [7], sec. 4 of Chap. 1).

4. Reduced Powers of the Real Number System

Let R denote the real number system and consider a higher-order reduced power of the theory of real numbers with respect to some proper filter $\mathfrak{D}$ of subsets of some set I. The set of individuals of this reduced power will be denoted by $'R$. Thus $R \subset {'R}$. The operations of addition and multiplication of R are extended to $'R$ as well as the ordering of R. We recall the definition. If $a,b,c \in {'R}$, then $a + b = c$ holds in $'R$ if and only if $\{i\colon a(i) + b(i) = c(i)\} \in \mathfrak{D}$, and $ab = c$ if and only if $\{i\colon a(i)b(i) = c(i)\} \in \mathfrak{D}$; and $a \leq b$ if and only if $\{i\colon a(i) \leq b(i)\} \in \mathfrak{D}$. The reader can easily check that under these operations $'R$ is an ordered commutative ring with a unit element, the unit 1 of R, of which R is a subfield. Since $\mathfrak{D}$ is not necessarily an ultrafilter we cannot show that $'R$ has no divisors of zero. In general, $'R$ will have divisors of zero. Furthermore, the ordering of $'R$ does not in general totally order $'R$ but it does satisfy the two basic properties of being translation-invariant and $a \geq 0$, $b \geq 0$ implies $ab \geq 0$. It is important to observe that $'R$ is a *lattice*. Indeed, let $a,b \in {'R}$; then the mapping $i \to c(i) = \max(a(i), b(i))$ of I into R determines an element $c \in {'R}$ such that $c = \max(a, b)$, and similarly $\min(a, b)$ exists. For every $a \in {'R}$ we shall write $a^+ = \max(a, 0)$, $a^- = \max(-a, 0)$. Then $a = a^+ - a^-$ and we denote $a^+ + a^-$ by $|a|$. To the structure of $'R$ one usually refers to as the structure of a *com-*

mutative Riesz ring with unit, which in our case has the additional property that it is an extension of R.

$'R$ as a Riesz space is not Archimedean ($a \geq 0$ and $na \leq 1$ for all $n = 1, 2, \cdots$ implies $a = 0$) if and only if $\mathfrak{D}$ is δ-incomplete. This justifies the following definition. An element $a \in {'R}$ will be called an *infinitesimal* whenever $|a| < r$ for all real numbers $0 < r \in R$. The set of all infinitesimal elements will be denoted by $\mathfrak{L}_1$. An element $a \in {'R}$ is called finite whenever there exists a positive real number $0 < r \in R$ such that $|a| < r$. The set of all finite elements of $'R$ will be denoted by $\mathfrak{L}_0$. It is easy to see that $\mathfrak{L}_0$ is a Riesz subring of $'R$ and that $\mathfrak{L}_1$ is an ideal of $\mathfrak{L}_0$ with the property that $a \in \mathfrak{L}_1$ and $|b| \leq |a|$ implies $b \in \mathfrak{L}_1$. From now on we shall consider $\mathfrak{L}_0$ as a lattice-ordered vector space (= *Riesz space*) over R.

In the Riesz space $\mathfrak{L}_0$ the multiplicative unit 1 is a strong order unit e; that is, for every $a \in \mathfrak{L}_0$ there exists a real number $0 < r \in \mathfrak{R}$ such that $|a| < re$. This shows that $\mathfrak{L}_0$ is a very special Riesz space. We can introduce on $\mathfrak{L}_0$ a Riesz *seminorm* by means of the following definition.

(*) *For every* $a \in \mathfrak{L}_0$ *we define* $\rho(a) = \inf(r\colon 0 < r \in R$ *and* $|a| \leq r)$.

Then it is easy to verify that ρ has the following properties.

(a) For all $a \in \mathfrak{L}_0$, $\rho(a) = \rho(|a|)$ and for all $0 < r \in R$, $\rho(r) = r$.
(b) ρ is a seminorm and $\rho(a) = 0$ if and only if $a \in \mathfrak{L}_1$.
(c) ρ is submultiplicative; that is, $\rho(ab) \leq \rho(a)\rho(b)$ for all $a,b \in \mathfrak{L}_0$.
(d) $\rho(\max(|a|, |b|)) = \max \rho(|a|, |b|)$ for all $a,b \in \mathfrak{L}_0$.

The reader will recognize immediately that the Riesz space $(\mathfrak{L}_0, \rho)$ is an abstract M-space in the sense of Kakutani (see [10], p. 100), and $\mathfrak{L}_0/\mathfrak{L}_1$ is the corresponding Archimedean quotient space containing R. The space $(\mathfrak{L}_0, \rho)$ will play a fundamental role in what follows.

5. The Hahn–Banach Extension Theorem

The Hahn–Banach extension theorem which we have been referring to is the following result.

***Theorem* (*HB*).** *Let V be a linear subspace of a real linear space E and let p be a sublinear functional on E (that is, $p(x + y) \leq p(x) + p(y)$ for all $x,y \in E$ and $p(rx) = rp(x)$ for all $0 \leq r \in R$ and $x \in E$). If φ is a linear functional defined on V such that $\varphi(x) \leq p(x)$ for all $x \in V$, then there exists a linear functional ψ on E such that $\psi = \varphi$ on V and $\psi(x) \leq p(x)$ for all $x \in E$.*

The proof of this result is based on the following weaker form of it due to Banach (see [11], p. 27).

Theorem **(*B*)**. *Under the same hypothesis as in the HB extension theorem, if* $x_1, \cdots, x_n \in E$ *and if* V_n *is the linear subspace generated by* V *and the elements* $x_1, \cdots, x_n$*, then there exists a linear functional* ψ_n *on* V_n *such that* $\varphi = \psi_n$ *on* V *and* $\psi_n(x) \leq p(x)$ *for all* $x \in V_n$.

(HB) follows from (B) upon the application of (AC) or (PI) (see [3] and [4]), whereas the proof of theorem (B) is constructive in the sense that the existence of ψ_n can be shown in Σ.

If we examine Theorem B a little closer we will recognize that it expresses the fact that the following binary relation is concurrent in x. "x is an element of E and ψ is a linear functional defined on some linear subspace of E such that $V \subset \text{dom } \psi$ and $\varphi = \psi$ on V and $x \in \text{dom } \psi$ and $\psi \leq p$ on dom ψ."

Thus from Theorem 3.1 the following kind of extension theorem holds in Σ.

Theorem 5.1. *Let* V *be a linear subspace of* E *and let* p *be a sublinear functional defined on* E*. If* φ *is a linear functional defined on* V *such that* $\varphi(x) \leq p(x)$ *for all* $x \in V$*, then there exists a higher-order reduced power structure of the theory of real numbers and a linear mapping of* T *of* E *into* $\mathfrak{L}_0$ *such that* $T = \varphi$ *on* V *and* $T(x) \leq p(x)$ *for* $x \in E$.

This shows that in Σ we can only prove the above weaker form of (HB).

6. On the Existence of Positive Linear Functionals on $\mathfrak{L}_0$

Let $'R$ be the set of numbers of some higher-order reduced power of the theory of real numbers. Since $(\mathfrak{L}_0, \rho)$ is a linear space with a seminorm it is natural to inquire whether there do exist linear functionals on $\mathfrak{L}_0$ which are bounded by ρ. The answer is contained in the following theorem.

Theorem 6.1. *The Hahn–Banach extension theorem is effectively equivalent to the statement. For every reduced power of the theory of real numbers there exists a real linear functional* l *on the Riesz space* $(\mathfrak{L}_0, \rho)$ *such that* $l(a) \geq 0$ *for all* $0 \leq a \in \mathfrak{L}_0$, $|l(a)| \leq \rho(a)$ *for all* $a \in \mathfrak{L}_0$ *and* $l(1) = 1$.

Proof. Assume first that (HB) holds. Then for every $a \in \mathfrak{L}_0$ we define $p(a) = \rho(a^+)$. Then it is easy to see that p is sublinear. Indeed, for all $a,b \in \mathfrak{L}_0$ and $0 \leq r \in R$ we have $p(a + b) = \rho((a + b)^+) \leq \rho(a^+ + b^+) \leq \rho(a^+) + \rho(b^+) = p(a) + p(b)$ and $p(ra) = \rho((ra)^+) = \rho(ra^+) = r\rho(a^+) = rp(a)$. Furthermore, $p(1) = \rho(1) = 1$, and $a \in \mathfrak{L}_1$ implies $p(a) = \rho(a^+) = 0$. Let V be the linear subspace of E generated by

$1 = e$ and let φ be the linear functional on V satisfying $\varphi(r) = r$ for all $r \in V = R$. Then $\varphi \leq p$ on V, and so, by (HB), there exists a real linear functional l on $\mathfrak{L}_0$ such that $l(a) \leq p(a)$ for all $a \in \mathfrak{L}_0$ and $l = \varphi$ on R, and so $l(1) = 1$. To prove that l is positive observe that if $0 \leq a \in \mathfrak{L}_0$, then $(-a)^+ = 0$, and so $-l(a) = l(-a) \leq p(-a) = \rho((-a)^+) = \rho(0) = 0$ implies $l(a) \geq 0$. This completes the proof of the first half. For the proof of the second half we use Theorem 5.1. Thus there is a linear transformation T of E into $(\mathfrak{L}_0, \rho)$ satisfying $T = \varphi$ on V and $T \leq p$. Now let l be a positive linear functional on $\mathfrak{L}_0$ such that $l(1) = 1$. Then $\psi = l \circ T$ is a real linear functional on E satisfying $\psi = l \circ T = l \circ \varphi = \varphi$ on V and $\psi(x) = l(T(x)) \leq l(p(x) = p(x)$ for all $x \in E$. Thus (HB) holds; and the proof is finished.

The above proof also shows that the following result holds.

Theorem 6.2. *The Hahn–Banach extension theorem is effectively equivalent to the following statement. For every reduced power of the theory of R and every $0 < a \in \mathfrak{L}_0$ such that $a \notin \mathfrak{L}_1$ there exists a positive linear functional l on $\mathfrak{L}_0$ such that $l(a) > 0$, $l(1) = 1$, and $l \leq \rho$.*

7. The Main Theorem

The purpose of this section is to establish the equivalence in Σ of (HB) and the statement there exists a (nontrivial) measure on every Boolean algebra. To this end, we shall first present the following introductory remarks.

For the terminology concerning Boolean algebras which is not explained below we refer to [12]. We shall consider only nondegenerate Boolean algebras. A mapping m of a Boolean algebra $\mathfrak{B}$ into R is called a *measure* whenever m satisfies the following conditions: (a) $m(x) \geq 0$ for all $x \in \mathfrak{B}$. (b) $x \wedge y = 0$ implies $m(x \vee y) = m(x) + m(y)$ for all $x,y \in \mathfrak{B}$ (additivity). (c) $m(1) > 0$, where 1 is the unit element of $\mathfrak{B}$.

We shall first prove the following Lemma.

Lemma 7.1. *The following statements are effectively equivalent.*

(a) *There exists a measure on every Boolean algebra.*
(b) *For every proper filter $\mathfrak{F}$ of elements of a Boolean algebra $\mathfrak{B}$ there exists a measure m on $\mathfrak{B}$ such that $m(x) = 1$ for all $x \in \mathfrak{F}$.*
(c) *For every proper ideal $\mathfrak{I}$ of elements of a Boolean algebra $\mathfrak{B}$ there exists a measure m on $\mathfrak{B}$ such that $m(x) = 0$ for all $x \in \mathfrak{I}$.*
(d) *For every Boolean algebra $\mathfrak{B}$ and for every element $0 \neq x \in \mathfrak{B}$ there exists a measure m on $\mathfrak{B}$ such that $m(x) \neq 0$.*

Proof. The only implication which needs to be shown is $(a) \Rightarrow$ (b). If $\mathfrak{F}$ is a proper filter of elements of a Boolean algebra $\mathfrak{B}$, then the set of the complements of the elements of $\mathfrak{F}$ is a proper ideal $\mathfrak{I}$. Then (a) implies that there exists a measure m on the quotient algebra $\mathfrak{B}/\mathfrak{I}$ such that $m(1) = 1$. Then this measure defines a measure on $\mathfrak{B}$ by saturation with respect to $\mathfrak{I}$ which is equal to 1 on the elements of $\mathfrak{F}$, and the proof is finished.

According to a result of Tarski it can be shown in Σ *that to every Boolean algebra* $\mathfrak{B}$ *there corresponds a set algebra* $\Lambda(\mathfrak{B})$, *that is, a subalgebra of the Boolean algebra of all subsets of a set, and a Boolean homomorphism h of* $\Lambda(\mathfrak{B})$ *onto* $\mathfrak{B}$. Indeed, we may take for $\Lambda(\mathfrak{B})$ the subalgebra of the Boolean algebra of all subsets of $\mathfrak{B}$ generated by the *principal* ideals of $\mathfrak{B}$ with an obvious definition of h. On the basis of this result we have the following theorem.

Theorem 7.2. *The following two statements are effectively equivalent.*

(a) *There exists a measure on every Boolean algebra.*
(b) *For every nonempty set* X *and for every proper filter* $\mathfrak{F}$ *of subsets of* X, *there exists a measure* m *on the Boolean algebra of all subsets of* X *such that* $m(E) = 1$ *for all* $E \in \mathfrak{F}$.
(c) *For every nonempty set* X *and for every proper ideal* $\mathfrak{I}$ *of subsets of* X, *there exists a measure* m *on the Boolean algebra of all subsets of* X *such that* $m(A) = 0$ *for all* $A \in \mathfrak{I}$.

Proof. We have only to show that (b) $\Rightarrow$ (a). To this end, let $\mathfrak{B}$ be a Boolean algebra. Then by Tarski's theorem there exists a subalgebra Λ of the Boolean algebra of all subsets of $\mathfrak{B}$ such that $\mathfrak{B}$ is a Boolean homomorphic image of Λ. Let $\mathfrak{I}_0$ be the kernel of that homomorphism h. Then $\mathfrak{I}_0$ is a proper ideal of Λ ($\mathfrak{B}$ is nondegenerate). Let $\mathfrak{I}$ be the ideal in the Boolean algebra of all subsets of $\mathfrak{B}$ generated by $\mathfrak{I}_0$. Then $\mathfrak{I}$ is also a proper ideal. Hence, by (c), which is obviously equivalent to (b), there is a measure m on the Boolean algebra of all subsets of $\mathfrak{B}$ such that $m(\mathfrak{I}) = 0$. Then the restriction m_0 of this measure m to Λ is nontrivial since $m(\mathfrak{B}) \neq \{0\}$; and $m_0(\mathfrak{I}_0) = 0$. Since $\Lambda/\mathfrak{I}_0$ is isomorphic to $\mathfrak{B}$, it follows that $\mathfrak{B}$ admits a measure in the sense defined above, and the proof is finished.

Remark. It is not without interest to observe that the above results in this section are analogous to the following list of effectively equivalent statements (see [12], par. 47).

(a) Every Boolean algebra has a prime ideal.
(b) Every Boolean algebra has a two-valued measure.

(c) Every ideal is contained in a prime ideal.
(d) Every proper filter of subsets of a nonempty set is contained in an ultrafilter.

We are now in a position to prove the main theorem of this paper.

Theorem 7.3. *The Hahn–Banach extension theorem is effectively equivalent to the statement that every Boolean algebra admits a (nontrivial) measure.*

Proof. Assume that the Hahn–Banach extension theorem holds. To prove that every Boolean algebra admits a measure it is sufficient to show according to Theorem 7.2 that for every nonempty set X and every proper ideal $\mathfrak{I}$ of subsets of X there exists a measure m on the Boolean algebra of all subsets of X such that $m(A) = 0$ for all $A \in \mathfrak{I}$. To this end, consider the Banach space $B(X)$ of all bounded real functions on X with the supnorm. Let $V = \{f: f \in B(X) \text{ and } \{x: f(x) \neq 0\} \in \mathfrak{I}\}$. Then V is a proper closed linear subspace of $B(X)$ such that $f \in V$ implies $|f| \in V$. Hence it follows from the Hahn–Banach extension theorem applied to $B(X)$, V, and $p(f) = \sup(f^+(x): x \in X)$ that there exists a positive linear functional φ on $B(X)$ such that $\varphi(1) = 1$, $\varphi \leq p$, and $\varphi(V) = 0$. Define $m(E) = \varphi(c_E)$, where c_E is the characteristic function of $E \subset X$. Then m is the required measure.

The converse is a little harder to show. According to Theorem 6.1 we have to show that for every $(I, \mathfrak{D})$-reduced power of the theory of R there exists a positive linear functional l on $(\mathfrak{L}_0, \rho)$ such that $l(\mathfrak{L}_1) = 0$ and $l(1) = 1$. From the hypothesis it follows that there exists a measure m on the Boolean algebra of all subsets of I such that $m(D) = 0$ for all $D \in \mathfrak{D}$. For every finitely valued real function $s = \sum_{i=1}^n s_i c_{E_i}$, $E_i \subset I$, $i = 1, 2, \cdots, n$, we define $\varphi(s) = \sum_{i=1}^n s_i m(E_i)$. Then φ defines a positive linear functional on the Riesz space $S(I)$ of all the real step functions. Since every bounded real function can be uniformly approximated by elements of S it follows immediately that φ can be extended uniquely by limits to $B(I)$. Then for every $a \in \mathfrak{L}_0$ we define $l(a) = \varphi(a)$. To justify this definition we have to show that $a = b \in \mathfrak{L}_0$ implies $l(a) = l(b)$. But $a = b$ if and only if $\{i: a(i) = b(i)\} \in \mathfrak{D}$, and so $\varphi(a) = \varphi(b)$. Furthermore, it is easy to see that l is a positive linear functional on $(\mathfrak{L}_0, \rho)$ such that $l(1) = 1$. Then also $l(a) = 0$ whenever $a \in \mathfrak{L}_1$ follows readily. This completes the proof of the theorem.

8. On Tarski's Extension Theorem for Measures on Boolean Algebras

In [13] Tarski showed that if m_0 *is a measure on a subalgebra* $\mathfrak{B}_0$ *of a Boolean algebra* $\mathfrak{B}$, *then there exists a measure* m *on* $\mathfrak{B}$ *such that* $m = m_0$

on $\mathcal{B}_0$ and the range $m(\mathcal{B})$ of m is contained in the closure of the range of m_0. In fact, he showed that this extension theorem for measures is effectively equivalent to the prime ideal theorem for Boolean algebras. For a proof of Tarski's result using ultrapowers the reader is referred to [14], sec. 4 of Chap. 6.

Tarski's result is based on the following theorem which is related to Tarski's theorem in the same way as Theorem (B) is related to (HB).

Let $\mathcal{B}_0$ be a subalgebra of a Boolean algebra $\mathcal{B}$ and let m_0 be a measure on $\mathcal{B}_0$. Then for every finite set of elements $x_1, \cdots, x_k$ of $\mathcal{B}$ there exists a measure m_k on the Boolean algebra $\mathcal{B}_k$ generated by $\mathcal{B}_0$ and the set $\{x_1, \cdots, x_k\}$ such that $m_k = m_0$ on $\mathcal{B}_0$, and the range of m_k is contained in the closure of the range of m_0.

As in the case of Theorem B of Section 5, we recognize that the above theorem is equivalent to the statement that the following binary relation is concurrent in x: "x is an element of $\mathcal{B}$ and m is a measure defined on some subalgebra $\mathcal{B}'$ of $\mathcal{B}$ such that $\mathcal{B}_0 \subset \mathcal{B}'$, $m = m_0$ on $\mathcal{B}_0$ and $x \in \mathcal{B}'$ and $m(\mathcal{B}') \subset \overline{m_0(\mathcal{B}_0)}$."

Thus using Theorem 3.1 we obtain the following weaker version of Tarski's theorem in Σ.

Theorem 8.1. *Let $\mathcal{B}_0$ be a subalgebra of a Boolean algebra $\mathcal{B}$ and let m_0 be a measure on $\mathcal{B}_0$. Then there exists a reduced power of the theory of R and a measure m on $\mathcal{B}$ with values in $(\mathcal{L}_0, \rho)$ such that $m = m_0$ on $\mathcal{B}_0$ and $m(\mathcal{B}) \subset \overline{m_0(\mathcal{B}_0)}$, where $\overline{m_0(\mathcal{B}_0)}$ denotes the closure of the range of m_0 in $'R$.*

If (HB) holds, then according to Theorem 6.1 there exists a positive linear functional l on the Riesz space of the finite elements of the $(I, \mathfrak{D})$-reduced powers of R such that $l(1) = 1$ and $|l(a)| \leq \rho(a)$ for all $a \in \mathcal{L}_0$. The positive linear functional l induces on $B(I)$ the space of bounded real functions a positive linear functional l' by saturation with respect to $\mathfrak{D}$. Using then the simple fact that $l'(a)$ is contained in the *closed convex hull of the range of* a, we obtain immediately the following lemma.

Lemma 8.2. *For every $A \subset R$ the set $\{l(a) : a \in {'A} \cap \mathcal{L}_0\}$ is contained in the closed convex hull of A.*

From Theorem 8.1, Theorem 7.3, Theorem 6.1, and Lemma 8.1 the following result follows.

Theorem 8.3. *The following two statements are effectively equivalent.*

(a) *The Hahn–Banach extension theorem.*
(b) *Let $\mathcal{B}_0$ be a subalgebra of a Boolean algebra $\mathcal{B}$ and let m_0 be a real measure on $\mathcal{B}_0$. Then there exists a real measure m on $\mathcal{B}$ such that*

$m = m_0$ on $\mathcal{B}_0$ and the range of m is contained in the closed convex hull of the range of m_0.

It is interesting to compare Theorem 8.3 with Tarski's result quoted above. The only difference is that on the basis of (HB) we can no longer show that there is an extension whose range is in the closure of the range of the given measure. This somehow illustrates the difference between the existence of measures on Boolean algebras and the existence of two-valued measures (= prime ideals) on Boolean algebras.

9. On the Existence of Strictly Positive Measures

A measure m on a Boolean algebra is called strictly positive whenever $m(a) = 0$ implies $a = 0$.

It is well known that there do exist Boolean algebras which do not admit strictly positive real-valued measures (see sec. 5 of Chap. 6 of [14]). Nikodym showed, however, that for every Boolean algebra $\mathcal{B}$ there exists a totally ordered field F with the property that $\mathcal{B}$ admits a strictly positive F-valued measure (see [15] and [14]). It was pointed out by A. Tarski at the meeting on Boolean algebras in Oberwolfach in the summer of 1962 that Nikodym's result is an immediate consequence of the compactness principle of model theory. This bases Nikodym's result on the prime ideal theorem for Boolean algebras rather than on the axiom of choice as in the case in Nikodym's proof. Tarski's proof in the form of ultrapowers was presented in [4] and [14].

If we now assume that the Hahn–Banach extension theorem holds, then we can still prove the following weaker form of Nikodym's theorem.

Theorem 9.1. *If the Hahn–Banach extension theorem holds, then for every Boolean algebra $\mathcal{B}$ there exists a $(I, \mathfrak{D})$-reduced power of R such that $\mathcal{B}$ admits a strictly positive measure with values in $(\mathfrak{L}_0, \rho)$.*

Proof. From Lemma 7.1 and Theorem 7.3 it follows that the following binary relation is concurrent in x: "x is an element of $\mathcal{B}$ and m is a real-valued measure on $\mathcal{B}$ such that $m(x) > 0$." Thus the result follows immediately from Theorem 3.1.

10. A Lemma

Let X be a nonempty set. Then by Ω we shall denote the Riesz space of all real functions on X which vanish off a finite set. For every $f \in R^X$ and every $\omega \in \Omega$ we define $\omega(f) = \Sigma_{x \in X}\omega(x)f(x)$. Then by means of this definition ω defines an order-bounded linear functional on the Riesz space R^X.

Some time ago, Dana Scott kindly pointed out to me that the Hahn–Banach extension theorem is a special case of the following folk lemma, which itself is an immediate consequence of the Tychonov product theorem for compact Hausdorff spaces [= the prime ideal theorem for Boolean algebras (see [16])].

Lemma 10.1 *Let* Ω_0 *be an arbitrary subset of* Ω *and let* $g_0, f_0 \in R^X$ *be such that* $g_0(x) \leq f_0(x)$ *for all* $x \in X$. *If for every finite subset* $\{\omega_1, \cdots, \omega_n\}$ *of* Ω_0 *there exists an element* $h \in H = \{h: g_0 \leq h \leq f_0\}$ *such that* $\omega_i(h) \geq 0$ *for* $i = 1, 2, \cdots, n$, *then there exists an element* $h_0 \in H$ *such that* $\omega(h_0) \geq 0$ *for all* $\omega \in \Omega_0$.

From the Tychonov product theorem for compact Hausdorff spaces it follows immediately that H is a compact subset of R^X in its product topology. Since for every $\omega \in \Omega$ the set $H_\omega = \{f: f \in H \text{ and } \omega(f) \geq 0\}$ is a closed convex subset of the compact subset H, it follows from the hypothesis—the family $\{H_\omega: \omega \in \Omega_0\}$ has the finite intersection property—that $\bigcap (H_\omega: \omega \in \Omega_0) \neq \emptyset$, and so the conclusion of the lemma follows.

We shall now prove, however, that Lemma 10.1 is effectively equivalent to the Hahn–Banach extension theorem.

Theorem 10.2. *The Hahn–Banach extension theorem is effectively equivalent to Lemma* 10.1.

Proof. We shall first present a proof of the fact that the Hahn–Banach extension theorem is a consequence of the lemma. To this end, assume that φ_0 is a linear functional defined on a linear subspace V of a real linear space E such that $\varphi_0 \leq p$ on V, where p is a sublinear functional on E. Then to apply the lemma we take for X the set E; g_0 and f_0 are defined as follows: $g_0(x) = -p(-x)$, $x \notin V$; $g_0(x) = \varphi_0(x)$, $x \in V$; $f_0(x) = p(x)$, $x \notin V$; and $f_0(x) = \varphi_0(x)$, $x \in V$; the system Ω_0 consists of all linear expressions of the type $\Sigma_{i=1}^k r_i f(x_i) - f(\Sigma_{i=1}^k r_i x_i) = 0$, where $x_1, \cdots, x_k \in E$ and $r_1, \cdots, r_k \in R$. Then Theorem B of Section 5 shows that the hypothesis of the lemma is satisfied, and so there exists a mapping φ of E into R such that $g_0(x) \leq \varphi(x) \leq f_0(x)$ for all $x \in E$ and $\Sigma_{i=1}^k r_i \varphi(x_i) = \varphi(\Sigma_{i=1}^k r_i x_i)$ for all $x_1, \cdots, x_k \in E$ and $r_1, \cdots, r_k \in R$. Thus φ is linear, $x \in V$ implies $\varphi(x) = \varphi_0(x)$ and $\varphi(x) \leq p(x)$ for all $x \in E$. Hence (HB) holds.

To prove the converse we observe that Lemma 10.1 is equivalent to the statement that the following binary relation is concurrent in ω: "ω is an element of Ω_0 and f is an element of H such that $\omega(f) \geq 0$." Hence it follows from Theorem 3.1 that there exists a reduced power

$'R$ of R and a mapping h of X into $'R$ such that $g_0(x) \leq h(x) \leq f_0(x)$ for all $x \in X$ and $\omega(h) \geq 0$ for all $\omega \in \Omega_0$. The former condition implies that $h(x) \in \mathfrak{L}_0$ for all $x \in X$. Since (HB) holds, there exists, by Theorem 6.1, a positive linear functional l on $\mathfrak{L}_0$ such that $l(1) = 1$. Hence $h_0 = l \circ h$ is a mapping of X into R such that $g_0(x) \leq h_0(x) \leq f_0(x)$ for all $x \in X$; that is, $h_0 \in H$ and $\omega(h_0) = \omega(l \circ h) = l(\omega(h)) \geq 0$ for all $\omega \in \Omega_0$. This shows that Lemma 10.1 holds and the proof is finished.

11. Convex Compactness

Let E be a normed linear space over R and let E' be the Banach dual of E; that is, E' is the Banach space of all bounded linear functionals on E. Then a well-known and important theorem of Bourbaki and Alaoglu (see [17] and [18]) states that the unit ball $E_1' = \{x' : x' \in E' \text{ and } \|x'\| \leq 1\}$ is compact in the weak dual topology $\sigma(E', E)$. It is interesting, however, that the theorem of Bourbaki and Alaoglu is effectively equivalent to the prime ideal theorem for Boolean algebras, as was shown in [16]. This suggests the question whether it is possible to formulate a property for E_1' which will turn out to be effectively equivalent to the Hahn–Banach extension theorem. The purpose of this section is to give an answer to this question. The details are as follows.

A subset A of a topological linear space E will be called *convex compact* whenever for any family of closed convex sets C_τ, $\tau \in \wedge$, of E such that the family $\{A \cap C_\tau : \tau \in \wedge\}$ has the finite intersection property

$$\bigcap (A \cap C_\tau : \tau \in \wedge) \neq \varnothing.$$

The reader who is familiar with Smulian's notion of convex compactness which deals with decreasing sequences of closed convex sets should observe that the above notion of convex compactness is stronger.

We shall now formulate an answer to the question raised above.

***Theorem* 11.1.** *The Hahn–Banach extension theorem is effectively equivalent to the statement that for every normed space E the unit ball of E' is convex compact in the $\sigma(E', E)$-topology.*

Proof. We shall first assume that (HB) holds. Let $\{C_\tau : \tau \in \wedge\}$ be a family of $\sigma(E', E)$-closed subsets of E_1', the unit ball of E'. We shall first show that for every $\tau \in \wedge$ there exists a subset Ω_τ of E such that

$$C_\tau = \bigcap (x' : x' \in E' \text{ and } (x, x') \leq 1 \text{ for all } x \in \Omega_\tau).$$

To this end, we have to show that for every $x_0' \notin C_\tau$ there exists an element

$x_0 \in E$ such that $1 < (x_0, x_0')$ and $(x_0, x') \leq 1$ for all $x' \in C_\tau$. Since C_τ is $\sigma(E', E)$-closed and $x_0' \notin C_\tau$, there exist elements $x_1, \cdots, x_n \in E$ such that $\max(|(x_i, x' - x_0')|: i = 1, 2, \cdots, n) \leq 1$ implies $x' \notin C_\tau$. It is obvious that there is no loss in generality to assume that the elements $x_1, \cdots, x_n$ are linearly independent. Consider then the mapping $x' \to ((x_1, x'), \cdots, (x_n, x'))$ of E' into R^n. This mapping maps C_τ into a convex subset K_τ of R^n and x_0' is mapped into an element y_0 of R^n such that $y_0 \notin K_\tau$ and there exists a sphere with center y_0 which does not intersect K_τ. Then the Minkowski separation theorem for finite-dimensional spaces implies that there exists an element $z_0 \in R^n$ such that $(y_0, z_0) > 1$ and $(y, z_0) \leq 1$ for all $y \in K_\tau$. Thus there exist real constants $c_1, \cdots, c_n$ in R such that $(y, z_0) = (\Sigma_{i=1}^n c_i x_i, x')$ for all $x' \in E'$, where y is the image of x' under the mapping defined above, and so $\Sigma_{i=1}^n c_i x_i$ is the required element. Now, let $\Omega_0 = \bigcup (\Omega_\tau: \tau \in \wedge)$. Then since the family $\{C_\tau: \tau \in \wedge\}$ has the finite intersection property, it follows that Ω_0 has the following property. For every finite subset $\{x_1, \cdots, x_k\}$ of Ω_0 there exists an element $x' \in E_1'$ such that $(x_1, x') \leq 1, \cdots, (x_k, x') \leq 1$. Then it follows from Lemma 10.1 and Theorem 10.2 that there exists an element $x' \in E_1'$ such that $(x, x') \leq 1$ for all $x \in \Omega_0$. Hence $x' \in \bigcap (C_\tau: \tau \in \wedge)$, which shows that E_1' is convex compact.

To prove the converse we have to show by Theorems 7.3 and 7.2 that for every proper filter of subsets of a nonempty set X there exists a measure m on the Boolean algebra of all subsets of X such that $m(F) = 1$ for all $F \in \mathfrak{F}$. To this end, let $B(X)$ be the Banach space of all bounded real functions on X, and let B_1' denote the unit ball of the dual space of $B(X)$. It is easy to see that the mapping $x \to f(x)$, $f \in B$ maps X into B_1' in a one-to-one manner. Then consider the family of those subsets of B_1' which are the $\sigma(B', B)$-closed convex hulls of the elements of $\mathfrak{F}$. Since this family has the finite intersection property ($\mathfrak{F}$ is proper) and B_1' is $\sigma(B', B)$-convex compact there exists an element $\varphi \in B_1'$ which is an element of every set of the family. Then we define $m(E) = \varphi(c_E)$, where c_E is the characteristic function of $E \subset X$. Since φ is linear and positive, the latter follows from the fact that φ is a $\sigma(E', E)$-limit point of a set of positive linear point functionals, m is a measure on the Boolean algebra of all subsets of X. To complete the proof we have to show that $m(F) = 1$ for all $F \in \mathfrak{F}$. To this end we shall denote by F_c the $\sigma(B', B)$-closed convex hull of F as a subset of B_1'. Since $\varphi \in F_c$, it follows that for every $\epsilon > 0$ and every $f \in B$ there exist elements $x_1, \cdots, x_n$ in F and positive constants $c_1, \cdots, c_n$ such that $\Sigma_{i=1}^n c_i = 1$ and $|\Sigma c_i f(x_i) - \varphi(f)| < \epsilon$. For $f = c_F$, we obtain $|\Sigma c_i c_F(x_i) - \varphi(c_F)| = |1 - \varphi(c_F)| = |1 - m(F)| < \epsilon$ for all $\epsilon > 0$, and so $m(F) = 1$, and the proof is finished.

Remarks

1. The same method can be used to show that the prime ideal theorem for Boolean algebras is effectively equivalent to the theorem of Bourbaki and Alaoglu.

2. In the theory of locally convex spaces the theorem of Bourbaki and Alaoglu takes the form. If U is a neighborhood of 0 of a locally convex space E, then its polar set U^0 is compact in the $\sigma(E', E)$-topology.

With the technique of this section it can readily be shown that this result is effectively equivalent to (PI). Furthermore, if we replace compact by convex compact in the above statement, then it becomes a statement that is effectively equivalent to (HB).

References

1. W. SIERPINSKI, *Hypothèse du Continn.* New York: Chelsea, 2nd ed., 1956.
2. H. RUBIN AND J. RUBIN, *Equivalents of the Axiom of Choice.* (Studies in Logic and the Foundations of Mathematics). Amsterdam: North-Holland, 1963.
3. J. LOŚ AND C. RYLL-NARDZEWSKI, On the Applications of Tychonov's Theorem in Mathematical Proofs, *Fundamenta Math. 38* (1951), 233–237.
4. W. A. J. LUXEMBURG, Two Applications of the Method of Construction by Ultrapowers to Analysis, *Bull. Am. Math. Soc. 68* (1962), 416–419.
5. J. D. HALPERN, The Independence of the Axiom of Choice from the Boolean Prime Ideal Theorem, *Fundamenta Math. 55* (1964), 57–66.
6. K. GÖDEL, *The Consistency of the Continuum Hypothesis* (*Annals of Mathematics Studies*). Princeton, N. J.: Princeton Univ. Press, 1940.
7. W. A. J. LUXEMBURG, A General Theory of Monads (this volume).
8. T. FRAYNE, C. MOREL, AND D. S. SCOTT, Reduced Direct Products, *Fundamenta Math. 51* (1962), 195–228.
9. A. ROBINSON, *Non-Standard Analysis* (Studies in Logic and the Foundations of Mathematics). Amsterdam: North-Holland, 1966.
10. M. DAY, *Normed Linear Spaces, Ergeb. Math. 21* (1958).
11. S. BANACH, *Théorie des opérations linéaires.* Warsaw: 1932.
12. R. SIKORSKI, *Boolean Algebras, Ergeb. Math. 25* (1964).
13. A. TARSKI, Une Contribution à la théorie de la mesure, *Fundamenta Math. 15* (1930), 42–50.
14. W. A. J. LUXEMBURG, *Non-Standard Analysis.* Pasadena: California Institute of Technology, 1962, and rev. ed., 1964.
15. O. NIKODYM, Sur le Mesure non-archimedienne effective sur une tribu de Boole arbitraire, *Compt. Rend. 251* (1960), 2113–2115.
16. J. E. RUBIN AND D. S. SCOTT, Some Topological Theorems Equivalent to the Boolean Prime Ideal Theorem, *Bull. Am. Math. Soc. 60* (1954), 389.
17. N. BOURBAKI, Sur les Espaces de Banach, *Compt. Rend. 206* (1938), 1701–1704.
18. L. ALAOGLU, Weak Topologies of Normed Linear Spaces, *Ann. Math. 41* (1940), 252–267.

Germs

by ABRAHAM ROBINSON

1. Introduction

Let S and T be a pair of topological spaces and let p and q be any two elements of S and T, respectively. We define an equivalence relation in the set of subsets of S by putting $V_1 \sim V_2$ for any $V_1 \subset S$, $V_2 \subset S$ if there exists an open neighborhood U of p such that $V_1 \cap U = V_2 \cap U$. The equivalence classes with respect to this relation are called the *germs of sets* (or, briefly, *set germs*) *at* p. For any two set germs of p, α and β, we define an inclusion relation, $\subset$, by putting $\alpha \subset \beta$ if there exist $V_1 \subset \alpha$, $V_2 \subset \beta$ and an open neighborhood U of p such that $\alpha \cap U \subset \beta \cap U$. Then $\alpha = \beta$ if and only if $\alpha \subset \beta$ and $\beta \subset \alpha$. Similarly, we define formal operations of union and intersection for set germs α, β at p by putting $\alpha \cup \beta = \gamma$ (or $\alpha \cap \beta = \gamma$) if γ is the (uniquely defined) set germ such that there exist $V_1 \in \alpha$, $V_2 \in \beta$, $V_3 \in \gamma$ for which $V_1 \cup V_2 = V_3$ (or $V_1 \cap V_2 = V_3$).

Let F be the class of functions into T whose domain is a subset of S and includes an open neighborhood of p. For any $A \subset S$, $f \in F$, $f \mid A$ shall denote the restriction of f to A (so that the domain of definition of $f \mid A$ is the intersection of A with the domain of definition of f). We define an equivalence relation in F by putting $f_1 \sim f_2$ for any $f_1 \in F$, $f_2 \in F$ if there exists an open neighborhood U of p such that $f_1 \mid U = f_2 \mid U$. The equivalence classes with respect to this relation are called the *germs of functions* (briefly, *function germs*) at p. If ϕ is a function germ, then the set germ α is called the *local variety* or *variety germ* of ϕ at p (for the given $q \in T$) if there exist $f \in \phi$, $V \in \alpha$ and an open neighborhood U of p which belongs to the domain of definition of f such that

$$V = \{x \mid x \in U \text{ and } f(x) = q\}.$$

A Normal Form Theorem for Germinal Calculators

If T is endowed with a ring structure, this induces a ring structure also on the function germs, as follows. If ϕ and ψ are function germs, choose $f_1 \in \phi$ and $f_2 \in \psi$ and an open neighborhood U of B such that both f_1 and f_2 are defined on U, and let $\phi + \psi$ at $\phi\psi$ be the function germs which include the functions $f_1 + f_2$, $f_1 f_2$ as defined on U by pointwise addition and multiplication, respectively.

The language of germs is in wide use at present since it provides a convenient framework for the analysis of the local behavior of functions. However, it will be observed that set germs are not actual sets of points, and function germs are not actual functions; in other words, the individual points are lost in the passage to germs. In the present paper, we shall show how to remedy the situation by the use of nonstandard analysis. Thus we shall replace set germs and function germs by actual sets and actual functions, and we shall give an effective application of this procedure.

2. Nonstandard Germs

Retaining the notation of Section 1, let $^*S$ and $^*T$ be enlargements of S and T, respectively (supposed embedded, as usual, in a common enlarged universe, $^*M$). The monad of p in $^*S$, $\mu(p)$, is defined as the intersection of the extensions to $^*S$, of the standard open neighborhoods of p in S, $\mu(p) = \bigcap_{\nu} {}^*U_\nu$ (see [2], Chap. 4). Let $f \in F$; then we shall, for clarity, denote the extension of f to $^*S$ by $^*f$ (and not by f, as in [2]).

An *n.s.* (nonstandard) *set germ at* p is defined as the intersection $^*V \cap \mu(p)$ for any subset V of S. Similarly, an *n.s. function germ at* p is defined as the restriction of $^*f$ to $\mu(p)$, $^*f \mid \mu(p)$, for any $f \in F$. In this connection, observe that $^*f$, and hence the corresponding n.s. function germ, is defined *on* $\mu(p)$. For any set germ α, define $\rho(\alpha)$ as $^*V \cap \mu(p)$ for arbitrary $V \in \alpha$; and for any function germ ϕ define $\sigma(\phi)$ as $^*f \mid \mu(p)$ for arbitrary $f \in \phi$. Using elementary considerations from nonstandard analysis, it is not difficult to verify that these rules establish one-to-one mappings, ρ and σ between the standard and nonstandard germs of sets and of functions, respectively. Moreover, $\rho(\alpha) \subset \rho(\beta)$ if and only if $\alpha \subset \beta$ and $\rho(\alpha \cup \beta) = \rho(\alpha) \cup \rho(\beta)$, $\rho(\alpha \cap \beta) = \rho(\alpha) \cap \rho(\beta)$. Notice that there is no need to *define* the symbols $\subset$, $\cup$, $\cap$ for n.s. set germs since these are actual sets. Similarly, if T is endowed with a ring structure, then $\sigma(f + g) = \sigma(f) + \sigma(g)$, $\sigma(f, g) = \sigma(f)\sigma(g)$.

For any finite set of function germs, $\phi_1, \cdots, \phi_k$, the variety germ of $(\phi_1, \cdots, \phi_k)$ at p is defined by

$$v(\phi_1, \cdots, \phi_k) = v(\phi_1) \cap \cdots \cap v(\phi_k),$$

where the $v(\phi_j)$ on the right side denote the variety germs of individual function germs introduced in the preceding section, for a given $q \in T$. The corresponding notion for a set of n.s. function germs, $\psi_1, \cdots, \psi_k$ is that of the n.s. variety germ of $(\psi_1, \cdots, \psi_k)$, which is defined by

$$v(\psi_1, \cdots, \psi_k) = \{x \mid x \in \mu(p) \quad \text{and} \quad \psi_j(x) = q, j = 1, \cdots, k\}.$$

This definition extends immediately to an infinite set of n.s. function germs $\{\psi_\nu\}$. For finite sets $\phi_1, \cdots, \phi_k$ only we have

$$\sigma(v(\phi_1, \cdots, \phi_k)) = v(\rho(\phi_1), \cdots, \rho(\phi_k)).$$

3. Rückert's Nullstellensatz

Suppose now that S is the n-dimensional complex space C^n, for some (standard) positive integer n where T coincides with the field of complex numbers, C, and $g = 0$, while $p = (0, \cdots, 0)$ is the origin of C^n. We consider only *analytic function germs*, that is, function germs which contain functions $f(z_1, \cdots, z_n)$ that are analytic in a neighborhood of the origin.

A central result in the theory of analytic function germs is

***Theorem* 3.1 (*Rückert's Nullstellensatz*).** *Let $\phi_1, \cdots, \phi_k$, $k \geq 1$, and ψ, be analytic function germs (at the origin of C^n) such that*

3.2. $$v(\psi) \supset v(\phi_1, \cdots, \phi_k).$$

Then there exist analytic function germs $\psi_1, \cdots, \psi_k$ and a positive integer ρ such that

3.3. $$\psi\rho = \psi_1\phi_1 + \cdots + \psi_k\phi_k.$$

That is, 3.2 implies that a power of ψ belongs to the ideal generated by $\phi_1, \cdots, \phi_k$ in the ring of analytic function germs at the origin.

Theorem 3.1 is the analogue, for function germs, of the classical

***Theorem* 3.4 (*Hilbert's Nullstellensatz*).** *Let $\phi_1, \cdots, \phi_k$, $k \geq 1$, and ψ be polynomials of n variables such that*

3.5. $$v(\psi) \supset v(\phi_1, \cdots, \phi_k),$$

where $v(\psi)$ and $v(\phi_1, \cdots, \phi_k)$ are the algebraic variables of ψ and $(\phi_1, \cdots, \phi_k)$. Then there exist polynomials $\psi_1, \cdots, \psi_k$ and a positive integer ρ such that

3.6. $$\psi^\rho = \psi_1\phi_1 + \cdots + \psi_k\phi_k;$$

that is, a power of ψ belongs to the ideal generated by $\phi_1, \cdots, \phi_k$.

Actually, the statement of Theorem 3.4 is ambiguous. If we suppose that the coefficients of the polynomials in question are in a field Φ and that 3.5 holds if we take the varieties in any extension of Φ, then we obtain a weak form of Hilbert's Nullstellensatz. If, on the other hand, we suppose only that 3.5 holds for the varieties in the algebraic closure $\bar{\Phi}$ of Φ, then we obtain the strong form of the theorem (for example, if both the coefficients and the varieties are taken in the field of complex numbers).

An expeditious proof of the weak form of Hilbert's Nullstellensatz, mentioned above, is as follows. Suppose that $\phi_1, \cdots, \phi_k$, and ψ belong to the ring of polynomials $\Phi[z_1, \cdots, z_n]$, where Φ is a given field and suppose that 3.6 does not hold for any ρ. That is to say, the ideal $J \subset R[z_1, \cdots, z_n]$ which is generated by $\phi_1, \cdots, \phi_k$ does not include any power of ψ. By Zorn's lemma, there exists an ideal J', $J \subset J' \subset R[z_1, \cdots, z_n]$, which is maximal with respect to the property of excluding all powers of ψ. A familiar elementary argument shows that J' is prime. Let Φ' be the field of quotients of the quotient ring $R[z_1, \cdots, z_n]/J'$ and let $\zeta_1, \cdots, \zeta_n$ be the canonical images of $z_1, \cdots, z_n$ in Φ'. Then $\zeta = (\zeta_1, \cdots, \zeta_n)$ is a generic point for J'; that is, for any $f(z_1, \cdots, z_n) \in R[z_1, \cdots, z_n]$, $f(\zeta_1, \cdots, \zeta_n) = 0$ if and only if $f(z_1, \cdots, z_n) \in J'$. Hence, in particular, $\phi_j(\zeta, \cdots, \zeta_n) = 0$, $j = 1, \cdots, k$, but $\psi(\zeta_1, \cdots, \zeta_n) \neq 0$. This shows that the variety of ψ in Φ' does not include the variety of $(\phi_1, \cdots, \phi_k)$ in Φ' and proves the weak form of Theorem 3.4.

Although we shall not make use of this fact subsequently, we may mention in passing that the model completeness of the notion of an algebraically closed field now provides an easy transition to the strong form of Theorem 3.4. For $\zeta_1, \cdots, \zeta_n$ as introduced above may be regarded also as elements of the algebraic closure $\bar{\Phi}'$ of Φ', and so the sentence "there exist $w_1, \cdots, w_n$ such that $\phi_1(w_1, \cdots, w_n) = 0, \cdots, \phi_k(w_1, \cdots, w_n) = 0, \psi(w_1, \cdots, w_n) \neq 0$" holds in Φ'. The model completeness of the notion of an algebraically closed field now shows that the sentence in quotation marks holds also in the algebraic closure $\bar{\Phi}$ of Φ, and so the variety of ψ in $\bar{\Phi}$ cannot include the variety of $(\phi_1, \cdots, \phi_k)$ in $\bar{\Phi}$. This completes the proof.

4. Proof of Rückert's Theorem

It is natural to ask whether there does not exist an analogous proof of Theorem 3.1.

The argument applied previously to polynomials still shows that if G_n is the ring of analytic function germs of n variables at the origin, and $\phi_1, \cdots, \phi_k$ and ψ are elements of G_n such that the ideal $J = (\phi_1,$

$\cdots, \phi_k) \subset G_n$ excludes all powers of ψ, then there exists a prime ideal J' such that $J \subset J' \subset G_n$, where J' excludes all powers of ψ (and is, in fact, maximal with respect to this property). The same holds true in the ring of n.s. analytic function germs of n variables at the origin, to be denoted by Γ_n, since the mapping ρ introduced in Section 2 provides an isomorphism between G_n and Γ_n. On the other hand, it does not now make sense to talk of a generic point for a prime ideal J in G_n. However, we are going to show that the corresponding fact is still true in Γ_n, more precisely.

Theorem 4.1. *Let J be a prime ideal in Γ_n, $J \neq \Gamma_n$, where n is a standard positive integer and let μ be the monad of the origin in C^n. Then there exists a point $\zeta = (\zeta_1, \cdots, \zeta_n) \in \mu$ such that for any $\phi(z_1, \cdots, z_n) \in \Gamma_n$, $\phi(\zeta_1, \cdots, \zeta_n) = 0$ if and only if $\phi \in J$.*

A point ζ as described in the theorem will be called a *generic point* for J.

In order to prove Theorem 4.1 we require the following results of Weierstrass', which form the starting point also of the standard proof of Rückert's Nullstellensatz.

Let $f(z_1, \cdots, z_n)$ be a function of n complex variables which is analytic at the origin, and let

$$f(z_1, \cdots, z_n) = \sum_{j=0}^{\infty} f_j(z_1, \cdots, z_n),$$

where $f_k(z_1, \cdots, z_n)$ is the homogeneous polynomial of degree j in the power-series expansion of $f(z_1, \cdots, z_n)$ around the origin, $j = 1, 2, 3, \cdots$. $f(z)$ is said to be *regular in z_n of order $k > 0$* if $f_j(z_1, \cdots, z_n) \equiv 0$ for $j < k$ and z_n^k has a nonvanishing coefficient in $f_k(z_1, \cdots, z_n)$. If

$$f(z_1, \cdots, z_n) = \sum_{j=k}^{\infty} f_j(z_1, \cdots, z_n), \; f_k(z_1, \cdots, z_n) \not\equiv 0,$$

then it is easy to find a nonsingular linear transformation $z_j \to z_j'$ that transforms f into a function which is regular in z_n' of order k.

A *Weierstrass polynomial of degree $k > 0$ in z_n* is a function $h(z_1, \cdots, z_n)$ of the form

4.2. $$h(z_1, \cdots, z_{n-1}, z_n) = z_n^k + a_1(z_1, \cdots, z_{n-1})z_n^{k-1} + \cdots + a_k(z_1, \cdots, z_{n-1}),$$

where the $a_j(z_1, \cdots, z_{n-1})$ are analytic in a neighborhood of the origin and such that $a_j(0, \cdots, 0) = 0$, $j = 1, \cdots, k$. Notice that such a polynomial is regular in z_n of order k.

With these notions, we have the following theorems.

***Theorem* 4.3 (*Weierstrass' Preparation Theorem*).** *If $f(z_1, \cdots, z_n)$, $n \geq 1$ is analytic in the neighborhood of the origin and is regular in z_n of order $k > 0$, then in some neighborhood of the origin there exist a Weierstrass polynomial $h(z_1, \cdots, z_{n-1}, z_n)$ and an analytic function $u(z_1, \cdots, z_n)$, $u(0, \cdots, 0) \neq 0$, such that*

$$4.4. \qquad f(z_1, \cdots, z_n) = u(z_1, \cdots, z_n)h(z_1, \cdots, z_{n-1}, z_n).$$

***Theorem* 4.5 (*Weierstrass' Division Theorem*).** *Let $h(z_1, \cdots, z_{n-1}, z_n)$ be a Weierstrass polynomial of order k in z_n in some neighborhood of the origin and let $f(z_1, \cdots, z_n)$ be any function which is analytic at the origin. Then, in a suitable neighborhood V of the origin,*

$$4.6. \quad f(z_1, \cdots, z_n) = g(z_1, \cdots, z_n)h(z_1, \cdots, z_n) + v(z_1, \cdots, z_n),$$

where $g(z_1, \cdots, z_n)$ and $v(z_1, \cdots, z_n)$ are analytic in V and $v(z_1, \cdots, z_n)$ is a polynomial of degree $< k$ with respect to z_n. That is to say,

$$4.7. \quad v(z_1, \cdots, z_n) = b_1(z_1, \cdots, z_{n-1})z_n^{k-1} + \cdots + b_k(z_1, \cdots, z_{n-1}),$$

where the b_j are analytic at the origin.

We shall make use of these results in the specified enlargement. However, the polynomials and analytic functions that we shall consider will be assumed throughout to be (the extensions of) standard functions.

Proof of Theorem 4.1. By induction with respect to n. Suppose $n = 1$. If $J = (0)$, then any point $\zeta = (\zeta_1)$ with $0 \neq \zeta \in \mu$ will do for the ζ of the theorem. If $J \neq (0)$, let $0 \neq \phi(\zeta_1) \in J$. Then $\phi(0) = 0$, for otherwise $\phi(\zeta_1)$ would possess an inverse in Γ_1 and $J = \Gamma_1$. Hence $\phi(z_1) = z_1^k\psi(z_1)$, where $\psi(0) \neq 0$ and so $z_1^k \in J$, $z_1 \in J$. It follows that $\zeta = (0)$ will do in this case.

Since every n.s. analytic function germ is the restriction of an analytic function to μ, we may transfer to n.s. analytic function germs the notion of regularity of order k with respect to z_n. Disregarding the case $\zeta = (0)$, which is again trivial, let $0 \neq \phi\ (z_1, \cdots, z_n) \in J$, so that, as before, $\phi(0, \cdots, 0) = 0$ and, if necessary, perform a standard linear transformation $z_j \to z_j'$ so that the transform of ϕ is a regular function in z_n' of order $k \geq 1$. The transformation carries prime ideals into prime ideals and zeros of functions into zeros of the corresponding functions, and so we may as well suppose from the outset that J contains an element $\phi(z_1, \cdots, z_n)$ which is regular with respect to z_n, of order $k \geq 1$.

An n.s. Weierstrass polynomial germ of degree $k > 0$ in z_n is an n.s. function germ $h(z_1, \cdots, z_n)$ which is of the form 4.2, where the $a_j(z_1, \cdots, z_{n-1})$ are now n.s. analytic function germs such that $a_j(0, \cdots, 0) = 0$. Thus an n.s. Weierstrass polynomial germ is the restriction to μ of a Weierstrass polynomial, Theorem 4.3 shows that the function germ $\phi(z_1, \cdots, z_n) \in J$ introduced above can be written in the form 4.4, where $h(z_1, \cdots, z_n)$ is an n.s. Weierstrass polynomial germ and $u(z_1, \cdots, z_n)$ is an invertible element of Γ_n; that is, $u(0, \cdots, 0) \neq 0$. Since J is prime, but $J \neq \Gamma_n$, we may conclude that $h(z_1, \cdots, z_n)$ belongs to J.

Let Π_n be the set of elements of Γ_n which are polynomials with respect to z_n, that is, such that there is a bound on the powers of z_n which appear in their power-series expansion. Then Π_n is an integral domain which, as far as its algebraic structure is concerned, may be identified with $\Gamma_{n-1}[z_n]$. In particular, Π_n contains the n.s. Weierstrass polynomial germs as given by 4.2. Thus $h(z_1, \cdots, z_n) \in J$ belongs to Π_n and, in the sense just explained, may also be regarded as an element of $\Gamma_{n-1}[z_n]$.

Let $J' = J \cap \Gamma_{n-1}$; then J' also is a prime ideal which does not contain an element invertible in Γ_{n-1}. Thus $J' \neq \Gamma_{n-1}$, and so, by the assumption of induction, J' possesses a generic point $\zeta' = (\zeta_1, \cdots, \zeta_{n-1}) \in \mu$, that is, for any $f(z_1, \cdots, z_{n-1}) \in \Gamma_{n-1}$, $f(z_1, \cdots, z_{n-1}) \in \zeta'$ if and only if $f(\zeta_1, \cdots, \zeta_{n-1}) = 0$. Accordingly, the evaluation map of Γ_{n-1} with $^*C$ at the point ζ' is a homomorphism with kernel J'. This yields a monomorphism from Γ_{n-1}/J' into $^*C$, to be denoted by τ.

Consider the quotient ring Γ_n/J. Since $J \cap \Gamma_{n-1} = J'$ we may regard Γ_n/J as an extension of Γ_{n-1}/J'. We claim that this extension is finite algebraic. Indeed, let λ be the canonical map $\Gamma_n \to \Gamma_n/J$. Since $h \in J$, we then have, by 4.2,

4.8. $$0 = \lambda(h) = (\lambda(z_n))^k + \lambda(a_1)(\lambda(z_n))^{k+1} + \cdots + \lambda(a_k)$$

But $\lambda(a_j) \in \Gamma_{n-1}/J'$ for $j = 1, \cdots, k$. This shows that $\lambda(z_n)$ is algebraic over Γ_{n-1}/J'.

Now let $f(z_1, \cdots, z_n)$ be any other element of Γ_n. The division theorem, 4.5, shows (by restriction to μ) that f can be written in the form 4.6, where v is given by 4.7 and g and the b_j are n.s. analytic function germs, $g \in \Gamma_n$, $b_j \in \Gamma_{n-1}$. Hence

$$\begin{aligned}\lambda(f) &= \lambda(g)\lambda(h) + \lambda(v)\\ &= \lambda(b_1)(\lambda(z_n))^{k-1} + \cdots + \lambda(b_k).\end{aligned}$$

This shows that $\lambda(f)$ is a polynomial of $\lambda(z_n)$ with coefficients in Γ_{n-1}/J' and proves our assertion.

Let Δ be the field of quotients of Γ_{n-1}/J'. Then

$$p(x) = x^k + \lambda(a_1)x^{k-1} + \cdots + \lambda(a_k) \in \Delta[x]$$

and $$p(\lambda(z_n)) = 0.$$

It follows that $\lambda(z_n)$ is a root of an irreducible factor of $p(x)$ in $\Delta[x]$, to be denoted by $q(x)$. There is a canonical extension of the mapping τ from Γ_{n-1}/J' into $^*C$, to a mapping from Δ into $^*C$, which will still be denoted by τ. Applying τ to the coefficients of $p(x)$ and $q(x)$, respectively, we obtain polynomials $p_\tau(x)$ and $q_\tau(x)$ with coefficients in $^*C$ such that $q_\tau(x)$ divides $p_\tau(x)$ in $\Delta[x]$. Let ζ_n be any root of $q(x)$ in $^*C$. Then we claim that ζ_n must be infinitesimal.

Indeed, $q_\tau(\zeta_n) = 0$ entails $p_\tau(\zeta_n) = 0$. Now

$$\begin{aligned} p_\tau(x) &= x^k + \tau(\lambda(a_1))x^{k-1} + \cdots + \tau(\lambda(a_k)) \\ &= x^k + a_1(\zeta_1, \cdots, \zeta_{n-1})x^{k-1} + \cdots + a_k(\zeta_1, \cdots, \zeta_{n-1}), \end{aligned}$$

and since $a_j(0, \cdots, 0) = 0$, $j = 1, \cdots, k$, and $(\zeta_1, \cdots, \zeta_{n-1})$ is in the monad of the origin of C^{n-1}, it follows that $a_j(\zeta_1, \cdots, \zeta_{n-1})$ is infinitesimal. Suppose now that ζ_n is not infinitesimal. Then

$$\zeta_n = d_1 + d_2\zeta_n^{-1} + \cdots + d_k\zeta^{1-k},$$

where $d_j = -a_j(\zeta_1, \cdots, \zeta_{n-1})$, so that the terms on the right side are all infinitesimal. This shows that ζ_n also must be infinitesimal, proving our assertion by contradiction. It follows that $(\zeta_1, \cdots, \zeta_n)$ belongs to the monad of the origin of C^n, μ.

In particular, let $q(x)$ be a polynomial with coefficients in Γ_{n-1}/J', which is irreducible over the field of quotients of that ring and such that $q(\lambda(z_n)) = 0$. Then $q(x)$ is determined uniquely up to nonzero factors from Γ_{n-1}/J'. Let $\zeta_n \in {}^*C$ be any root of $q(\zeta_n) = 0$. We are going to show that $\zeta = (\zeta_1, \cdots, \zeta_n)$ is a generic point for J.

As we have seen already, $\zeta \in \mu$. Also

$$\begin{aligned} 0 = p_\tau(\zeta_n) &= \zeta_n^{\,k} + a_1(\zeta_1, \cdots, \zeta_{n-1})\zeta_n^{\,k-1} + \cdots + a_k(\zeta_1, \cdots, \zeta_{n-1}) \\ &= h(\zeta_1, \cdots, \zeta_n), \end{aligned}$$

and so, by 4.6,

$$f(\zeta_1, \cdots, \zeta_n) = r(\zeta_1, \cdots, \zeta_n)$$

for any $f(z_1, \cdots, z_n) \in \Gamma_n$, where v is given by 4.7, with $b_j \in \Gamma_{n-1}$, $j = 1, \cdots, k$. At the same time, $\lambda(f(z_1, \cdots, z_n)) = \lambda(v(z_1, \cdots, z_n))$, since $h \in J$. Accordingly, the proof of Theorem 4.1 will be complete as soon as we show that $r(\zeta_1, \cdots, \zeta_n) = 0$ if and only if $r(z_1, \cdots, z_n) \in J$ for any $r(z_1, \cdots, z_n)$ of the form 4.7, with $b_j(z_1, \cdots, z_n) \in \Gamma_{n-1}$, $j =$

$1, \cdots, k$, that is, for any $r \in \Gamma_{n-1}[z_n]$. In other words, we have to verify that for any $r(z_1, \cdots, z_n) \in \Gamma_{n-1}[z_n]$ the evaluation map η at $\zeta_1, \cdots, \zeta_n$ is a homomorphism with kernel $J \cap \Gamma_{n-1}[z_n]$, that is, η induces a monomorphism from $\Gamma_{n-1}[z_n]/J \cap \Gamma_{n-1}[z_n]$ into $^*C$. But we know that the restriction of η to Γ_{n-1} induces a monomorphism, called previously τ, from Γ_{n-1}/J' into $^*C$. Thus we only have to show that the addition and specification $\lambda(z_n) \to \zeta_n$ extends τ to a monomorphism from $\Gamma_{n-1}[z_n]/J \cap \Gamma_{n-1}[z_n]$ into $^*C$. But this follows from the choice of ζ_n, since $\lambda(z_n)$ and ζ_n are roots of the irreducible polynomials $q(x)$ and $q_\tau(x)$, respectively, which correspond under the mapping τ. This completes the proof of Theorem 4.1.

Rückert's Nullstellensatz (Theorem 3.1) now follows immediately by the argument used in the proof of Theorem 3.4. As we compare our procedure with a standard proof of Theorem 3.1 (for example, [1]) we may notice the great advantage obtained from the introduction of the notion of a generic point. In particular, we did not require the result that Γ_n is Noetherian. In Section 5 we shall consider a situation where the rings under consideration are in fact no longer Noetherian, but where the conclusion of Theorem 3.1 is valid all the same.

5. Function Germs of an Unbounded Number of Variables

Let $\nu = \{I\}$ be an index set of arbitrary cardinality and let C^I be the direct product of $\bar{\bar{I}}$ copies of the complex numbers indexed in I. We consider the class Φ of functions from C^I into C which depend only on a finite number of coordinates $\nu \in I$, and we may, for simplicity, use ordinary integers $0, 1, 2, \cdots$ to indicate the coordinates on which the function in question may depend. The elements of Φ will be called *cylindrical functions*. The generalization of the theory of the preceding sections to functions of this kind presents itself naturally in a nonstandard setting. Accordingly, we shall approach the problem in this framework.

Passing to enlargements, C is extended to $^*C$ and C^I is extended to $^*C^{*I}$, where we have to bear in mind that any *internal* points are to be regarded as elements of $^*C^{*I}$. The *monad of* $^*C^{*I}$, μ, will be defined as the set of internal points $a \in {}^*C^{*I}$ such that the νth coordinate of a, a_ν, is infinitesimal for all standard ν. μ is, in fact, the monad of the origin in the product topology of $^*C^{*I}$ [2]. By an *n.s. set germ* we mean an intersection $A \cap \mu$ where $A = {}^*B$ is the extension of any $B \subset C^I$ to $^*C^{*I}$ (that is, A is any *standard* set).

By an *n.s. function germ* (more precisely, a *nonstandard cylindrical analytic function germ at the origin*) we mean the restriction of a cylindrical function $f(z_1, \cdots, z_n)$ which is analytic for sufficiently small $|z_1|, \cdots, |z_n|$ to the monad μ. The n.s. function germs constitute an integral domain, to be denoted by Γ. If J is an ideal in Γ which excludes all (standard) powers g^0 of some $g \in \Gamma$, then there exists a prime ideal $J' \supset J$ which still excludes all powers of g.

Let $A \subset \Gamma$. The *n.s. variety germ* of A, $v(A)$, is defined as the set of all points $\zeta \in \mu$ such that $f(\zeta) = 0$ for all $f \in A$ [where we write $f(\zeta)$ briefly for $f(\cdots, \zeta_\nu, \cdots)$]. The n.s. variety germ of the ideal generated by A coincides with the n.s. variety germ of A. If A consists of a single element, $A = \{f\}$, then $v(A)$ is an n.s. set germ. For if $f = f(z_1, \cdots, z_n)$, then f is the restriction of a standard function $^*g(z_1, \cdots, z_n)$ which is analytic for $|z_j| < \rho$, $j = 1, \cdots, n$, for sufficiently small standard positive ρ, and $v(A)$ is then the restriction to μ of the set of zeros of $^*g$ which satisfy $|z_j| < \rho, j = 1, \cdots, n$. A similar argument shows, more generally, that if A is a finite set, or a finitely generated ideal, then $v(A)$ is an n.s. set germ.

Let J be an ideal in Γ, at point $\zeta \in \mu$ will be said to be *generic for* J if for any $f \in \Gamma$, $f(\zeta) = 0$ if and only if $f \in J$. We are going to prove

Theorem 5.1. *Let* J *be a prime ideal in* Γ, $J \neq \Gamma$. *Then* J *possesses a generic point.*

Proof. Given the prime ideal J, let G be any finite subset of Γ, put $H = J \cap G$, $K = G - H$, and suppose that H and K are not empty. Since G is finite, there exists a finite subset I' of I such that the elements of G are independent of coordinates with subscripts in $I - I'$. Let Γ' be the set of elements of Γ which depend only (that is, at most) on coordinates with subscripts in I', and let $J' = \Gamma' \cap J$. Then J' includes H and excludes K and hence is a prime ideal in Γ' which is different from Γ'. Let $I' = \{\nu_1, \cdots, \nu_m\}$; then Theorem 4.1 shows that there exist infinitesimal complex numbers $\zeta_{\nu_1}, \cdots, \zeta_{\nu_m}$ such that for any $f(z_{\nu_1}, \cdots, z_{\nu_m}) \in \Gamma'$, $f(\zeta_{\nu_1}, \cdots, \zeta_{\nu_m}) = 0$ if and only if $f(z_{\nu_1}, \cdots, z_{\nu_m}) \in J'$. It follows that, for any standard positive integer n, the following statement holds in the enlargement.

5.2. "There exist a positive $\rho < 1/n$ and complex numbers ζ_{ν_j}, $j = 1, \cdots, m$ such that $|\zeta_{\nu_j}| < \rho$ and the elements of $G = H \cup K$ are analytic for $|z_{\nu_j}| < \rho$, $j = 1, \cdots, m$ and $f(\zeta_{\nu_1}, \cdots, \zeta_{\nu_m}) = 0$ for all $f \in H$ while $f(\zeta_{\nu_1}, \cdots, \zeta_{\nu_m}) \neq 0$ for all $f \in K$."

Bearing in mind that the set G is finite and consists of standard functions only, we see that 5.2 must hold also in the standard domain, for certain standard ρ, $\zeta_{\nu_1}, \cdots, \zeta_{\nu_m}$, provided we replace the n.s. function germs $f(z_{\nu_1}, \cdots, z_{\nu_m})$ by standard analytic functions whose restrictions they are.

Let Γ_0 be obtained from Γ by replacing each element f of Γ by an appropriate standard analytic function f_0 from which f is attained by restriction, $f \leftrightarrow f_0$. Let J_0 be the image of J under this mapping. Then the argument just applied to 5.2 shows that for every finite subset H_0 of J_0 and for every finite subset K_0 of $\Gamma_0 - J_0$ there exist a standard $\rho < 0$ and standard complex $\zeta_{\nu_1}, \cdots, \zeta_{\nu_m}$ such that $|\zeta_{\nu_j}| < \rho$ and the elements of $G_0 = H_0 \cup K_0$ depend only on $z_{\nu_1}, \cdots, z_{\nu_m}$ and are analytic for $|z_{\nu_j}| < \rho$ and $f(\zeta_{\nu_1}, \cdots, \zeta_{\nu_m}) = 0$ for all $f \in H_0$ while $f(\zeta_{\nu_1}, \cdots, \zeta_{\nu_m}) \neq 0$ for all $f \in k_0$.

Consider the binary relation $R(x, y)$ which is defined as follows. x is an array $\langle n, H_0, K_0\rangle$ where n is a (standard) positive integer, H_0 is a finite subset of J_0, and K_0 is a finite subset of $\Gamma_0 - J_0$; and y is a set of complex numbers $\{\zeta_\nu\}$ indexed in I such that if $z_{\nu_1}, \cdots, z_{\nu_m}$ are the variables on which the functions of $H_0 \cup K_0$ depend, then $|\zeta_{\nu_j}| < 1/n$ for $j = 1, \cdots, m$, and the functions of $H_0 \cup K_0$ are analytic for $(\zeta_{\nu_1}, \cdots, \zeta_{\nu_m})$ and $f(\zeta_{\nu_1}, \cdots, \zeta_{\nu_m}) = 0$ for $f \in H_0$ and $f(\zeta_{\nu_1}, \cdots, \zeta_{\nu_m}) \neq 0$ for $f \in K_0$. Then the discussion following the statement of 5.2 shows that $R(x, y)$ is concurrent. It follows that there exists a set of $\zeta_\nu \in {}^*C$ indexed in ${}^*I$ such that the relations $R(\langle n, H_0, K_0\rangle, \{\zeta_\nu\})$ hold for all n, H_0, K_0 as specified above, simultaneously. Accordingly, $|\zeta_\nu| < 1/n$ for $\nu \in I$ and all standard n; that is, ζ_ν is infinitesimal for $\nu \in I$ and hence $\{\zeta_\nu\} = \zeta$ belongs to the monad μ. Also, since every $f \in \Gamma$ is the restriction of some $f_0 \in \Gamma_0$ it follows that $f(\zeta) = 0$ if and only if $f \in J$. This shows that ζ is a generic point for J and proves Theorem 5.1.

Similarly as before, the argument of Section 3 above leads from Theorem 5.1 to the following Nullstellensatz.

Theorem 5.3. *Let $A \subset I$ and let g be an element of Γ such that $g(\zeta) = 0$ for all $\zeta \in v(A)$. Then there exist a standard positive integer ρ and n.s. function germs $f_1, \cdots, f_n \in A$, $g_1, \cdots, g_n \in \Gamma$ such that*

$$g^0 = g, f_1 + \cdots + g_n f_n.$$

For finite Γ, Theorem 5.3 includes Theorem 3.1, but is in fact seen to be no stronger than Theorem 3.1 if account is taken of the fact that I_n is Noetherian. For it then follows that for any $A \subset I_n$, $v(A) = v(A')$ for some finite subset A' of A, so that Theorem 5.3 reduces to Theorem 3.1 in this particular case. However, for infinite I, the ring Γ is no longer Noetherian, and Theorem 5.3, which is formulated in nonstandard language, then provides a natural generalization of Theorem 3.1.

References

1. R. C. GUNNING AND H. ROSSI, *Analytic Functions of Several Complex Variables.* Englewood Cliffs, N. J.: Prentice-Hall, 1965.
2. A. ROBINSON, *Non-Standard Analysis* (Studies in Logic and the Foundations of Mathematics). Amsterdam: North-Holland, 1966.

Nonstandard Analysis of Almost Periodic Functions

by LAWRENCE D. KUGLER[1]

1. Introduction

In this paper we shall show how the methods of A. Robinson's nonstandard analysis can be applied to H. Bohr's theory of almost-periodic functions to give (1) new characterizations of almost-periodic functions which may have some intuitive appeal, (2) new proofs of the fundamental theorems on almost-periodic functions, and (3) nonstandard characterizations of certain character groups related to almost-periodic functions which are of interest in themselves. A detailed and comprehensive presentation of nonstandard analysis may be found in Robinson's book on the subject [7], and it will be assumed that the reader is familiar with the first four chapters of that work. The following is a brief summary of the notation and basic results which will be needed.

Following Robinson's notation, let $^*M$ be an enlargement of a higher-order structure M. Then $^*M$ is an elementary extension of M, and we say that for a sentence defined in M, its truth value in M or $^*M$ may be deduced by *transfer* from its truth value in $^*M$ or M, respectively. Any relation or individual of $^*M$ is called *internal*, and relations not in $^*M$ are called *external*. If an internal relation or individual of $^*M$ corresponds to a relation or individual R of M, it is called *standard* and is designated by $^*R$.

Suppose Φ is a relation which specifies the open sets of a topology on a nonempty set A. In an enlargement of such a topological space, the *monad* $\mu(p)$ of a standard point $p \in A$ is defined by $\mu(p) =$

[1] This paper is an abridgment of the author's doctoral dissertation which was submitted to the University of California, Los Angeles, in 1966. The research was supported by National Science Foundation Grant, GP-4038 and was supervised by A. Robinson.

$\bigcap_{p \in U \in \Phi} {}^*U$. It is easy to see that if the relation Φ_0 determines an open basis for the topological space (A, Φ), then $\mu(p) = \bigcap_{p \in U \in \Phi} {}^*U$. Points of $\bigcup_{p \in A} \mu(p)$ are called *near-standard.*

The three theorems stated next are nonstandard characterizations of important topological concepts. Proofs may be found in Robinson [7].

***Theorem* 1.1.** *(A, Φ) is a Hausdorff space iff distinct points of A have disjoint monads.*

***Theorem* 1.2.** *(A, Φ) is compact iff every point of ${}^*A$ is near-standard.*

***Theorem* 1.3.** *A function f from (A, Φ_A) into (B, Φ_B) is continuous iff for every $a \in A$, ${}^*f(\mu(a)) \subset \mu(f(a))$.*

If **C** and **R** are the complex and real fields, respectively, their enlargements are the fields ***C** of *nonstandard complex numbers* and ***R** of *nonstandard real numbers.* Standard relations in ***C** and ***R** will generally be written as they are in **C** and **R**, in accordance with ordinary mathematical usage, for example, the symbol $<$ will be used for the ordering relation in both **R** and ***R**, and if f is a standard function on **C**, its extension on ***C** will usually be designated by f also.

If **C** is endowed with the usual topology, the monad of zero is designated by $\mathbf{M}_1$ and elements of $\mathbf{M}_1$ are called *infinitesimals.* Thus a number $a \in {}^*\mathbf{C}$ is infinitesimal if and only if $|a| < |c|$ for every nonzero $c \in \mathbf{C}$. Near-standard elements of ***C** are called *finite* and their totality is denoted by $\mathbf{M}_0$. By the completeness of **C**, $a \in \mathbf{M}_0$ if and only if there is a number $c \in \mathbf{C}$ such that $|a| \leq |c|$. Elements of ${}^*\mathbf{C} - \mathbf{M}_0$ are said to be *infinite* (such elements exist since **C** is not compact). It is not hard to show that $\mathbf{M}_1$ and $\mathbf{M}_0$ are external and that $\mathbf{M}_1$ is an ideal in $\mathbf{M}_0$. For $a,b \in \mathbf{C}$, we write $a \simeq b$ if and only if $a - b$ is infinitesimal. For every finite number $a \in {}^*\mathbf{C}$, the unique standard number ${}^0(a)$ such that $a \simeq {}^0(a)$ is called the *standard part* of a.

The above definitions and remarks apply also to **R** in its usual topology.

The following theorems characterize various notions concerning functions defined on **R** with values in **C**. Proofs may be found in Robinson [7].

***Theorem* 1.4.** *A standard complex-valued function on* **R** *is uniformly continuous iff for all x,y in* ***R**, *$f(x) \simeq f(y)$ whenever $x \simeq y$.*

***Theorem* 1.5.** *If f is a standard complex-valued function on* **R**, *then $\lim_{x \to \infty} f(x) = b$ iff for every infinite $x > 0$ in* ***R**, *$f(x) \simeq b$.*

Let $\mathbf{Z} \subset \mathbf{C}$ be the set of positive integers. A (standard) sequence is a function σ defined on $\mathbf{Z}$ and is represented by the symbol $\{s_n\}$, where $s_n = \sigma(n)$, $n = 1, 2, \cdots$. The sequence $^*\{s_n\}$ is then the extension function $^*\sigma$ of σ defined on $^*Z$.

Theorem 1.6. *If $\{f_n\}$ is a standard sequence of complex-valued functions on $\mathbf{R}$, then $\{f_n\}$ converges uniformly to a (standard) function f iff for every infinite positive integer n and every $x \in {}^*\mathbf{R}$, $f_n(x) \simeq f(x)$.*

2. Definitions and Basic Properties of Almost-Periodic Functions

The definition of almost periodicity is most conveniently stated in two parts:

Definition 2.1. A set $E \subset \mathbf{R}$ is *relatively dense* (*r.d.*) if there is a number $d > 0$ such that every interval of length d contains an element of E.

Definition 2.2. A function f: $\mathbf{R} \to \mathbf{C}$ is (*uniformly*) *almost periodic*, $f \in$ UAP if f is continuous and for every $\epsilon > 0$,

$$E(\epsilon, f) = \{\tau\colon (\forall x)[|f(x + \tau) - f(x)| < \epsilon]\} \text{ is r.d.}$$

In this section we establish three nonstandard characterizations of the class UAP. The first is obtained by characterizing r.d. sets, the second replaces the sets $E(\epsilon, f)$ by a single set $E(f)$, and the third is related to a characterization of UAP due to Bochner. For the remainder of this section, f is assumed to be continuous.

The following lemma characterizes relatively dense sets in $^*\mathbf{R}$ in terms of cosets of its additive subgroup $\mathbf{M}_0$.

Lemma 2.3. *A set $E \subset \mathbf{R}$ is r.d. iff $^*E$ contains an element of every coset $\mathbf{M}_0 + a$ of $\mathbf{M}_0$, $a \in {}^*\mathbf{R}$.*

Proof. ($\to$) Choose $d > 0$ in $\mathbf{R}$ so that Definition 2.1 is satisfied for E. By transfer from $\mathbf{R}$, the sentence $(\forall a)(\exists\tau)[\tau \in (a, d + a) \cap {}^*E]$ holds in $^*\mathbf{R}$. But $(a, d + a) \subset \mathbf{M}_0 + a$ for any $a \in {}^*\mathbf{R}$, so that $\mathbf{M}_0 + a$ also intersects $^*E$.

($\leftarrow$) Let $\omega > 0$ be infinite. Then for each $a \in {}^*\mathbf{R}$, the interval $(a - \omega, a + \omega)$ contains $M_0 + a$. Hence the sentence $(\exists d)(\forall a)(\exists\tau)[\tau \in (a - d/2, a + d/2) \cap {}^*E]$ is true in $^*\mathbf{R}$ and thus also in $\mathbf{R}$, where it simply asserts that E is r.d.

***Theorem* 2.4 (*Characterization I*).** $f \in \text{UAP}$ *iff given* $\epsilon > 0$ *in* $\mathbf{R}$, *every coset of* $\mathbf{M}_0$ *contains a number* $\tau \in {}^*\mathbf{R}$ *such that for all* $x \in {}^*\mathbf{R}$, $|f(x + \tau) - f(x)| < \epsilon$.

Proof. The theorem follows directly from Definition 2.2 and Lemma 2.3 by setting $E = E(\epsilon, f)$.

The second characterization of UAP eliminates the sets $E(\epsilon, f)$ of translation numbers by introducing a single set $E(f) \subset {}^*\mathbf{R}$ such that the graphs of f and its translate by any $\tau \in E(f)$ match everywhere on ${}^*\mathbf{R}$ with only infinitesimal error. The frequency of occurrence of elements of $E(f)$ is such that every interval of infinite length intersects $E(f)$.

The following lemma concerning the sets $E(\epsilon, f)$ will be needed to derive the desired properties of $E(f)$.

***Lemma* 2.5.** For $f \in UAP$, *define* $d(\epsilon) = \inf\{d > 0\colon d$ *satisfies Definition* 2.1 *for* $E = E(\epsilon, f)\}$. *Then:*

(a) $d(\epsilon)$ *is a decreasing function of* ϵ.
(b) *If* f *is not periodic,* $\lim_{\epsilon \to 0} d(\epsilon) = \infty$.
(c) *For every* a, *there exists* $\tau \in [a, d(\epsilon) + a]$ *such that for all* x,

$$|f(x + \tau) - f(x)| \leq \epsilon.$$

The proof is straightforward.

***Theorem* 2.6 (*Characterization II*).** $f \in UAP$ *iff for every* $a \in {}^*\mathbf{R}$ *and every infinite* $\omega > 0$ *there exists a number* $\tau \in [a, \omega + a]$ *such that* $f(x + \tau) \simeq f(x)$ *for all* $x \in {}^*\mathbf{R}$.

Proof. $(\rightarrow)$ If f is periodic, the implication is trivial, since the set of periods of f is r.d. Assume, therefore, that f is not periodic and consider the function $d(\epsilon)$ defined in Lemma 2.5. Given an infinite $\omega > 0$, there is a number $\epsilon_0 \simeq 0$ such that $d(\epsilon_0) \leq \omega$, for, if not, the internal set $\{\epsilon \neq 0\colon d(\epsilon) > \omega \text{ or } d(-\epsilon) > \omega\}$ would contain the external set $\mathbf{M}_1 - \{0\}$ properly, so that there would be a positive $\epsilon \not\simeq 0$ such that $d(\epsilon) > \omega$, contradicting the fact that $d(\epsilon)$ is finite for all positive $\epsilon \not\simeq 0$. Hence by (c) of Lemma 2.5 interpreted in ${}^*\mathbf{R}$, we conclude that for any $a \in {}^*\mathbf{R}$, there exists $\tau \in [a, d(\epsilon_0) + a] \subset [a, \omega + a]$ such that for all $x \in {}^*\mathbf{R}$, $|f(x + \tau) - f(x)| \leq \epsilon_0 \simeq 0$.

$(\leftarrow)$ Choose $\epsilon > 0$ in $\mathbf{R}$. Then the sentence $(\exists d)(\forall a)(\exists \tau)(\forall x)[\tau \in (a, a + d) \wedge |f(x + \tau) - f(x)| < \epsilon]$ is true in ${}^*\mathbf{R}$ (take d infinite). It is therefore true in $\mathbf{R}$, so that by definition, $f \in UAP$.

Numbers $\tau \in {}^*\mathbf{R}$ such that for all $x \in {}^*\mathbf{R}$, $f(x + \tau) \simeq f(x)$ will be called *near-periods* for f. The (external) set of such τ will be denoted by

$E(f)$. $E(f)$ is clearly an additive subgroup of $^*\mathbf{R}$, in analogy with the group of periods of a periodic function.

By way of comparison with characterization I, note that intervals of infinite length are larger than cosets of $\mathbf{M}_0$, since any two elements of $\mathbf{M}_0 + a$ are only a finite distance apart. The question of whether $E(f)$ in fact intersects every coset of $\mathbf{M}_0$ is answered by the following theorem, the proof of which may be found in [5].

Theorem 2.7. *If $f \in UAP$ and $E(f)$ intersects every coset of $\mathbf{M}_0$, then f is periodic.*

The third characterization of UAP deals with translations of almost-periodic functions, not only by near-periods, but by any number $a \in {}^*\mathbf{R}$. The next lemma asserts some important facts about almost-periodic functions which we shall need.

Lemma 2.8. *Let $f \in UAP$. Then f is bounded and uniformly continuous.*

Both the standard and the nonstandard proofs of this lemma are simple and are left to the reader.

We now consider translates of an almost-periodic function by arbitrary elements of $^*\mathbf{R}$.

Lemma 2.9. *Let $a \in {}^*R$ and $f \in UAP$. Define g_a: $\mathbf{R} \to \mathbf{C}$ by $g_a(x) = {}^0(f(x + a))$. Then $g_a(x) \in UAP$.* (Note that Lemma 2.8 and Theorem 1.4 ensure that g_a is well defined.)

Proof. To show that $g_a(x)$ is continuous, let $\epsilon > 0$ in $\mathbf{R}$. By Lemma 2.8, $\delta \in \mathbf{R}$ can be chosen so that the sentence $(\forall y_1)(\forall y_2)[|y_1 - y_2| < \delta \to |f(y_1) - f(y_2)| < \epsilon/2]$ is true in $\mathbf{R}$ and thus also in $^*\mathbf{R}$. Now suppose $|x_1 - x_2| < \delta$, where $x_1,x_2 \in \mathbf{R}$. Setting $y_1 = x_1 + a$ and $y_2 = x_2 + a$ yields $|f(x_1 + a) - f(x_2 + a)| < \epsilon/2$. It follows from the triangle inequality and the definition of g_a that $|g_a(x_1) - g_a(x_2)| < \epsilon$, so g_a is (uniformly) continuous.

Now suppose $\tau \in \mathbf{R}$ is chosen so that the sentence $(\forall y)[|f(y + \tau) - f(y)| < \epsilon/3]$ is true in $\mathbf{R}$ and hence in $^*\mathbf{R}$. Then for any $x \in {}^*\mathbf{R}$, we may set $y = x + a$ to obtain $|g_a(x + \tau) - g_a(x)| < \epsilon/2$. This inequality shows that $E(\epsilon/3, f) \subset E(\epsilon/2, g_a)$, so that the latter is r.d. By Definition 2.2, $g_a \in UAP$.

Theorem 2.10 (***Characterization III***). *$f \in UAP$ iff for every $a \in {}^*\mathbf{R}$ there is a standard function $g_a(x)$ such that for all $x \in {}^*\mathbf{R}$, $f(x + a) \simeq g_a(x)$.*

Proof. $(\to)$ Define $g_a(x)$ as in Lemma 2.9 and choose $x \in {}^*\mathbf{R}$ and $\epsilon > 0$ in $\mathbf{R}$. By Theorem 2.4, there is a number $\tau \in \mathbf{M}_0 + x$ such that $|f(x + a) - f(x - \tau + a)| < \epsilon/3$, and by the proof of Lemma 2.9,

$|g_a(x) - g_a(x - \tau)| < \epsilon/2$. Using these facts together with the continuity of f and g_a and the definition of g_a, we find that

$$\begin{aligned}|f(x + a) - g_a(x)| \leq\\ &|f(x + a) - f(x - \tau + a)| + |f(x - \tau + a) - f({}^0(x - \tau) + a)|\\ &+ |f({}^0(x - \tau) + a) - g_a({}^0(x - \tau))| + |g_a({}^0(x - \tau)) - g_a(x - \tau)|\\ &+ |g_a(x - \tau) - g_a(x)| <\\ &\frac{\epsilon}{2} + \frac{\epsilon}{2} = \epsilon.\end{aligned}$$

Hence, for each $x \in {}^*\mathbf{R}$, $f(x + a) \simeq g_a(x)$.

($\leftarrow$) If $f \notin$ UAP, then by Theorem 2.4 there are numbers $a \in {}^*\mathbf{R}$ and $\epsilon > 0$ in $\mathbf{R}$ such that for each $\tau \in \mathbf{M}_0 + a$ there exists $y \in {}^*\mathbf{R}$ such that $|f(y + \tau) - f(y)| \geq \epsilon$. On the other hand, for each $\tau \in \mathbf{M}_0 + a$ there is by hypothesis a standard function g_τ such that for all $x \in {}^*\mathbf{R}$, $g_\tau(x) \simeq f(x + \tau)$. These two statements imply that for each $\tau \in \mathbf{M}_0 + a$ there exists $y \in {}^*\mathbf{R}$ such that $|g_\tau(y) - f(y)| \geq \epsilon/2$.

The set of functions $\{g_\tau(x) \colon \tau \in \mathbf{M}_0 + a\}$ is closed under translation by any $\tau' \in \mathbf{R}$, since for all y, $g_\tau(y - \tau') \simeq f(y + \tau - \tau') \simeq g_{\tau-\tau'}(y)$, and the fact that g_τ and $g_{\tau-\tau'}$ are standard functions implies that equality must hold. Also, for each $\tau \in \mathbf{M}_0 + a$ and $\tau' \in \mathbf{R}$, $\tau - \tau' \in \mathbf{M}_0 + a$. It follows that there exists $y \in {}^*\mathbf{R}$ such that $|g_\tau(y - \tau') - f(y)| = |g_{\tau-\tau'}(y) - f(y)| \geq \epsilon/2$. Hence by setting $x = y - \tau'$, we find that for each $\tau \in \mathbf{M}_0 + a$ and $\tau' \in \mathbf{R}$, the sentence $(\exists x)[|g_\tau(x) - f(x + \tau')| > \epsilon/2]$ is true in ${}^*\mathbf{R}$. Since each g_τ and τ' is standard, each of these sentences is defined and true in $\mathbf{R}$. So for each $\tau \in \mathbf{M}_0 + a$, the sentence $(\forall \tau')(\exists x)[|g_\tau(x) - f(x + \tau')| \geq \epsilon/2]$ is true in $\mathbf{R}$ and therefore in ${}^*\mathbf{R}$. Now choose any $\tau \in \mathbf{M}_0 + a$ and set $\tau' = \tau$. Then $(\exists x)[|g_\tau(x) - f(x + \tau)| \geq \epsilon/2]$ is true in ${}^*\mathbf{R}$, contradicting the hypothesis.

In the sequel, the various characterizations of *UAP* will be referred to simply by I, II, or III.

We now wish to consider the characterization of *UAP* due to Bochner.

Let $C(\mathbf{R})$ denote the Banach space of continuous complex-valued functions on $\mathbf{R}$ under the supnorm. The monad of $f \in C(\mathbf{R})$ consists of the functions $g(x) \in {}^*C(\mathbf{R})$ such that $g(x) \simeq f(x)$ for all $x \in {}^*\mathbf{R}$. The following lemma is a nonstandard characterization of the closure $\bar{F}$ of a set $F \subset C(\mathbf{R})$, the proof of which is left to the reader.

Lemma 2.11. *If $F \subset C(\mathbf{R})$, then $g \in \bar{F}$ iff there is a function $f \in {}^*F$ such that f is in the monad of g.*

We shall now show how Bochner's characterization of *UAP* can be deduced from III.

Theorem 2.12 (**Bochner**). *$f \in UAP$ iff the closure of the set F of translates of f is compact in $C(\mathbf{R})$.*

Proof. ($\rightarrow$) The set $G = \{g_a: a \in {}^*\mathbf{R}\}$ is the closure of the set F. To see this, choose any $a \in {}^*\mathbf{R}$, and let $h(x) = f(x + a)$ on ${}^*\mathbf{R}$. By III, $h(x) \simeq g_a(x)$ for all $x \in {}^*\mathbf{R}$. Hence, by Lemma 2.11, $G = \bar{F}$. Now let $g \in {}^*G$. By transfer from $C(\mathbf{R})$ of the definition of closure, we see that given an infinitesimal $\epsilon > 0$, there is a number $a \in {}^*\mathbf{R}$ such that $\sup_{x \in {}^*\mathbf{R}} |f(x + a) - g(x)| < \epsilon$ and *a fortiori* $f(x + a) \simeq g(x)$ for all $x \in {}^*\mathbf{R}$. Since $g_a(x) \simeq f(x + a)$ for all $x \in {}^*\mathbf{R}$, $g(x)$ is in the monad of $g_a(x)$. Hence by Theorem 1.2, $G = \bar{F}$ is compact.

($\leftarrow$) Let $h \in {}^*F \subset {}^*(\bar{F})$. Then by Theorem 1.2, there is a function $g \in \bar{F}$ such that h is in the monad of g. By III, $f \in UAP$, since $h(x) \equiv f(x + a)$ for some $a \in {}^*\mathbf{R}$.

We now use III to give a simple proof that UAP is an algebra.

Theorem 2.13. *If f_1 and $f_2 \in UAP$, then $f_1 + f_2$ and $f_1 \cdot f_2 \in UAP$.*

Proof. For a, $x \in {}^*\mathbf{R}$, let $g_{1,a}(x) = f_1(x + a)$, $g_{2,a}(x) = f_2(x + a)$. Then $(f_1 + f_2)(x + a) = f_1(x + a) + f_2(x + a) \simeq g_{1,a}(x) + g_{2,a}(x)$, which is standard. By a similar argument, using the boundedness of f_1 and f_2, $f_1 \cdot f_2(x + a) \simeq g_{1,a}(x) \cdot g_{2,a}(x)$. Thus $f_1 + f_2$ and $f_1 \cdot f_2 \in UAP$, by III.

The next theorem is easy to prove by either standard or nonstandard methods.

Theorem 2.14. *If a sequence $\{f_n\}$ of functions in UAP converges uniformly to f on $\mathbf{R}$, then $f \in UAP$.*

Corollary 2.15. *A uniformly convergent series $\Sigma_{n=1}^{\infty} a_n e^{i\lambda_n x}$, $\lambda_1, \lambda_2, \cdots$ in $\mathbf{R}$, is an almost-periodic function.*

3. Mean Values and Fourier Series of Almost-Periodic Functions

In this section we show how mean values and Fourier series for almost-periodic functions may be obtained, using integrals in ${}^*\mathbf{R}$ over intervals of infinite length.

By transfer from $\mathbf{R}$, the formal properties of integrals in ${}^*\mathbf{R}$ and in $\mathbf{R}$ are the same, and this fact will be used from now on without further comment.

Before proceeding to the proof of existence of mean values, we state a lemma concerning integrals in ${}^*\mathbf{R}$.

Lemma 3.1. *If f is bounded and integrable on $\mathbf{R}$, and $X, X' \in {}^*\mathbf{R}$ with $(X - X')/X' \simeq 0$, then $(1/X) \int_0^X f(x)\, dx \simeq (1/X') \int_0^{X'} f(x)\, dx$.*

The proof is straightforward.

Theorem 3.2. *The mean value* $M(f) = \lim_{x\to\infty} (1/X) \int_0^X f(x)\,dx$ *of any function* $f \in UAP$ *exists.*

Proof. By Theorem 1.5, it suffices to show that for any infinite $T_1, T_2 > 0$ in $^*\mathbf{R}$, $(1/T_1) \int_0^{T_1} f(x)\,dx \simeq (1/T_2) \int_0^{T_2} f(x)\,dx$. These integrals are finite since f is bounded. By II, an infinite $T \in E(f)$ may be chosen so that $0 < T < \min(\sqrt{T_1}, \sqrt{T_2})$, and hence $(T/T_1) \simeq (T/T_2) \simeq 0$. Define integers n_1, n_2 by $n_1 T < T_1 \leq (n_1 + 1)T$ and $n_2 T < T_2 \leq (n_2 + 1)T$, and for each $k = 1, 2, \cdots, n_1$, choose $\tau_k \in E(f) \cap ((k-1)T, kT)$.

Then $$\frac{1}{T}\int_{(k-1)T}^{kT} f(x)\,dx \simeq \frac{1}{T}\int_{\tau_k}^{T+\tau_k} f(x)\,dx \simeq \frac{1}{T}\int_0^T f(x)\,dx.$$

So $$\frac{1}{n_1 T}\int_0^{n_1 T} f(x)\,dx = \frac{1}{n_1}\sum_{k=1}^{n_1} \frac{1}{T}\int_{(k-1)T}^{kT} f(x)\,dx \simeq \frac{1}{T}\int_0^T f(x)\,dx.$$

Similarly, $(1/n_2 T) \int_0^{n_2 T} f(x)\,dx \simeq (1/T) \int_0^T f(x)\,dx$. Now, by Lemma 3.1,

$$\frac{1}{T_i}\int_0^{T_i} f(x)\,dx \simeq \frac{1}{n_i T}\int_0^{n_i T} f(x)\,dx \simeq \frac{1}{T}\int_0^T f(x)\,dx,\ i = 1, 2,$$

and the proof is complete. We have shown, incidentally, that for every infinite $T > 0$ and $f \in UAP$, $M\{f\} = {}^0\!\left((1/T) \int_0^T f(x)\,dx\right)$.

Corollary 3.3. *For all* $a \in {}^*\mathbf{R}$, $f \in UAP$, *and infinite* $T > 0$ *in* $^*\mathbf{R}$.

$$\frac{1}{T}\int_0^T f(x)\,dx \simeq \frac{1}{T}\int_a^{a+T} f(x)\,dx.$$

Proof. The sentence $(\forall a)[M\{f(x+a)\} = M\{f(x)\}]$ can easily be shown to hold in $\mathbf{R}$ and thus it also holds in $^*\mathbf{R}$. Define $g_a(x)$ as in III. Then $M\{g_a(x)\} = M\{f(x)\}$, since $g_a(x) \simeq f(x+a)$ and both f and g_a are standard. Hence

$$\frac{1}{T}\int_a^{a+T} f(x)\,dx \simeq \frac{1}{T}\int_0^T g_a(x)\,dx \simeq M\{g_a(x)\}$$
$$= M\{f(x)\} \simeq \frac{1}{T}\int_0^T f(x)\,dx.$$

Theorem 3.4. *For* $f \in UAP$, *let* $a(\lambda) = M\{f(x)e^{-i\lambda x}\}$ *for each* $\lambda \in \mathbf{R}$. *Then* $a(\lambda) = 0$ *for all but countably many* λ, *and for all* λ_n *such that* $a(\lambda_n) = A_n \neq 0$, *the inequality* $\Sigma_{n=1}^{\infty} |A_n|^2 \leq M\{|f(x)|^2\}$ *holds.*

These results are obtained by standard arguments in a straightforward way. $M\{f(x)e^{-i\lambda x}\}$ exists by Theorems 3.2 and 2.13.

Because of Theorem 3.4, each $f \in UAP$ has a *Fourier series:* $f(x) \sim \Sigma_{n=1}^{\infty} A_n e^{i\lambda_n x}$.

The set $S(f) = \{\lambda_n \colon a(\lambda_n) = A_n \neq 0\}$ of Fourier exponents is called the *spectrum* of f.

Lemma 3.5. *If $f \in UAP$ is real, nonnegative, and $M\{f(x)\} = 0$, then $f(x) = 0$ for all x in* $\mathbf{R}$.

Proof. By hypothesis, given any infinite $T > 0$ in $^*\mathbf{R}$,

$$\left(\frac{1}{T}\right) \int_0^T f(x)\, dx \simeq 0.$$

If f is not identically zero, there is a number $x_0 > 0$ in R such that $f(x_0) = a_0 > 0$. Given $\delta = \epsilon^2 \simeq 0$, let N be the least positive integer such that $N > \epsilon T/a_0$. It is not hard to see that T/N is infinite, so for each $k = 1, 2, \cdots, N$, τ_k may be chosen so that $(\tau_k - \epsilon, \tau_k + \epsilon) \subset ((k-1)T/N, kT/N)$ and $\tau_k \in E(f)$, and therefore $f(x_0 + \tau_k) > 2a_0/3$. Now for every $\tau \in (\tau_k - \epsilon, \tau_k + \epsilon)$, $f(x_0 + \tau) \geq a_0/2$ by uniform continuity, and the intervals $(\tau_k - \epsilon, \tau_k + \epsilon)$ are disjoint. Hence

$$\frac{1}{T} \int_0^T f(x)\, dx \geq \frac{1}{T} \sum_{k=1}^{N} \int_{\tau_k - \epsilon}^{\tau_k + \epsilon} f(x)\, dx \geq \frac{N 2\epsilon (a_0/2)}{T} > \epsilon^2 = \delta.$$

Thus $(1/T) \int_0^T f(x)\, dx$ is larger than every infinitesimal, contradicting the hypothesis.

We now give proofs of the uniqueness theorem and the Parseval equation for $f \in UAP$. The first step is the following lemma.

Lemma 3.6. *If $f \in UAP$ and $M\{f(x)e^{-i\lambda x}\} = 0$ for every $\lambda \in \mathbf{R}$, then for every $\lambda \in {}^*\mathbf{R}$ and infinite $T > 0$, $(1/T) \int_0^T f(x)e^{-i\lambda x}\, dx \simeq 0$.*

Proof. The hypothesis is equivalent to the statement that

$$\left(\frac{1}{T}\right) \int_0^T f(x)e^{-i\lambda x}\, dx \simeq 0$$

for every infinite $T > 0$ and $\lambda \in \mathbf{R}$.

Suppose first that λ is finite. Then $\lambda = \lambda_0 + \epsilon$, where $\lambda_0 \in \mathbf{R}$ and $\epsilon \simeq 0$. Given an infinite $T > 0$, choose an infinite T' and an integer $N > 0$ so that $T' \in E(f)$, $T'\epsilon \simeq 0$, and $T'N < T \leq T'(N + 1)$. Then

$$\frac{1}{NT'}\int_0^{NT'} f(x)e^{-i\lambda x}\,dx \simeq \frac{1}{NT'}\sum_{k=1}^{N} e^{-i\epsilon(k-1)T'}\int_{(k-1)T'}^{KT'} f(x)e^{-i\lambda_0 x}\,dx.$$

But by Corollary 3.3, $(1/T')\int_{(k-1)T'}^{kT'} f(x)e^{-i\lambda_0 x}\,dx \simeq 0$, so, by Lemma 3.1,

$$\frac{1}{T}\int_0^{T} f(x)e^{-i\lambda x}\,dx \simeq \frac{1}{NT'}\int_0^{NT'} f(x)e^{-i\lambda x}\,dx \simeq 0.$$

Suppose now that λ is infinite. Given an infinite $T > 0$, define $\eta \simeq 0$ and an infinite positive integer N by $\lambda\eta = 2\pi$ and $N|\eta| < T \leq (N+1)|\eta|$. For each $k = 1, 2, \cdots, N$, define $M_k = f((k-1)|\eta|)$. Then $f(x) \simeq M_k$ for $x \in ((k-1)|\eta|, k|\eta|)$, and we have

$$\frac{1}{N|\eta|}\int_0^{N|\eta|} f(x)e^{-i\lambda x}\,dx \simeq \frac{1}{N|\eta|}\sum_{k=1}^{N} M_k\int_{(k-1)|\eta|}^{k|\eta|} e^{-i\lambda x}\,dx.$$

Since
$$\int_{(k-1)|\eta|}^{k|\eta|} e^{-i\lambda x}\,dx = 0,$$

it follows from Lemma 3.1 that

$$\frac{1}{T}\int_0^{T} f(x)e^{-i\lambda x}\,dx \simeq \frac{1}{N|\eta|}\int_0^{N|\eta|} f(x)e^{-i\lambda x}\,dx \simeq 0,$$

and the lemma is proved.

***Lemma* 3.7.** *Let $f \in UAP$ and $T \in {}^*\mathbf{R}$. Define functions $g(x)$ and $G(T; x)$ on ${}^*\mathbf{R}$ by*

$$g(x) = \lim_{X\to\infty}\frac{1}{X}\int_0^{X} f(x+t)\bar{f}(t)\,dt \text{ and } G(T; x) = \frac{1}{T}\int_0^{T} f(x+t)\bar{f}(t)\,dt.$$

Then for all $x \in {}^*\mathbf{R}$ and infinite $T > 0$, $g(x) \simeq G(T; x)$, and $g \in UAP$.

Proof. We note first that by Theorems 2.13 and 3.2, $g(x)$ is well defined. If $T \in \mathbf{R}$, then $G(T; x) \in UAP$, for if $\tau \in E(f)$, then

$$G(T; x+\tau) - G(T; x) = \frac{1}{T}\int_0^{T} (f(x+t+\tau) - f(x+t))\bar{f}(t)\,dt \simeq 0.$$

By III, if $x \in {}^*\mathbf{R}$, there is a standard almost-periodic function $h_x(t)$ such that $h_x(t) \simeq f(x+t)$ for all $t \in {}^*\mathbf{R}$. Then, for infinite $T > 0$,

$$g(x) \simeq \frac{1}{T}\int_0^{T} h_x(t)\bar{f}(t)\,dt \simeq G(T; x),$$

which also shows that $g(x) = \lim_{T\to\infty} G(T; x)$ uniformly on $\mathbf{R}$, so $g(x) \in UAP$, by Theorem 2.14.

Theorem 3.8. *If $f \in UAP$ and $a(\lambda) = 0$ for all $\lambda \in \mathbf{R}$, then $f(x) = 0$ for all $x \in \mathbf{R}$.*

Proof. Let $F(T; x)$ be the periodic function with infinite positive period $T \in E(f)$ defined by $F(T; x) = f(x)$ for $x \in [0, T)$, and for each integer k let $A_k(T) = 1/T \int_0^T F(T; x) \exp(-2\pi ikx/T)\, dx$ be its ordinary kth Fourier coefficient. Now define a periodic function $G_1(T; x)$ by

$$G_1(T; x) = \frac{1}{T} \int_0^T F(T; x + t)\bar{F}(T; t)\, dt$$

and define $G(T; x)$ as in Lemma 3.7. Since $T \in E(f)$, $G_1(T; x) - G(T; x) \simeq 0$ if $x \in [0, T)$. A simple computation using the periodicity of F shows that the Fourier coefficients of G_1 are $|A_k(T)|^2$, $k = 0, \pm 1, \pm 2, \cdots$. Now $\sup_k |A_k(T)| \simeq \sup_k |a(2\pi k/T)| \simeq 0$ by Lemma 3.6, so that

$$\sum_{-\infty}^{\infty} |A_k(T)|^4 \leq \sup_k |A_k(T)|^2 \sum_{-\infty}^{\infty} |A_k(T)|^2 \simeq 0.$$

But the Parseval relation holds for G_1, so

$$\frac{1}{T} \int_0^T |G_1(T; x)|^2\, dx = \sum_{-\infty}^{\infty} |A_k(T)|^4 \simeq 0.$$

Since $G_1(T; x) \simeq G(T; x) \simeq g(x)$ for $x \in [0, T)$ by Lemma 3.7, it follows that $(1/T) \int_0^T |g(x)|^2\, dx \simeq 0$ for each infinite $T \in E(f)$. If, now, $T' > 0$ is infinite but is not in $E(f)$, choose an infinite $T \in E(f)$ so that $(T - T')/T$. Then, by Lemma 3.1,

$$\frac{1}{T'} \int_0^{T'} |g(x)|^2\, dx \simeq \frac{1}{T} \int_0^T |g(x)|^2\, dx \simeq 0.$$

By Lemma 3.5, $g(x) = 0$ for all $x \in \mathbf{R}$, so that $g(0) = M\{|f(x)|^2\} = 0$. By Lemma 3.5 again, $f(x) = 0$ for all $x \in \mathbf{R}$.

Corollary 3.9. *If $f,g \in UAP$ have the same Fourier series, then $f(x) = g(x)$ for all $x \in R$.*

Theorem 3.10 (***Parseval Equation***). *If $f \in UAP$ and $f(x) \sim \Sigma_{n=1}^{\infty} A_n e^{i\lambda_n x}$, then $M\{|f(x)|^2\} = \Sigma_{n=1}^{\infty} |A_n|^2$.*

Proof. Define $g(x)$ as in Lemma 3.7. A straightforward computation shows that $M\{g(x)e^{-i\lambda_n x}\} \simeq |A_n|^2$, and, since g is standard, equality holds. Thus $g(x) \sim \Sigma_{n=1}^{\infty} |A_n|^2 e^{i\lambda_n x}$, which is uniformly convergent since $\Sigma_{n=1}^{\infty} |A_n|^2 < \infty$. Hence

$$g(x) = \sum_{n=1}^{\infty} |A_n|^2 e^{i\lambda_n x} \qquad \text{and} \qquad g(0) = \sum_{n=1}^{\infty} |A_n|^2 = M\{|f(x)|^2\}.$$

4. Properties of Near-Periods of Almost-Periodic Functions

We now give an arithmetical characterization of the group $E(f)$, where $f \in UAP$.

***Theorem* 4.1.** *If $f \in UAP$ and $f \sim \Sigma_{n=1}^{\infty} A_n e^{i\lambda_n x}$, then $\tau \in E(f)$ iff $\tau\lambda_n \cong 0 (\mathrm{mod}\ 2\pi)$ for each (standard) n.*

Proof. ($\rightarrow$) Choose $\tau \in E(f)$ and an infinite $T > 0$. Then, by Corollary 3.3,

$$A_n \simeq \frac{1}{T}\int_0^T f(x)e^{-i\lambda_n x}\,dx \simeq \frac{1}{T}\int_\tau^{T+\tau} f(x)e^{-i\lambda_n x}\,dx.$$

Therefore, $$A_n \simeq e^{i\lambda_n \tau}\cdot \frac{1}{T}\int_0^T f(x)e^{-i\lambda_n x}\,dx \simeq e^{i\lambda_n\tau}\cdot A_n.$$

Since $A_n \not\simeq 0$, division by A_n yields $1 \simeq e^{i\lambda_n\tau}$, which implies $\lambda_n\tau \cong 0 (\mathrm{mod}\ 2\pi)$.

($\leftarrow$) Suppose $\tau\lambda_n \cong 0 (\mathrm{mod}\ 2\pi)$ for each standard n, and define $g_\tau(x)$ as in III. Then if $T > 0$ is infinite and $\lambda \in \mathbf{R}$,

$$M\{g_\tau(x)e^{-i\lambda x}\} \simeq \frac{1}{T}\int_0^T f(x+\tau)e^{-i\lambda x}\,dx \simeq e^{i\lambda\tau}M\{f(x)e^{-i\lambda x}\}.$$

If $\lambda = \lambda_n$ for some n, then $e^{i\lambda_n\tau} \simeq 1$, so that $M\{g_\tau(x)e^{-i\lambda_n x}\} \simeq A_n$. If $\lambda \neq \lambda_n$, $M\{g_\tau(x)e^{-i\lambda x}\} \simeq e^{i\lambda\tau}a(\lambda) = 0$. In either case, equality holds since g_τ is standard, so the Fourier coefficients of f and g_τ are the same. By Corollary 3.9, $f(x) = g_\tau(x) \simeq f(x+\tau)$ for all $x \in {}^*\mathbf{R}$, so $\tau \in E(f)$.

5. Limit Periodic Functions

We now give an application of the arithmetic characterization of $E(f)$ by investigating a class of functions called limit periodic functions.

***Definition* 5.1.** A function $f(x)$ is *limit periodic*, $f \in LMP$, if it is the uniform limit of a sequence $\{f_k(x)\}$ of continuous purely periodic functions.

Theorem 5.2. *$f \in LMP$ iff there is a continuous periodic function $f_\omega(x)\colon {}^*\mathbf{R} \to {}^*\mathbf{C}$ such that for all $x \in {}^*\mathbf{R}$, $f(x) \simeq f_\omega(x)$.*

Proof. ($\to$) Extend the sequence $\{f_k(x)\}$ to ${}^*\{f_k(x)\}$ and choose an infinite positive integer ω. Then $f_\omega(x) \simeq f(x)$ for all $x \in {}^*\mathbf{R}$ by uniform convergence, and $f_\omega(x)$ is continuous and periodic, since this is true for all $f_k(x)$.

($\leftarrow$) For each positive standard integer n, the sentence $(\exists\omega)(\forall x)[\omega$ is a positive integer, f_ω is continuous and periodic, and $|f_\omega(x) - f(x)| < 1/n]$ holds in ${}^*\mathbf{R}$ and hence in $\mathbf{R}$, so Definition 5.1 is satisfied.

Theorem 5.3. *$f \in LMP$ iff $f \in UAP$ and all its Fourier exponents λ_n are rational multiples of the same real number.*

Proof. ($\to$) Choose $f_\omega(x)$ as in Theorem 5.2, and let $T > 0$ be an infinite period of $f_\omega(x)$. The Fourier exponents of $f_\omega(x)$ are among the numbers $2\pi k/T$, where k runs through the integers of ${}^*\mathbf{R}$. Since $(1/T)\int_0^T (f(x) - f_\omega(x))e^{-i\lambda x}\,dx \simeq 0$ for all $\lambda \in {}^*\mathbf{R}$, all the standard Fourier exponents λ of f occur among the standard numbers $2\pi k/T$, $k = 0, \pm 1, \pm 2, \cdots$. The ratio of any two such λ is clearly standard and rational.

($\leftarrow$) Let $(p_n/q_n)\cdot r = \lambda_n$ be the Fourier exponents of f, let N be an infinite positive integer, and let $\tau = (2\pi/r)\,\Pi_{n=1}^N q_n$. Then $\tau\lambda_n \equiv 0 (\mathrm{mod}\ 2\pi)$ for every finite positive integer n, so that, by Theorem 4.1, $\tau \in E(f)$. Note also that $k\tau \in E(f)$ for every integer $k \in {}^*\mathbf{R}$.

Now for $0 \le x < \tau$, let $f_\omega(x) = f(x) - (x/\tau)(f(\tau) - f(0))$. If we extend the domain of $f_\omega(x)$ to ${}^*\mathbf{R}$ periodically, it is clear that $f_\omega(x)$ is continuous in ${}^*\mathbf{R}$. For any $x \in {}^*\mathbf{R}$, define an integer k by $k\tau \le x < (k+1)\tau$. Then

$$f_\omega(x) = f_\omega(x - k\tau) = f(x - k\tau) - \frac{x - k\tau}{\tau}(f(\tau) - f(0)) \simeq f(x).$$

Thus, by Theorem 5.2, $f \in LMP$.

6. Bohr Compactifications and the Approximation Theorem

To prove the trigonometric polynomial approximation theorem for almost-periodic functions, it is convenient to use the language of the theory of topological groups. We begin with some general definitions.

Definition 6.1. If G is an Abelian topological group (written additively), then a function $\chi\colon G \to \mathbf{C}$ satisfying

(a) $\chi(x + y) = \chi(x)\cdot\chi(y)$
(b) $|\chi(x)| = 1$

for all x, y in G is called a *character* of G. The *continuous* characters of G form a (multiplicative) group $\hat{G}$, called the *character group* of G. $\hat{G}$ is a topological group with a basis of open sets at the identity given by $N'(\epsilon, F) = \{\chi: |\chi(x) - 1| < \epsilon, \text{ all } x \in F\}$, where $\epsilon > 0$ and F is compact in G.

If $S \subset \mathbf{R}$, denote by S_d the additive subgroup of $\mathbf{R}$ generated by S, with the discrete topology. The topological group $\hat{S}_d$ will be denoted by $b_s\mathbf{R}$.

Theorem 6.2. *The group $b_s\mathbf{R}$ is compact and Hausdorff.*

Proof. By Theorems 1.1 and 1.2, it suffices to show that the monads in $^*b_S\mathbf{R}$ of points of $b_S\mathbf{R}$ are disjoint and that every point of $^*b_S\mathbf{R}$ is in such a monad. For any $\chi_0 \in b_S\mathbf{R}$, the monad of χ_0 is given by $\{\chi \in {}^*b_S\mathbf{R}: \chi(x) \simeq \chi_0(x) \text{ for all } x \in S_d\}$, by the definition of a monad in a topological space. Suppose $\chi_0 \neq \chi_1$ in $b_S\mathbf{R}$, so that there is a point $x_0 \in S_d$ such that $\chi_0(x_0) \neq \chi_1(x_0)$, and suppose $\chi \in {}^*b_S\mathbf{R}$ is in the monad of χ_0; that is, $\chi(x) \simeq \chi_0(x)$ for all $x \in S_d$. Then, since χ_1 is standard, $\chi(x_0) \not\simeq \chi_1(x_0)$, which implies that χ is not in the monad of χ_1. Thus the monads of χ_0 and χ_1 are disjoint and $b_S\mathbf{R}$ is Hausdorff.

If now $\chi \in {}^*b_S\mathbf{R}$, the function ${}^0(\chi(x))$ defined for all $x \in S_d$ is easily seen to be a character of S_d, that is an element of $b_S\mathbf{R}$. (Note that because of the discrete topology on S_d, every character of S_d is continuous.) By the definition of monads, χ is in the monad of the standard character ${}^0(\chi(x))$, and thus $b_S\mathbf{R}$ is compact.

The Diophantine approximation theorem which we now state will be needed for what follows. For $x \in \mathbf{R}$, denote by $||x||$ the (nonnegative) distance from x to the integer nearest x.

Theorem 6.3 (***Kronecker***). *Given any real numbers θ_i, α_i, $1 \leq i \leq n$, the following are equivalent:*

(a) *For each $\epsilon > 0$, there is an integer q such that simultaneously $||q\theta_i - \alpha_i|| < \epsilon$, $1 \leq i \leq n$.*
(b) *If $u_1, u_2, \cdots, u_n$ are integers such that $||\Sigma_{i=1}^n u_i\theta_i|| = 0$, then $||\Sigma_{i=1}^n u_i\alpha_i|| = 0$.*

Theorem 6.4. *If $S \subset \mathbf{R}$, then the characters χ in $b_S\mathbf{R} = \hat{S}_d$ are just the functions $\chi: S_d \to \mathbf{C}$ defined by $\chi(x) = {}^0(e^{i\tau x})$, $\tau \in {}^*\mathbf{R}$.*

Proof. A simple computation shows that every function ${}^0(e^{i\tau x})$, $\tau \in {}^*\mathbf{R}$, is in $\hat{S}_d$. Now let $\chi \in S_d$ and set $\chi(x) = e^{2\pi i f(x)}$, where $f: S_d \to \mathbf{R}$ and $f(x) + f(y) \equiv f(x + y) (\text{mod } 1)$. By Theorem 6.3 and the fact that $f(nx) \equiv nf(x) (\text{mod } 1)$ for each $x \in S_d$ and integer n, it is easy to show that given $\delta > 0$ in R and $x_1, \cdots, x_n \in S_d$, there is an integer q such that

$$\|qx_j - (f(1)x_j - f(x_j))\| < \delta,\ 1 \leq j \leq n.$$

Hence, given $\epsilon > 0$ in $\mathbf{R}$ and $x_1, \cdots, x_n \in S_d$, there is a real number $\tau = 2\pi(f(1) - q)$ such that

$$|e^{i\tau x_j} - \chi(x_j)| < \epsilon,\ 1 \leq j \leq n.$$

Therefore, the relation $R(x, \epsilon, \tau)$ defined by the formula $[\epsilon > 0 \wedge x \in S_d \wedge |e^{i\tau x} - \chi(x)| < \epsilon]$ is concurrent on $\mathbf{R}$, so there exists $\tau \in {}^*\mathbf{R}$ such that $e^{i\tau x} \simeq \chi(x)$ for all $x \in S_d$. Hence, for all $x \in S_d$, $\chi(x) = {}^0(e^{i\tau x})$.

Theorem 6.5. *For $S \subset \mathbf{R}$, let $E_S = \{\tau \in {}^*\mathbf{R}\colon \lambda\tau \cong 0 (\mathrm{mod}\ 2\pi)$ for all $\lambda \in S_d\}$. Then E_S is an additive subgroup of ${}^*\mathbf{R}$ and $b_S\mathbf{R}$ is isomorphic to ${}^*\mathbf{R}/E_S$.*

Proof. It is obvious that E_S is a subgroup of ${}^*\mathbf{R}$. Now let $\chi_1, \chi_2 \in b_S\mathbf{R}$. By Theorem 6.4, there exist $\tau_1, \tau_2 \in {}^*\mathbf{R}$ such that $\chi_1(x) = {}^0(e^{i\tau_1 x})$ and $\chi_2(x) = {}^0(e^{i\tau_2 x})$ for all $x \in S_d$. Clearly then, $\chi_1 = \chi_2$ if and only if $\tau_1\lambda \cong \tau_2\lambda\ (\mathrm{mod}\ 2\pi)$ for all $\lambda \in S_d$, that is, if and only if $\tau_1 - \tau_2 \in E_S$. The mapping $G\colon {}^*\mathbf{R}/E_S \to b_S\mathbf{R}$ defined by $G(\bar{\tau}) = {}^0(e^{i\tau x})$, $\bar{\tau} \in {}^*\mathbf{R}/E_S$ is the required isomorphism between ${}^*\mathbf{R}/E_S$ and $b_S\mathbf{R}$.

For each $\epsilon > 0$ in $\mathbf{R}$ and finite $F \subset S$, let

$$N(\epsilon, F) = \{\bar{\tau} \in {}^*\mathbf{R}/E_S\colon |\tau\lambda| < \epsilon\ (\mathrm{mod}\ 2\pi) \text{ for all } \tau \in \bar{\tau} \text{ and all } \lambda \in F\}.$$

The sets $N(\epsilon, F)$ form an open basis at the indentity for a topology on ${}^*\mathbf{R}/E_S$. Using Theorem 6.4 we can see that the isomorphism G between ${}^*\mathbf{R}/E_S$ and $b_S\mathbf{R}$ is also a homeomorphism. Since $\mathbf{M}_1 \subset E_S$, we can identify each $\tau \in \mathbf{R}$ with its coset $\bar{\tau} \in {}^*\mathbf{R}/E_S$ and with $G(\bar{\tau}) \in b_S\mathbf{R}$, so that $b_S\mathbf{R}$ may be regarded as an extension of $\mathbf{R}$, called the *Bohr compactification* of $\mathbf{R}$ with respect to S. The proof of Theorem 6.4 shows that under this identification, $\mathbf{R}$ is dense in $b_S\mathbf{R}$.

Theorem 6.6. *Let S be a countable subgroup of $\mathbf{R}$. Then the class $\{f \in UAP\colon S(f) \subset S\} = UAP(S)$ of almost-periodic functions with spectrum contained in S is isometrically isomorphic, in the sense of the supnorm, to the space $C(b_S\mathbf{R})$ of all complex-valued continuous functions on $b_S\mathbf{R}$.*

Proof. If $f \in UAP(S)$, then, by Theorem 4.1, $E(f) \supset E_S$. By Theorem 6.4, a function $\hat{f}$ with values in $\mathbf{C}$ may be defined on $b_S\mathbf{R} = G({}^*\mathbf{R}/E_S)$ by $\hat{f}(G(\bar{\tau})) = {}^0(f(\tau))$. By Theorem 6.5, $\hat{f}$ is well defined, for if $\tau_1, \tau_2 \in \bar{\tau} \in {}^*\mathbf{R}/E_S$, then $\tau_1 - \tau_2 \in E_S \subset E(f)$, so that ${}^0(f(\tau_1)) = {}^0(f(\tau_2))$. If the topology on ${}^*\mathbf{R}/E_S$ is restricted to $\mathbf{R}$, so that the basic open sets at the origin are

$$N(\epsilon, F) = \{\tau \in \mathbf{R}\colon |\tau\lambda| < \epsilon (\mathrm{mod}\ 2\pi) \text{ for all } \lambda \in F\},$$

where $\epsilon > 0$ in **R** and $F \subset S$ is finite, then the resulting monad of zero is

$$\mu(0) = \{\tau \in {}^*\mathbf{R}: \tau\lambda \cong 0 \pmod{2\pi} \text{ for all } \lambda \in S\} = E_S.$$

Since $\tau_1 - \tau_2 \in E_S$ implies $f(\tau_1) \simeq f(\tau_2)$, f is uniformly continuous on **R** with respect to this topology. It follows that if $\eta > 0$ in **R**, a basic open set $N(\epsilon, F)$ can be chosen at the origin of **R** such that $\tau_1 - \tau_2 \in N(\epsilon, F)$ implies $|f(\tau_1) - (\tau_2)| < \eta/2$. Now since F is finite, we have $F = {}^*F$, and so by transfer from **R**,

$${}^*N(\epsilon, F) = \{\tau \in {}^*\mathbf{R}: |\tau\lambda| < \epsilon \pmod{2\pi} \text{ for all } \lambda \in F\}$$

and $\tau_1 - \tau_2 \in {}^*N(\epsilon, F) \subset {}^*\mathbf{R}$ implies $|f(\tau_1) - f(\tau_2)| < \eta/2$. Using the fact that G is a homeomorphism, we may choose $\delta > 0$ in **R** so that for all $\bar{\tau} \in {}^*\mathbf{R}/E_S$, if $G(\bar{\tau})$ is in the neighborhood $N'(\delta, F)$ of the identity in $b_S\mathbf{R}$, then $\bar{\tau} \in N(\epsilon, F)$ in ${}^*\mathbf{R}/E_S$. Hence if $G(\bar{\tau}_1)/G(\bar{\tau}_2) \in N'(\delta, F)$, we have $\tau_1 - \tau_2 \in {}^*N(\epsilon, F)$ for every $\tau_1 \in \bar{\tau}_1$ and $\tau_2 \in \bar{\tau}_2$, so that

$$|\hat{f}(G(\bar{\tau}_1)) - \hat{f}(G(\bar{\tau}_2))| = |{}^0f(\tau_1) - {}^0f(\tau_2)| < \eta,$$

which proves that $\hat{f}$ is continuous on $b_S\mathbf{R}$.

Suppose now that h is defined and continuous on $b_S\mathbf{R}$. Define a function f on **R** by $f(\tau) = h(e^{i\tau x})$. By transfer from **R**, this equation also holds for every $\tau \in {}^*\mathbf{R}$. Now if $\tau_1 - \tau_2 \in E_S$, then $\tau_1\lambda \cong \tau_2\lambda \pmod{2\pi}$ for all $\lambda \in S$, so that the functions $e^{i\tau_1 x}$ and $e^{i\tau_2 x}$ are in the same monad in ${}^*b_S\mathbf{R}$. By the compactness of $b_S\mathbf{R}$, h is uniformly continuous, so it follows that $f(\tau_1) = h(e^{i\tau_1 x}) \simeq h(e^{i\tau_2 x}) = f(\tau_2)$. This shows that the elements of E_S are near-periods for f. Now since S is countable, it is the spectrum of a suitably chosen function $g \in UAP$, and therefore $E_S = E(g)$ intersects every infinite interval in ${}^*\mathbf{R}$. Thus by II, $f \in UAP$ and it is clear that $S(f) \subset S$. Since for every $\tau \in {}^*\mathbf{R}$,

$$\hat{f}(G(\bar{\tau})) = {}^0(f(\tau)) = {}^0(h(e^{i\tau x})) = h(G(\bar{\tau})),$$

we see that the mapping $H\colon UAP(S) \to C(b_S\mathbf{R})$ defined by $H(f) = \hat{f}$ is onto.

If $f_1 \neq f_2$ in $UAP(S)$, then there exists $\tau_0 \in \mathbf{R}$ such that $f_1(\tau_0) \neq f_2(\tau_0)$, and since $f_1(\tau) = \hat{f}_1(e^{i\tau x})$ and $f_2(\tau) = \hat{f}_2(e^{i\tau x})$ for $\tau \in \mathbf{R}$, $\hat{f}_1(e^{i\tau_0 x}) \neq \hat{f}_2(e^{i\tau_0 x})$; that is, $\hat{f}_1 \neq \hat{f}_2$. The mapping H is therefore one-to-one, and a simple computation shows that H is an isomorphism. That H is an isometry is clear from the fact that

$$\sup_{\tau \in \mathbf{R}} |f(\tau)| = \sup_{\tau \in {}^*\mathbf{R}} |f(\tau)| = \sup_{\bar{\tau} \in {}^*\mathbf{R}/E_S} |{}^0(f(\tau))| = \sup_{\chi \in b_S\mathbf{R}} |\hat{f}(\chi)|.$$

Theorem 6.7 (***Approximation by Trigonometric Polynomials***). *Let $f \in UAP$ and let S be the subgroup of* **R** *generated by $S(f)$. Then, given $\epsilon > 0$, there is a polynomial $g(x) = \Sigma_{k=1}^{n} B_k e^{i\lambda_k x}$, $\lambda_k \in S$, such that $|f(x) - g(x)| < \epsilon$ for every $x \in$* **R**.

Proof. By Theorem 6.2, $b_S\mathbf{R}$ is a compact Hausdorff space. If $H: UAP(S) \to C(b_S\mathbf{R})$ is defined as in Theorem 6.6, then the functions $H(e^{i\lambda x})$, $\lambda \in S$, are in $C(b_S\mathbf{R})$. Since S is a group, these functions generate a subalgebra A of $C(b_S\mathbf{R})$ which contains the unit function identically equal to 1 and which is closed under complex conjugation. Now suppose $\bar{y}_1 \neq \bar{y}_2$ in $^*\mathbf{R}/E_S$. Then for some $\lambda_0 \in S$, $\lambda_0 y_1 \not\equiv \lambda_0 y_2 (\text{mod } 2\pi)$. Thus the function $H(e^{i\lambda_0 x}) \in A$ has the property that $H(e^{i\lambda_0 y_1}) \neq H(e^{i\lambda_0 y_2})$, so A separates points of $b_S\mathbf{R}$. Applying the Stone–Weierstrass theorem, A is dense in $C(b_S\mathbf{R})$. Hence, given $\epsilon > 0$, there is a polynomial $\hat{g} = \Sigma_{k=1}^{n} B_k H(e^{i\lambda_k x})$, $\lambda_k \in S$, in $C(b_S\mathbf{R})$ such that $|\hat{g}(\chi) - \hat{f}(\chi)| < \epsilon$ for every $\chi \in b_S\mathbf{R}$. Since H is an isometric isomorphism, $H^{-1}(\hat{g}) = g = \Sigma_{k=1}^{n} B_k e^{i\lambda_k x}$ and $|g(x) - f(x)| < \epsilon$ for every $x \in \mathbf{R}$.

References

1. A. S. BESICOVITCH, *Almost Periodic Functions*. New York: Dover, 1954.
2. H. BOHR, *Almost Periodic Functions*. New York: Chelsea, 1947.
3. N. DUNFORD AND J. T. SCHWARTZ, *Linear Operators*, Parts I and II. New York: Wiley-Interscience, 1958.
4. E. HEWITT, Linear Functionals on Almost Periodic Functions, *Trans. Am. Math. Soc. 74* (1953), 303–322.
5. L. D. KUGLER, *Nonstandard Analysis of Almost Periodic Functions*, Doctoral dissertation, Los Angeles: Univ. of Calif., 1966.
6. W. A. J. LUXEMBURG, *No-standard Analysis* (lectures on A. Robinson's theory of infinitesimals and infinitely large numbers). Pasadena: California Institute of Technology, 1964.
7. A. ROBINSON, *No-standard Analysis* (Studies in Logic and the Foundations of Mathematics). Amsterdam: North-Holland, 1966.

On Some Properties of Bounded Internal Functions

by R. F. TAYLOR

The following question seems to arise frequently in nonstandard analysis. If $\mathfrak{F}$ is some class of complex-valued functions on a space X, and if, for $f \in {}^*\mathfrak{F}$,

$$\text{st}[f](x) = \begin{cases} \text{st}[f(x)], & \text{if } f(x) \text{ is finite} \\ \infty, & \text{if } f(x) \text{ is infinite,} \end{cases}$$

where st denotes the standard part, for all $x \in X$, then under what conditions is $\text{st}[f] \in \mathfrak{F}$? For example, Robinson [1] has shown that if f is analytic in some S-open set of points $B \subset {}^*C$, and B contains only finite points, then if $f(z)$ is finite on B, $\text{st}[f]$ is analytic in $\text{st}[B]$.

In particular, we are interested in the question of measurability. Denote by $M = M[0, 1]$, the measurable functions on $[0, 1]$. Under what conditions does $f \in {}^*M$ have the property that $\text{st}[f]$ is measurable and what is the relationship between f and ${}^*[\text{st}[f]]$? Finiteness of f is not sufficient to ensure $\text{st}[f] \in M$, for Luxemburg [2] has demonstrated the existence of an infinitely large ω such that $\text{st}[\cos \omega x]$ is nonmeasurable. The following demonstrates a larger class of such ω, using more elementary methods; then we show existence of ω such that $\text{st}[\sin \omega x]$ is measurable.

Vietoris [3] has shown that the only measurable functions $C\colon R \to R$ satisfying

$$C(x + y) + C(x - y) = 2C(x)C(y) \tag{1}$$

are the continuous ones, of the form $C(x) = \cos ax$, $a \in R$. This result follows from the simpler functional equation result $f(x + y) = f(x) + f(y)$, and f measurable implies $f(x) = ax$.

Consider $\omega \in {}^*N \sim N$ with the following divisibility properties:

(a) $\exists$ an increasing sequence $n_1, n_2, \cdots, n_k, \cdots$ in N such that n_k divides ω, $k = 1, 2, \cdots$.

(b) $\exists$ an integer p such that p does not divide ω.

***Lemma* 1.** *For such ω, st[cos ωx] is not measurable.*

Proof. We consider, for simplicity, $\cos 2\pi\omega x$. Let $a_k = 1/pn_k$. Then $a_k \to 0$ as $k \to \infty$. But

$$\omega a_k = \frac{\omega}{n_k}\frac{1}{p} = \frac{M_k}{p} = N_k + \frac{r_k}{p}, \qquad 1 \leq r_k \leq p - 1.$$

Then $\cos 2\pi\omega a_k = \cos 2\pi[N_k + (r_k/p)] = \cos 2\pi(r_k/p)$. Then

$$\lim_{k\to\infty} \text{st}[\cos 2\pi\omega a_k] = \lim_{k\to\infty} \cos 2\pi(r_k/p) \neq 1,$$

even if lim exists. That is, st[$\cos 2\pi\omega x$] is not continuous at $x = 0$. But st[$\cos 2\pi\omega x$] satisfies (1), since $\cos 2\pi\omega x$ satisfies (1) and st is linear and multiplicative. Hence the Vietoris result assures us that st[$\cos 2\pi\omega x$] is not measurable.

Denote by $(\omega x) = \omega x \bmod 1$. We see immediately that the truly nonmeasurable part of st[$\cos 2\pi\omega x$] is (ωx). For

$$\text{st}[\cos 2\pi\omega x] = \text{st}[\cos 2\pi(\omega x)] = \cos 2\pi[\text{st}(\omega x)],$$

since $\cos 2\pi y$ is S-continuous in y.

Hence st(ωx) is nonmeasurable. It follows easily that, for any $a \in R$, and measurable $f\colon R \to R$ with period 1, st[$f(a\omega x)$] is not measurable.

It seems clear that the extreme non-S-continuity of (ωx) is the essential factor in ensuring the nonmeasurability of st(ωx). Indeed, the following is true.

***Lemma* 2.** *If f is bounded, $f \in M$, then $^*f$ is S-continuous in the following sense: For every standard $\epsilon > 0$, there exists an internal closed set $A \subset {}^*[0, 1]$ such that $\mu(A) > 1 - \epsilon$, and f is S-continuous on A.*

Conversely, if f satisfies the above S-continuity property, then st[f] *is measurable, and, in this case,*

$$^*\!\int f - {}^*[\text{st}\, f]\, d\mu =_1 0.$$

But this lemma is a trivial consequence of the standard theorem concerning almost-continuity of measurable functions, and as yet there has been no effective nonstandard approach to even this elementary fact of measure theory.

Difficulties also present themselves in nonstandard approaches to the usual convergence theorems. Namely, if $f_n(x) \to 0$ boundedly, then $\mathrm{st}[f_\omega(x)] \equiv 0$, but we cannot immediately conclude that $\int^*[\mathrm{st}\, f_\omega] - f_\omega =_1 0$, which would, of course, yield the theorem. For, in an enlargement, [0, 1] can be embedded in a Q-finite set, which must necessarily have $^*\mu$ measure 0. Hence there exists g such that $\mathrm{st}[g] \equiv 0$, but $g = 1$ $^*\mu$-almost everywhere.

This digression leads us to question as to whether the extreme non-S-continuity of $\sin \omega x$ will always ensure that $\mathrm{st}[\sin \omega x]$ is not measurable. The answer is negative, and it is an immediate consequence of the following, n-dimensional Dirichlet principle [4].

Theorem. *Given $\zeta_1, \zeta_2, \cdots, \zeta_n \in R$, and any positive $\epsilon > 0$, there exists an integer q such that $q\zeta_i$ differs from an integer by at most ϵ.*

Embedding R into a Q-finite set $R' = \{\zeta_1, \cdots, \zeta_\mu\}$, and letting $\epsilon =_1 0$, we are assured of the existence of $\omega \in {}^*N$ such that $(\omega\zeta_i) =_1 0$ or 1, $i = 1, 2, \cdots, \mu$. Hence $\sin 2\pi\omega x =_1 0$ all $x \in R$, so $\mathrm{st}[\sin 2\pi\omega x] \equiv 0$.

Finally, we considered the question as to whether or not the power of the enlargement was necessary to obtain the result. In particular, if one considers $R^N/\mathfrak{U}$ for some ultrafilter $\mathfrak{U}$ on N, does there exist $\omega \in N^N/\mathfrak{U}$ such that $\mathrm{st}[\sin 2\pi\omega x] \equiv 0$? This has a more interesting equivalent statement in standard language: Does there exist an ultrafilter on N such that $\sin 2\pi nx \to 0$ modulo $\mathfrak{U}$, even though $\int_0^1 |\sin 2\pi nx|\, dx \to 1/\pi$ modulo $\mathfrak{U}$? The answer is yes, but we require the former result to show it. Taking for the enlargement $^*R$ an ultrapower $R^I/\mathfrak{U}$, there exists $\omega_0 \in {}^*N$ such that $\sin 2\pi\omega_0 x =_1 0$ all $x \in R$. $\omega_0 = (\Omega_0(\nu))$ mod $\mathfrak{U}$. Define an ultrafilter $\mathfrak{U}_N$ on N via the following. Let $A_n = \{\nu \in I \mid \Omega_0(\nu) = n\}$. $F \in \mathfrak{U}_N \Leftrightarrow \bigcup_{n \in F} A_n \in \mathfrak{U}$. That $\mathfrak{U}_N$ is an ultrafilter on N is easily verified. We construct $R^N/\mathfrak{U}_N$, and map it into $R^I/\mathfrak{U}$ via φ, defined by $\varphi(p) = p' \Leftrightarrow p = (P(n)),\ p' = (P'(\nu))$, where $P'(\nu) = P(n) \forall \nu \in A_n$. φ is a well-defined, order-preserving isomorphism into $R^I/\mathfrak{U}$ (see Theorem 2.2, Chap. 6, of [5]). Furthermore, for $w_0 = (W_0(n) = n) \in R^N/\mathfrak{U}_N$, $\varphi(w_0) = \omega_0 \in {}^*R$, where ω_0 was the integer such that $\mathrm{st}[\sin \omega_0 x] = 0$, $x \in R$.

***Lemma* 3.** $\mathrm{st}[\sin \omega_0 x] = 0$, *for all $x \in R$.*

Proof. Fix $x \in R$, and $\epsilon > 0$. $\mathrm{st}[\sin \omega_0 x] =_1 0$ implies there exists a set $B \in \mathfrak{U}$ such that for every $\nu \in B$, $|\sin \Omega_0(\nu)x| < \epsilon$, where $\omega_0 = (\Omega_0)$. Let $C = \{n \mid \Omega_0(\nu) = n$, for some $\nu \in B\}$. $C \in \mathfrak{U}_N$, since $\bigcup_{n \in C} A_n \supset B$, and $|\sin nx| < \epsilon$ for all $n \in C$. Therefore, $\sin nx \to 0$ modulo $\mathfrak{U}_N$, or $\mathrm{st}[\sin \omega_0 x] = 0$, for all $x \in R$.

References

1. A. ROBINSON, *Non-Standard Analysis* (Studies in Logic and the Foundations of Mathematics). Amsterdam: North-Holland, 1966.
2. W. A. J. LUXEMBURG, Addendum to "On the Measurability of a Function Which Occurs in a Paper by A. C. Zaanen," *Proc. Acad. Sci. Amsterdam, 65* (1963), 587–590.
3. L. VIETORIS, Zur Kennzeichuung des Sinus und Verwandter Funktionen durch Funktionalgleichungen *J. Reine Augew. Math., 186* (1942), 1–15.
4. G. H. HARDY AND E. M. WRIGHT, *An Introduction to the Theory of Numbers.* New York: Oxford, 1954, p. 170.
5. W. A. J. LUXEMBURG, *Non-Standard Analysis.* Pasadena: Mathematics Department, California Institute of Technology, 1962.

Nonstandard Measure Theory

by ALLEN R. BERNSTEIN[1]
and FRANK WATTENBERG

Introduction

This paper is motivated by the following question. Suppose that a dart is thrown, using the unit interval as a target; then what is the probability of hitting a given point? Clearly this probability cannot be a positive real number, yet to say that it is zero violates the intuitive feeling that, after all, there is some chance of hitting the point. With the development by A. Robinson of nonstandard analysis, a rigorous theory of infinitesimals, another alternative presents itself: the probability of hitting a point should be a positive infinitesimal, that is, a number bigger than zero yet less than any positive real number.

It is our purpose here to show that, in fact, a nonstandard measure can be constructed on the unit interval such that the measure of any real number in the interval is a fixed infinitesimal. Furthermore, the measure of a set of real numbers is obtained by counting the number of points in that set in a suitable manner. We obtain a measure μ which is infinitely close to Lebesgue measure in the sense that if A is any Lebesgue measurable set, then $\mu(A)$ is a nonstandard number which is infinitely close to the Lebesgue measure of A. In particular, nonempty sets of Lebesgue measure zero will have positive infinitesimal measure. Thus, for example, it is now possible to say that the probability of hitting a rational number in the interval $[0, \frac{1}{4})$ is exactly half that of hitting a rational number in the interval $[0, \frac{1}{2})$, despite the fact that both sets in question have Lebesgue measure zero.

Finally, the measure μ is constructed so that it is defined on all subsets of the interval. Hence by taking the standard part of it we obtain a

[1] Financial support received from the National Science Foundation, Grant GP-5913 and the Office of Naval Research, Grant 1467.

finitely additive measure for arbitrary subsets of the interval which agrees with Lebesgue measure where the latter is defined. This measure, of course, cannot be countably additive, but it is a finitely additive, translation-invariant extension of Lebesgue measure to all sets in the interval. Thus it provides a natural solution to the "easy problem of measure" solved first by Banach [3].

The measure μ is constructed as a point measure, finite in the sense of nonstandard analysis. That is, we select a suitable set F of points in the nonstandard unit interval such that: (1) F contains all standard real numbers in the interval, (2) F is finite in the sense of nonstandard analysis, and (3) F is well distributed. Then given a set A in the unit interval the measure $\mu(A)$ is defined to be the number of points of the set F which lie in A divided by the total number of points in F. It will follow from condition (1) that the measure of a single standard real number in the interval is an infinitesimal: the reciprocal of the number of points in F. Condition 3 will guarantee that μ is infinitely close to Lebesgue measure and that it behaves well with respect to translation.

1. Nonstandard Analysis

In this section is presented a brief sketch of that part of Robinson's theory of nonstandard analysis needed later on. The reader is urged to consult [5] for a complete account.

Let $\mathcal{R}$ be the set of real numbers. The theory of nonstandard analysis is based upon the existence of an extension $^*\mathcal{R}$ of $\mathcal{R}$ which has the feature that any suitably formulated statement which is true about $\mathcal{R}$ is also true about $^*\mathcal{R}$. Since we must deal not only with elements of $\mathcal{R}$ but also with sets of elements of $\mathcal{R}$ and relations over such sets, and so on, it is necessary to work within the framework of a higher-order model theory which includes these kinds of objects.

The class T of *types* is defined inductively as follows. (a) 0 is a type; (b) if $\tau_1, \tau_2, \cdots, \tau_n$ are types, then $(\tau_1, \tau_2, \cdots, \tau_n)$ is also a type; (c) T is the smallest class satisfying (a) and (b).

A *higher-order structure* is defined to be a generalized sequence $\{A_\tau\}_{\tau\in T}$ (that is, a mapping which assigns to each type τ a set A_τ) such that A_0 is nonempty and, if $\tau \neq 0$, $\tau = (\tau_1, \tau_2, \cdots, \tau_n)$, then A_τ is a set of subsets of $A_{\tau_1} \times A_{\tau_2} \times \cdots \times A_{\tau_n}$. If $\sigma = (\tau)$, then the preceding Cartesian product is understood to be just the set A_τ, and $A_\sigma = A_{(\tau)}$ is then a set of subsets of A_τ. If $a \in A_0$, then a is called an *individual* of the higher-order structure. If $Q \in A_\tau$, $\tau = (\tau_1, \tau_2, \cdots, \tau_n)$, then Q is called a *relation* of the higher-order structure. Q is then a set of tuples $\langle a_1, a_2, \cdots, a_n\rangle$, where $a_i \in A_{\tau_i}$ and we say that $Q(a_1, a_2, \cdots, a_n)$ *holds* whenever $\langle a_1, a_2,$

$\cdots, a_n\rangle \in Q$. The *complete structure* of the set A_0 is the higher-order structure in which each A_τ, $\tau = (\tau_1, \tau_2, \cdots, \tau_n)$, is the set of all subsets of $A_{\tau_1} \times A_{\tau_2} \times \cdots \times A_{\tau_n}$.

Now let $A_0 = \mathcal{R}$, the set of real numbers, and let $\mathfrak{M}$ be the complete structure of $\mathcal{R}$. Thus among the relations of $\mathfrak{M}$ are all sets and relations of real numbers, all sets of such sets and relations, all relations of these sets and relations, and so on. In particular, the set $\mathfrak{N}$ of positive integers, being a subset of $\mathcal{R}$, would be a relation of $\mathfrak{M}$, that is, $\mathfrak{N} \in A_{(0)}$. Let Q be a two-placed relation of $\mathfrak{M}$, so that $Q \in A_{(\sigma,\tau)}$ for some types σ, τ. The *domain* of Q is defined to be the set of those x in A_σ for which there is a y in A_τ such that $Q(x, y)$ holds. The relation Q is said to be *finitely satisfiable* if given any finite set $\{a_1, a_2, \cdots, a_n\}$ of elements in the domain of Q there is a y such that $Q(a_i, y)$ holds for each a_i. For example, if $Q(x, y)$ is the relation which holds whenever x is strictly less than y, then $Q(x, y)$ is finitely satisfiable, since given any finite set $\{a_1, a_2, \cdots, a_n\}$ we may choose $y = \max \{a_1, a_2, \cdots, a_n\} + 1$.

Next we choose an appropriate higher-order formal language L which includes distinct constant symbols for each individual and relation of $\mathfrak{M}$, as well as the usual connectives: & (and), $\vee$ (or), $\neg$ (not), $\Rightarrow$ (implication), and quantifiers: $\forall$ (for all), $\exists$ (there exists). L also contains variables ranging over each type and quantification is permitted over all such variables. A suitable notion of when a sentence of L is true in a higher-order structure (under a correspondence between the constant symbols of L and the individuals and relations of the higher-order structure) may then be defined (see [2] or [5]). It then follows from a completeness theorem of Henkin [2] that there exists a higher-order structure $^*\mathfrak{M} = \{B_\tau\}_{\tau \in T}$, where B_0 properly includes A_0, such that under a suitable correspondence between the constant symbols of L and the elements of the B_τ's any sentence of L which is true in $\mathfrak{M}$ is also true in $^*\mathfrak{M}$. Furthermore, any constant symbol of L which denotes some individual of A_0 in $\mathfrak{M}$ will denote the same individual in $^*\mathfrak{M}$ now regarded as an element of B_0. $^*\mathfrak{M}$ will not be the complete structure of B_0, so that, for example, there will be subsets of B_0 which are not in $B_{(0)}$. However, in $^*\mathfrak{M}$ the variables of L range only over the elements of the B_τ's, so that, for example, a sentence of L which asserts that a certain property is true for all subsets of $A_0 = \mathcal{R}$ in $\mathfrak{M}$ will assert in $^*\mathfrak{M}$ that this property is true for only those subsets of B_0 which occur in $B_{(0)}$. The elements of the B_τ's, $\tau \neq 0$, are called *internal*.

Now if Q is an individual or relation of $\mathfrak{M}$, say $Q \in A_\tau$, then Q is denoted by some constant symbol β of the language L and β must denote some element of B_τ in $^*\mathfrak{M}$. This element will be written $^*Q$. In particular, if Q happens to be in A_0, then $^*Q = Q$ but this may not be true if Q is in A_τ for $\tau \neq 0$. However, in $^*\mathfrak{M}$, $^*Q$ will have exactly the same properties as Q in $\mathfrak{M}$ insofar as they can be expressed in the language L. In particular, $\mathcal{R}$ and $\mathfrak{N}$ will extend to sets $^*\mathcal{R}$ and $^*\mathfrak{N}$, respectively, which are called the nonstandard reals and nonstandard positive integers. These sets will contain in addition to the standard reals or positive integers other nonstandard points which are not elements of $\mathcal{R}$ or $\mathfrak{N}$.

Any function f of n variables is in fact a relation of $n + 1$ variables. Hence if f is any function in $\mathfrak{M}$ it extends to a relation $^*f$ in $^*\mathfrak{M}$ which is also a function since the property of being a function is expressible in the language L. Similarly, the relations of addition, multiplication, absolute value, and so on, on $\mathcal{R}$ which make $\mathcal{R}$ an ordered field extend to $^*\mathcal{R}$, where they are also associative, commutative, and so on. For these common relations we use the usual symbols $+$, $\cdot$, $|\cdot|$ for their extensions to $^*\mathfrak{M}$. Under these relations $^*\mathcal{R}$ is also an ordered field, since this fact can be expressed in the language L.

The relation $^*\mathfrak{M}$ may be chosen in such a manner that, in addition to having the property that it satisfies any sentence true in $\mathfrak{M}$, it has the following property. If Q is any finitely satisfiable relation of $\mathfrak{M}$, $Q \in A_{(\sigma,\tau)}$, then there is an element z of $^*\mathfrak{M}$, $z \in B_\tau$ such that given any x in the domain of Q, $^*Q(^*x, z)$ holds and we say that Q is simultaneously satisfied by z. Thus, for example, if we consider the relation $Q(x, y)$ which holds whenever x and y are reals and x is less than y, we obtain in $^*\mathcal{R}$ an element that is larger than all the reals in $\mathcal{R}$. Such elements are called infinite elements of $^*\mathcal{R}$. Similarly, we obtain infinite positive integers in $^*\mathfrak{N}$. By taking the reciprocal of an infinite element, we obtain a number closer to zero than any of the elements in $\mathcal{R}$.

Any higher-order structure which has the properties described above is sufficient for the purposes of this paper. However, we shall assume a particular one $^*\mathfrak{M}$ has been chosen which will be used throughout this paper. We shall tacitly assume that any sets or relations mentioned in the following pages are internal unless otherwise stated. $\mathfrak{M}$ will always be referred to as the *standard* model of the reals, and the individuals and relations of $\mathfrak{M}$ will be called *standard*. $^*\mathfrak{M}$ will be referred to as the *nonstandard* model of the reals and $^*\mathcal{R}$ and $^*\mathfrak{N}$ will be called the *nonstandard* reals and *nonstandard* positive integers, respectively.

In the nonstandard model any real that is closer to zero than any standard real number is called an *infinitesimal*. In particular, if n is any infinite integer, then its reciprocal is an infinitesimal. An element of $^*\mathcal{R}$ whose absolute value is less than some standard real is said to be finite. Note that an element of $^*\mathfrak{N}$ which is finite must in fact be already in $\mathfrak{N}$. This is demonstrated by observing that the statement $(\forall n)(n \in \mathfrak{N}\ \&\ |n| < r \Rightarrow n = 0 \vee n = 1 \vee \cdots \vee n = [r])$, where $[r]$ is the greatest integer in r, is true in $\mathfrak{M}$ and therefore must also be true in $^*\mathfrak{M}$ with $\mathfrak{N}$ replaced by $^*\mathfrak{N}$.

If x and y are two nonstandard reals, then we say that x is *infinitely close* to y ($x \sim y$) whenever $|x - y|$ is an infinitesimal. If x is any finite nonstandard real, then one can consider the set of all standard real numbers less than x. Since this set is bounded, it has a supremum s. It is easy to see that $s \sim x$ and that s is the only standard real which is infinitely close to x. We call s the *standard part* of x and write $s = \text{st}(x)$.

If $\{s_n\}$ is a standard sequence of real numbers in the model $\mathfrak{M}$ (that is, a function from the positive integers into the reals), then $\{s_n\}$ extends to a sequence $^*\{s_n\}$ of nonstandard reals in the model $^*\mathfrak{M}$ (that is, a function from the nonstandard positive integers into the nonstandard reals). One then can obtain, for instance, the following characterization of the limit of a sequence [5]. The standard number s is the limit of the standard sequence $\{s_n\}$ if and only if for every infinite integer ν the term s_ν of the corresponding nonstandard sequence $^*\{s_n\}$ is infinitely close to s.

Let us now consider the set X in the model $\mathfrak{M}$, which consists of all finite sets of real numbers. In the model $^*\mathfrak{M}$ this extends to the set $^*X$ and we call any element of $^*X$ a **finite set.* While $^*X$ contains some sets which have an infinite number of elements (for example, the set $\{1, 2, \cdots, \nu\}$, where ν is any infinite integer), every element of $^*X$ has all the properties of finiteness which can be expressed in L. In particular, the relation which assigns to each finite set F in X a positive integer which is its cardinality extends to $^*X$ in $^*\mathfrak{M}$ and assigns to each *finite set F a positive integer in $^*\mathfrak{N}$ which is its nonstandard cardinality. This integer will be denoted $\|F\|$. In addition, the sum operation which is defined in the model $\mathfrak{M}$ on the set X extends to the set $^*X$ in the model $^*\mathfrak{M}$.

2. Measure Theory

If F is any finite set, there is an obvious way to assign a measure to any subset A of F by dividing the number of elements in A by the number of elements in F. Clearly this gives a nonnegative additive measure in which the whole space F has measure 1. If F is an infinite *finite set in the nonstandard model $^*\mathfrak{M}$, then a measure can be defined on F in the same way. This raises the possibility of obtaining a measure theory for infinite sets in the same way as is used for finite sets.

It will be convenient for the purposes of this paper to construct a measure on the circle $\mathfrak{S}$ with unit circumference. $\mathfrak{S}$ may be thought of as the unit interval [0, 1] with end points identified, as the half-open interval [0, 1), or as the real numbers modulo 1. Points and addition on $\mathfrak{S}$ will be written modulo 1. Thus $\frac{1}{2} + \frac{3}{4} = \frac{1}{4}$. In the model $^*\mathfrak{M}$ there is a corresponding circle $^*\mathcal{S}$. Operations such as addition in $^*\mathfrak{M}$ which strictly speaking should be denoted by $^*+$ will be denoted by the usual $+$. The asterisk on the term *finite will be retained to emphasize the nonstandard meaning of the term. We shall denote by $L(A)$ the Lebesgue measure of a Lebesgue measurable set A.

Definition 2.1. A *finite subset of $^*\mathcal{S}$ will be called a *sample.* Any sample F has an associated *sample measure* which assigns to every subset A of $^*\mathcal{S}$ a nonstandard real number $\mu_F(A)$ defined by

$$\mu_F(A) = \frac{\|F \cap A\|}{\|F\|}.$$

For any sample F the following facts are immediate from the *finiteness condition on F.

Theorem 2.2. (a) *$\mu_F(^*\mathcal{S}) = 1$; $\mu_F(\phi) = 0$; $\mu_F(A) \geq 0$, for any subset A of $^*\mathcal{S}$.*

(b) *If $A \subseteq B$, then $\mu_F(A) \leq \mu_F(B)$.*

(c) *If $\{A_i\}_{i \in {}^*\mathfrak{N}}$ is any sequence of disjoint subsets of* $^*\mathcal{S}$ (notice that the index i ranges over the nonstandard positive integers), *then there is a nonstandard integer L such that if $i > L$, then $\mu_F(A_i) = 0$ and*

$$\mu_F(\cup_{i \in {}^*\mathfrak{N}} A_i) = \Sigma_{i=1}^{L} \mu_F(A_i).$$

Definition 2.3. If $n \in {}^*\mathfrak{N}$ and F is a sample, we say that F is *n-invariant* if and only if $F = F + 1/n$; that is, if whenever x is in F so is $x + 1/n$ (recall that addition is modulo 1).

Theorem 2.4. *If F is n-invariant, then:* (a) *For any subset A of $^*\mathcal{S}$, $\mu_F(A) = \mu_F(A + 1/n)$.*

(b) *$\mu_F((a, a + t/n]) = t/n$ for any $t \in {}^*\mathfrak{N}$, $0 \leq t \leq n$.*

(c) *$|\mu_F((a, b]) - (b - a)| \leq 1/n$.*

Proof. (a) is immediate. (b) follows from (a) by observing that

$$1 = \mu_F\left(\left(a, \frac{a+1}{n}\right]\right) + \mu_F\left(\left(\frac{a+1}{n}, \frac{a+2}{n}\right]\right) + \cdots$$
$$+ \mu_F\left(\left(\frac{a+(n-1)}{n}, a\right]\right) = n\mu_F\left(\left(a, \frac{a+1}{n}\right]\right).$$

Hence $\mu_F((a, a + 1/n]) = 1/n$ and $\mu_F((a, a + t/n]) = t/n$ by additivity. (c) is obtained by observing that if t is the greatest integer such that

$t/n < (b - a)$, then

$$\frac{t}{n} = \mu_F\left(\left(a, \frac{a+t}{n}\right]\right) \leq \mu_F((a, b]) \leq \mu_F\left(\left(a, \frac{a+(t+1)}{n}\right]\right) = \frac{t+1}{n}$$

and therefore $|\mu_F((a, b]) - (b - a)| \leq 1/n$.

***Theorem* 2.5.** *If F is a sample which is n-invariant for every standard positive integer n, then there is an infinite positive integer P such that for any $k \in {}^*\mathfrak{N}$, $k \leq P$, F is k-invariant.*

Proof. Let T be the set of all integers n such that F is k-invariant for any positive integer $k \leq n$. T is an internal set which contains all the finite positive integers. Furthermore, T is bounded and hence must contain a maximal element P. P cannot be finite and hence must be infinite. The infinite integer P thus obtained is called the *mesh* of F.

***Theorem* 2.6.** *Let F be a sample which is n-invariant for every standard positive integer n and which has mesh P. Then:*

(a) *If p and q are positive integers in ${}^*\mathfrak{N}$ with $p \leq q \leq P$, then $\mu_F((a, a + p/q]) = p/q$.*
(b) $|\mu_F((a, b]) - (b - a)| \leq 1/p \sim 0$.

Proof. Follows immediately from Theorem 2.4.

One can easily construct a sample function which is n-invariant for every standard positive integer n and which includes all the standard points of $\mathcal{S}$. This kind of sample produces a sample measure which gives the appropriate measure to intervals and gives each standard point an infinitesimal measure $1/\|F\|$. However, this kind of sample may produce a sample measure which gives very inaccurate measures to some Lebesgue measurable sets and which behaves poorly with respect to translation of subsets. For example, given any sample of this kind, by adding a large number of nonstandard rational numbers to it one can obtain a sample which is still n-invariant for each standard positive integer n but which gives the rational numbers a very large measure. The following definition lists the properties which we want F to possess.

***Definition* 2.7.** A sample F is called a *premeasure* and its associated sample measure is called a *measure* provided the following conditions are satisfied:

(a) Every point of $\mathcal{S}$ is in F.
(b) For every standard positive integer n, F is n-invariant.

(c) If A is any Lebesgue measurable set, then $\mathrm{st}(\mu_F(*A))$ is its Lebesgue measure.
(d) If α is any standard point of $*\mathcal{S}$ and A is any subset of $*\mathcal{S}$, then $\mu_F(A) \sim \mu_F(A + \alpha)$.

The first condition above forces the measure of each standard point to be the infinitesimal $1/\|F\|$. The restriction to standard Lebesgue measurable sets in the third condition is necessary since F itself being a *finite set is a *Lebesgue measurable set of *Lebesgue measure zero in $*\mathfrak{M}$ yet $\mu_F(F) = 1$.

In Lebesgue theory measure is actually translation invariant. However, since the translate of a set may actually be smaller than the original set, it is impossible for a measure in the above sense to be strictly translation invariant. Thus condition (d) is the best one can hope for. To see this more specifically, consider the set T consisting of all the points of the form kx for a positive integer k and a fixed irrational x (recall multiplication is modulo 1). Since we have $T = (T + x) \cup \{x\}$, the measure of T must be infinitesimally larger than the measure of $T + x$.

We conclude this section by listing some properties which are equivalent to condition (c) above.

***Theorem* 2.8.** *If F is a sample, then the following conditions on F are equivalent:*

(a) *For every standard open set O, $\mathrm{st}(\mu_F(*O)) \leq L(O)$, where $L(O)$ is the Lebesgue measure of O.*
(b) *For every standard set A, if $\overline{m}(A)$ is its outer measure and $\underline{m}(A)$ is its inner measure, then $\underline{m}(A) \leq \mathrm{st}(\mu_F(*A)) \leq \overline{m}(A)$.*
(c) *For every Lebesgue measurable set A, $\mathrm{st}(\mu_F(*A)) = L(A)$.*

Proof. (a) $\Rightarrow$ (b). If A is any standard set, then

$$\overline{m}(A) = \inf\{L(O) : O \text{ open}, A \subseteq O\}.$$

But $\mathrm{st}(\mu_F(*A)) \leq \mathrm{st}(\mu_F(*O)) \leq L(O)$, so that $\mathrm{st}(\mu_F(*A)) \leq \underline{m}(A)$.

$$\underline{m}(A) = 1 - \overline{m}(\mathcal{S} - A) \leq 1 - \mathrm{st}(\mu_F(*\mathcal{S} - *A)) = \mathrm{st}(\mu_F(*A)).$$

The other implications are clear.

3. Proof of the Existence of Measures

This section is devoted to proving the main result of this paper, Theorem 3.9, which states that premeasures and hence measures exist in the model $*\mathfrak{M}$.

The first requirement on a premeasure F is that it be n-invariant for each standard positive integer n. This requirement alone, however, does not force μ_F to assign appropriate values to Lebesgue measurable sets. If we concentrate on a specific positive integer n and a single Lebesgue measurable set V we can force $\mu_F(V)$ to be low by adding to the n-invariant sample F enough points which are not in V. However, to retain the n-invariance of F each time a point x is added to the sample all the translates of x of the form $x + k/n$ for k an integer must also be added to F. Thus it is vital to be able to choose points x such that not too many of the points $x + k/n$ lie in V. The following lemma in the standard model $\mathfrak{M}$ enables us to do just that.

***Lemma* 3.1.** *Suppose that V is any Lebesgue measurable set with Lebesgue measure $L(V)$. Suppose further that p and q are integers such that $p/q \leq L(V)$ and $(p + 1)/q > L(V)$. Then there is a point x in $\mathcal{S}$ such that at most p of the points in the set*

$$T(x) = \left\{\frac{x + t}{q} : 0 \leq t \leq q,\ t \in \mathfrak{N}\right\}$$

are in V.

Proof. Suppose to the contrary that for each x in $\mathcal{S}$ at least $p + 1$ of the points in $T(x)$ are in V. Under this assumption we will show that $L(V) \geq (p + 1)/q$, which contradicts the hypotheses of the lemma. Let E_i denote the interval $[(i - 1)/q,\ i/q)$ for $1 \leq i \leq q$. For each j, $1 \leq j \leq p + 1$, let V_{ij} be the set of all points x in E_i such that x is the jth point in the sequence $x - (i - 1)/q, \cdots, x, x + 1/q, \cdots, x + (q - i)/q$ which lies in the set V. Notice that the V_{ij}'s are disjoint subsets of $E_i \cap V$. Let $V'_{ij} = V_{ij} - (i - j)/q$. Thus the V'_{ij}'s are disjoint subsets of E_j. Let x be any point of E_j, $1 \leq j \leq p + 1$. Since at least $p + 1$ of the points in the sequence $x - (j - 1)/q, \cdots, x, x + 1/q, \cdots, x + (q - j)/q$ lie in V, there is a jth element of this sequence in V. This element lies in some $V_{j+r,j}$, where $1 \leq r \leq q$, and hence $x \in V'_{j+r,j}$. Thus $E_j = \bigcup_i V'_{ij}$ and we obtain

$$L(V) \geq L(\bigcup V_{ij}) = L(\bigcup V'_{ij}) = L\left(\left[0, \frac{p + 1}{q}\right]\right) = \frac{p + 1}{q}.$$

***Corollary* 3.2.** *Suppose V, p, and q are as above. If in addition we are given a set Z of Lebesgue measure zero, then a point x can be chosen satisfying the conclusions of the lemma and such that no point of $T(x)$ lies in the set Z.*

Proof. Apply the lemma to the set

$$W = V \cup Z \cup \frac{Z + 1}{q} \cup \cdots \cup \frac{Z + (q - 1)}{q}.$$

Given an integer $n \in \mathfrak{N}$ we can obtain n-invariance for a sample by adding to the sample all the translates of points x in the sample by k/n, where k is an integer. Similarly for any real number y, in order to obtain a sample which assigns to a set A a measure close to the measure it assigns to $A + y$, we can add to the sample a lot of the translates of points x in the sample by ky, where k is an integer. The following definition and lemmas are needed to enable us to do this without losing control of the sample we obtain.

Definition 3.3. The standard points $z_1, z_2, \cdots, z_t$ of $\mathcal{S}$ are said to be *independent* if whenever $\Sigma_{i=1}^{t} k_i z_i = 0$ for standard integers k_i then all of the k_i's must be zero. Notice that since addition is modulo 1 if any one of the z_i's is a rational number, then the points $z_1, z_2, \cdots, z_t$ are not independent.

Lemma 3.4. *Let $z_1, z_2, \cdots, z_t$ be independent, x be any point of $\mathcal{S}$, and $T = \{x + t/q : t \in \mathfrak{N}\}$ for a given positive integer q. Then all the sets of the form $T \neq \Sigma_{i=1}^{t} k_i z_i$ for integers k_i are pairwise disjoint.*

Proof. If they were not pairwise disjoint there would be a point y which could be expressed as $x + p/q + \Sigma k_i z_i$ and as $x + p'/q + \Sigma k_i' z_i$ with some $k_i' \neq k_i$. Then $(p - p')/q + \Sigma(k_i - k_i')z_i = 0$ and, since we're working modulo 1, $\Sigma(qk_i - qk_i')z_i = 0$. But this contradicts the independence of the z_i's, since for some i, $qk_i - qk_i' \neq 0$.

Lemma 3.5. *Suppose $y_1, y_2, \cdots, y_s$ are given irrational points of $\mathcal{S}$. Then there is a set of points $z_1, z_2, \cdots, z_t$ which are independent and an integer T such that each y_i is of the form $\Sigma_{i=1}^{t} k_i z_i$ for some integers k_i with $|k_i| \leq T$.*

Proof. The proof proceeds by induction on the number s. If $s = 1$, then the single point y_1 is independent because it is irrational. Now assume the lemma is true for $s - 1$. If the points $y_1, y_2, \cdots, y_s$ are independent, we are done. If they are not independent, then there are integers k_i such that $\Sigma_{i=1}^{s} k_i y_i = 0$ and not all the k_i's are zero. Without loss of generality we may assume $k_s \neq 0$. Then let $w_i = y_i/k_s$ for $1 \leq i \leq s - 1$. Let $T' = sk_1 .\ k_2 \cdots k_s$. Now apply the inductive hypothesis to the points $w_1, w_2, \cdots, w_{s-1}$ to obtain a set of points $z_1, z_2, \cdots, z_t$ and an integer T'' such that each of the points w_i is of the form $\Sigma_{i=1}^{t} l_i z_i$ with $|l_i| \leq T''$. Let $T = T''T'$. Now for $1 \leq j \leq s - 1$, $y_j = w_j k_s$ and hence is of the form $\Sigma k_s l_i z_i$ with $|k_s l_i| \leq T$. $y_s = \Sigma_{i=1}^{s-1} (-k_i)w_i$ and hence is also of the form $\Sigma_{i=1}^{t} l_i z_i$ with $|l_i| \leq T$.

In building up a sample we always have a few points over which we have no control and which may contribute very badly to the sample.

This problem is avoided by adding enough points to the sample to overwhelm these bad points. The following technical lemma allows us to do this. The corollary that follows enables us to obtain a sample which keeps the measure of any set A close to the measure of $A + y$ for a standard real y.

Lemma 3.6. *Suppose F and H are samples with $\|H\|/\|F\| < \epsilon$ for some standard positive real number ϵ. Let $F' = F \cup H$. Then for any set A, $|\mu_F(A) - \mu_{F'}(A)| < \epsilon$.*

Proof. Let $\mu_F(A) = p/\|F\|$. Then the smallest $\mu_{F'}(A)$ can possibly be is $p/(\|F\| + \epsilon\|F\|)$. But

$$\frac{p}{\|F\|} - \frac{p}{\|F\| + \epsilon\|F\|} = \frac{p}{\|F\|}\frac{1 - 1}{1 + \epsilon} \leq \frac{\epsilon}{1 + \epsilon} < \epsilon.$$

Thus $\mu_{F'}(A) \geq \mu_F(A) - \epsilon$. At the other extreme $\mu_{F'}(A)$ cannot be larger than $(p + \|H\|)/\|F\|$. But

$$\frac{p + \|H\|}{\|F\|} - \frac{p}{\|F\|} = \frac{\|H\|}{\|F\|} < \epsilon.$$

Thus $\mu_{F'}(A) \leq \mu_F(A) + \epsilon$. Hence $|\mu_F(A) - \mu_{F'}(A)| < \epsilon$.

Corollary 3.7. *Let y be a standard real number and suppose that F' is a sample such that $F' \cap (F' + ky) = \varnothing$ for each integer k. Let F be the sample given by*

$$F = \{x + ky : x \in F', |k| \leq L\}.$$

Then for any set A, $|\mu_F(A) - \mu_F(A + y)| < 1/L$.

Proof. Let $H = F \cap (F - y)$. Notice that H and $H + y$ are both subsets of F and that $(\|F - H\|)/\|F\| < 1/2L$, and $(\|F - (H + y)\|/\|F\| < 1/2L$. Now let $H' = H + y$. Then $\mu_{H'}(A + y) = \mu_H(A)$; but by the lemma $|\mu_H(A) - \mu_F(A)| < 1/2L$ and $|\mu_{H'}(A + y) - \mu_F(A + y)| < 1/2L$. Thus $|\mu_F(A) - \mu_F(A + y)| < 1/L$.

The proof of the existence of premeasures and measures is accomplished by showing that the following relation is finitely satisfiable. As described in Section 1, it will then follow that there will be some element in $^*\mathfrak{M}$ which will simultaneously satisfy the relation for all standard objects in its domain. Note that the four parts of the relation below correspond exactly to the four parts of Definition 2.7, so that the element obtained in $^*\mathfrak{M}$ will in fact be a premeasure.

Definition 3.8. Let $Q(\langle O, n, \epsilon, x, y\rangle, F)$ be the relation which holds between a sample F and a quintuple consisting of an open set O, an integer $n \in \mathfrak{N}$, a positive real number ϵ, a point x of $\mathcal{S}$, and an irrational real number y, if and only if the following conditions are satisfied:

(a) $x \in F$.
(b) F is an n-invariant sample.
(c) $|\mu_F(O) - L(O)| < \epsilon$, where $L(O)$ denotes the Lebesgue measure of O.
(d) $|\mu_F(A) - \mu_F(A + y)| < \epsilon$ for every subset A of $\mathcal{S}$.

***Main Theorem* 3.9.** *The relation defined above is finitely satisfiable and hence both premeasures and measures exist.*

Proof. To show that the relation is finitely satisfiable, given any finite collection of quintuples $\langle O_1, n_1, \epsilon_1, x_1, y_1\rangle, \cdots, \langle O_s, n_s, \epsilon_s, x_s, y_s\rangle$ in the domain of Q we must construct a sample which satisfies Q for these quintuples.

First we apply Lemma 3.5 to the points $y_1, y_2, \cdots, y_s$ and obtain a set of independent points $z_1, z_2, \cdots, z_t$ and an integer T_1 such that each y_i is of the form $\Sigma_{j=1}^t k_j z_j$ for integers k_j with $|k_j| \leq T_1$. Next let $\epsilon = \min(\epsilon_1, \epsilon_2, \cdots, \epsilon_s)/4$ and let $T_2 \in \mathfrak{N}$ be chosen such that $1/T_2 < \epsilon$. Let $T = tT_1T_2$.

Now let W be the finite collection of open sets consisting of all sets of the form $O_i + \Sigma_{j=1}^t k_j z_j$, where $|k_j| \leq T$. Enumerate the elements of W, $W = \{W_1, W_2, \cdots, W_r\}$. Since each W_i is an open set, it has a representation as a countable union of disjoint open intervals $W_i = \bigcup_j I_{ij}$. Pick a fixed integer J such that for each i, $L(\bigcup_{j>J} I_{ij}) < \epsilon/2^i$. Let $O = \bigcup_{j>J;1\leq i\leq r} I_{ij}$ and note that $L(O) \leq \epsilon$. Now let J' be any integer greater than J/ϵ and let n be the product $J'n_1n_2 \cdots n_s$. Clearly any sample which is n-invariant will be n_i-invariant for each i.

Let

$$H = \left\{\frac{x_i + k}{n} : 1 \leq i \leq s,\ k \in \mathfrak{N}\right\}.$$

This is an n-invariant sample containing all the x_i's, but we have no control over the measure it assigns to O. The next step is to construct another n-invariant sample K which satisfies conditions (b)–(d) and is large enough to overwhelm H. The sample we desire will then be $H \cup K$. The construction proceeds inductively.

Let p be the integer such that $p/n \leq \epsilon$ and $(p + 1)/n > \epsilon$. Using Lemma 3.1 choose a point v such that at most p of the points of

$$T(v) = \left\{\frac{v + k}{n} : k \in \mathfrak{N}\right\}$$

lie in O. Let $F_1 = T(v)$. Notice that $\mu_{F_1}(O) \leq \epsilon$. By Lemma 3.4 the samples $F_1 + \Sigma_{i=1}^t k_i z_i$ are all pairwise disjoint.

Suppose inductively that F_u has been chosen so that $\mu_{F_u}(O) \leq \epsilon$, and the samples $F_u + \Sigma_{i=1}^t k_i z_i$ are pairwise disjoint. Let

$$Z = \left\{v + \sum_{i=1}^{t} k_i z_i \colon v \in F_u,\ k_i \text{ integers}\right\}.$$

Since Z is countable $L(Z) = 0$. Hence we can apply Corollary 3.2 to obtain a point v such that at most p of the points in $T(v)$ lie in O and none of them lie in Z. Let $F_{u+1} = F_u \cup T(v)$. Clearly $\mu_{F_{u+1}}(O) \leq \epsilon$. Now let k_i' and k_i'' be integers, $1 \leq i \leq t$, and look at

$$\|(F_{u+1} + \Sigma k_i' z_i) \cap (F_{u+1} + \Sigma k_i'' z_i)\| = \|(F_{u+1} + \Sigma k_i z_i) \cap F_{u+1}\|,$$

where $k_i = k_i' - k_i''$. Since $F_{u+1} = F_u \cup T(v)$ we have

$$\begin{aligned}
&(F_{u+1} + \Sigma k_i z_i) \cap F_{u+1} = \\
&\quad ((F_u + \Sigma k_i z_i) \cup (T(v) + \Sigma k_i z_i)) \cap (F_u \cup T(v)) = \\
&\quad ((F_u + \Sigma k_i z_i) \cap F_u) \cup ((T(v) + \Sigma k_i z_i) \cap T(v)) \cup ((F_u + \Sigma k_i z_i) \\
&\qquad\qquad \cap T(v)) \cup (F_u \cap (T(v) + \Sigma k_i z_i)).
\end{aligned}$$

The first term is ϕ by the inductive hypothesis. The second term is ϕ by Lemma 3.4. v was chosen so that the third term is ϕ. Finally, since

$$\|F_u \cap (T(v) + \Sigma k_i z_i)\| = \|(F_u - \Sigma k_i z_i) \cap T(v)\|$$

the last term is also ϕ. Thus the samples $F_{u+1} + \Sigma k_i z_i$ are pairwise disjoint.

We proceed in this way until we obtain a sample $G = F_\omega$ such that $\|H\|/\|G\| < \epsilon$, G is n-invariant, $\mu_G(O) \leq \epsilon$, and the samples $G + \Sigma k_i z_i$ are pairwise disjoint.

Let

$$K = \bigcup_{|k_i| \leq T} \left(G + \sum_{i=1}^{t} k_i z_i\right) = \left\{g + \sum_{i=1}^{t} k_i z_i \colon g \in G,\ |k_i| \leq T\right\}.$$

Finally, let $F = H \cup K$. We wish to show that F satisfies the requirements of the theorem, that is, that conditions (a)–(d) are satisfied by F.

Condition (a) is satisfied by F since it is satisfied already by H.

To verify condition (b) for F simply note that H is n-invariant by construction and that K is n-invariant since G is. Therefore, F is n-invariant and this in turn implies that F is n_i-invariant for $1 \leq i \leq s$.

If W_i is a set in W, then $W_i = \cup_j I_{ij} = (\cup_{j \leq J} I_{ij}) \cup (\cup_{j > J} I_{ij})$ and thus $\mu_G(W_i) = \mu_G(\cup_{j \leq J} I_{ij}) + \mu_G(\cup_{j > J} I_{ij})$. Then since $\cup_j I_{ij} \subset O$ and $\mu_G(O) \leq \epsilon$, we obtain $|L(W_i) - L(\cup_{j<J} I_{ij})| \leq \epsilon$, and $|\mu_G(W_i) - \mu_G(\cup_{j<J} I_{ij})| \leq \epsilon$. Since G is n-invariant, we get by Theorem 2.4 that $|\mu_G(I_{ij}) - L(I_{ij})| < 1/n$ and hence $|\mu_G(\cup_{j \leq J} I_{ij}) - L(\cup_{j \leq J} I_{ij})| \leq J/n < \epsilon$ by our choice of n. Putting these all together we obtain $|\mu_G(W_i) - L(W_i)| < 3\epsilon$.

Let X be the set of all points y of the form $y = \Sigma_{i=1}^{t} k_i z_i$ where $|k_i| \le T$. For each of the original O_i's and each $y \in X$ we have $\mu_{G+y}(O_i) = \mu_G(O_i - y)$ and since $(O_i - y) \in W$, $|\mu_{G+y}(O_i) - L(O_i)| < 3\epsilon$. But since $K = \bigcup_{y \in X}(G + y)$ and G was chosen so that the sets of the form $G + y$ with $y \in X$ are pairwise disjoint, it follows that $|\mu_K(O_i) - L(O_i)| < 3\epsilon$. By Lemma 3.6 $|\mu_F(O_i) - \mu_K(O_i)| < \epsilon$, so that $|\mu_F(O_i) - L(O_i)| < 4\epsilon < \epsilon_j$ for $1 \le i, j \le s$. Hence F satisfies condition (c).

For each z_i let

$$K_i = \left\{v + \sum_{j=1}^{t} k_j z_j : v \in G, |k_j| \le T, k_i = 0\right\}.$$

By applying Corollary 3.7 to K_i and $K = \{x + kz_i : x \in K_i, |k| \le T\}$ we obtain $|\mu_K(A) - \mu_K(A + z_i)| < 1/T$ for any set A. Since each $y_j = \Sigma_{i=1}^{t} k_i z_i$ for some k_i with $|k_i| \le T_1$, we get by repeated applications of the above inequality with the triangle inequality that

$$|\mu_K(A) - \mu_K(A + y_j)| < \frac{tT_1}{T} \le \frac{1}{T_2} < \epsilon.$$

Since $|\mu_K(A) - \mu_F(A)| \le \epsilon$ and $|\mu_K(A + y_j) - \mu_F(A + y_j)| \le \epsilon$, we obtain finally,

$$|\mu_F(A) - \mu_F(A + y_j)| < 3\epsilon < \epsilon_i, \qquad 1 \le i \le s.$$

Thus F satisfies condition (d), completing the proof of the main theorem.

4. Integration

In this section we define the integral $\int f\, d\mu$ of a function f with respect to a sample measure μ and show that if f is a bounded standard Lebesgue measurable function and μ is a measure, then $\int f\, d\mu$ is infinitely close to the Lebesgue integral of f.

Definition 4.1. If F is any sample and $f: {}^*\mathcal{G} \to {}^*\mathcal{C}$ is any nonstandard complex function, then the integral of f with respect to $\mu = \mu_F$ is defined by $\int f\, d\mu = \Sigma_{x \in F} f(x)/\|F\|$. We also define $\int_A f\, d\mu = \int f \cdot \chi_A\, d\mu$, where A is any subset of ${}^*\mathcal{G}$ and χ_A is the characteristic function of A.

The following properties of the integral are immediate from the *finiteness of the sample.

Theorem 4.2. (a) $\int 0\, d\mu = 0$.

(b) $\int_A d\mu = \int \chi_A\, d\mu = \mu(A)$, *where* χ_A *is the characteristic function of the set* A.

(c) *If* $f \leq g$, *then* $\int f\, d\mu \leq \int g\, d\mu$, *where* f *and* g *are real-valued functions.*
(d) $\int (f + g)\, d\mu = \int f\, d\mu + \int g\, d\mu$.
(e) *If* c *is any nonstandard complex number, then* $\int cf\, d\mu = c\int f\, d\mu$.
(f) $|\int f\, d\mu| \leq \int |f|\, d\mu$.

Definition 4.3. A function f: $^*\mathcal{S} \to {}^*\mathcal{C}$ is said to be *μ-measurable* if whenever $\mu(A) \sim 0$, then $\int_A |f|\, d\mu \sim 0$. For example, if $|f|$ is bounded by a standard real number, then f is μ-measurable for any μ.

Theorem 4.4 (**Dominated Convergence**). *Suppose* $\{f_n\}$ *is a standard sequence of Lebesgue measurable functions converging to* f. *Suppose that* μ *is a measure and that there is a* μ*-measurable function* g *such that for each* n, $|f_n| \leq g$. *Then* $\mathrm{st}(\int f_n\, d\mu)$ *converges to* $\mathrm{st}(\int f\, d\mu)$.

Proof. Pick any standard $\epsilon > 0$. Define the sequence of sets E_n by

$$E_n = \left\{x: k \geq n \Rightarrow |f_k(x) - f(x)| < \frac{\epsilon}{2}\right\}.$$

Notice that $E_n \subseteq E_{n+1}$ and that $\cup_n E_n = \mathcal{S}$. For any infinite integer ν, $|\int f_\nu\, d\mu - \int f\, d\mu| \leq \int |f_\nu - f|\, d\mu = \int_{E_\nu} |f_\nu - f|\, d\mu + \int_{^*\mathcal{S} - E_\nu} |f_\nu - f|\, d\mu \leq \epsilon/2 + \int_{^*\mathcal{S} - E_\nu} 2g\, d\mu < \epsilon$, since $\mu(^*\mathcal{S} - E_\nu) \sim 0$ and $2g$ is μ-measurable. Now let T be the set of all positive nonstandard integers ν such that for $k \geq \nu$, $|\int f_k\, d\mu - \int f\, d\mu| < \epsilon$. Since T is an internal set it must contain a least element r, and since all the infinite positive integers are in T, r must be finite. This completes the proof of Theorem 4.4.

Corollary 4.5. *If* f *is any standard bounded Lebesgue measurable function, then* $\mathrm{st}(\int f\, d\mu)$ *is the Lebesgue integral of* f.

Proof. This follows immediately from Theorem 4.4 since f is the limit of simple functions, and by Theorem 4.2, if s is a simple function, then $\mathrm{st}(\int s\, d\mu)$ is the Lebesgue integral of s.

References

1. P. HALMOS, *Measure Theory*. Princeton, N. J.: Van Nostrand, 1950.
2. L. HENKIN, Completeness in the Theory of Types. *J. Symbolic Logic 15* (1960), 81–91.
3. I. NATANSON, *Theory of Functions of a Real Variable*. New York: Ungar, 1955.
4. A. ROBINSON, Non-Standard Analysis, *Indagationes Math. 23* (1961), 432–440.
5. A. ROBINSON, *Non-Standard Analysis* (Studies in Logic and the Foundations of Mathematics). Amsterdam: North-Holland, 1966.

Nonstandard Proofs of Invariance Principles in Probability Theory

by D. W. MÜLLER[1]

Let $\{Y_n(t): n \in N, t \in T\}$($N$ the set of natural numbers, T some index set) be a sequence of stochastic processes. A theorem which—under general assumptions about the Y_n—asserts the existence of a process $\{Y(t): t \in T\}$ having some specified asymptotic properties of the Y_n is called an invariance principle. In the case the properties in question are preserved by weak approximation the theory of tight measures turns out to be an appropriate tool for proving asymptotic invariance. We shall formulate a condition characterizing these measures in terms of nonstandard analysis and then derive a new proof of the Donsker–Prokhorov invariance principle [1, 5] which is less technical than the classical approach to this problem (see also [4]; another (classical) proof coming nearest to ours is due to V. Strassen (unpublished)); moreover, by nonstandard methods the proof is reduced to a well-known classical argument used to establish the continuity of paths for the Wiener process (see [2]).

I would like to thank W. A. J. Luxemburg for pointing out an error in the original manuscript.

1. Nonstandard Characterization of Tight Measures

Let E be a metric space[2] and $^*E$ an enlargement of E (containing the structure of the set R of real numbers).[3] Denote by ns$^*E$ the set of

[1] The author's work done on this subject was supported by the Deutsche Fortschungsgemeinschaft, from which he also received a special grant which enabled him to attend the Symposium on Nonstandard Analysis.

[2] The statements of this section will also be valid in the case of a general Hausdorff (or completely regular) space if the model of E is assumed to be saturated (see this volume, p. 66). In this case Lemma 2 can be stated for Baire measures. But we shall not use this fact.

[3] For terminology see [6].

near-standard points of $*E$; that is, $\{x: x \in *E$, there exists $x_0 \in E$ such that $x \in \mu(x_0)\}$.

The main tool of our approach will be the following

***Lemma* 1.** *Let S be an internal subset of* ns$*E$. *Then* ^0S *is compact.*

Here is a proof: It suffices to verify sequential compactness. Suppose $\{x_n\}$ to be a sequence of elements of ^0S; then it is immediate that $\text{dist}(x_n, S)$ is infinitesimal, $< 1/n$ say, for all $n \in N$. We conclude this assertion to be still valid for some $n_0 \in *N \sim N$, whence $x_{n_0} \in \mu(x_0)$ for some $x_0 \in {}^0S$. So x_0 turns out to be a limit point of $\{x_n\}$.

Let us remark that S need not be contained in any standard compact set. This is the case for every internal subset of ns $*E$ if and only if the topology of E is locally compact.

Now consider the space $\mathfrak{M}_+^1$ of all normalized positive Borel measures on E. We call $P \in *\mathfrak{M}_+^1$ *tight* if for preassigned standard $\epsilon > 0$ there exists a standard compact set $K \subset E$ such that $P*K > 1 - \epsilon$. Let $\mathcal{C}E$ be the space of all real-valued continuous bounded functions on E endowed with the uniform norm $\|\cdot\| = \sup\{|\cdot(x)|: x \in E\}$ and let $\mathcal{C}E'$ be the dual of $\mathcal{C}E$. By definition call a positive linear form $\mathcal{P} \in *(\mathcal{C}E')$ tight, if for preassigned standard $\epsilon > 0$ there exist a standard $\delta > 0$ and a standard compact $K \subset E$ such that the conditions

$$\mathcal{C}E \ni f \geq 0,\ \|f\| \leq 1,\ \text{Rest}_K f < \delta \text{ imply } \mathcal{P}f < \epsilon.$$

Clearly, if $P \in *\mathfrak{M}_+^1$ is tight, then also $\mathcal{P}_P \cdot = \int \cdot\, dP$ as an element of $*(\mathcal{C}E')$; the converse, however, is not true in general.

For every (not necessarily internal) subset S of $*E$ define $\mathbf{P}S = \sup\{^0PF: F \subset S, F \text{ internal Borel set}\}$.

***Lemma* 2.** *For* $P \in *\mathfrak{M}_+^1$, *the following assertions are equivalent:*

(a) $\mathbf{P}(\text{ns}*E) = 1$.

(b) $\mathcal{P}_P$ *is tight.*

Proof. (a) implies (b): Given a standard $\epsilon > 0$, the hypothesis implies the existence of an internal set $F \subset \text{ns}*E$ such that $PF \geq 1 - \epsilon/2$. Then if

$$0 \leq f \in \mathcal{C}E,\ \|f\| \leq 1,\ \text{Rest}_F f < \delta := \frac{\epsilon}{2}, \tag{1}$$

we get $$\mathcal{P}_P f = \int_F f\, dP + \int_{\mathbf{0}F} f\, dP < \frac{\epsilon}{2} PF + \|f\|\, P\mathbf{C}F \leq \epsilon.$$

Now let $K = {}^0F$ (compact after Lemma 1). Then

$$0 \leq g \in \mathcal{C}E,\ \|g\| \leq 1,\ \text{Rest}_K g < \delta \text{ imply } \text{Rest}_F g < \delta,$$

since g is standard. So (1) holds for g instead of f and thus implies $\mathcal{P}_P g < \epsilon$.

(b) implies (a): Let $\epsilon > 0$ be a given standard real number and let K be a standard ϵ-compact set; that is, there exists $\delta > 0$ standard such that the conditions $0 \leq f \in \mathcal{C}E$, $\|f\| \leq 1$, $\text{Rest}_K f < \delta$ imply $\mathcal{P}_P f < \epsilon$. Now, by compactness of K and complete regularity of E, given a standard $\eta > 0$ we find $f_\eta \in \mathcal{C}E$ such that $(1 - \delta)\chi_K \leq f_\eta \leq \chi_{K^\eta}$; here χ denotes the characteristic function of a set and K^η the set of all points having $\text{dist}(\cdot, K) < \eta$. Thus by tightness of $\mathcal{P}_P$, $\mathcal{P}_P f_\eta > 1 - \epsilon$, and consequently $P^*K^\eta > 1 - \epsilon$, true for all standard $\eta > 0$. We conclude this inequality to hold also for some infinitesimal $\eta_0 > 0$. Then, by Robinson's compactness criterion, we see that $^*K^{\eta_0} \subset \text{ns}^*E$.

2. Application to Invariance Principles

We are now in the position to deduce a sufficient (and also necessary) condition for weak convergence of probability measures on $E = \mathcal{C}[0, 1]$.

Lemma 3. *Let $\{P_n: n \in N\}$ be a sequence of normalized Borel measures on $E = \mathcal{C}[0, 1]$ having weakly convergent marginal distributions. Suppose that for every $n \in {}^*N \sim N$ $\mathbf{P}_n$ $(\text{ns}^*E) = 1$. Then the P_n converge in the weak topology of $\mathcal{C}E'$ induced by $\mathcal{C}E$.*

Proof. Let e_t: $E \ni x \to x(t)$ be the evaluation mapping at the point t. Denote by $\mathfrak{F}$ the subspace of $\mathcal{C}E$ consisting of those functions of $\mathcal{C}E$ which depend only on finitely many of the e_t $(0 \leq t \leq 1)$. Then the unit ball of $\mathfrak{F}$ is dense in the unit ball $\mathcal{C}E$ with respect to the topology T of uniform convergence on compacta; this is a consequence of the order-theoretic form of the Stone–Weierstrass theorem, since $\mathfrak{F}$ is a vector sublattice of $\mathcal{C}E$ which separates the points and contains the constants. For $f \in \mathcal{C}E$, define $\mathcal{P}_n f = {}^0(\int f\, dP_n)$, where $n \in {}^*N \sim N$. Then for $f \in \mathfrak{F}$, $\mathcal{P}_n f$ is independent of n by weak convergence of finite-dimensional distributions. But $\int \cdot\, dP_n$, and so $\mathcal{P}_n$, being a tight functional on $\mathcal{C}E$ according to the preceding lemma, is T-continuous on the unit ball of $\mathcal{C}E$. So $\mathcal{P}_n f$ does not depend on $n \in {}^*N \sim N$ for all $f \in \mathcal{C}E$ and the desired conclusion follows.

The necessity of the conditions stated in the lemma is obvious, since every normalized Borel measure on $\mathcal{C}[0, 1]$ is tight.

Now the proof of the Donsker–Prokhorov invariance principle is easy. It essentially consists of an argument familiar from the theory of path continuity. Indeed what we have to prove according to Lemma 3 (since the convergence of finite-dimensional distributions will be evident) is the "macroscopic" continuity of the approximating paths. Besides, it is noteworthy that establishing the near-standard property of paths we need not bother about their interpolation part.

***Theorem* (*Prokhorov*).** *Let* $\{X_{nk}: n \in N,\ 1 \leq k \leq k_n\}$ *be an array of random variables all having* $EX_{nk} = 0$ *and* $0 < EX_{nk}^2 < \infty$, *which, for fixed* n, *are independent and have* $\Sigma_k EX_{nk}^2 = 1$. *Moreover, let Lindeberg's condition be satisfied. Define* $t_{nk} = \Sigma_{i \leq k} EX_{ni}^2$ $(= 0$ *if* $k = 0)$.

If $\{Y_n(t): t \in [0, 1]\}$ *is a random process with values in* $\mathcal{C}[0, 1]$ *being monotonic in each interval* $[t_{n,k-1}, t_{nk}]$ *such that* $Y_n(t_{nk}) - Y_n(t_{n,k-1}) = X_{nk}$ *and* $Y_n(0) = 0$, *then the distributions of* $\{Y_n\}$ *converge weakly to the Wiener measure on* $\mathcal{C}[0, 1]$. (The existence of the Wiener measure on $\mathcal{C}[0, 1]$ follows from our proof.)

Proof. Consider a fixed enlargement of the whole structure assumed in the theorem. Since the convergence of the finite-dimensional distributions to those of the Wiener measure is guaranteed by the central limit theorem, only the second condition of Lemma 3 must be checked.

For fixed $n \in {}^*N \sim N$, let T_n be the subset of the unit interval consisting of all t_{nk} $(0 \leq k \leq k_n)$. For positive γ and δ satisfying $\delta \geq \max_{1 \leq k \leq k_n} EX_{nk}^2$ ($\simeq 0$ after Lindeberg's condition) define

$$\alpha_\delta(\gamma) = \sup_{\substack{s,t \in T_n \\ |s-t| \leq \delta}} \Pr[|Y_n(t) - Y_n(s)| \geq \gamma].$$

Then in analogy to the case of continuous Markov processes we have the inequality (for a proof see the Appendix)

$$\Pr[\sup_{\substack{s,t \in T_n \\ |s-t| \leq \delta}} |Y_n(t) - Y_n(s)| \geq 4\gamma] \leq 2\delta^{-1}\alpha_{2\delta}(\gamma). \tag{2}$$

Now for preassigned standard $\epsilon > 0$ and $m \in N$ we find a standard $\delta_m > 0$ such that

$$\Pr[\sup_{\substack{s,t \in T_n \\ |s-t| \leq \delta_m}} |Y_n(t) - Y_n(s)| \geq 4/m] \leq 2^{-m}\epsilon. \tag{3}$$

For according to (2) it suffices to make $2\delta_m{}^{-1}\alpha_{2\delta_m}(1/m)$ smaller than $2^{-m}\epsilon$; the existence of such a δ_m then follows from the fact that (by normal approximation)

$$\Pr[|Y_n(t) - Y_n(s)| \geq 1/m] \simeq (2\pi|t - s|)^{-1/2} \int \exp\left(-\frac{u^2}{2|t - s|}\right) du \qquad |u| \geq \frac{1}{m}$$

decreases to zero with exponential velocity for $|t - s| \not\simeq 0$ or else is infinitesimal by Čebyšev's inequality. Having chosen, for $m \in N$, the

δ_m, we conclude that there exists some $m_0 \in {}^*N \sim N$ such that (3) and $\delta_m \geq \max_{1 \leq k \leq k_n} EX_{nk}^2$ are valid for $m = 1, \cdots, m_0$. Now put

$$S = \bigcap_{m=1}^{m_0} \left[\sup_{\substack{s,t \in T_n \\ |s-t| \leq \delta_m}} |Y_n(t) - Y_n(s)| < \frac{4}{m} \right].$$

Then by (3) $\Pr[S \leq \epsilon \Sigma_{m=1}^{m_0} 2^{-m} \leq \epsilon$, whence $\Pr S \geq 1 - \epsilon$. Evidently $Y_n S \subset ns^*\mathcal{C}[0, 1]$, by monotonicity of interpolation. This completes the proof.

Finally, let us show how the methods used to prove Lemma 3 can be modified if the paths are no longer assumed to be continuous. Let $E = \mathfrak{D}[0, 1]$ be the space of all real-valued functions on the unit interval without discontinuities of the second kind, endowed with Skorokhod's topology J, that is, the space of all functions x such that

(a) for all $0 < t \leq 1$, $x(t - 0)$ exists;
(b) $x(1 - 0) = x(1)$;
(c) for all $0 \leq t < 1$, $x(t + 0)$ exists;
(d) for all $0 \leq t < 1$, $x(t + 0) = x(t)$.

The topology J can be described by a metric ρ (see [3]): By definition call $x,y \in E$ ϵ-equivalent ($x \in y$), if there exist $k \in N$ and two subdivisions of the unit interval

$$0 = t_0 < t_1 < \cdots < t_k = 1,$$
$$0 = t_0' < t_1' < \cdots < t_k' = 1,$$

such that for $\kappa = 1, \cdots, k$

$$|t_k - t_k'| \leq \epsilon \qquad \text{and} \qquad \sup_{\substack{t \in (t_{k-1}, t_k) \\ t' \in (t'_{k-1}, t'_k)}} |x(t) - y(t')| \leq \epsilon;$$

put $\rho(x, y) = \inf\{\epsilon : x \in y\}$.

Skorokhod [7] has stated conditions guaranteeing weak convergence of all J-continuous functionals on E in case it holds for the marginal distributions of the given sequence $\{Y_n(t) : n \in N, t \in [0, 1]\}$ of stochastic processes in E. Here the limit process is assumed to have values in E. We get rid of this condition by an additional (but not very restrictive) equiboundedness assumption.

Theorem. *Suppose the following conditions are satisfied:*

(a) *The finite-dimensional distributions of the Y_n belonging to $t \in D$, D a countable dense subset of* [0, 1], *are weakly convergent.*

(b) *For every* $\epsilon > 0$,

$$\lim_{\gamma \to 0} \overline{\lim_{n \to \infty}} \Pr[\Delta_\gamma(Y_n) > \epsilon] = 0.$$

Here

$$\Delta_\gamma(x) = \sup_{\substack{|t''-t'| \leq \gamma \\ 0 \leq t' \leq t \leq t'' \leq 1}} \min\{|x(t'') - x(t)|, |x(t) - x(t')|\} + \sup_{t \leq \gamma} (|x(t) - x(0)| + |x(1-t) - x(1)|).$$

(c) *For every* $\epsilon > 0$,

$$\lim_{\delta \to 0} \overline{\lim_{n \to \infty}} \sup_{|t-s| \leq \delta} \Pr[|Y_n(t) - Y_n(s)| > \epsilon] = 0.$$

(d) $\lim_{\eta \to \infty} \overline{\lim_{n \to \infty}} \Pr[\sup_{0 \leq t \leq 1} |Y_n(t)| > \eta] = 0.$

Then there exists a tight measure on E being the weak limit of the distributions P_n of Y_n; its marginal distributions (belonging to $t \in D$) are the weak limits of the marginal distributions of the Y_n.

Proof. 1. First we show $P_n(\text{ns}^*E) = 1$ for all $n \in {}^*N \sim N$. Let $n \in {}^*N \sim N$ be fixed. Then given $\epsilon > 0$ standard, one finds for every $m \in N$ $\gamma_m > 0$ standard such that

$$\Pr\left[\Delta_{\gamma_m}(Y_n) > \frac{1}{m}\right] < 2^{-m}\epsilon.$$

Denote this event by A_m. In addition there is an $\eta > 0$ standard such that

$$\Pr[\sup_{0 \leq t \leq 1} |Y_n(t)| > \eta] < \frac{\epsilon}{4};$$

denote this event by B. Let $m_0 \in {}^*N \sim N$ such that $\Pr A_m < 2^{-m}\epsilon$ for all $m = 1, \cdots, m_0$. Denote the elements of D by $d_1, d_2, \cdots$. According to (c) we find standard positive $\delta_{mi} < \gamma_m/2$ such that

$$\Pr\left[|Y_n(d_i + \delta_{mi}) - Y_n(d_i - \delta_{mi})| > \frac{1}{m}\right] < \left(\frac{\epsilon}{4} 2^{-i}\right) 2^{-m}$$

$(i, m \in N)$; denote this event by C_{mi}. We conclude this statement to be valid for all $i \leq i_m \in {}^*N \sim N$; let i_m be maximal, whence it is defined for all $m \in {}^*N$. Put

$$C = \bigcup_{m=1}^{m_0} A_m \cup B \cup \bigcup_{m=1}^{\infty} \bigcup_{i=1}^{i_m} C_{mi} \quad \text{and} \quad S = \complement C.$$

Then

$$\Pr C \leq \frac{\epsilon}{2} + \frac{\epsilon}{4} + \frac{\epsilon}{4} \sum_{m=1}^{\infty} \sum_{i=1}^{i_m} 2^{-i} 2^{-m} \leq \epsilon \quad \text{and} \quad \Pr S \geq 1 - \epsilon.$$

Let E_1 be the set of all paths having no jumps for $t \in D$. Then we show $Y_nS \subset \text{ns}^*E$ and ${}^0(Y_nS) \subset E_1$. For this purpose take $x \in Y_nS$ and put $x_0(t) = {}^0(x(t))$ for all standard t, which is defined since $|x| \leq \eta$. Then we claim that $x_0{}^+(t) = x_0(t + 0)$ exists and is $\in E_1$. To show this let $t_0 \in (0, 1)$. Of course, $\Delta_{\gamma_m}(x) \leq 1/m$ implies $\Delta_{\gamma_m}(x_0) \leq 1/m$ (m standard). Now assume the right limit of x_0 in t_0 does not exist. Then $|x_0| \leq \eta$ implies the existence of two limit points $a \neq b$ ($|b - a| = d$) of $\{x_0(s_k)\}$, where $\{s_k\}$ is a suitably chosen sequence decreasing to t_0. So we get two cofinal subsequences of $\{s_k\}$ converging to a and b, namely $\{s_k'\}$ and $\{s_k''\}$ (containing some elements repeatedly if necessary), such that $s_k' < s_k < s_k''$ and $|x_0(s_k'') - x_0(s_k)| > d/2$, $|x_0(s_k) - x_0(s_k')| > d/2$ for $k > k_0$, say. This yields

$$\min\{|x_0(s_k'') - x_0(s_k)|, |x_0(s_k) - x_0(s_k')|\} > \frac{d}{2},$$

even if finally $s_k'' - s_k' < \gamma_m$, leading to a contradiction if $1/m \leq d/2$. The existence of right (and also left) limits for all t then follows from the smallness of the boundary terms of $\Delta_{\gamma_m}(x_0)$.

To finish the proof of the second part of our assertion suppose $x_0{}^+$ has a jump of magnitude $>\beta > 0$ in $d_i \in D$. To derive a contradiction take $m > 3/\beta$. Clearly x has a jump of magnitude $>\beta$ in $\mu(d_i)$; that is, there exist τ and τ' such that $d_i - \delta_{mi} < \tau < \tau' < d_i + \delta_{mi}$ and $|x(\tau) - x(\tau')| > \beta > 3/m$. But because of $\Delta_{\gamma_m}(x) \leq 1/m$, $x(d_i + \delta_{mi})$ or $x(d_i - \delta_{mi})$ lies in the $1/m$-neighborhood of $x(\tau)$ and $x(\tau')$, and this together with $|x(d_i + \delta_{mi}) - x(d_i - \delta_{mi})| \leq 1/m$ yields $|x(\tau) - x(\tau')| \leq 3/m$, contrary to the above. So we have proved $x_0{}^+ \in E_1$.

It remains to show $x \in \mu(x_0{}^+)$. To prove the ϵ-equivalence, for each standard $\epsilon > 0$, of $x_0{}^+$ and x, subdivide [0, 1] by $0 < t_1 < \cdots < t_{k-1} < 1$ such that at every point of discontinuity of x_0 different from all t_k the jump is smaller than $\epsilon/2$. Then in $\mu(t_k)$ we have exactly one point of discontinuity t_k' of x with jump $>\epsilon/2$, as is seen by considering Δ. Now the partition $0 < t_1 < \cdots < 1$ can be refined by standard numbers such that the variation of x_0 on each subinterval is less than ϵ. Refining $0 < t_1' < \cdots < 1$ by the same standard numbers yields the desired ϵ-equivalence, and $Y_nS \subset \text{ns}^*E$ is proved.

Thus we obtain $\mathbf{P}_n(\text{ns}^*E) = 1$.

2. Let $\mathfrak{F}$ be the space of all functions of the form

$$g \cdot (e_{t_1}, \cdots, e_{t_k}),$$

such that $g \in \mathfrak{C}(R^k)(k \in N)$ and $t_i \in D(i = 1, \cdots, k)$. Every $f \in \mathfrak{F}$ has the remarkable property

$$f(\mu(x) \cap Y_nS) \subset \mu(f(x)) \qquad \text{for all } x \in E,$$

allowing us to apply the arguments of Lemma 2 for $\mathfrak{F} + \mathcal{C}E$ instead of $\mathcal{C}E$ and with $F = Y_n S$. Thus we obtain that P_n defines a tight standard functional $\mathcal{P}_n$ on $\mathfrak{F} + \mathcal{C}E$ (clearly, the meaning of "tight" must be slightly modified in this connection).

To prove weak convergence we have to show that $\mathcal{P}_n = \mathcal{P}_{n'}$ for all $n' \in {}^*N \sim N$, already knowing that it is valid on $\mathfrak{F}$. If $g \in \mathcal{C}E$, $\|g\| \leq 1$ say, then given a standard $\epsilon > 0$ there exist a standard compact $K \subset E_1$ and $\delta > 0$ standard such that $\text{Rest}_K|f - g| < \delta (f \in \mathfrak{F}, \|f\| \leq 1)$ implies $|\mathcal{P}_n(f - g)| < \epsilon$; an analogous assertion is true for $\mathcal{P}_{n'}$: $\text{Rest}_{K'}|f - g| < \delta'$ implies $|\mathcal{P}_{n'}(f - g)| < \epsilon$. The $f \in \mathfrak{F}$ being continuous on E_1, we can apply the order-theoretic Stone–Weierstrass theorem to approximate g on the compact $K \cup K'$ by some $f_0 \in \mathfrak{F}(\|f_0\| \leq 1)$ such that

$$\text{Rest}_{K \cup K'}|f_0 - g| < \min(\delta, \delta').$$

Thus we obtain

$$|\mathcal{P}_n g - \mathcal{P}_{n'} g| \leq |\mathcal{P}_n(g - f_0)| + |\mathcal{P}_{n'}(g - f_0)| < 2\epsilon,$$

whence $\mathcal{P}_n g = \mathcal{P}_{n'} g$. Put $\mathcal{P} = \mathcal{P}_n$.

It remains to show that $\mathcal{P}$ has the desired marginal distributions; that is, $\mathcal{P}f = \int f\, d\mathcal{P}$ for $f \in \mathfrak{F}$ (here the integral is obtained by usual measure-theoretic extension of the linear form $\mathcal{P}$ from $\mathcal{C}E$ to the class of Borel sets; this can be done since $\mathcal{P}$ is tight on $\mathcal{C}E$). For this purpose let $K \subset E_1$ be a standard ϵ-compact set for $\mathcal{P}$. Then χ_K is the limit of a monotone decreasing sequence of functions $g_k \in \mathcal{C}E$ with norm ≤ 1. Therefore, $\int_K d\mathcal{P} = \lim_{k \to \infty} \mathcal{P}g_k$, whence $\int_K d\mathcal{P} \geq 1 - \epsilon$.

Consequently, for $f \in \mathfrak{F}$ (such that $\|f\| \leq 1$),

$$\int f\, d\mathcal{P} = \int_K f\, d\mathcal{P} + \int_{\complement K} f\, d\mathcal{P},$$

where the absolute value of the second term is $\leq \epsilon$. So if $g \in \mathcal{C}E(\|g\| \leq 1)$ satisfies $g = f$ on K, then $|\int f\, d\mathcal{P} - \mathcal{P}g| \leq 2\epsilon$, which, by $|\mathcal{P}f - \mathcal{P}g| < 2\epsilon$, yields $|\int f\, d\mathcal{P} - \mathcal{P}f| < 4\epsilon$. Since ϵ was arbitrary, the theorem follows.

Appendix

Proof of (2): To prove (2) we need the following estimate (here $a,b \in T_n$ may be assumed without restriction of generality):

$$\Pr[\sup_{s,t \in T_n \cap [a,b]} |Y_n(t) - Y_n(s)| \geq 4\gamma] \leq \Pr[\sup_{t \in T_n \cap [a,b]} |Y_n(t) - Y_n(a)| \geq 2\gamma]$$
$$\leq \Pr[|Y_n(b) - Y_n(a)| \geq \gamma] + \Pr[|Y_n(b) - Y_n(a)| < \gamma \text{ and } \sup_t |Y_n(t)$$
$$- Y_n(a)| \geq 2\gamma] \leq \alpha_{b-a}(\gamma) + \sum_t \Pr[|Y_n(t) - Y_n(a)| \geq 2\gamma \text{ for the}$$
$$\text{first time and } |Y_n(b) - Y_n(t)| \geq \gamma].$$

As by independence of the summands the term under the summation sign decomposes into a product, we obtain as estimate

$$\alpha_{b-a}(\gamma)(1 + \sum_t \Pr[|Y_n(t) - Y_n(a)| \geq 2\gamma \text{ for the first time}])$$

and thus

$$\Pr[\sup_{s,t \in T_n \cap [a,b]} |Y_n(t) - Y_n(s)| \geq 4\gamma] \leq 2\alpha_{b-a}(\gamma). \tag{4}$$

Now let $h = 1 + [1/\delta]$. Application of (4) yields

$$\Pr[\sup_{\substack{s,t \in T_n \\ |s-t| \leq \delta}} |Y_n(t) - Y_n(s)| \geq 4\gamma] \leq \sum_{k=0}^{h-2} \Pr[\sup_{\substack{s,t \in T_n \cap \\ [k/h,(k+2)/h]}} |Y_n(t) - Y_n(s)|$$
$$\leq 2(h-1)\alpha_{2\delta}(\gamma), \text{ whence (2) follows.}$$

References

1. M. D. DONSKER, An Invariance Principle for Certain Probability Limit Theorems, *Mem. Am. Math. Soc. 6* (1951), 1–12.
2. J. R. KINNEY, Continuity Properties of Sample Functions of Markov Processes, *Trans. Am. Math. Soc. 74* (1953), 280–302.
3. A. N. KOLMOGOROV, On Skorokhod Convergence, *Theoret. Probability Appl. 1* (1956), 215–222.
4. K. KRICKEBERG, Wahrscheinlichkeitsoperatoren von Verteilungen in Vektorräumen, *Transactions of the Third Prague Conference on Information Theory, Stat. Decision Functions, Random Processes, 1962.* (1964), pp. 441–452.
5. Y. V. PROKHOROV, Convergence of Random Processes and Limit Theorems in Probability Theory, *Theoret. Probability Appl. 1* (1956), 157–214.
6. A. ROBINSON, *Non-Standard Analysis* (Studies in Logic and the Foundations of Mathematics). Amsterdam: North-Holland, 1966.
7. A. V. SKOROKHOD, *Studies in the Theory of Random Processes* (English translation) 1965, p. 137.

Remarks on the Nonstandard Real Axis[1]

by ELIAS ZAKON

Introduction

Nonstandard structures have so far mainly been treated as a tool, rather than an object, of research. In particular, very little has been done to clarify the topological and order properties of the nonstandard real number system, henceforth denoted by $^*E^1$ (E^1 being the standard real axis). It is known (see [5], 3.1.5) that the order type α of the nonstandard natural number system $^*N$ has the form $\omega + (\omega^* + \omega)\theta$, where θ is a dense order type; but a deeper study of $^*N$ and $^*E^1$ is still missing, both from the viewpoint of ordering and that of topology. In the present paper (which is intended as a continuation and supplement to sec. 3.2 and 4.4 of [5]) we shall study $^*E^1$ more closely, as an ordered set and as a uniform space. For our purposes it will be convenient to adopt the set-theoretical approach presented in [8]. We briefly recall, in Section 1, the notions involved.

1. **Preliminaries**

In [8] we defined the *superstructure* $\hat{A}$ on a set $A = A_0$ of "individuals" by $\hat{A} = \bigcup_{n=0}^{\infty} A_n$, where A_{n+1} is the set of all subsets of $\bigcup_{k=0}^{n} A_k$. In our case, $A = A_0 \supseteq E^1$. We also recall the first-order language L described in [8, sec. 3]: Its constants are identified with the elements of $\hat{A}$, and its atomic formulas have the form $(x_1, \cdots, x_m) \in y$, where y and the x_k are variables or constants. Well-formed formulas (wff) and sentences (wfs) are defined as in [5, p. 7], with the restriction that all quantifiers must have the form "$(\forall x \in C)$" or "$(\exists x \in C)$," with C a *constant* ($C \in \hat{A}$). We denote by K the set of all wfs which are true in $\hat{A}$, with the usual interpretation of the membership symbol $\in$ and the usual

[1] We wish to acknowledge our indebtedness to A. Robinson for many valuable ideas and for his competent advice.

inductive definition of ordered m-tuples: $(x_1, \cdots, x_m) = ((x_1, \cdots, x_{m-1}), x_m)$, $(x_1) = x_1$, $(a, b) = \{\{a, b\}, \{b\}\}$. Sentences which are elements of K (that is, are true in $\hat{A}$) are briefly called *K-sentences*. Thus $\hat{A}$ is a model of K, by definition.[2]

As is shown in [8], other models of K can be obtained by using certain injective maps Φ (called *monomorphisms*) of $\hat{A}$ into other superstructures $\hat{B}$. We write $*X$ for $\Phi(X)$ (*not to be confused with* $\Phi[X] = \{*x | x \in X\}$), and put $*A = \bigcup_{n=0}^{\infty} *A_n$. Elements of $*\hat{A}$ are called the *Φ-internal* (briefly, *internal*) members of B; noninternal elements of $\hat{B}$ are called *external*. Elements of the form $*X$ ($X \in \hat{A}$) are called *Φ-standard* (briefly, *standard*). Given a wff α, we denote by $*\alpha$ the formula obtained from α by replacing in it each *constant* $c \in \hat{A}$ by $*c$, *without changing anything else;* $*\alpha$ is called the *Φ-transform* of α. The injection $\Phi: \hat{A} \to \hat{B}$ is called a *monomorphism* iff $*\hat{A}$ is a model of K in the following sense[3]: *A wff α holds in $\hat{A}$ (that is, is a K-sentence) iff $*\alpha$ holds in $*\hat{A}$.* In this case, as is known, all standard elements are internal, and so are all elements of internal elements. We always identify $*x$ with x if $x \in A_0$. The monomorphism Φ is assumed to be *normal* (see [8], 2.5′), that is, such that $*\Delta$ is the identity map on $*C$ whenever Δ is the identity on C (that is, the diagonal of $C \times C$).

We identify each relation R with its graph. A binary relation $R \in \hat{A}$ is called *concurrent* if, for every finite number of elements $a_1, \cdots, a_m$ of its domain D_R, there is $b \in \hat{A}$ such that $(a_k, b) \in R$, $k = 1, \cdots, m$. The monomorphism Φ is said to be *enlarging* (and $*\hat{A}$ is called an *enlargement* of $\hat{A}$) if, for every concurrent relation $R \in \hat{A}$, there is $b \in *\hat{A}$ such that $(*x, b) \in *R$ for *all* $x \in D_R$. The model $*\hat{A}$ (and Φ) are said to be *comprehensive* if, for every mapping $f: C \to *D$ ($C, D \in \hat{A}$), there is an *internal* map $g: *C \to *D$ ($g \in *\hat{A}$) such that $f(x) = g(*x)$ for all $x \in C$. It is known that $\hat{A}$ always has comprehensive normal enlargements (see [7] and [8], 4.2). However, unless otherwise stated, we only assume that $*\hat{A}$ is a *nonstandard* model of K, that is, such that E^1 is a *proper* subset of $*E^1$. This suffices for the proof (given in [5], p. 51ff.) of the fact that the standard natural numbers (elements of N) are less than all "infinite" naturals (elements of $*N - N$),[4] as well as for other facts stated below; in particular, that $*E^1$ is an ordered field.

[2] For simplicity, $\hat{A}$ will also denote the *structure* based on the object set $\hat{A}$, with atomic predicates described above. Thus $\hat{A}$ is a *model* (of K), along with $*\hat{A}$ as defined in Section 1.

[3] We use this here as a *definition*. In [8] it is Theorem 3.2. A purely set-theoretical definition consists of Postulates 2.1–2.6 of [8].

[4] Note that $*E^1 - E^1 \neq \emptyset$ implies $*N - N \neq \emptyset$. For, if $*N = N$, then the ordered dense subset of all rationals in $*E^1$ would be the same as in E^1, implying $*E^1 \subseteq E^1$.

Turning now specifically to $^*E^1$, we write (as in [5]) $x \sim y$ ($x,y \in {}^*E^1$) iff there is some positive $c \in E^1$ such that $|x - y| < c$; and $x \simeq y$ iff $|x - y| < c$ for *all* such c. The equivalence class of $x \in {}^*E^1$ under the relations $\sim$ and $\simeq$ is called, respectively, the *galaxy* and the *monad* of x, denoted $G(x) = G_x$ and $M(x) = M_x$ (written $\mu(x)$ in [5]). $G(0) = G_0$ is a subring of $^*E^1$; its elements are called *finite* numbers. $M(0) = M_0$ is an additive subgroup of $^*E^1$ and an ideal in G_0; its elements are called *infinitesimals*. The order types of E^1, $^*E^1$, G_0, and M_0 (under the ordering of $^*E^1$) are denoted by λ, λ', λ_0, and μ, respectively. Since these are types of ordered *groups*, in which the map $x \leftrightarrow -x$ is an inverse order isomorphism, they coincide with their inverse types. An ordering (compatible with addition) in the quotient groups $^*E^1/G_0$ and $^*E^1/M_0$ is obtained by setting $G_x \leq G_y$ iff $x < y$ or $x \sim y$, and $M_x \leq M_y$ iff $x < y$ or $x \simeq y$. Thus $^*E^1/G_0$ (the group of all galaxies) and $^*E^1/M_0$ (the group of all monads) are additive *ordered* groups.

The term "ordered" always means "totally ordered." A subset B of an ordered set C is called *convex* iff $x < z < y$ (x, $y \in B$, $z \in C$) implies $z \in B$. We put $C(\cdots a) = \{x \in C \mid x < a\}$, $C(\cdots a] = \{x \in C \mid x \leq a\}$, $C(a,b) = \{x \in C \mid a < x < b\}$, $C[a,b] = \{x \in C \mid a \leq x \leq b\}$; similarly for $C(a, \cdots)$, $C[a \cdots)$, and so on, dropping C if confusion is unlikely. $C(\cdots a)$ and $C(\cdots a]$ are called, respectively, the open and closed *left* (or *initial*) segments of C, with *end point* a; similarly for the *right* segments, $C(a \cdots)$ and $C[a \cdots)$. A Dedekind cut (X, Y) in C is called a *gap* if sup X and inf Y do not exist in C. If there are no gaps, C is called *order-complete* (even if it has no least and no largest element); C is *totally incomplete* iff gaps occur in every open interval $C(a, b) \neq \emptyset$.

The positive parts of E^1 and $^*E^1$ (without 0) are denoted by $E_+{}^1$ and $^*E_+{}^1$, respectively. Two numbers $x,y \in {}^*E_+{}^1$ are said to have the same *rank* or *order of magnitude* if x/y is finite but not infinitesimal, that is, $x/y \in G_0 - M_0$. This is, obviously, an equivalence relation in $^*E_+{}^1$; the equivalence class of an element $a \in E_+{}^1$ is called the *rank of* a, denoted $R(a) = R_a$. In particular, R_1 (the rank of 1) is exactly the positive part of $G_0 - M_0$; R_1 is a *multiplicative* subgroup of $E_+{}^1$. The quotient group $E_+{}^1/R_1$; that is, the group of all ranks, with multiplication defined by $R_aR_b = R_{ab}$, admits a (compatible) ordering: $R_a < R_b$ iff $a/b \simeq 0$. We call $^*E_+{}^1/R_1$, so ordered, the (*multiplicative*) *valuation group* of $^*E^1$. The rank R_a is said to be *infinite* or *infinitesimal* according as $R_a > R_1$ or $R_a < R_1$. An infinite rank splits into many disjoint galaxies (all positive, that is, $> G_0$). All infinitesimal ranks are contained in the positive part of M_0, the monad of 0. In Section 2 we shall show that $^*E_+{}^1/R_1$ is isomorphic with $^*E^1/G_0$. As a by-product we shall also obtain a shorter proof of the density of θ. We always implicitly assume a given monomorphism $\Phi\colon \hat{A} \to \hat{B}$ (where $\hat{B}$ is an arbitrary superstructure), such that $^*A_0 \supseteq {}^*E^1$, and $^*E^1$ properly contains E^1. If $^*\hat{A}$ is supposed to be an enlargement, we prefix "(ENL)" before stating the proposition in question.

2. The Quotient Groups $^*E^1/G_0$ and $^*E_+{}^1/R_1$

We start by listing some rather familiar facts, for later reference.

2.1. (a) *For every* $x \in {}^*E^1$, *there is a unique* $n \in {}^*N$ *such that* $n \leq x < n + 1$.

(b) *The only internal convex subsets of* $^*E^1$ *(that is, those which belong to* $^*A_1$*) are intervals, left and right segments, and* $^*E^1$ *itself.*

(c) $^*E^1$ *is order-isomorphic with any of its left or right open segments and with any of its nondegenerate open intervals* $a, b \neq \varnothing$.

(d) *All galaxies* G_x *(and all monads* M_x*) in* $^*E^1$ *are external convex sets, without end points (that is, infima or suprema). All* G_x *are mutually disjoint and order-isomorphic, of type* λ_0. *Similarly for the* M_x *(which are all of type* μ*).*

(e) $^*E^1$ *is a non-Archimedean (hence incomplete) ordered field.*

We give a brief proof, mainly to illustrate the use of K-sentences (that is, passage from $\hat{A}$ to $^*\hat{A}$) as a method of proof; later such proofs will be omitted.

Assertions (a)–(c) are clearly true, with $^*E^1$, $^*N$, and $^*A_1$ replaced by E^1, N, and A_1, respectively. Moreover, after this replacement, they can be formally written as wff in L, and so become K-sentences in the sense of Section 1. Hence, by properties of monomorphisms, their Φ-transforms are true, and our assertions (a)–(c) result. For the proof of (d) we note that the isomorphisms $G_a \cong G_0$ and $M_a \cong M_0$ are established by the map $x \leftrightarrow x + a$; thus the order types of G_a and M_a are those of G_0 and M_0, respectively, that is, λ_0 and μ. The G_a (and M_a) are equivalence classes, hence disjoint; they are obviously convex since $x < z < y$ $(x, y \in G_a)$ implies $|x - z| < |x - y| < c \in E^1$, that is, $z \in G_a$; and similarly for monads. They are external (the proof given in [5, pp. 54, 58] works also if $^*\hat{A}$ is no enlargement). Hence none of them can have even a single end point; for, by the symmetry of the order types λ_0 and μ (see Section 1), this would entail also the existence of the other end point, which is impossible for an external convex set, that is, not an interval. Thus (d) is proved. We omit the obvious proof of (e).

Theorem 2.2

(a) *The additive Abelian group* $^*E^1/G_0$ *of all galaxies in* $^*E^1$ *is algebraically and order-isomorphic with the multiplicative valuation group* $^*E_+{}^1/R_1$; *moreover, it is divisible and non-Archimedean.*

(b) *Both groups are densely ordered and totally order-incomplete.*

(c) *The order type of the positive part of* $*E^1/G_0$ *(and that of the infinite part of* $*E_+{}^1/R_1$*) is* θ*, where* θ *is the same as in*

2.2.1. $\alpha = \omega + (\omega^* + \omega)\theta =$ *order type of* $*N$.

Proof. As is well known (see [8], 2.6, 2.7(ix), and 3.6), the exponential map $x \to e^x$ extends, on passage from $\hat{A}$ to $*\hat{A}$, to a map $x \to e^x$ on $*E^1$ (it is an *extension* of the original map, by [8], 2.6). Thus e^x is defined for all $x \in *E^1$. By using appropriate K-sentences, one easily shows that it still satisfies $e^{x+y} = e^x e^y$, $e^0 = 1$, and $e^x > 1$ for $x > 0$, and thus e^x increases with x on $*E^1$. We now define a mapping f: $(*E^1/G_0) \to (*E^1_+/R_1)$ by setting $f(G_x) = R(e^x) =$ rank of e^x $(x \in *E^1)$. This is unambiguous. Indeed, if $y \in G_x$ is another representative of G_x and if $x < y$, say, then, by the definition of G_x, $z = y - x \in G_0$ and hence $e^y/e^x = e^z \in G_0$ ($e^z < e^n$ for some $n \in N$; so e^z is *finite*). Moreover, $z > 0$ implies $e^z > 1$, and so $e^z \notin M_0$. Thus $e^y/e^x \in G_0 - M_0$; that is, $R(e^y) = R(e^x)$ by the definition of rank. This proves the validity of the definition of f. Furthermore, f is an order-isomorphism. For if $G_x < G_y$ in the sense of the ordering of $*E^1/G_0$ (see Section 1), then $z = y - x$ is positive *infinite;* hence so is $e^z = e^y/e^x$, implying $R(e^x) < R(e^y)$ in $*E^1/R_1$. As is readily seen, f also preserves the operations defined in $*E^1/G_0$ and $*E^1_+/R_1$ and thus is an algebraic isomorphism as well. Hence, for the rest, we may consider $*E^1/G_0$ alone.

Let $G_a \in *E^1/G_0$ and let $n \in N$, $n \neq 0$. As $*E^1$ is a field, there is an $x \in *E^1$ such that $a = nx = x + x + \cdots + x$ (n times), whence $G_a = G_x + G_x + \cdots + G_x = nG_x$ in $*E^1/G_0$. Thus each G_a is divisible by any $n \in N$ $(n \neq 0)$. In other words, $*E^1/G_0$ is a *divisible* group, hence densely ordered.[5] Next, let $G_a > G_0$, that is, G_a is "positive" in $*E^1/G_0$, so that a is positive *infinite*, and so is $b = \sqrt{a}$ (this root exists in $*E^1$ by the corresponding K-sentence for E^1). Then $G(b) > G_0$ and $G(b) = G(a/b) \leq G(a/n) = G_a/n$ for any $n \in N$, $n \neq 0$. Thus $G(b)$ is a "*nonzero*" (positive) lower bound of the set $\{G_a/n \mid n \in N,\ n \neq 0\}$ in $*E^1/G_0$, and so $*E^1/G_0$ is not Archimedean. Moreover, if $G_x > G_0$ is any positive lower bound of the set $\{G_a/n \mid n \in N,\ n \neq 0\}$, then, as is easily seen, $2G_x$ is a *larger* bound of that set; hence there is no *greatest* lower bound. This shows that the open interval (G_0, G_a) in $*E^1/G_0$ contains a gap, for any $G_a > G_0$. Since translations are order-automorphisms in any ordered group, it follows that *any* open interval in $*E^1/G_0$ has gaps. Thus $*E^1/G_0$ is totally order-incomplete.

Finally, by 2.1(a), each galaxy $G_a > G_0$ contains some $n_a \in *N - N$, $n_a \leq a < n_a + 1$ (n_a is infinite, for a is). We call the set $N \cap G_a \neq \varnothing$,

[5] This shortens the proof of the density θ, given in [5], p. 52 (the idea is essentially the same). It also shows that θ is the type of a set without a first or last element.

denoted N_a, the *natural part* of G_a; its type is $\omega^* + \omega$, since it consists of those $n \in {}^*N$ which differ from n_a by *finite* naturals only. Clearly, the map $G_a \leftrightarrow N_a$ is an order-isomorphism from all positive galaxies onto the set of their natural parts, ordered by the same rule as are the G_a (see Section 1). Let θ denote the order type of either set, in particular, of the succession of the N_a inside ${}^*N - N$. As each N_a is of type $\omega^* + \omega$, Formula 2.2.1 results, and the proof is complete.

As usual, the inverse of an order type ξ is denoted by ξ^*, and its cardinal by $|\xi|$.[6] With this notation (and that of Section 1), we have the following corollaries.

Corollaries 2.3

(a) *The order type of* ${}^*E^1/G_0$ *and* ${}^*E_+^1/R_1$ *is* $\theta^* + 1 + \theta$.

(b) *The order types of* ${}^*E^1$, M_x, *and* G_x $(x \in {}^*E^1)$ *are, respectively:* $\lambda' = \lambda_0(\theta^* + 1 + \theta)$, $\mu = \lambda_0\theta + 1 + \lambda_0\theta^*$ *and* $\lambda_0 = \mu\lambda$, *where* λ *is the order type of* E^1.

(c) $|\lambda'| = |\mu| = |\lambda_0|$.

(d) ${}^*E^1$, M_0, *and* G_0 *are totally order-incomplete and non-Archimedean.*

Proof. As θ is the type of the positive part of ${}^*E^1/G_0$ (by Theorem 2.2), θ^* is that of the negative part. Inserting also the zero of ${}^*E^1/G_0$ (that is, G_0, treated as a *single* element), we obtain $\theta^* + 1 + \theta$ as the type of all of ${}^*E^1/G_0$ [hence also of E_+^1/R_1, by Theorem 2.2(a)], as asserted. It follows that ${}^*E^1$ is built from a $(\theta^* + 1 + \theta)$-type succession of disjoint galaxies, each of type λ_0 [see 2.1(d)]; and so its type is $\lambda' = \lambda_0(\theta^* + 1 + \theta)$. Similarly, G_0 consists of all monads of standard points, forming a set of type λ; thus the type of G_0 (hence of each G_x) is $\lambda_0 = \mu\lambda$ (μ being the type of a monad and λ that of E^1). Next, the positive part of M_0 is, clearly, the image of ${}^*E_+^1 - G_0$ (positive infinite numbers) under the inverse order-isomorphism $x \leftrightarrow 1/x$. Thus its type is the inverse of $\lambda_0\theta$ (the type of ${}^*E_+^1 - G_0$), that is, $(\lambda_0\theta)^* = \lambda_0{}^*\theta^* = \lambda_0\theta^*$, while the negative part of M_0 is of type $\lambda_0\theta$. Including also 0, we obtain $\mu = \lambda_0\theta + 1 + \lambda_0\theta^*$ as the type of M_0 (and of any M_x). This proves (b), and easily implies (c).

Finally, to prove (d), it suffices to consider infinitely small intervals of the form $(0, 1/a)$, where a is positive infinite. Exactly as in the proof of Theorem 2.2, one shows that all points of the form $1/a + n$, $n \in N$, constitute a set with positive lower bounds in $(0, 1/a)$, but with no infimum. This exhibits a gap in $(0, 1/a)$; hence in any arbitrarily small interval of ${}^*E^1$ (by translation), and assertion (d) easily follows. Thus all is proved.

[6] Similarly, the power of a set C is denoted by $|C|$.

3. Some Properties of the Order Type θ and of the Set $^*N$

Theorem 3.1

(a) *Any nondegenerate interval in an ordered set of type θ has at least continuum power, $2^{\aleph_0}$. The same applies to intervals $^*N(m, n)$ of infinite length $n - m$.*

(b) *Hence the cardinal of $^*N$ and of θ (denoted $|\theta|$) is $\geq 2^{\aleph_0}$.*

(c) *$|\theta|$ is also the number of all monads in $^*E^1$.*

Proof. Fix an infinite natural n, $n \in {}^*N - N$. Then the points $0, 1/n, 2/n, \cdots, (k+1)/n, \cdots, k < n, k \in {}^*N$, constitute a partition of the interval $^*E^1[0, 1]$ into subintervals $[k/n, (k+1)/n]$ (the fact that $[0, 1] = \bigcup_{k<n}[k/n, (k+1)/n]$ easily follows from 2.1(a)). As the length $1/n$ of these intervals is infinitesimal (n being infinite), each of them is contained in exactly one of the disjoint monads M_x that cover $[0, 1]$, and each such M_x, with $x \in [0, 1]$, contains at least one such interval. Hence the number of these intervals cannot be less than that of the M_x, $x \in [0, 1]$; that is, *it is* $\geq 2^{\aleph_0}$ (recall that there are as many such M_x as there are *standard* points in $[0, 1]$). But the intervals $[k/n, (k+1)/n]$ are in one-to-one correspondence with the values of k, $k \in {}^*N[0, n-1]$, and so their number equals the cardinal of the interval $^*N[0, n-1]$. Thus this cardinal is $\geq 2^{\aleph_0}$. By translation, this applies to any interval $^*N[m, m+n-1]$ of infinite length. The (uncountable) power of such intervals will not change also if each component N_a of $^*N$ (of type $\omega^* + \omega$) is replaced by a single point, thus transforming $^*N - N$ into some set C of type θ ($\cong$ to the positive part of $^*E^1/G_0$). Moreover, it is obvious that infinite intervals in $^*N - N$ correspond exactly to nondegenerate intervals of C (that is, those containing at least two points). This proves assertions (a) and (b). Furthermore, the number of all monads in G_0 (hence in each G_x) equals the cardinal of E^1, that is, $2^{\aleph_0}$, so it is $\leq |\theta|$. On the other hand, by Theorem 2.2(c), $|\theta|$ also equals the number of all galaxies G_x, so it cannot exceed the number of all monads in these galaxies. Thus $|\theta| \cdot 2^{\aleph_0} = |\theta|$ is the number of all monads in $^*E^1$. This completes the proof.

A set $D \in {}^*\hat{A}$ is said to be *star-finite* (**finite*) if there is an internal bijective mapping of D onto some interval of $^*N$. By Theorem 3.1, any such set is either finite or of power $\geq 2^{\aleph_0}$. More can be said if $^*\hat{A}$ is an enlargement:

Theorem 3.2 (***ENL***). *For each $n \in N$, there are *finite sets (hence also intervals in $^*N$ and in any set of order type θ) of power $> |\hat{A}_n|$, the cardinal of A_n, with $|A_0| \geq |E^1| = 2^{\aleph_0}$ and $|A_{n+1}| = 2^{|A_n|}$. Moreover, $|\theta| \geq |\hat{A}|$ (= power of $\hat{A}$).*

Proof. We shall use a known proposition (see [4], 1.5.1) which, in our set-theoretical language, can be expressed as follows:

3.2.1. *If a monomorphism* $\Phi: \hat{A} \to \hat{B}$ *is enlarging then, for every set* $P \in \hat{A}$, *there is a *finite set* Q *such that* $*P \supseteq Q \supseteq \Phi[P] = \{*x \mid x \in P\}$, $Q \in *\hat{A}$.

[Indeed, this is trivial if P is finite. In the infinite case, the proof is based on the concurrence of the binary relation $R = \{(x, Y) \mid x \in Y \subseteq P, |Y| < \aleph_0\}$, on noting that $*R = \{(x, Y) \mid x \in Y \subseteq *P, Y$ star-finite$\}$; see [8], 3.2(b).]

Setting here $P = A_n$, we obtain a *finite set $Q \supseteq \Phi[A_n]$, whence, as Φ is injective, $|Q| \geq |A_n|$. Moreover, the *finiteness of Q implies, by definition, that Q has the same power as some interval of $*N$, hence also as some interval in any set of order type θ (by the argument used in the proof of Theorem 3.1). This proves the first clause of Theorem 3.2. The fact that $|A_0| \geq |E^1| = 2^{\aleph_0}$ and that $|A_{n+1}| = 2^{|A_n|}$, $n = 0, 1, 2, \cdots$ follows directly from our inductive definition of A_n (see Section 1). Finally, by what was shown above, the power $|\theta|$ of the entire set $*N$ must exceed *each* $|A_n|$, and hence $|\theta| \geq |\bigcup_{n=0}^{\infty} A_n| = |\hat{A}|$.[7] Thus all is proved.

NOTE 1. The requirement that $*\hat{A}$ be an enlargement is essential in Theorem 3.2. Otherwise, it may well occur that $|\theta| = |*N| = |*E^1| = 2^{\aleph_0}$. See example constructed in [6], p. 243.

As a result of Theorem 3.2, Corollary 3.3 can be strengthened (replacing $2^{\aleph_0}$ by $|\hat{A}|$) if $*\hat{A}$ is an enlargement. In the general case, however, we only have

Corollary 3.3. *With the notation of Corollaries* 2.3, *we have* $2^{\aleph_0} \leq |\theta| \leq |\mu| = |\lambda_0| = |\lambda'| \leq 2^{|\theta|}$, *where* $|\xi|$ *denotes the cardinal of an order type* ξ.

Indeed, noting that the power of $*N$ is $|\theta|$, we obtain the inequality $|\lambda'| \leq 2^{|\theta|}$ from the K-sentence[8] "$*E^1$ can be mapped, one to one, on the family of all *internal* subsets of $*N$." The rest is immediate from Theorem 3.1 and Corollaries 2.3.

Theorem 3.4. *Any set of order type* θ, λ', λ_0, *or* μ *(for example,* $*E^1$, G_0, *or* M_0*) has dense subsets of power* $|\theta|$ *but no dense subsets of power* $< |\theta|$.

[7] Indeed, it is easy to see that $*N$ contains a sequence of disjoint intervals $[m_k, n_k]$, $k = 0, 1, 2, \cdots$, with $[m_k, n_k]$ of power $\geq |A_k|$. Thus $*N$ has a subset equipollent with $\bigcup_{k=0}^{\infty} A_k$, and our assertion follows.

[8] In a wider sense, the term "K-sentence" means also "any sentence equivalent to a K-sentence"; this includes also the Φ-transform of a K-sentence.

Proof. We consider the positive part of $^*E^1/G_0$ as a typical set of type θ. If a set D of positive galaxies is dense in it, we choose from each member of D a representative *belonging to* $^*N - N$, thus obtaining a set $N' \subset {}^*N - N$, of the same power as D, with the following property:

3.4.1. *For any m, $n \in {}^*N$, with $n - m \in {}^*N - N$, there is $k \in N'$ such that $m < k < n$.*

Let F be the least subfield of $^*E^1$ that contains N'. Then F has the same power as N' and D, since F consists of all finite "rational combinations" of elements of N'. Moreover, F is dense in $^*E^1$. Indeed, let $a < b$, a, $b \in {}^*E_+^1$ (it suffices to consider the *positive* part of $^*E^1$). By 3.4.1, there is $n \in N'$ with $n > 1/(b - a)$ so that $1/n < b - a$. By 2.1(a), there is $k \in {}^*N$ such that $k - 1 \leq an < k$, and so $a \leq k/n < b$. Moreover, n can be chosen so large that $a \leq k/n < (k + 1)/n < b$; that is, $a \leq nk/n^2 < (nk + n)/n^2 < b$. Now, since $(nk + n) - nk = n$ is *infinite* (for $n \in N'$), 3.4.1 yields a number $q \in N'$ such that $nk < q < nk + n$, whence $a < q/n^2 < b$. Here q/n^2 belongs to the field F (for q, $n \in N'$), and so the density of F in $^*E^1$ is proved. But this implies that every monad M_x (being a convex set) must contain an element of F, and so, by the disjointness of the M_x, the cardinal of F (hence that of D) cannot be less than $|\theta|$, the number of all monads in $^*E^1$ [see 3.1(c)]. This proves Corollary 3.3 for sets of type θ, and also for $^*E^1$ (the fact that $^*E^1$ does have dense subsets of power $|\theta|$ is obvious, since numbers of the form m/n, $m,n \in {}^*N - \{0\}$, are dense in $^*E^1$, as was shown above). By 2.1(c), then, Theorem 3.4 also applies to intervals, hence to convex sets in $^*E^1$, such as M_0 and G_0.

Corollaries 3.5

(a) *If an ordered set E has a subset of type θ, then E has no dense subsets of power $< |\theta|$.*

(b) *Any ordered set of type θ, λ', λ_0, or μ has at least $|\theta|$ gaps.*

(c) *E^1 has no subsets of type θ.*

Proof

(a) Suppose that E has a subset C of type θ and a dense subset D. Then C is densely ordered, and so, by the density of D in E, each interval $E(a, b)$ with $a,b \in C$ contains some a', $b' \in D$ such that $a' < x_{a'b'} < b'$ for some $x_{a'b'} \in C$. We now fix such an $x_{a'b'}$ for each pair of elements a', $b' \in D$ with $C \cap E(a', b') \neq \varnothing$. Then, clearly, all $x_{a'b'}$ so chosen form a dense subset C' of C whose power does not exceed that of $D \times D$. On the other hand, by Theorem 3.4, C' has power $|\theta|$ at least. *A fortiori* this applies to $D \times D$, hence to D (for D must be infinite). This proves (a), and also (c), since E^1 has *countable* dense subsets.

(b) Let C be a set of type θ, hence totally incomplete, by Theorem

2.2(b). This implies that the set D of all gaps of C is dense in the order completion $\bar{C}$ of C. Thus, by (a), D must have power $|\theta|$ at least. A similar proof applies to any set of type λ' on noting that $*E^1$ has subsets of type θ. By 2.1(c), it also applies to any interval in $*E^1$, hence also to M_0 and G_0, by convexity.

Theorem 3.6. *The set* $\mathfrak{N}$ *of all gaps in the infinite natural number system* $*N - N$ *is order-isomorphic with the set of all Dedekind cuts* (X, Y) *in the positive part of* $*E^1/G_0$ *(or in the infinite part of* $*E_+{}^1/R_1$*), including cuts in which* X *has a largest, or* Y *has a least, element. Its power is* $\geq |\theta|$.

Proof. Recall that $*N - N$ is of type $(\omega^* + \omega)\theta$, where $\omega^* + \omega$ is the order type of the natural part N_a of any galaxy $G_a > G_0$. As $\omega^* + \omega$ has no gaps, the gaps in $*N - N$ lie between "whole" galaxies G_a (for N_a is both cofinal and coinitial with G_a). More precisely, they correspond to Dedekind cuts (X, Y) in the positive part of the set $*E^1/G_0$ of all galaxies. Such a cut may, but need not, be a gap in $*E^1/G_0$ itself. Indeed, even if X has the form $(G_0, G_a]$ or (G_0, G_a), that is, it consists of all positive galaxies $G_x \leq G_a$ (or $G_x < G_a$) the cut (X, Y) still defines a gap in $*N - N$, which immediately "follows" or "precedes" N_a, in a self-evident sense. Thus to obtain *all* gaps in $*N - N$ one must take *all* cuts in the positive part of $*E^1/G_0$, including those cuts (X, Y) in which X has the form $(G_0, G_a]$ or (G_0, G_a), so that the number of the gaps is $|\theta|$ at least. Finally, by Theorem 2.2, we may replace $*E^1/G_0$ by $*E_+{}^1/R_1$ in this argument. This completes the proof.

NOTE 2. It also follows that the set $\mathfrak{N}$ of all gaps in $*N - N$ is not densely ordered, since *there are pairs of gaps with no intermediate gap between them,* namely those defined by cuts (X, Y) and (X', Y'), with $X = (G_0, G_a)$ and $X' = (G_0, G_a]$ (we then say that the two gaps are *adjacent*). However, $\mathfrak{N}$ becomes densely ordered if gaps of the form $X' = (G_0, G_a]$ are excluded. Then $\mathfrak{N}$ becomes order-isomorphic to the completion of a set of type θ.

Theorem 3.7. *In a comprehensive model* $*\hat{A}$ *(see Section 1), the set* $*N - N$ *of infinite naturals has no cofinal or coinitial subsets of power* $\leq \aleph_0$*; nor does any set of type* θ, λ', *or* μ *have such subsets.*

Proof. We use the K-sentence "For each $k_0 \in N$, every sequence $S = \{n_k \mid k < k_0\}$, $n_k \in N$, has a largest term" (being a *finite* sequence of naturals). Hence it follows that, for each $k_0 \in *N$ (finite or infinite), every *internal* sequence $\{n_k \mid k < k_0\}$, $n_k \in *N$, has a largest term. This shows that $*N$ has no *internal* cofinal subsets of power $\leq \aleph_0$ (for the proof, take an *infinite* k_0). Now suppose that $S = \{n_k \mid k \in N\}$,

$n_k \in {}^*N$, is external (that is, not a member of ${}^*\hat{A}$). Then, as the monomorphism $x \to {}^*x$ is comprehensive, there is an *internal* function $g: {}^*N \to {}^*N$ such that $g({}^*k) = g(k) = n_k$ for $k \in N$, that is, for $n_k \in S$. Fix an infinite $k_0 \in {}^*N$. Then, by what was said above, the (internal) subsequence $\{g(k) \mid k < k_0\}$ has a largest term $g(\bar{k})$ for some $\bar{k} < k_0$, so that $g(k) \leq g(\bar{k})$ for all $k < k_0$, and certainly for $k \in N$, that is, for $g(k) = n_k \in S$. Thus any countable set $S \subset {}^*N$ has an upper bound in ${}^*N$. This proves the first clause of Theorem 3.7, for *cofinal* sets. For coinitial subsets, it was proved in [7]. Next, suppose that a set C of type θ has a countable cofinal subset. Then, as is easily seen, the formula $\alpha = \omega + (\omega^* + \omega)\theta$ (see 2.2.1) yields a countable cofinal subset for ${}^*N$ as well (contradiction!). Similarly for coinitial subsets. Thus Theorem 3.7 holds for sets of type θ, hence also for those of type λ' or μ, as follows from Corollaries 2.3. Thus the theorem is proved.

NOTE 3. The theorem does not apply to λ_0, the type of G_0, since G_0 does have countable cofinal subsets (for example, N). Thus, *under a comprehensive monomorphism, λ_0 is different from θ, λ', and μ.*

As ${}^*N$ is totally ordered, it has a cofinal wellordered subset ${}^\#N$. We choose ${}^\#N$ of least possible type, denoted Ω, and call Ω the *character* of ${}^*N$ (and of θ). Because of its minimality, it is a regular initial ordinal, so that the segment of ordinals $(\cdots\Omega)$ has no cofinal subsets of smaller type or power. We may think of ${}^\#N$ as of a strictly increasing Ω-type sequence of naturals $m_\eta \in {}^*N$ ($\eta < \Omega$), at infinite distances $|m_\eta - m_\xi|$ from each other. Fixing this sequence once and for all, we call it the *${}^\#N$-sequence* (in ${}^*N$). By Theorem 3.7, $|\Omega| > \aleph_0$ if ${}^*\hat{A}$ is comprehensive.

Assuming that ${}^*\hat{A}$ is also an enlargement, we can use Theorem 3.2 to choose, by induction, for each $n \in N$ a term of the ${}^\#N$-sequence $m_{\eta_n} = m'_n$ in such a manner that $m'_n < m'_{n+1}$ and that the power $|A_n|$ of A_n is less than that of the interval ${}^*N[m_n, m_{n+1})$, $n = 0, 1, 2, \cdots$. The ω-type sequence $\{m'_n \mid n \in N\}$ is *not* cofinal with ${}^\#N$ (since $\omega < \Omega$, by the assumed comprehensiveness of ${}^*\hat{A}$), so it has an upper bound m' in ${}^\#N$. By construction, ${}^*N[0, m']$ has a subset equipollent to $\bigcup_{n=0}^{\infty} \hat{A}_n = \hat{A}$, and so $[{}^*N[0, m']| \geq |\hat{A}|$. We thus obtain:

***Theorem* 3.8 (*ENL*).** *In a comprehensive enlargement, there are intervals in ${}^*N$ (and in any set of order type θ), of power $\geq|\hat{A}|$. Hence there also are star-finite sets of such power.*

Furthermore, we have:

***Theorem* 3.9.** *In a comprehensive model ${}^*\hat{A}$, no ordered set of type θ, λ_0, λ', or μ has open intervals with a countable cofinal or coinitial subset.*

Proof. $^*E^1$ can have no such intervals by Theorem 3.7 and 2.1(c), since all intervals in $^*E^1$ are of type λ', as is $^*E^1$ itself. *A fortiori* there are no such intervals in G_0 and M_0, for they are also intervals in $^*E^1$. This proves the theorem for sets of type λ', λ_0, and μ. As a typical set of type θ, we take again the positive part of $^*E^1/G_0$ and consider an open interval (G_a, G_b), $G_a < G_b$. Seeking a contradiction, suppose it has a cofinal countable subset which we put in an increasing sequence $\{G_{x_k} \mid k \in N\}$, $G_k < G_{k+1} < G_b$. Then $\{x_k\}$ is an increasing sequence in $^*E_+{}^1$. On the other hand, G_b is a set of type λ_0, and so it contains a coinitial decreasing sequence of elements $\{y_k \mid k \in N\}$, with $x_k < y_k$ for $k \in N$. By the assumed comprehensiveness of $^*\hat{A}$, there are two *internal* functions $f, g\colon {}^*N \to {}^*E_+{}^1$ such that $f(k) = x_k$ and $g(k) = y_k$ for $k \in N$. Now let P be the set of all $n \in {}^*N$ with the property that $f(k) < f(n) < g(n) < g(k)$ for each $k < n$. Obviously P is internal (for f, g are), and $P \supseteq N$. As N is external (see [5], p. 54), $P \neq N$; so P must contain some $n_0 \in {}^*N - N$. This implies $f(k) < f(n_0) < g(n_0) < g(k)$ for all $k < n_0$, hence certainly for $k \in N$. Thus, setting $p = f(n_0)$, $q = g(n_0)$, we have $x_k = f(k) < p < q < g(k) = y_k$ for $k \in N$. It follows that $q \notin G_b$ for, by assumption, the y_k cannot have a lower bound in G_b. Thus $G_q < G_b$. On the other hand, as $x_k < q$ for all $k \in N$, G_q is an upper bound of the sequence of galaxies $G_{x_k} \in (G_a, G_b)$, contrary to the assumed cofinality of $\{G_{x_k}\}$ in (G_a, G_b). This settles the cofinal case of the theorem. The coinitial case is treated in a similar manner. Thus all is proved.

Corollary 3.10. *In a comprehensive model $^*\hat{A}$, the set $^*E^1$ has no Dedekind cuts (X, Y) in which X has a cofinal, while Y has a coinitial, countable subset.*

The proof is quite analogous to that of Theorem 3.9. We omit the details.

Thus, if $^*\hat{A}$ is comprehensive, a point or a gap can *never* be defined by a countable sequence of nondegenerated nested intervals in $^*E^1$. But there are gaps (X, Y) in which *either* X has a cofinal, *or* Y has a coinitial, countable subset, for example, the gap between G_0 and $E_+{}^1 - G_0$.

4. The Uniform Topology of $^*E^1$

A deeper insight into the structure of $^*E^1$ can be gained by treating it as a uniform space. In this respect we shall have to supplement the topological notions of [5] by some ideas of [4]; however, as before, we shall not need the assumption that $^*\hat{A}$ is an enlargement (let alone a saturated ultrapower in the sense of [4]). In topology we shall use the terminology of Kelley [3], slightly modifying his notation.

On passage from $\hat{A}$ to $^*\hat{A}$, the standard metric $\rho(x, y) = |x - y|$ of E^1 extends to a $^*E^1$-valued metric $^*\rho(x, y) = |x - y|$ in $^*E^1$. We denote by τ the standard topology of (E^1, ρ) ("topology" means "the family of all open sets," throughout). On passage to $^*\hat{A}$, τ turns into $^*\tau$. As is well known, $^*\tau$ is a base for a topology in $^*E^1$, called the *Q-topology*, which we denote by $\overline{^*\tau}$; its members are called *Q-open* sets. Moreover, the base $^*\tau$ consists exactly of all *internal* members of $\overline{^*\tau}$ (see [5], 4.2.9), that is, internal Q-open sets (called simply "open" sets in [5]). Another base of $\overline{^*\tau}$, contained in $^*\tau$, consists of all Q-open *balls*, that is, sets of the form $\{x \in {^*E^1} \mid |x - a| < r\}$, $a \in {^*E^1}$, $r \in {^*E_+^1}$. All such balls are internal, hence members of $^*\tau$.

A subset of $E^1 \times E^1$ is called an *entourage* (in E^1) if it contains a set of the form $\{(x, y) \mid x, y \in E^1, |x - y| < r\}$, $r \in E_+^1$. The set $\mathbf{u}$ of all such entourages is a filter, called the *standard uniformity* on E^1.[9] On passage to $^*\hat{A}$, $\mathbf{u}$ is transformed into an internal family $^*\mathbf{u} = \Phi(\mathbf{u})$ of subsets of $^*E^1 \times {^*E^1}$, to be distinguished from its subfamily $\Phi[\mathbf{u}] = \{^*U \mid U \in \mathbf{u}\}$. We have:

Theorem 4.1

(a) *The set families $^*u$ and $\Phi[u]$ are bases for certain uniformities on $^*E^1$, denoted by $\overline{^*\mathbf{u}}$ and $\overline{\Phi[\mathbf{u}]}$, respectively, with $\overline{^*\mathbf{u}} \supset \overline{\Phi[\mathbf{u}]}$, properly.*

(b) *Another base for $\overline{^*\mathbf{u}}$ consists of all sets* (called *metric entourages in* $^*E^1$) *of the form $U_r = \{(x, y) \mid x, y \in {^*E^1}, |x - y| < r\}, r \in {^*E_+^1}$.*

(c) *All those U_r in which $r \in E_+^1$ (though $x,y \in {^*E^1}$) form a base for* $\overline{\Phi[\mathbf{u}]}$.

(d) *The uniform topology of $(^*E^1, \overline{^*\mathbf{u}})$ is exactly the Q-topology, $\overline{^*\tau}$.*

Proof. From the definition of the standard uniformity $\mathbf{u}$ in E^1 it follows, on passage to $^*\hat{A}$, that $^*\mathbf{u}$ consists exactly of those subsets of $^*E^1 \times {^*E^1}$ which are *internal* supersets of metric entourages U_r defined in (b). These U_r, however, are a base for a uniformity on $^*E^1$ (call it $\overline{^*u}$) consisting of *all* supersets of the U_r (the proof that $\overline{^*\mathbf{u}}$ is, indeed, a uniformity is the same as in ordinary metric spaces). Since $^*\mathbf{u} \subset \overline{^*\mathbf{u}}$, and each member of $^*\mathbf{u}$ contains some U_r, it follows that $^*\mathbf{u}$ is another (larger) base for the same uniformity $\overline{^*\mathbf{u}}$. Note that each U_r is in $^*\mathbf{u}$, being an *internal* superset of itself.

Similarly, all U_r with *standard* r ($r \in E_+^1$) form a base for a uniformity $\overline{\Phi[\mathbf{u}]}$. Also, if $U \in \mathbf{u}$, then, by definition, $U \supseteq \{(x, y) \mid x, y \in E^1,$

[9] For the general notion of a uniformity, see [3], p. 176.

$|x - y| < r\}$ for some $r_0 \in E_+{}^1$, and hence $^*U \supseteq U_{r_0} = \{(x, y) \mid x, y \in {}^*E^1, |x - y| < r_0\}$. Thus each $^*U$ contains some U_{r_0} with $r_0 \in E_+{}^1$, and so $\Phi[\mathbf{u}] = \{^*U \mid U \in \mathbf{u}\}$ is another base for $\overline{\Phi[\mathbf{u}]}$. As $\Phi[\mathbf{u}] \subset {}^*\mathbf{u}$, we have $\overline{\Phi[\mathbf{u}]} \subseteq \overline{^*\mathbf{u}}$. This inclusion is *proper* because $\overline{^*\mathbf{u}}$ contains, by definition, *all* U_r, whereas no U_r with $r \simeq 0$ can belong to $\overline{\Phi[\mathbf{u}]}$; otherwise, it would be (by the definition of $\overline{\Phi[\mathbf{u}]}$) a superset of some U_{r_0} with $r_0 \in E_+{}^1$, which is clearly impossible. Thus, indeed, $\overline{\Phi[\mathbf{u}]} \neq \overline{^*\mathbf{u}}$.

Finally, since all U_r $(r \in {}^*E_+{}^1)$ form a base for $\overline{^*\mathbf{u}}$, the uniform topology of $(^*E^1, \overline{^*\mathbf{u}})$ has a base consisting of all sets of the form $U_r(x) = \{y \mid (x, y) \in U_r\} = \{y \in {}^*E^1 \mid |x - y| < r\}$, $r \in {}^*E_+{}^1$, that is, of all Q-open balls. But, as is well known, these balls are also a base for the Q-topology, $\overline{^*\tau}$. Thus the latter must coincide with the $\overline{^*\mathbf{u}}$-topology. This completes the proof of the theorem.

In this connection, we shall call $\overline{^*\mathbf{u}}$ the *Q-uniformity* on $^*E^1$. On the other hand, all sets of the form $U(x) = \{y \mid (x, y) \in U\}$, $U \in \overline{\Phi[\mathbf{u}]}$, $x \in {}^*E^1$, constitute the neighborhood system of the (coarser) topology determined by the uniformity $\overline{\Phi[\mathbf{u}]}$. It is easy to show that this is exactly the *S-topology*, as defined in [5], pages 106–107.[10] Therefore we shall call $\overline{\Phi[\mathbf{u}]}$ the *S-uniformity* on $^*E^1$. By Theorem 4.1, the S-topology is *strictly* coarser than the Q-topology.

In the proof of Theorem 4.1 we also have established the following fact:

Corollary 4.2. *The base* $^*\mathbf{u}$ *consists exactly of all internal members of the Q-uniformity* $\overline{^*\mathbf{u}}$. *It includes all metric entourages* U_r $(r \in {}^*E_+{}^1)$.

We shall now exhibit some *external* entourages and thus show that $^*\mathbf{u}$ and $\Phi[\mathbf{u}]$ are not filters, that is, that $^*\mathbf{u} \neq \overline{^*\mathbf{u}}$ and $\Phi[\mathbf{u}] \neq \overline{\Phi[\mathbf{u}]}$. (*Note:* "Entourage" means "member of $\overline{^*\mathbf{u}}$," unless another uniformity is specified.)

Corollary 4.3. *The sets* $M = \{(x, y) \mid x, y \in {}^*E^1, x \simeq y\}$ *and* $G = \{(x, y) \mid x, y \in {}^*E^1, x \sim y\}$ *are external members of the Q-uniformity* $\overline{^*\mathbf{u}}$ *on* $^*E^1$.

In fact, we have $G \supset M \supset U_r = \{(x, y) \mid x, y \in {}^*E^1, |x - y| < r\}$ for any infinitesimal $r > 0$, and $G \supset U_{r'}$ for any $r' \in E_+{}^1$. Since $U_r \in {}^*\mathbf{u}$ (= base of the filter $\overline{^*\mathbf{u}}$) and $U_{r'} \in \Phi[\mathbf{u}]$ (= base of $\overline{\Phi[\mathbf{u}]}$), we have $M, G \in \overline{^*\mathbf{u}}$ and $G \in \overline{\Phi[\mathbf{u}]}$. Moreover, as is easily seen, the neighborhoods

[10] In fact, each $U(x)$ contains a "ball" $U_r(x)$ with $r \in E_+{}^1$, and hence the S-ball $S(x, r)$ as defined in [5]. Conversely, each S-ball contains some $U_r(x)$, $r \in E_+{}^1$. Thus the two neighborhood systems are equivalent. *Note:* $U_r(x)$ is *not* S-open.

$M(x)$ and $G(x)$, $x \in {}^*E^1$, are, respectively, the monad of x and the galaxy of x, as previously defined. As the latter are external sets [see 2.1(d)], so must be M and G as well; for, otherwise, the sets $M(x) = \{y \mid x, y \in M\}$ and $G(x) = \{y \mid x, y \in G\}$ would be internal. This proves Corollary 4.3, and yields a new approach to M_x and G_x.

The entourage M defined in Corollary 4.3 is called the *monad* of the Q-uniformity $\overline{{}^*\mathbf{u}}$. Set-theoretically, M and G are simply the equivalence relations $\simeq$ and $\sim$, respectively. An entourage $U \in \overline{{}^*\mathbf{u}}$ is said to be *infinitesimal* iff $U \subset M$,[11] *finite* iff $U \subseteq G$, and *infinite* iff $U \supset G$ (properly). This does not exhaust all kinds of entourages in $\overline{{}^*\mathbf{u}}$. An infinitesimal or infinite entourage may be internal (take a metric entourage U_r with $r \simeq 0$, or infinite r).

***Corollary* 4.4.** *$(E^1, \mathbf{u})$ is a uniform subspace of $({}^*E^1, \overline{\Phi[\mathbf{u}]})$, not of $({}^*E^1, \overline{{}^*\mathbf{u}})$.*

Proof. We must show that all $U \in \mathbf{u}$ are exactly the "traces" in $E^1 \times E^1$ of members of $\overline{\Phi[\mathbf{u}]}$. Now, if $W \in \overline{\Phi[\mathbf{u}]}$, then (as the standard entourages ${}^*U$ form a base of $\overline{\Phi[\mathbf{u}]}$) there is $U \in \mathbf{u}$ such that ${}^*U \subseteq W \subseteq {}^*E^1 \times {}^*E^1$. Since $U \subseteq {}^*U$, we get $U = (E^1 \times E^1) \cap {}^*U \subseteq (E^1 \times E^1) \cap W \subseteq (E^1 \times E^1) \cap ({}^*E^1 \times {}^*E^1) = E^1 \times E^1$, which shows that $(E^1 \times E^1) \cap W$ is an entourage in $(E^1, \mathbf{u})$. Conversely, each $U \in \mathbf{u}$ is the trace of the corresponding ${}^*U \in \overline{\Phi[\mathbf{u}]}$. Thus $(E^1, \mathbf{u})$ is indeed a subspace of $({}^*E^1, \overline{\Phi[\mathbf{u}]})$, but not of $({}^*E^1, \overline{{}^*\mathbf{u}})$, for the trace of the monad $M \in \overline{{}^*\mathbf{u}}$ is the diagonal $\Delta \notin \mathbf{u}$.

5. Dedekind Cuts in E_+^1. Quasimetric and Monadic Entourages

After the general remarks of Section 4 (which, to a great extent, apply to all metric spaces) we now turn to some special properties of ${}^*E^1$, linking its topology to Dedekind cuts in its positive part, ${}^*E_+^1$. From Section 4 we recall that a *metric entourage* is a set of the form $U_r = \{(x, y) \mid x, y \in {}^*E^1, |x - y| < r\}$, $r \in {}^*E_+^1$. Now, given a Dedekind cut (X, Y) in ${}^*E_+^1$, we put $U_X = \bigcup \{U_r \mid r \in X\}$ (equivalently, $U_X = \bigcap \{U_r \mid r \in Y\}$) and call U_X the *quasimetric entourage* determined by (X, Y). In particular, each metric entourage U_r is also quasimetric; it is determined by the cut (X, Y) where $X = {}^*E^1(0, r)$ and $Y = {}^*E^1[r \cdots)$. We have $U_X \subseteq U_{X'}$ iff $X \subseteq X'$, provided we exclude cuts with a largest

[11] We use $\subset$ for *proper* inclusion and $\subseteq$ for ordinary inclusion. We exclude M from infinitesimal entourages mainly for symmetry: M and G are *both* neither infinite nor infinitesimal. This convention simplifies formulations (as in Corollary 5.2).

element in X. Thus the set of all quasimetric entourages is totally ordered by inclusion, being order-isomorphic with the so-depleted set of all cuts in $*E_+^1$.

We shall apply the names "Q-topology" and "S-topology" (see Section 4) also to the corresponding product topologies in $*E^1 \times *E^1$. In this sense, an entourage may be Q-open, S-closed, and so on, as a subset of $*E^1 \times *E^1$. In accordance with the now common usage, "*clopen*" means "both open and closed." A quasimetric entourage is always Q-open and symmetric, as easily follows from the fact that it is a union of metric entourages possessing these properties; it is in general not S-open, even if it belongs to the S-uniformity $\overline{\Phi[\mathbf{u}]}$. Given any entourage U and a set $C \subseteq *E^1$, we put $U[C] = \bigcup \{U(x) \mid x \in C\}$, where $U(x) = \{y \mid x, y \in U\}$. Thus all entourages (in particular, M and G, as defined in Section 4) are operators on subsets of $*E^1$. We call $U[C]$ the *U-neighborhood* of C; it is Q- or S-open if U is. As is readily seen, $U(x)$ is a convex set if U is quasimetric; it is an *interval* (hence internal) if U is a metric entourage, and then U itself is internal, too. It follows by 2.1(b) that *a quasimetric entourage U_X is internal iff it is metric, that is, iff the corresponding cut (X, Y) is not a gap in $*E_+^1$.*

The entourages M and G introduced in Section 4 are quasimetric. Indeed, by definition, $M = \{(x, y) \mid |x - y| \simeq 0\} = \bigcap \{U_r \mid r \in E_+^1\} = \bigcup \{U_r \mid 0 < r \in M_0\}$, and so $M = U_X$, where X is the positive part of M_0, the monad of 0. Similarly, $G = U_{X'}$, where X' is the positive part of G_0, the galaxy of 0. From Section 4 we recall that all metric entourages U_r, with $r \in E_+^1$, constitute a base for the S-uniformity $\overline{\Phi[\mathbf{u}]}$, and so do all standard entourages $*U$, $U \in \mathbf{u}$. Since equivalent bases must have the same intersection, we obtain $\bigcap \{U_r \mid r \in E_+^1\} = \bigcap \{*U \mid U \in \mathbf{u}\} = M$. As we know, G and M are *equivalence relations* ($\sim$ and $\simeq$). We shall now single out *all* quasimetric entourages which are equivalence relations. Such entourages will be called *monadic* (because of their resemblance to M).

Theorem 5.1. *A quasimetric entourage U_X is monadic iff $X \supseteq R_x$ (= rank of x) for all $x \in X$; that is, the corresponding cut (X, Y) determines also a cut $(\mathbf{X}, \mathbf{Y})$ in the multiplicative valuation group $*E_+^1/R_1$, with $\mathbf{X} = \{R_x \mid x \in X\}$, $\mathbf{Y} = \{R_y \mid y \in Y\}$ (here max $\mathbf{X}$ or min $\mathbf{Y}$ may exist in $*E_+^1/R_1$).*

Proof. If U_X is monadic, that is, an equivalence relation, and if $r \in X$, then $|x - y| < r$ implies $x,y \in U_X$, by the definition of U_X. Hence $(\frac{1}{4}r, r) \in U_X$, $(r, 7r/4) \in U_X$ and so, by transitivity, $(r/4, 7r/4) \in U_X$. It follows that $r \in X$ implies $|(7r/4) - (r/4)| = \frac{3}{2}r < x$ for some

$x \in X$, and so $3/2r \in X$. By induction, $r \in X$ implies $(3/2)^n r \in X$ for any $n \in N$, and hence $ar \in X$ for any finite $a > 0$. This, in turn, implies that $X \supseteq R_r$ (= rank of r). Thus $X \supseteq R_r$ whenever $r \in X$. Conversely, if this is true and if $(x, y) \in U_X$ and $(y, z) \in U_X$, then $|x - y| < r'$ and $|y - z| < r''$ for some $r', r'' \in X$; hence $|x - z| < r$, where $r = \max(2r', 2r'')$ belongs to X, by our assumption, and so $(x, z) \in U_X$, proving the transitivity of U_X. As U_X is a quasimetric entourage, it is also reflexive and symmetric, hence an equivalence relation. Thus the theorem is proved.

***Corollary* 5.2.** *The inclusion-ordered set of all infinite (infinitesimal) monadic entourages is directly (inversely) order-isomorphic with the set of all gaps in the infinite natural number system $*N - N$. Hence it is order-complete, has no last or first element, and is of power $\geq |\theta| \geq 2^{\aleph_0}$.*

Indeed, by Theorem 5.1, monadic entourages correspond to cuts (X, Y) in $*E_+^1/R_1$ including cuts in which max X or min Y exist. Hence, by Theorem 3.6, the first clause of Corollary 5.2 follows for *infinite* monadic entourages. For infinitesimal ones, it holds by the inverse order-isomorphism $x \to 1/x$ in $*E_+^1$. The order-completeness of either set follows from the fact that the set of *all* Dedekind cuts, in any ordered set, is always order-complete. Finally, the rest of Corollary 5.2 is true because the set $\mathfrak{N}$ of all gaps in $*N - N$ has no first or last element and is of power $\geq |\theta|$.

We thus have obtained a characterization of the set of all gaps in $*N - N$.

***Corollary* 5.3.** *For every quasimetric entourage U there is a largest monadic one U', and a smallest monadic one U'', such that $U' \subseteq U \subseteq U''$.* [$U'$ and U'' are called *adjacent* monadic entourages (for U).]

In fact, if U is itself monadic, then $U' = U = U''$. If U is not monadic, then $U = U_X$ for some cut (X, Y) *inside* some rank R_a, and the adjacent entourages U' and U'' are determined by the cuts (X', Y') and (X'', Y'') which immediately "precede" or "follow" R_a, that is, cuts between which R_a is contained in $*E_+^1$, so that $X'' = X' \cup R_a$. Between U' and U'' there is no other monadic entourage. (See also Note 2 after Theorem 3.6.) In particular, M and G form a pair of adjacent monadic entourages, since they correspond to cuts bordering R_1 (rank of 1).

***Theorem* 5.4.** *If $U = U_X$ is a monadic entourage in $*E^1$, then:*
(a) *The neighborhoods $U(a)$, $a \in *E^1$, are mutually disjoint (when distinct), convex, external Q-clopen sets, forming a partition of $*E^1$ (the "U-induced partition").*

(b) *These partitions are totally ordered by refinement, becoming finer as U decreases. More precisely, if U and U' are monadic with $U \supset U'$, then each $U(a)$ splits into one and the same infinite ($\geq \aleph_0$) number of disjoint sets $U'(x)$, $x \in U(a)$.*[12]
(c) *If $U \subseteq G$, then the total number of disjoint sets $U(a)$ equals $|\theta|$.*
(d) *For each set $C \subseteq {}^*E^1$, the U-neighborhood $U[C]$ is Q-clopen. So are, in particular, all sets of the form $M[C]$ and $G[C]$.*[13]
(e) *$U(0)$ is an additive subgroup of ${}^*E^1$. All other sets $U(a)$, $a \in {}^*E^1$, are its order-isomorphic cosets (translates).*

Proof

(a) The sets $U(a)$ are disjoint since they are equivalence classes (U being an equivalence relation). Their convexity follows from the fact that U is a quasimetric entourage. Moreover, by Theorem 5.1, $U = U_X$ corresponds to some cut (X, Y) between "whole" ranks, so that *sup X and inf Y do not exist.* It easily follows that $U(a) = \cup \{U_r(a) \mid r \in X\}$ has no supremum or infimum, and so $U(a)$ is external, by 2.1(b). As U is Q-open (as noted above), so is each $U(a)$; $U(a)$ is also Q-closed, being the complement of the other Q-open $U(x)$ combined. This proves (a) and immediately implies (d). Indeed, by definition, $U[C] = \cup \{U(x) \mid x \in C\}$ is Q-open, for so are all $U(x) \subseteq C$. But the disjointness of distinct $U(x)$ shows that also ${}^*E^1 - U[C]$ consists exactly of those $U(x)$ which are *not* in $U[C]$, and so both $U[C]$ and its complement are Q-open, that is, $U[C]$ is clopen.

(b) If $U \supset U'$, then, clearly, $U(a) \supset U'(a)$ for each $a \in {}^*E^1$, and so the U'-induced partition must be finer than that induced by U, that is, each $U(a)$ consists of a number of disjoint sets $U'(x)$, $x \in U(a)$. This number is the same for each $U(a)$, by translation (recall that any translation is an order-automorphism in ${}^*E^1$). Seeking a contradiction, suppose that this number is finite, n_0 say. As $U = U_X$ and $U' = U_{X'}$ are monadic, they correspond (by Theorem 5.1) to certain cuts (gaps) separated by at least one rank R_p, so that $X - X' \supseteq R_p$. Choosing from R_p two elements r and r' such that $r > 2n_0r' > 0$, we obtain two metric entourages U_r and $U_{r'}$ satisfying $U' \subset U_{r'} \subset U_r \subset U$ and, obviously, $U_r(0)$ contains *more* than n_0 disjoint sets of the form $U_{r'}(x)$. *A fortiori* the larger set $U(0)$ contains more than n_0 smaller sets $U'(x)$, which is the desired contradiction.

(c) If U is finite, that is, $U \subseteq G$, then the U-induced partition of ${}^*E^1$ is *finer* than the partition into galaxies $G(a)$, whose total number is $|\theta|$. Thus we only have to show that the number of disjoint sets $U(a)$ is $\leq |\theta|$. Choose a metric entourage $U_r \subset U$, so that $U_r(a) \subset U(a)$ for each

[12] This number depends however on the choice of U and U'.

[13] Note that all Q-clopen sets other than $\varnothing$ and ${}^*E^1$ are external. See Theorem 6.3.

$a \in {}^*E^1$, and every $U(x)$ contains many (not necessarily disjoint) sets $U_r(a)$. The family G of all sets $U_r(a)$, $a \in {}^*E^1$, is an internal set; moreover, it is a covering of ${}^*E^1$ by internal Q-open sets (that is, sets from ${}^*\tau$). Now, the Lindelöf property of E^1 can be expressed as a K-sentence whose Φ-transform is: Every internal Q-open covering of ${}^*E^1$ (by sets from ${}^*\tau$) contains a subcovering G' for which there is an internal surjective map $f\colon {}^*N \to G'$. Thus the family G introduced above contains a subcovering G', of power $\leq |{}^*N| = |\theta|$, by sets of the form $U_r(a) \subset U(a)$. *A fortiori* ${}^*E^1$ is covered by not more than $|\theta|$ *disjoint* sets $U(a)$, and (c) is proved.

(d) Let $U = U_X$, as in Theorem 5.1. If $x, y \in U(0)$, then, by the definition of U_X, there are $r, s \in X$ such that $|x - 0| = |x| < r$ and $|y| < s$, and so $|x \pm y| < r + s$. As $(r + s) \in X$ (by Theorem 5.1), we obtain $(x \pm y) \in U(0)$. Thus $U(0)$ is closed under addition and subtraction, and hence is an additive subgroup of ${}^*E^1$. The fact that all other neighborhoods $U(a)$ are order-isomorphic translates (that is, cosets) of $U(0)$ was already stated before. Thus the theorem is proved.

NOTE 1. By convexity, each $U(x)$ contains an interval $(a, b) \neq \emptyset$ whose power equals that of ${}^*E^1$, by 2.1(c). It follows that $U(x)$ has the same power, $|\lambda'|$. However, the order type of $U(x)$ under the ordering of ${}^*E^1$ depends on U. For example, the types μ and λ_0 (of M_x and G_x, respectively) may be *different* (see Note 3 after Theorem 3.7).

NOTE 2. As $U(0)$ is a subgroup, we may consider the quotient group ${}^*E^1/U(0)$. By Theorem 5.4(b), its power is $|\theta|$ if $U \subseteq G$. We order it by setting $U(a) \leq U(b)$ iff $a < b$ or $(a, b) \in U$; as is readily seen, this is a valid definition [by the convexity and disjointness of the sets $U(x)$], and it yields a total ordering, compatible with the addition defined in ${}^*E^1/U(0)$: $U(a) + U(b) = U(a + b)$. Special cases are the groups ${}^*E^1/G_0$ and ${}^*E^1/M_0$ considered before. As we know, ${}^*E^1/G_0$ is totally order-incomplete, by 2.2(b), whereas ${}^*E^1/M_0$ has a convex order-complete subset $G_0/M_0 \cong E^1$. This shows that the order types of the groups ${}^*E^1/U(0)$ depend on the choice of U and may be different.

Corollary 5.5. *If $U = U_X$ and $U' = U_{X'}$ are two nonadjacent monadic entourages, with $U \supset U'$, then each $U(a)$ splits into at least $2^{\aleph_0}$ disjoint sets $U'(x)$.*

Indeed, as U and U' are not adjacent, they correspond to gaps in ${}^*E^1$ which are separated by *several* distinct ranks. Thus we can choose r, $r' \in X - X'$ in such a manner that $r = nr'$ for some *infinite* $n \in {}^*N$ (it suffices to choose r and r' of different rank). Now, we have ${}^*E^1[0, r] = \bigcup_{k=0}^{n-1} {}^*E^1[kr', (k + 1)r]$ and, by Theorem 3.1, the number of the intervals ${}^*E^1[kr', (k + 1)r']$ is $2^{\aleph_0}$ at least, since they are in one-to-one correspondence with the elements k of the *infinite* interval $*N[0, n - 1]$ whose power is $\geq 2^{\aleph_0}$. It follows that there are at least $2^{\aleph_0}$ disjoint sets of the form $U_{r'}(x) = (x - r', x + r')$ inside $U_r(0) = (-r, r) \subset U(0)$, with $U' \subset U_{r'} \subset U_r \subset U$. *A fortiori* $U(0)$ contains at least $2^{\aleph_0}$ disjoint smaller sets $U'(x)$. By translation, this applies to *each* $U(a)$, $a \in *E^1$. Thus Corollary 5.5 is proved.

NOTE 3. The example $U = G$, $U' = M$, shows that Corollary 5.5 may hold also for adjacent entourages. We do not know whether it holds in general.

NOTE 4. Obviously, by choosing U' sufficiently small, we can make the number $n \in *N - N$ (occurring in the proof of Corollary 5.5) as large as we like. Thus the number of the disjoint sets $U'(x)$ inside $U(a)$ can be made so large as to reach the power of any interval of $*N$. If $*\hat{A}$ is an enlargement, then this number can be made greater than $|A_n|$, for any prescribed n (see Theorem 3.2).

Corollary 5.6. *Every monadic entourage U is an external Q-clopen subset of $*E^1 \times *E^1$, with $U = \cup \{U(x) \times U(x) \mid x \in *E^1\}$.*[14]

Indeed, the last equality easily follows from the fact that U is an equivalence relation. By Theorem 5.4(a), the disjoint sets of the form $U(x) \times U(x)$, $x \in *E^1$, are Q-open in $*E^1 \times *E^1$. Hence so also is their union U, *as well as the complement of U;* for the latter is exactly the union of those sets $U(x) \times U(x)$ which are not subsets of U. Thus U is *Q-clopen.* It is external for, otherwise, the sets $U(a) = \{x \mid (a, x) \in U\}$ would be internal, contrary to Theorem 5.4(a).

Corollary 5.7. *Every monadic entourage U is a closure operator on subsets of $*E^1$; that is, we have:*

(a) $U[\varnothing] = \varnothing$.

(b) *For any set* $C \subseteq *E^1$, $C \subseteq U[C] = U[U[C]]$.

(c) *For any subsets C and D of $*E^1$, $U[A \cup B] = U[A] \cup U[B]$ (the last property holds even for infinite unions).*

Indeed, all this is an easy consequence of the definition: $U[C] = \bigcup_{x \in C} U(x)$. The equality $U[C] = U[U[C]]$ follows from the fact that U is an equivalence relation, so that $U = U \circ U$.

We say that C is *U-saturated* if $C = U[C]$, that is, $U(x) \subseteq C$ for all $x \in C$. Instead, we may also say that C is *U-closed,* that is, closed in the topology defined by U as a closure operator (briefly, "U-topology").

[14] Note that, by Theorem 5.4(a), the sets $U(x) \times U(x)$ are disjoint when distinct.

6. Some Further Topological Inferences

Throughout this section, V will denote a fixed (although arbitrary) monadic entourage determined by a cut (X_v, Y_v) in $^*E_+{}^1$. Clearly, all metric entourages $U_r \subset V$, that is, those with $r \in X_v$, form a base for the Q-uniformity, $\overline{^*\mathbf{u}}$; by Corollary 5.3, so also do all *monadic* entourages $U' \subset V$. Consider, however, the set $\mathbf{u}_v$ of all metric entourages $U_r \supset V$, that is, those with $r \in Y_v$. By Theorem 5.1, if $r \in Y_v$, then also $s = \frac{1}{2}r \in Y_v$, so that $U_s \in \mathbf{u}_v$, and obviously $U_s \circ U_s \subseteq U_r$. Since this holds for every $U_r \in \mathbf{u}_v$, and since all such U_r are totally ordered by inclusion, $\mathbf{u}_v$ is a base for a uniformity $\overline{\mathbf{u}_v}$ on $^*E^1$ which we shall call the *S_v-uniformity;* the corresponding topology is called the *S_v-topology* (imitating the term "S-topology," which is simply the S_v-topology for $V = M$). By its very definition, the S_v-uniformity is (strictly) coarser than the Q-uniformity; it is coarser or finer than the S-uniformity $\Phi[\mathbf{u}]$ according as $V \supset M$ or $V \subset M$. The most important case is, of course, the case $V = M$ (S-topology), because of Corollary 4.4. Apart from Corollary 4.4, however, any S_v-topology closely resembles the S-topology. In fact, most of the S-topological theorems proved in [5] carry over to the S_v-topology, and the proofs (for $^*E^1$) can even be simplified, inasmuch as the assumption of an enlargement is unnecessary. We have:

Theorem 6.1. *The assertions of Theorem 5.4(a, d) and Corollary 5.6 hold also with "Q-clopen" replaced by "S_v-clopen," provided $U \supset V$. Hence each galaxy G_x is S-clopen.*

Indeed, if $U \supset V$, there is a metric entourage U_r with $U \supset U_r \supset V$, $r \in Y_v$. As U is monadic, we have, for any $x \in U(a)$, $U(a) = U(x) \supset U_r(x)$, with $U_r \in \mathbf{u}_v$. Thus $U(a)$ is S_v-open. The rest of the proof is exactly as in Section 5. The assertion about galaxies is the special case: $V = M \subset G = U$ (it is Theorem 4.4.4 of [5]).

Theorem 6.2. *For any set $C \subseteq {}^*E^1$, the S_v-closure (in particular, the S-closure) of C equals that of $V[C]$ ($M[C]$ for S-closures). Thus $V[C]$ is a subset of the S_v-closure of C, but contains the Q-closure of C. In particular, $M[C]$ is a subset of the S-closure of C.*

Proof. By a well-known formula (see [3], p. 179), the S_v-closure $\bar{C}$ of C satisfies $\bar{C} = \bigcap \{U[C] \mid U \in \mathbf{u}_v\} = \bigcap \{U[U[C]] \mid U \in \mathbf{u}_v\} \supseteq \bigcap \{U[V[C]] \mid U \in \mathbf{u}_v\} = \overline{V[C]}$ (for $U \in \mathbf{u}_v$ implies $U \supset V$). Thus $\overline{V[C]} \subseteq \bar{C} \subseteq \overline{V[C]}$, and Theorem 6.2 follows on noting that $V[C]$ certainly contains the finer Q-closure of C, by Theorem 5.4(d).

NOTE 1. The same closure formula (used above) also shows that $V(c)$ is the S_v-closure of the singleton $\{c\}$, $c \in {}^*E^1$. For another proof, see Theorem 6.4.[15]

Theorem 6.3. *All S_v-closed and all S_v-open sets in ${}^*E^1$ are V-saturated [that is, contain $V(x)$ together with any x in them] and Q-clopen. Hence they are external, except for $\varnothing$ and ${}^*E^1$. With this exception, then, no internal set $C \subset {}^*E^1$ can be V-saturated, S_v-closed, S_v-open, or Q-clopen.*

Proof. Under any uniform topology, every open or closed set C contains the closure of each $\{x\} \subseteq C$. Hence, if C is S_v-open or S_v-closed, we have $V(x) = \overline{\{x\}} \subseteq C$ for $x \in C$, and so $V[C] \subseteq C \subseteq V[C]$, that is, $C = V[C]$ and C is V-saturated. Now, as V is by assumption a monadic entourage, $C = V[C]$ is Q-clopen, by Theorem 5.4(d), and so the first clause of Theorem 6.3 is proved. Next, as E^1 is a connected space, it has no clopen subsets other than $\varnothing$ and E^1. This fact can be expressed as a K-sentence whose Φ-transform states that ${}^*E^1$ has no *internal* Q-clopen subsets (that is, members of ${}^*\tau$ whose complements are likewise in ${}^*\tau$), except $\varnothing$ and E^1. *A fortiori* there are no internal V-saturated sets (since they are all Q-clopen). This, combined with the first clause, shows that there are no internal S_v-closed or S_v-open sets other than $\varnothing$ and ${}^*E^1$. This completes the proof.

NOTE 2. With $V = M$, the theorem applies to the S-topology in any connected metric space. We may treat it as a nonstandard characterization of connectedness: *A metric space (T, ρ) is connected iff ${}^*T$ has no internal S-open (or S-closed) subsets other than $\varnothing$ and ${}^*T$.*

We now recall some S-topological theorems of [5], and extend them to S_v = topology when possible. As in [5], we put ${}^0C = E^1 \cap M[C]$ ("standard part of C") for each set $C \subseteq {}^*E^1$; ${}^0C$ is also denoted by st(C) or st$_v(C)$ (in [4]).

Theorem 6.4. *If the set $C \subseteq {}^*E^1$ is internal, then:*

(a) *The S_v-interior of C equals $\{x \in {}^*E^1 \mid V(x) \subseteq C\}$, and its S_v-closure is $V[C]$ (with $V = M$ for S-topology). Hence its S_v-boundary is $V[C] \cap V[{}^*E^1 - C]$.*

(b) *Its standard part ${}^0C = E^1 \cap M[C]$ is closed in E^1. If, in particular, $C = {}^*D$ for some $D \subseteq E^1$, then ${}^0C = {}^0({}^*D) = \bar{D}$ in E^1; moreover, D is*

[15] Thus ${}^*E^1$ is not a Hausdorff space under its S_v-topology; but we can make it one by passing to the quotient space ${}^*E^1/V(0)$, briefly denoted by ${}^*E_v{}^1$.

closed in E^1 *iff* $C \cap G_0 = {}^*D \cap G_0 \subseteq M[D]$; D *is open in* E^1 *iff* $C \cap G_0 = {}^*D \cap G_0 \supseteq M[D]$ (*equivalently*, ${}^*D \supseteq M[G]$).

Proof

(a) If p is in the S_v-interior of C, there is a metric entourage $U_r \in \mathbf{u}_v$ ($U_r \supset V$), with $C \supseteq U_r(p) \supset V(p)$, so that $p \in \{x \in {}^*E^1 \mid V(x) \subseteq C\}$. Conversely, fix any p with $V(p) \subseteq C$, and let $E = \{r \in {}^*E_+^1 \mid U_r(p) \subseteq C\}$. Then E is internal (for C is). Obviously, $E \supseteq X_v$ [(X_v, Y_v) being the cut that determines the monadic entourage V]. As the cut is a *gap*, X_v is external, and so $E \neq X_v$; that is, E contains some $r \in Y_v$, so that $U_r \in \mathbf{u}_v$. As $r \in E$, we have $U_r(p) \subseteq C$, and so p is in the S_v-interior of C. This proves the first clause of (a). The closure clause easily follows by taking complements, and the rest of (a) is obvious.

(b) By (a), the S-closure of C is $M[C]$, and so $M[C]$ is S-closed. Hence $E^1 \cap M[C] = {}^0C$ is closed in E^1 as a subspace of ${}^*E^1$ with S-topology (see Corollary 4.4). This proves the first clause of (b) (and simplifies the proof given in [5]). The rest of (b) is only a rephrasing of Theorems 4.3.4 and 4.1.4–4.1.6 of [5].

NOTE 3. Part (a) of Theorem 6.4 may sometimes hold also if C is external. For example, the S-closure of E^1 is $M[E^1] = G_0$. Indeed, by Theorems 6.1 and 6.2, $M[E^1] = G_0$ is S-closed and contained in the S-closure of E^1, hence equals it. On the other hand, if $C \subset E^1$ and C is not closed in E^1, then $M[C]$ is not S-closed; for, otherwise, $C = E^1 \cap M[C]$ would be closed, by Corollary 4.4.

NOTE 4. This example also shows that S-topology is different from (and coarser than) the topology defined by M as a closure operator (see Corollary 5.7). For internal sets, however, S_v-closures coincide with V-closures, and so Corollary 5.7(c) holds for S_v-closures of arbitrary (even infinite) internal unions of internal sets.

NOTE 5. By the argument used in Theorem 6.4(b), if C is internal, then ${}^0C$ is the closure (in E^1) of $E^1 \cap C$ (the trace of C in E^1). Setting here $C = {}^*D$, ($D \subseteq E^1$), we see that ${}^0({}^*D)$ is the closure of both $E^1 \cap {}^*D$ and D.

While the preceding propositions hold in any nonstandard model ${}^*\hat{A}$, the assumption of an enlargement seems to be unavoidable in Theorems 4.1.13 and 4.1.15 of [5]. In our present notation, we can restate them both thus:

Theorem 6.5 (***ENL***). *A set* $D \subseteq E^1$ *is compact iff* ${}^*D \subseteq M[D]$. (*Proof:* See [5], 4.1.5.) Observe that, by Theorem 6.4(b), D is closed iff ${}^*D \cap G_0 \subseteq M[D]$.

***Theorem* 6.6.** *If V is the smaller of two adjacent monadic entourages, V and U, then $^*E^1$ is pseudometrizable under its S_v-uniformity, and so the quotient space $^*E_v{}^1 = E^1/V(0)$ is metrizable.*[16]

Proof. As is well known (see [3], p. 186), a uniform space is pseudometrizable iff its uniformity has a countable base. To construct such a base in our case, we recall from Theorem 5.1 and Corollary 5.3 that two adjacent monadic entourages U and V $(U \supset V)$ correspond to two cuts (X_u, Y_u) and (X_v, Y_v) in $^*E_+{}^1$, such that $X_u - X_v = R_a$ (= the rank of a) for some $a \in {}^*E_+{}^1$. Let $r_n = a/n$ $(n \in N)$, and consider the sequence of metric entourages $U_{r_n} = \{(x, y) \mid x, y \in {}^*E^1, |x - y| < r_n\}$, $n \in N$. By the definition of rank, all $r_n = a/n$ are in $R_a = X_u - X_v$, hence in Y_v (for they are not in X_v). This means that $V \subset U_{r_n} \in \mathbf{u}_v$ for all $n \in N$. Moreover, the sequence $\{U_{r_n} \mid n \in N\}$ is another base for the S_v-uniformity $\overline{\mathbf{u}_v}$. In fact, by definition, every entourage $U' \in \overline{\mathbf{u}_v}$ contains some $U_r \in \mathbf{u}_v$, and we can choose r so small that $r \in R_a \subset Y_v$. Then, by definition of R_a, $r = ca$ for some finite but *not infinitesimal* $c \in {}^*E_+{}^1$. Thus, for sufficiently large $n \in N$, $r_n = a/n < ca = r$, and so $U_{r_n} \subset U_r \subseteq U'$. This shows that, indeed, each $U' \in \overline{\mathbf{u}_v}$ contains some U_{r_n}, and so the U_{r_n} $(n \in N)$ constitute a countable base for $\overline{\mathbf{u}_v}$. This completes the proof. In particular, taking $V = M$, $U = G$, we see that the S-topology admits a pseudometric with values in E^1, and so the quotient space $^*E_M{}^1 = {}^*E^1/M_0$ (corresponding to T_μ in the notation of [5], p. 108) is metrizable. (This supplements [5], where a metric was constructed only for each galaxy separately. Our present proof applies, of course, to $^*E^1$ only.)

The theorem may fail without the assumption made. In fact, we have:

***Theorem* 6.7.** *In a comprehensive model $^*\hat{A}$, the S_v-topology in $^*E^1$ is not pseudometrizable if V is the larger of two adjacent monadic entourages U and V; moreover, the Q-topology is not metrizable either, and no point has a countable local neighborhood base, under either topology.*

Proof. By assumption, U and V correspond to two cuts (X_u, Y_u) and (X_v, Y_v) in $^*E_+{}^1$ with $X_u \subset X_v$ and $X_v - X_u = R_a$ for some $a \in {}^*E_+{}^1$. Seeking a contradiction, suppose that some point $p \in {}^*E^1$ has a countable neighborhood base in the S_v-topology. Then necessarily there is a decreasing sequence of metric entourages U_{r_n}, $r_n \in Y_v$, such that the balls $U_{r_n}(p)$ form another local base at p $(n \in N)$.[17] Since $R_a =$

[16] By this we mean that the uniformity of the space is compatible with some metric with values *in* E^1 (although different from the standard metric $\rho(x, y) = |x - y|$). It is, of course, trivial that it admits a metric with values in $^*E^1$. For the definition of a pseudometric, see [3], pp. 118–119.

[17] Here, as before, $U_r = \{(x, y) \mid x, y \in {}^*E^1, |x - y| < r\}$, in the sense of the $^*E^1$ = valued metric $^*\rho$ defined in $^*E^1$. An E^1-valued metric is not assumed.

$X_v - X_u \subset X_v$ and $r_n \in Y_v$, we have $r_n \notin R_a$ and $r_n > a$ for $n \in N$, and so $R_a < R_{r_n}$ under the ordering of the valuation group $^*E_+^1/R_1$. Moreover, the sequence $\{R_{r_n}\}$ cannot have a lower bound $R_r > R_a$; for this would imply the existence of a ball $U_r(p)$ strictly smaller than all $U_{r_n}(p)$, contrary to the fact that the balls $U_{r_n}(p)$ form a local base at p. Thus the sequence $\{R_{r_n}\}$ is coinitial with an interval (R_a, R_b) of $^*E_+^1/R_1$, a set of type $\theta^* + 1 + \theta$, by Theorem 2.2(c). But this is the desired contradiction; for, under a comprehensive monomorphism (here assumed) such a set has no intervals possessing a countable coinitial subset, as follows from Theorem 3.9. Thus, in the given S_v-topology, no point has a countable local neighborhood base, and this excludes pseudometrizability as well. The proof for Q-topology is analogous (even simpler), since Theorem 3.9 also applies to intervals in $^*E^1$, a set of type λ'. Thus the theorem is proved.

We do not know whether Theorem 6.7 holds also without the assumption of comprehensiveness, or for nonadjacent monadic entourages V. In any case, it shows that metrizability cannot be *proved in general*. On the other hand, if Q-topology could be metrized in some (noncomprehensive) model $^*\hat{A}$, the metric would have to be a rather "weird" one, in view of the Q-clopen base described in Theorem 5.4.

7. Completeness in the Topological Sense

In this section, the term "*completeness*" (to be distinguished from *order-completeness*) will mean the completeness of a space under its uniform topology (see [3], p. 190ff.). As is well known, an ordered uniform space may well be complete even though it has gaps as an ordered set. For densely ordered Abelian *groups*, under their usual uniformity (see [1]), completeness is equivalent to the absence of *regular* gaps (called "*Dedekindean*" in [1]), that is, those gaps (X, Y) in which X is not invariant under any translation.[18] It is also known that any such group is a *nested* uniform space; that is, its uniformity has a base $\mathbf{U}$ which is totally ordered by inverse inclusion, $\supset$; thus one can select from $\mathbf{U}$ a cofinal base $\mathbf{U}' \subset \mathbf{U}$ which is *well-ordered* by $\supset$ and is of the least possible order type (denoted ξ^* in [1]) under that ordering. By its minimality, ξ^* is a regular initial ordinal, uniquely determined by the given nested uniformity; it is called the *type* or *character* of that uniformity (and of the given space).[19] In particular, the Q-uniformity in $^*E^1$ is of type $\xi^* = \Omega$ as defined in Section 3 (after Theorem 3.7); indeed, the

[18] Equivalently, (X, Y) is a regular cut iff, for every positive element p of the group, there is $x \in X$ with $x + p \in Y$.

[19] We exclude from consideration the trivial case $\xi^* = 1$.

well-ordered Ω-type base $\mathbf{U}'$ can be chosen to consist of all metric entourages $U_r = \{(x,y) \mid x, y \in {}^*E^1, |x - y| < r\}$ in which r is of the form $r = 1/m_\eta$, $m_\eta \in \#N$ (see Section 3); these U_r may also be replaced by monadic entourages closest to them (such as U' in Corollary 5.3). A space is uniformly pseudometrizable iff it is of type $\xi^* = \omega$.

We may put the well-ordered base $\mathbf{U}'$ in a decreasing ξ^*-type sequence: $\mathbf{U}' = \{U_\nu \mid \rho < \xi^*\}$. Then, as shown in [2], all problems of convergence, completeness, and so on, can be treated in much the same manner as in metric spaces, with ordinary sequences replaced by those of type ξ^*. In particular, a sequence $\{a_\nu \mid \nu < \xi^*\}$ in a ξ^*-type space T is a *Cauchy sequence* iff (with ϵ, δ, ν, κ, η, $\cdots$ denoting ordinals $<\xi^*$) for every ϵ there is a δ such that $(a_\nu, a_\kappa) \in U_\epsilon$ for all $\nu,\kappa \geq \delta$. The space T is *complete* iff every Cauchy sequence converges, in a self-evident sense.[20] We first consider a case of an S_v-uniformity in ${}^*E^1$; its character will be denoted by ξ_v^*.

***Theorem* 7.1.** *In a comprehensive model ${}^*\hat{A}$, let V be the smaller of two adjacent monadic entourages (V, U) in ${}^*E^1$. Then ${}^*E^1$ is complete under the corresponding S_v-uniformity, and so is each $U(a)$, $a \in {}^*E^1$, as a subspace.*

Proof. In our case, by Theorem 6.6, the S_v-uniformity has a countable base consisting of metric entourages $U_{r_n} \subset U$ $(n \in N,\ r_n > r_{n+1})$. Thus $\xi^* = \xi_v^* = \omega$, and we need only consider ordinary ω-type sequences. Let $\{x_n \mid n \in N\}$ be an S_v-Cauchy sequence in ${}^*E^1$. [No generality is lost by assuming that it is contained in some $U(a)$, because $U_{r_n} \subset U$, and so $x_n \in U(x_{n_0})$ for sufficiently large n, and suitable n_0.] By the Cauchy property, we can inductively select from $\{x_n\}$ and $\{r_n\}$ (as above) two subsequences $\{x_n'\} \subset \{x_n\}$ and $\{r_n'\} \subset \{r_n\}$ such that $|x_n' - x_m'| < r_n'$ for $m \geq n$ $(m, n \in N)$. It suffices to show that the subsequence $\{x_n'\}$ is S_v-convergent. Now, by the assumed comprehensiveness of ${}^*\hat{A}$, the subsequences $\{x_n'\}$ and $\{r_n'\}$ have *internal* extensions $\{x_n'' \mid n \in {}^*N\}$ and $\{r_n'' \mid n \in {}^*N\}$ such that $x_n'' = x_n'$ and $r_n'' = r_n'$ for $n \in N$. Let P be the set of all $m \in {}^*N$ such that $|x_n'' - x_m''| < r_n''$ for all $n \leq m$, $n \in {}^*N$. As is readily seen, P is internal, and $P \supseteq N$; so P must also contain some $m_0 \in {}^*N - N$ (henceforth fixed). Let $p = x_{m_0}''$. Then, by the definition of P, $|x_n'' - p| < r_n''$ for all $n \leq m_0 \in {}^*N - N$; hence certainly $|x_n' - p| < r_n'$, that is, $x_n' \in U_{r_n'}(p)$, for all $n \in N$. As the entourages $U_{r_n'}$ obviously form a base for our S_v-uniformity, this implies that $x_n' \to p$ in the S_v-topology. It follows that ${}^*E^1$ is complete under that S_v-uniformity. So also is each $U(a)$, being an S_v-*closed* subspace, by Theorems 6.1 and 5.4(d). Thus all is proved.

[20] For nested spaces, this definition of completeness is equivalent to that based on Cauchy *nets* ([3], p. 190ff.) or Cauchy filters [4].

NOTE 1. In the special case $V = M$, $U = G$, Theorem 7.1 holds also without the comprehensiveness assumption. In fact, as noted above, we may always assume that the Cauchy sequence $\{x_n\}$ lies in some $U(a) = G(a)$. Thus all reduces to showing that $G(a)$ is complete as a subspace; moreover, by translation, it suffices to consider $G(0)$, so that all x_n are finite. Moreover, nothing essential will change if each x_n is replaced by some $y_n \in \overline{\{x_n\}} = M(x_n)$, for example, by the standard part ${}^0x_n$ of x_n. Thus we may assume that x_n is in E^1. But, then, the above proof works with $\{x_n''\}$ and $\{r_n''\}$ replaced by $^*\{x_n'\}$ and $^*\{r_n'\}$, respectively (note that $r_n \in E^1$, in the case of the S-uniformity). The required internal extensions result here simply by passage from $\hat{A}$ to $^*\hat{A}$.

The proof of Theorem 7.1 fails for Q-topology. To overcome this difficulty partially, we shall construct a *completion* of $^*E^1$ inside a larger nonstandard model.[21] A general completion procedure was suggested in [4, p. 112]. For *nested* uniform spaces, it is convenient to use a simplified version of it which we shall briefly sketch below, first in general terms, and then for $^*E^1$ as a special case.

Let T be a (not necessarily Hausdorff) uniform space whose uniformity has a ξ^*-type base $\mathbf{U} = \{U_\nu \mid \nu < \xi^*\}$ such that $U_\nu \subset U_\kappa$ whenever $\kappa < \nu < \xi^*$. Let Z be the ordered set of all ordinals $< \xi^*$, and let $h\colon \hat{B} \to \hat{C}$ be a monomorphism, with $T \cup Z \subseteq B = B_0$. Writing $'x$ for $h(x)$, we put $'\hat{B} = \bigcup_{n=0}^{\infty} {'B_n}$, so that $'\hat{B}$ is a model of the set of all wfs which hold in $\hat{B}$ (see Section 1). On passage from $\hat{B}$ to $'\hat{B}$, Z turns into a totally ordered set $'Z \supseteq Z$, and $\mathbf{U}$ turns into a family $'\mathbf{U}$ of subsets of $'T \times {'T}$, with $'\mathbf{U} = \{V_\nu \mid \nu \in {'Z}\}$ and with $V_\nu \subset V_\kappa$ whenever $\kappa < \nu$ ($\nu, \kappa \in {'Z}$). Henceforth we assume that $'\hat{B}$ is a *nonstandard* model, that is, that $'Z$ has an element greater than each $\nu \in Z$; $'\hat{B}$ may, but need not, be an enlargement of $\hat{B}$.

As is easily seen, the sets $'\mathbf{U}$ and $h[\mathbf{U}] = \{'U_\nu \mid \nu \in Z\}$ are bases for certain uniformities, $\overline{'\mathbf{U}}$ and $\overline{h[\mathbf{U}]}$, on $'T$ (called the Q^*- and S^*-uniformities, respectively).[22] The set $M^* = \bigcap \{'U_\nu \mid \nu \in Z\}$ is a member of $\overline{'\mathbf{U}}$; we call it the *monad* of $\overline{'\mathbf{U}}$. Clearly, $M^*(x) = \{y \mid x, y \in M^*\} = \bigcap_{\nu \in Z} {'U_\nu}(x)$ for $x \in {'T}$. Hence, as the U_ν ($\nu \in Z$) are a base for the S^*-uniformity, $M^*(x)$ is exactly the S^*-closure of $\{x\} \subset {'T}$. But, as is

[21] A complete uniform space $\bar{T}$ is called a *completion* of a uniform space T if T is uniformly homeomorphic with a dense subspace of $\bar{T}$. If such a completion $\bar{T}$ is *separated* (that is, a Hausdorff space), it is unique to within uniform homeomorphism. In general, there are many nonseparated completions of T. The separated completion of a Hausdorff space T is also simply called *the completion* of T.

[22] We use "starred" Q and S to avoid confusion with similar notions previously defined for $^*E^1$. Similarly for M^* below.

well known, one-point closures are either identical or disjoint, in any uniform topology. Thus the distinct sets $M^*(x)$ form a partition of $'T$, and hence M^* is an equivalence relation in $'T$. As before, we put $M^*[X] = \bigcup_{x \in X} M^*(x)$ for $X \subseteq {'T}$. In particular, we consider the set $M^*[T]$ whose elements are called *near-standard* points of $'T$. We treat $M^*[T]$ as a uniform subspace of $('T, \overline{h[\mathbf{U}]})$, that is, of $'T$ with *S^*-uniformity*. Then, as is readily seen, the separated quotient space of $M^*[T]$ is uniformly homeomorphic to that of T (or to T itself if T is separated). Moreover, T is a uniform subspace of $M^*[T]$, hence of $('T, \overline{h[\mathbf{U}]})$. Below, $\bar{X}$ will denote the *S^*-closure* of $X \subseteq {'T}$, unless otherwise stated.

Theorem 7.2. *With the above notation and assumptions, we have:*

(a) *The S^*-closure $\bar{T}$ of T is a completion of T; moreover,* $\bar{T} = \overline{M^*[T]}$.
(b) *Hence the separated quotient space of $\bar{T}$ is the (unique to within uniform homeomorphism) completion of the separated quotient space of T.*
(c) *T is complete iff $\bar{T} = M^*[T]$, that is, iff $M^*[T]$ is S^*-closed.*

Proof. The fact that $\bar{T} = \overline{M^*[T]}$ is obvious since $\bar{T}$ contains the S^*-closure $\overline{\{x\}} = M^*(x)$ of each $x \in T$, that is, $\bar{T} \supseteq M^*[T]$, and hence $\bar{T} \supseteq \overline{M^*[T]} \supseteq \bar{T}$. To show that $\bar{T}$ is complete [as a subspace of $('T, \overline{h[\mathbf{U}]})$], it suffices to consider ξ^*-type Cauchy sequences $\{x_\nu \mid \nu < \xi^*\} = \{x_\nu \mid \nu \in Z\}$ *of elements of* T (for T is dense in $\bar{T}$); and here we may simply apply the *original* uniformity of T (since T is a uniform subspace of $('T, \overline{h[\mathbf{U}]})$), as previously noted. In particular, we may use in T the given ξ^*-type base $\mathbf{U} = \{U_\nu \mid \nu \in Z\}$. Thus, given a Cauchy sequence $\{x_\nu \mid \nu \in Z\} \subseteq T$, we may assume (by passage to a subsequence if necessary) that $(x_\nu, x_\mu) \in U_\nu$ whenever $\nu \leq \mu$ $(\nu, \mu \in Z)$. Now, on passage from $\hat{B}$ to $'\hat{B}$, the sequence $\{x_\nu \mid \nu \in Z\} \subseteq T$ extends to $\{x_\nu \mid \nu \in {'Z}\} \subseteq {'T}$, with $(x_\nu, x_\mu) \in V_\nu$ whenever $\nu \leq \mu$ $(\nu, \mu \in {'Z})$; here the V_ν are members of the *Q^*-uniformity* in general; but we have $V_\nu = {'U_\nu} \in h[\mathbf{U}]$ if $\nu \in Z$. Let κ be an upper bound of Z in $'Z$ (it exists, by our assumption that $'\hat{B}$ is a *nonstandard* model), and put $p = x_\kappa$. Then it easily follows (as in the proof of Theorem 7.1) that the sequence $\{x_\nu \mid \nu \in Z\}$ converges to p in the S^*-topology; moreover, since $\{x_\nu \mid \nu \in Z\} \subseteq T$, we have $p \in \bar{T}$. This shows that $\bar{T}$ is S^*-complete; and as T is S^*-dense in $\bar{T}$, the latter is a completion of T, by definition. Thus assertion (a) is proved, and the remaining two assertions are easy consequences of (a).

NOTE 2. The preceding argument generalizes (and simplifies) Theorems 4.4.5 and 4.4.6 of [5], using essentially the same ideas. Actually, with slight changes, it can be extended to *all* (not necessarily nested) uniform spaces. It is closely related to the completion procedure suggested in [4], p. 112; however, it does not need a separate theory of "pre-near-standard" points (here replaced by the notion of S^*-closure).

When applying Theorem 7.2 to $T = {}^*E^1$, we may use either Q- or S_v-topology for ${}^*E^1$. On passage to $'\hat{B}$, this yields *different* S^*-topologies, called the S_q^*- *and* S_v^*-*topologies* (with the corresponding monads M_q^* and M_v^*, and ξ^*-type sets Z_q and Z_v), respectively. No generality is lost by assuming that the set B_0 of individuals in $\hat{B}$ contains ${}^*E^1$, as well as Z_q and Z_v for all monadic entourages V. By Theorem 7.2, the S_q^*-closure of ${}^*E^1$, henceforth briefly denoted by $\overline{{}^*E}$, is S_q^*-*complete*, that is, complete as a subspace of $'{}^*E^1 = h({}^*E^1)$, *with* S_q^*-*uniformity*. We now ask in what cases it is also S_v^*-*complete*. In this respect, we have:

Theorem 7.3. *The* S_q^*-*closure* $\overline{{}^*E}$ *of* ${}^*E^1$ *in* $'{}^*E^1$ *is* S_v^*-*complete if and only if* ${}^*E^1$ *is* S_v-*complete (for example, in the case described in Theorem* 7.1).

Proof. Obviously, the S_v^*-completeness or incompleteness of a subspace $X \subseteq {}^*E^1$ is not affected if each singleton $\{x\} \subseteq X$ is replaced by its S_v^*-closure, $M_v^*(x)$. *Hence* X *is* S_v^*-*complete iff so is* $M_v^*[X]$. Furthermore, as is easily seen, M_v^* is a member of the S_q^*-uniformity. Therefore, $M_v^*[{}^*E^1] \supseteq \overline{{}^*E}$ ($= S_q^*$-closure of ${}^*E^1$) whence $M_v^*[\overline{{}^*E}] \subseteq M_v^*[M_v^*[{}^*E^1]] = M_v^*[{}^*E^1]$ (for M_v^* is an equivalence relation). Thus $M_v^*[\overline{{}^*E}] = M_v^*[{}^*E^1]$. Now, if $\overline{{}^*E}$ is S_v^*-complete, then, as noted above, so also is $M_v^*[\overline{{}^*E}] = M_v^*[{}^*E^1]$. Hence it easily follows that $M_v^*[{}^*E^1]$ is S_v^*-closed and so, by Theorem 7.2(c), ${}^*E^1$ is S_v-complete. Conversely, if so, then Theorem 7.2(c) shows that the S_v^*-closure of ${}^*E^1$ equals $M_v^*[{}^*E^1] = M_v^*[\overline{{}^*E}]$ and, by Theorem 7.2(c), it is S_v^*-complete. Hence so also are $M_v^*[\overline{{}^*E}]$ and $\overline{{}^*E}$. Thus all is proved.

We denote by $\overline{{}^*E_q}$ and $\overline{{}^*E_v}$ the *separated* completions of ${}^*E^1$ and ${}^*E_0{}^1 = {}^*E^1/V(0)$, under the Q- and S_v-uniformities, respectively. By Theorem 7.2(b), $\overline{{}^*E_q}$ is uniformly homeomorphic with the quotient space $\overline{{}^*E}/M_q^*$ obtained by identifying x with y in $\overline{{}^*E}$ whenever $x,y \in M_q^*$. In the case described in Theorem 7.1, we have $\overline{{}^*E_v} \cong {}^*E_v{}^1 = {}^*E^1/V(0)$ and also $\overline{{}^*E_v} \cong \overline{{}^*E}/M_v^*$, by Theorems 7.3 and 7.2(b). As is readily seen, the completions $\overline{{}^*E_q}$ and $\overline{{}^*E_v}$ are nested uniform spaces, of types Ω and ξ_v^*, respectively. If V is as in Theorem 7.1, we have $\xi_v^* = \omega$, by Theorem 6.6.

From Section 5, Note 2, we recall that ${}^*E_v{}^1 = {}^*E^1/V(0)$ is a densely ordered Abelian group (density follows in the same manner as in the proof of Theorem 2.2). Now, as is shown in [1], the separated topological completion $\bar{H}$ of a densely ordered Abelian group H (under its usual uniformity) is itself such a group, with H its subspace and subgroup. Moreover, $\bar{H}$ can be constructed as the group H_D of all *regular* Dedekind cuts in H, with the usual addition and ordering of cuts. If, in particular, H is an ordered *field*, so also is H_D, as was proved by Scott [9]. Thus, summarizing, we have:

Theorem 7.4

(a) *The separated completion* $\overline{{}^*E_q}$ *of* $({}^*E^1, \overline{{}^*\mathbf{u}})$ *is an ordered field and a nested uniform space of the same type* Ω *as is* ${}^*E^1$*; it contains* ${}^*E^1$ *as a dense subfield and subspace.*

(b) *The separated topological completion* $\overline{{}^*E_v}$ *of* ${}^*E^1/V(0)$ *(*V *being any monadic entourage in* ${}^*E^1$*) is a densely ordered Abelian group and a nested uniform space of the same type* ξ_v^* *as is* ${}^*E_v{}^1 = {}^*E^1/V(0)$*; it contains* ${}^*E_v{}^1$ *as a dense subgroup and subspace.*

(c) *If* ${}^*E_v{}^1$ *is complete (as in the case described in Theorem* 7.1*), then* ${}^*E_v \cong {}^*E_v{}^1 \cong \overline{{}^*E}/M_v^*$*, and* $\overline{{}^*E}$ *is* S_v^**-complete.*

(d) *As ordered groups,* $\overline{{}^*E_q}$ *and* $\overline{{}^*E_v}$ *have no regular gaps.*

In fact, (d) follows from the fact (noted above) that all regular gaps are "filled" on passage from H to H_D. The rest is clear from previous remarks.

Thus the completion $\overline{{}^*E_q}$ of ${}^*E^1$ preserves the algebraic nature of ${}^*E^1$ as an ordered field and its character Ω as a nested uniform space. It also preserves the completeness of the quotient spaces ${}^*E_v{}^1$ whenever they are complete in the original nonstandard model ${}^*\hat{A}$, under the corresponding S_v-uniformities.[23] It remains, however, an open question whether Q-completeness and S_v-completeness (beyond Theorem 7.1) can already be achieved in ${}^*\hat{A}$ itself, even if ${}^*\hat{A}$ is a comprehensive or saturated enlargement.

8. Connectedness. Final Remarks. Unsolved Questions

We shall say that a uniform space is *totally disconnected* iff its components (that is, maximal connected subsets) are closures of singletons, $\overline{\{x\}}$. For Hausdorff spaces, these are the singletons themselves. The total order incompleteness of ${}^*E^1$ by no means implies its total disconnectedness under *all* topologies so far defined in ${}^*E^1$. In fact, we have:

Theorem 8.1. (a) *Under* S*-topology, the components of* ${}^*E^1$ *are exactly all galaxies* $G(a)$, $a \in {}^*E^1$.

[23] In particular, it preserves the completeness of ${}^*E^1$ under the S-uniformity (see Note 1). Thus $\overline{{}^*E_q}$ and $\overline{{}^*E_M}$ are both complete.

(b) *More generally, if V is the smaller of two adjacent monadic entourages V and U ($V \subset U$), and if $^*E^1$ is S_v-complete (as in the case of Theorem 7.1), then the S_v-components of $^*E^1$ are exactly all $U(a)$, $a \in {^*E^1}$.*

Proof of (b). By Theorems 6.1 and 5.4(a), the sets $U(a)$ are S_v-clopen and thus cannot have *proper* connected supersets. It remains to show that each $U(a)$ is connected. Seeking a contradiction, suppose that $U(a) = C \cup D$ for two disjoint S_v-clopen sets C, $D \neq \emptyset$, and let $c \in C$ and $d \in D$, with $c < d$, say. Now, by using a classical bisection process, one can construct an ω-type sequence of nested intervals $F_n = [c_n, d_n]$ such that $c_n \in C$, $d_n \in D$, $F_n \supset F_{n+1}$, and $|d_n - c_n| = (d - c)/2^n < r_n$, where $r_n = (d - c)/n$ ($n = 1, 2, \cdots$). With r_n so defined, the metric entourages U_{r_n}, $n = 1, 2, \cdots$, constitute a base for the S_v-uniformity, $\overline{\mathbf{u}_v}$, as easily follows by the argument used in the proof of Theorem 6.6. Since $|d_n - c_n| < r_n$, we also have $d_n, c_n \in U_{r_n}$, $n = 1, 2, \cdots$, and obviously the sequences $\{c_n\}$ and $\{d_n\}$ are S_v-Cauchy. Thus, by the assumed S_v-completeness of $^*E^1$, they are S_v-convergent to one and the same limit $p \in C \cap D$ (for C and D are S_v-closed).[24] This, however, is the desired contradiction, since $C \cap D = \emptyset$. Thus all is proved.

The situation is different for the other topologies in $^*E^1$:

Theorem 8.2. *$^*E^1$ is totally disconnected under Q-topology and under S_v-topology if the monadic entourage V is not the smaller of two adjacent ones.*

Proof. Seeking a contradiction, suppose there is a Q-connected set C with at least two elements $a, b \in C$, $a < b$. By the Hausdorff property and by Corollary 5.3, there is a metric entourage U_r and a monadic entourage $U' \subset U_r$ such that $U_r(a) \cap U_r(b) = \emptyset$ and hence also $U'(a) \cap U'(b) = \emptyset$, with $x < y$ for all $x \in U'(a)$ and $y \in U'(b)$. Setting $X = \bigcup_{x \leq a} U'(x)$ and $Y = {^*E^1} - X$, we have $X \cap Y = \emptyset$, $a \in X$, and $b \in Y$, with X and Y Q-clopen, as easily follows from Theorem 5.4(a). But, then, the sets $C \cap X$ and $C \cap Y$ are nonempty, disjoint, and clopen in C as a subspace, with $C = (C \cap X) \cup (C \cap Y)$. This contradicts the assumed connectedness of C and thus proves Theorem 8.2 for Q-topology. The proof for S_v-topology is analogous, on passage to the separated quotient space $^*E^1/V(0)$. One only has to choose $U' \subset U_r$ such that $U' \supset V$, properly. This is possible since $V \subset U_r$ (U_r being a member of the S_v-uniformity) and since V is, by assumption, *not* the smaller of two adjacent entourages U' and U'' for U_r (chosen as in Corollary 5.3); thus $V \subset U' \subset U_r$.

[24] The limit p, although not unique in a non-Hausdorff topology, can be chosen one and the same for both sequences.

The disconnectedness of $^*E^1$ immediately implies the following:

***Corollary* 8.3.** *Every mapping $f\colon E^1 \to T$ can be extended to a mapping $g\colon {}^*E^1 \to T$ such that $g(x) = f(x)$ for $x \in E^1$, and g is continuous on $^*E^1$ under Q-topology, as well as under S_v-topology, with V a monadic entourage properly contained in the monad M. The topology of T may be arbitrary.*

Proof. It suffices to make g constant on each of the disjoint sets $M(a)$, $a \in {}^*E^1$, setting in particular $g(a) = f(a)$ if $a \in E^1$. The continuity of g then follows because $M(a)$ is Q-clopen (by Theorem 5.4) and also S_v-clopen when $V \subset M$ (by Theorem 6.1).

***Corollary* 8.4.** *No proper nonempty subset of a galaxy $G(a)$, $a \in {}^*E^1$, is S-clopen. Similarly, no such subset of $V(a)$ is S_v-clopen if V is as in Theorem* 8.1.

Indeed, this is immediate from Theorem 8.1.

Summing up, we see that $^*E^1$ can be characterized as follows:

1. It is a non-Archimedean and totally order-incomplete ordered field with uncountably many gaps and no order-dense countable subsets. It contains E^1 as a proper subfield and shares with E^1 all properties expressible as wfs.

2. The $^*E^1$-valued metric $^*\rho(x, y) = |x - y|$ defines in $^*E^1$ a nested Hausdorff uniformity (the *Q-uniformity*) which agrees with the interval topology in $^*E^1$ as an ordered set, and which has a base consisting of equivalence relations (*monadic entourages*). Under Q-topology, $^*E^1$ is totally disconnected. It is not metrizable in the usual sense if the model $^*\hat{A}$ is comprehensive.

3. Under its S-uniformity (see Section 4), $^*E^1$ is a complete pseudometrizable (but not Hausdorff) uniform space; it is not connected, its components being the galaxies. Similar assertions hold (sometimes under the comprehensiveness assumption) for S_v-uniformity whenever V is the smaller of two adjacent monadic entourages (otherwise, $^*E^1$ is totally disconnected under S_v-topology). In all cases, Q-topology is strictly finer than S_v-topology. E^1 is a subspace of $^*E^1$ under the S-uniformity but not under other uniformities mentioned above.

Some questions remain unsolved; we give a tentative list:

1. Is the Q-uniformity metrizable (equivalently, does $^*E^1$ have countable cofinal subsets) if the model $^*\hat{A}$ is *not* comprehensive?
2. Does $^*E^1$ have regular gaps, that is, gaps (X, Y) with $X + a \neq X$ for all $a \in {}^*E^1$? Equivalently, is $^*E^1$ incomplete under the Q-uniformity?
3. Apart from the case of Theorem 7.1, is $^*E^1$ complete under S_v-uniformity?

4. Is $\theta = \theta^*$? Is a set of type θ order-isomorphic to its open intervals?
5. Is $^*E^1$ order-isomorphic with its monads $M(a)$, $a \in {}^*E^1$?

References

1. L. W. COHEN AND C. GOFFMAN, The Topology of Ordered Abelian Groups, *Trans. Am. Math. Soc. 67* (1949), 310–319.
2. L. W. COHEN AND C. GOFFMAN, A Theory of Transfinite Convergence, *Trans. Am. Math. Soc. 66* (1949), 65–74.
3. J. KELLEY, *General Topology*. Princeton, N. J.: Van Nostrand, 1955.
4. W. A. J. LUXEMBURG, A New Approach to the Theory of Monads (this volume, and Tech. Rept. 1), Pasadena: California Institute of Technology, 1967.
5. A. ROBINSON, *Non-Standard Analysis* (Studies in Logic and the Foundations of Mathematics). Amsterdam: North-Holland, 1966.
6. A. ROBINSON, *Introduction to Model Theory and to Metamathematics of Algebra*, Amsterdam: North-Holland, 1965.
7. A. ROBINSON, Non-standard Theory of Dedekind Rings, *Proc. Acad. Sci. Amsterdam A70* (1967), 444–452.
8. A. ROBINSON AND E. ZAKON, A Set-Theoretical Characterization of Enlargements (this volume).
9. D. SCOTT, On Completing Ordered Fields (this volume).

Infinite Quantifiers and Continuous Games

by H. JEROME KEISLER[1]

Introduction

There is a close connection between strings of quantifiers and games between two players. For example, in a game where the two players take turns making n moves, the statement that the second player has a winning strategy may be expressed in the form

$$\forall t_0 \, \exists u_0 \cdots \forall t_n \, \exists u_n \phi.$$

In a game with countably many alternating moves, the statement that the second player has a winning strategy is of the form

$$\forall t_0 \, \exists u_0 \, \forall t_1 \, \exists u_1 \cdots \phi,$$

with an infinite string of quantifiers. For a continuous game, where both players move continuously with time, the statement that a player has a winning strategy can be expressed using an infinite linearly ordered quantifier. Such infinite quantifiers belong to the infinitary logics of the type considered by Henkin in [6].

In this paper we shall exploit the connection between games and infinite quantifiers. This may be done in either direction.

In one direction, we may use ideas about games to obtain results in model theory. This was done by Ehrenfeucht in [3] for finitary logic. In Section 1 of this paper we shall obtain three results, Theorems C, D, and E, which were first suggested by the examples of continuous games of pursuit discussed in Section 3. Although games do not actually enter into the proofs of these theorems, they were very important in motivating the results. Section 1 consists of a series of results in the model theory of

[1] This research was supported in part by NSF, Grant GP-5913. The author is a fellow of the Alfred P. Sloan Foundation.

infinitary logic. Each of these theorems says that a formula with an infinite quantifier may be approximated in some way by formulas of a simpler nature. Thus we call them *approximation theorems*. The first of these approximation theorems, Theorem A, involved only well-ordered quantifiers and was proved by the author in [8]. That result was partially extended to arbitrary quantifiers by Malitz [10] (see Theorem B). Theorems C and D are improvements of Theorems A and B, respectively. The approximation theorems not only shed some light on the model theory for infinitary logic, but also have applications to the model theory of ordinary finitary logic; see [9].

Continuous games are motivated by actual physical games. Through the connection between games and quantifiers we can use some of this physical motivation to obtain new model-theoretic results for infinitary, and perhaps finitary, logic. It is possible that our series of approximation theorems for infinitary logic can be extended much further by continuing this approach.

In the other direction, infinitary logic may be a useful approach to the study of games with infinitely many moves. For one thing, it provides a way of stating general principles common to a wide variety of such games (as in Section 2). Moreover, infinitary logic suggests questions that are often quite different from those which arise from a purely game-theoretic viewpoint. Our discussion of games in this paper was strongly influenced by ideas that arise most naturally in infinitary logic.

In Section 2 we apply the approximation theorems to obtain some general existence theorems in game theory. It deals with games with a payoff function as well as games with a winner. However, we restrict our attention only to *pure* strategies for these games. The last section is a selection of natural examples of games, some with countably many moves, and some continuous games in which one player is pursuing another through a metric space. We discuss what our theorems in Section 2 say about these games. We wish to warn the reader that the motivation for Section 1 comes from the examples in Section 3. The best way to begin this paper is with a casual reading of Section 3, followed by a casual reading of Section 2.

1. Approximation Theorems for Infinitely Long Quantifiers

We shall denote by ${}^XY$ the set of all functions on X into Y. We shall also sometimes write $f\colon X \to Y$ to mean $f \in {}^XY$. We denote by $S_\omega I$ the set of all finite subsets of a set I. If f is a function, $f \upharpoonright X$ is the restriction of f to X.

We shall use an infinitary language $\mathfrak{L}$ of the type introduced by Henkin

[6]. The language $\mathfrak{L}$ has a set V of individual variables that may be uncountable. It has an identity symbol $=$, a set $\{P_\alpha\}$ of finitary predicate symbols, the usual finitary connectives $\wedge$, $\vee$, $\neg$, and quantifiers $\forall$, $\exists$. In addition, $\mathfrak{L}$ has an infinite conjunction $\bigwedge$ and disjunction $\bigvee$ that may be applied to any set of formulas of $\mathfrak{L}$ to form another formula of $\mathfrak{L}$. Finally, $\mathfrak{L}$ has dependent quantifiers (T, U, f), where T and U are disjoint (possibly infinite) subsets of V and f is a function on U into the power set of T. If ϕ is a formula of $\mathfrak{L}$, so is $(T, U, f)\phi$. The quantifier (T, U, f) has the following intuitive meaning (which will be captured in our definition of satisfaction). T is the set of universally quantified variables, U is the set of existentially quantified variables, and each $u \in U$ depends only on the set of variables $f(u)$.

A *model* $\mathfrak{A}$ for $\mathfrak{L}$ is a nonempty set A together with a relation R_l corresponding to each predicate symbol P_l. Let z be a function on V into A. The relation

$$\mathfrak{A} \models \phi[z],$$

read z satisfies ϕ in $\mathfrak{A}$, is defined as usual by an induction on the complexity of ϕ. The quantifiers (T, U, f) are interpreted as follows:

$$\mathfrak{A} \models (T, U, f)\phi[z]$$

if and only if there is a function $S\colon {}^TA \to {}^UA$ such that:

(a) For all $x,x' \in {}^TA$ and $u \in U$,

$$x \restriction f(u) = x' \restriction f(u) \text{ implies } (Sx)(u) = (Sx')(u).$$

[In other words, $(Sx)(u)$ depends only on $x \restriction f(u)$.]

(b) For all $x \in {}^TA$, $\mathfrak{A} \models \phi[z']$, where

$$z'(v) = \begin{cases} x(v) & \text{if } v \in T, \\ (Sx)(v) & \text{if } v \in U, \\ z(v) & \text{if } v \in V - (T \cup U). \end{cases}$$

If ϕ is a formula of $\mathfrak{L}$, then $\mathfrak{A} \models \phi$ is understood to mean that ϕ is satisfied in $\mathfrak{A}$ by *every* function $z\colon V \to A$; in other words, the universal closure of ϕ holds in $\mathfrak{A}$.

In dealing with satisfaction the following special notation will be convenient. If $z\colon V \to A$ and x is a function from a subset of V into A, then $(z; x)$ is the function defined by

$$(z; x)(v) = \begin{cases} x(v) & \text{if } v \in \text{domain } (x), \\ z(v) & \text{if } v \varnothing \text{ domain } (x). \end{cases}$$

If x, y are two functions from disjoint subsets of V into A, then the function $(z; x, y)$ is defined analogously. Thus (b) above may be written:

$$\text{For all } x \in {}^TA,\ \mathfrak{A} \models \phi[z; x, Sx].$$

A *strategy* for the quantifier (T, U, f) in A is a function $S\colon {}^T A \to {}^U A$ with the property (a) above. If S also has the property (b), it is called a *winning strategy* for $\mathfrak{A} \models (T, U, f)\phi[z]$. Thus we have

$$\mathfrak{A} \models (T, U, f)\phi[z]$$

if and only if there is a winning strategy for $\mathfrak{A} \models (T, U, f)\phi[z]$. This terminology suggests the game-theoretic interpretation of the quantifier (T, U, f).

A formula ϕ is said to be *elementary* if it is a formula of elementary logic, that is, ϕ is built up from atomic formulas using only finite connectives and elementary quantifiers $\forall$, $\exists$.

Dependent quantifiers which are linearly ordered are of particular interest. Let $<$ be a linear ordering of the set $T \cup U$. We shall denote by $(T, U, <)$ the quantifier (T, U, f) such that for each $u \in U$,

$$f(u) = \{t \in T\colon t < u\}.$$

We say that (T, U, f) is a *linearly ordered quantifier* if it is of the form $(T, U, <)$.

Let Φ be a set of formulas of $\mathfrak{L}$. A model $\mathfrak{A}$ is said to be *Φ-saturated* if for every subset $\Sigma \subset \Phi$ and every variable $v \in V$,

$$\mathfrak{A} \models (\bigwedge_{\Gamma \in S_\omega(\Sigma)} \exists v \wedge \Gamma) \to \exists v \wedge \Sigma.$$

This notion depends very strongly on the set Φ. Notice that the above formula may have free variables, and our convention is that a formula is true in $\mathfrak{A}$ if and only if its universal closure is true in $\mathfrak{A}$.

The usual notion of an $\mathfrak{m}$-saturated model (see [11] and [18]) is related to the notion of a Φ-saturated model as follows. Let $\mathfrak{m}$ be an uncountable cardinal and suppose $\mathfrak{L}$ has at least $\mathfrak{m}$ variables; that is, $|V| \geq \mathfrak{m}$. Then $\mathfrak{A}$ is $\mathfrak{m}$-saturated if and only if $\mathfrak{A}$ is Φ-saturated for every set Φ of elementary formulas such that $|\Phi| < \mathfrak{m}$. Similarly, $\mathfrak{A}$ is $\aleph_0$-saturated if and only if $\mathfrak{A}$ is Φ-saturated for every countable set Φ with finitely many free variables. It is known [11] that every first-order theory which has infinite models has $\mathfrak{m}^+$-saturated models of power $\mathfrak{p}^{\mathfrak{m}}$, for any cardinals $\mathfrak{p} > 1$ and $\mathfrak{m} \geq \aleph_0$. See also [14].

We are now ready to state two known approximation theorems and then prove two new generalizations of them.

Theorem A (see [8]). *Let $\mathfrak{m}$ be an infinite cardinal. Consider a formula*

$$(T, U, <) \wedge \Sigma$$

and a model $\mathfrak{A}$ such that:

(a) *$<$ is a well ordering of type $\leq \mathfrak{m}^+$.*
(b) *Σ is a set of elementary formulas.*

(c) *$(T, U, <) \wedge \Sigma$ has at most $\mathfrak{m}$ free variables and predicate symbols.*
(d) *$\mathfrak{A}$ is an $\mathfrak{m}^+$-saturated model.*

Then

$$\mathfrak{A} \models (\bigwedge_{\Gamma \in S_\omega \Sigma} (T, U, <) \wedge \Gamma) \leftrightarrow (T, U, <) \wedge \Sigma.$$

Theorem B (Malitz [10]). *Let $\mathfrak{m}$ be an infinite quantifier and assume $2^{\mathfrak{m}} = \mathfrak{m}^+$. Consider a formula*

$$(T, U, f) \wedge \Sigma$$

and a model $\mathfrak{A}$ such that:

(a) *$|U| \leq \mathfrak{m}^+$ and for all $u \in U$, $|f(u)| \leq \mathfrak{m}$.*
(b) *Σ is a set of elementary formulas.*
(c) *$(T, U, f) \wedge \Sigma$ has at most $\mathfrak{m}$ free variables and predicate symbols.*
(d) *$\mathfrak{A}$ is an $\mathfrak{m}^+$-saturated model of power $|A| \leq \mathfrak{m}^+$.*

Then

$$\mathfrak{A} \models (\bigwedge_{\Gamma \in S_\omega \Sigma} (T, U, f) \wedge \Gamma) \leftrightarrow (T, U, f) \wedge \Sigma.$$

Notice that in each of the above theorems, the implication $\leftarrow$ is trivial, while $\rightarrow$ is not. In the following results we have a similar situation.

We now state two new results. Theorem C improves Theorem A by dropping the assumption that $<$ is well-ordered, and replacing the infinite conjunction $\wedge\Sigma$ of elementary formulas by a conjunction $\wedge_{i \in I}(\psi_i \rightarrow \sigma_i)$ where only the σ_i are assumed to be elementary. Also, the cardinal $\mathfrak{m}^+$ is replaced by an arbitrary infinite cardinal $\mathfrak{n}$.

Theorem C. *Let $\mathfrak{n}$ be an infinite cardinal. Consider a formula*

$$(T, U, <) \bigwedge_{i \in I} (\psi_i \rightarrow \sigma_i),$$

and a model $\mathfrak{A}$ such that

(a) *$<$ is a linear order such that $|U| \leq \mathfrak{n}$ and each $u \in U$ has fewer than $\mathfrak{n}$ predecessors.*
(b) *$\Sigma = \{\sigma_i : i \in I\}$ is a set of elementary formulas.*
(c) *The formula $(T, U, <) \wedge_{i \in I} \sigma_i$ has fewer than $\mathfrak{n}$ free variables and predicate symbols.*
(d) *For each $j \in I$, no variable $u \in U$ occurs in ψ_j and no $t \in T$ occurs in both ψ_j and $\wedge_{i \in I} \sigma_i$.*
(e) *$\mathfrak{A}$ is an $\mathfrak{n}$-saturated model.*

Then

$$\mathfrak{A} \models (\bigwedge_{J \in S_\omega I} (T, U, <) \bigwedge_{j \in J} (\psi_j \rightarrow \sigma_j)) \leftrightarrow (T, U, <) \bigwedge_{i \in I} (\psi_i \rightarrow \sigma_i).$$

The next theorem is a similar improvement of Theorem *C*.

Theorem D. *Let* $\mathfrak{n}$, $\mathfrak{p}$ *be infinite cardinals such that*

$$\mathfrak{p} = \sum_{\mathfrak{m}<\mathfrak{n}} \mathfrak{p}^{\mathfrak{m}}.$$

(This happens, for example, if $\mathfrak{n} = \mathfrak{m}^+$ *and* $\mathfrak{p} = 2^{\mathfrak{m}}$.*) Consider a formula*

$$(T, U, f) \bigwedge_{i \in I} (\psi_i \to \sigma_i)$$

and a model $\mathfrak{A}$ *such that:*

(a) $|U| \leq \mathfrak{p}$ *and for all* $u \in U$, $|f(u)| < \mathfrak{n}$.
(b) $\Sigma = \{\sigma_i \colon i \in I\}$ *is a set of elementary formulas.*
(c) *The formula* $(T, U, f) \bigwedge_{i \in I} \sigma_i$ *has fewer than* $\mathfrak{p}$ *free variables and predicate symbols.*
(d) *For each* $j \in I$, *no variable* $u \in U$ *occurs in* ψ_j, *and no* $t \in T$ *occurs in both* ψ_j *and* $\bigwedge_{i \in I} \sigma_i$.
(e) $\mathfrak{A}$ *is a* $\mathfrak{p}$*-saturated model of power* $\leq \mathfrak{p}$. *Then*

$$\mathfrak{A} \models [\bigwedge_{J \in S_\omega I} (T, U, f) \bigwedge_{j \in J} (\psi_j \to \sigma_j)] \leftrightarrow (T, U, f) \bigwedge_{i \in I} (\psi_i \to \sigma_i).$$

We shall defer the proof until later.

Before proving Theorem C we shall give a still more general statement of it involving Φ-saturation instead of $\mathfrak{n}$-saturation. The new formulation of Theorem C enables us to avoid complicated conditions involving cardinality, and also has more applications to game theory.

Theorem C′. *Consider a formula*

$$(T, U, <) \bigwedge_{i \in I} (\psi_i \to \sigma_i),$$

where

(a) $<$ *is a linear ordering.*
(b) $\Sigma = \{\sigma_i \colon i \in I\}$ *is a set of elementary formulas.*
(c) *For each* $j \in I$, *no variable* $u \in U$ *occurs in* ψ_j, *and no* $t \in T$ *occurs in both* ψ_j *and* $\bigwedge_{i \in I} \sigma_i$.

Let Φ be the least set of elementary formulas such that $\Sigma \subset \Phi$; if $\phi, \phi' \in \Phi$, then $\phi \wedge \phi' \in \Phi$, and if $\phi \in \Phi$, $t \in T$, $u \in U$, then $\forall t \phi \in \Phi$, $\exists u \phi \in \Phi$. For each $u \in U$ let $\Phi_u = \{\phi \in \Phi \colon$ no free variable of ϕ is $> u\}$. Suppose $\mathfrak{A}$ is a model such that:

(d) $\mathfrak{A}$ is Φ-saturated, or at least Φ_u-saturated for all $u \in U$. Then

$$\mathfrak{A} \models [\bigwedge_{J \in S_\omega I} (T, U, <) \bigwedge_{j \in J} (\psi_j \to \sigma_j)] \leftrightarrow (T, U, <) \bigwedge_{i \in I} (\psi_i \to \sigma_i).$$

To see that Theorem C′ implies Theorem C, we need only observe that under the hypotheses of Theorem C, each set of formulas Φ_u has power $< \mathfrak{n}$, and hence every $\mathfrak{n}$-saturated model is Φ_u-saturated.

Proof of Theorem C′. Let $\mathfrak{A}$ be Φ_u-saturated for all $u \in U$. Let $z\colon V \to A$ and assume that

$$\mathfrak{A} \models \bigwedge_{J \in S_\omega I} (T, U, <) \bigwedge_{j \in J} (\psi_j \to \sigma_j)[z].$$

For each $J \in S_\omega I$, let S_J be a winning strategy for

$$\mathfrak{A} \models (T, U, <) \bigwedge_{j \in J} (\psi_j \to \sigma_j)[z].$$

We want to find a winning strategy S for

$$\mathfrak{A} \models (T, U, <) \bigwedge_{i \in I} (\psi_i \to \sigma_i)[z].$$

The strategy S will be constructed bit by bit in the following order. We shall enumerate all pairs $\langle x, u\rangle$, where $x\colon T \to A$ and $u \in U$, say $\langle x_\alpha, u_\alpha\rangle$, $\alpha = \delta$. First we shall choose the values of

$$(Sx_0)(w), \qquad w \leq u_0.$$

Then we shall choose the values of

$$(Sx_1)(w), \qquad w \leq u_1,$$

in such a way that if $w \leq u_0$, $w \leq u_1$, and $x_0(t) = x_1(t)$ for all $t < w$, then $(Sx_0)(w) = (Sx_1)(w)$. We shall continue in this way through all $\alpha < \delta$. We shall exploit the strategies S_J to carry out the above process in such a way that S will be a winning strategy. We now give the details of the proof.

Let T_0 be the set of all $t \in T$ which occur in $\bigwedge_{i \in I} \sigma_i$, and let $T_1 = T - T_0$. Thus no variable in $T_0 \cup U$ occurs in any ψ_i. For each $x\colon T_1 \to A$ and each $J \in S_\omega I$, define $\Phi^x(J)$ to be the set of all $\phi \in \Phi$ such that whenever

$$J \subset K \in S_\omega I, \qquad x \subset x' \in {}^T A,$$

we have

$$\mathfrak{A} \models \phi[z; x', S_K x'].$$

Let

$$\Phi^x = \bigcup \{\Phi^x(J) \colon J \in S_\omega I\}.$$

Thus $\Phi^x \subset \Phi$. Since each $\Phi^x(J)$ is closed under finite conjunction and

$$\Phi^x(J) \cup \Phi^x(K) \subset \Phi^x(J \cup K),$$

each set Φ^x is closed under finite conjunction. Since $\models \phi \to \exists u \phi$, it is obvious that if $\phi \in \Phi^x$ and $u \in U$, then $\exists u \phi \in \Phi^x$. On the other hand, if $\phi \in \Phi^x$, $t \in T_0$, and there is no $u \in U$, $u > t$, which occurs free in ϕ, then $\forall t\phi \in \Phi^x$. This is because if $x(t') = x'(t')$ except when $t' = t$, then $S_J x$ and $S_J x'$ are the same for all free u in ϕ, and so if $\phi \in \Phi^x(J)$,

$$\mathfrak{A} \models \forall t\phi[z;\, x,\, S_J x].$$

We also note that for any $\phi \in \Phi^x$,

$$(1) \qquad \mathfrak{A} \models (\exists u)_{u \in U}\phi[z;\, x],$$

because when $\phi \in \Phi^x(J)$,

$$\mathfrak{A} \models \phi[z;\, x,\, S_J x].$$

Moreover, since each S_J is a strategy, whenever

$$x(t) = x'(t) \text{ for all } t < u,$$

we have

$$\Phi^x \cap \Phi_u = \Phi^{x'} \cap \Phi_u.$$

For $x\colon T \to A$ let $\Phi^x = \Phi^{x \restriction T_1}$.

We shall now prove the following:

(a) For any $x\colon T \to A$ and $u \in U$, there exists $y\colon U \to A$ such that

$$\mathfrak{A} \models \bigwedge (\Phi^x \cap \Phi_u)[z;\, x,\, y].$$

Proof of (a). Notice that $\Phi^x \cap \Phi_u$ is closed under finite conjunction. Enumerate the variables $u' \leq u$ without repetitions, say

$$\{u_\alpha\colon \alpha < \beta\} = \{u' \in U\colon u' \leq u\}$$

and let Σ_α be the set of all $\phi \in \Phi^x \cap \Phi_u$ in which no u_γ, $\gamma \geq \alpha$, occurs free. Then each Σ_α is a subset of $\Phi^x \cap \Phi_u$ which is closed under finite conjunction. Using (1) and the hypothesis that $\mathfrak{A}$ is Φ_u-saturated, we may choose $y_0 \in A$ such that

$$\mathfrak{A} \models \bigwedge \Sigma_1[z;\, x,\, y_0].$$

Now whenever $\phi \in \Sigma_2$ we have $\exists u_1\phi \in \Sigma_1$, so again using Φ_u-saturatedness we may choose $y_1 \in A$ such that

$$\mathfrak{A} \models \bigwedge \Sigma_2[z;\, x,\, y_0,\, y_1].$$

Continuing in this way through all $\alpha < \beta$ we obtain $y\colon U \to A$ such that

$$\mathfrak{A} \models \bigwedge (\Phi^x \cap \Phi_u)[z;\, x,\, y].$$

Things work at limit ordinals α because $\Sigma_\alpha = \bigcup_{\gamma<\alpha} \Sigma_\gamma$. Thus (a) is proved.

Now we claim:

(b) Let W be an initial segment of $T \cup U$ with $U \cap W \neq 0$, and let $u \in U$. Suppose $x \in {}^T A$, $y \in {}^U A$, and

$$\mathfrak{A} \models \bigwedge (\Phi^x \cap \textstyle\bigcup_{w \in U \cap W} \Phi_w)[z;\, x,\, y].$$

Then there exists $y' \in {}^{U}A$ such that $y'(w) = y(w)$ for all $w \in U \cap W$, and

$$\mathfrak{A} \models \bigwedge (\Phi^x \cap \Phi_u)[z; x, y'].$$

The proof of (b) is trivial if $u \in W$. Otherwise the proof is like the proof of (a), except that we take an enumeration

$$\{u' \in U - W : u' \leq u\} = \{u_\alpha : \alpha < \beta\}$$

without repetitions.

Again let Σ_α be the set of all $\phi \in \Phi^x \cap \Phi_u$ for which no u_γ, $\gamma \geq \alpha$, occurs free. The crucial observation is that for each $\phi \in \Sigma_0$, if $t^1, \cdots, t^m$ are all the $t \in T - W$ occurring free in ϕ, then

$$(\forall t^1 \cdots \forall t^m \phi) \in \Phi^x \cap \bigcup_{w \in U \cap W} \Phi_w,$$

and hence $$\mathfrak{A} \models \forall t^1 \cdots \forall t^m\, \phi[z; x, y].$$

It follows that for all $\phi \in \Sigma_0$,

$$\mathfrak{A} \models \phi[z; x, y].$$

We now proceed exactly as in the proof of (a).

We now return to the proof of the theorem. Let us enumerate all pairs $\langle x, u\rangle$, where $x: T \to A$ and $u \in U$, say $\langle x_\alpha, u_\alpha\rangle$, $\alpha < \delta$. It does not matter how large δ is. For each $\alpha,\beta < \delta$ let

$$W_{\alpha\beta} = \{v \in T \cup U : v \leq u_\alpha,\ v \leq u_\beta, \text{ and for all } t \in T,\ t \leq v \text{ implies } x_\alpha(t) = x_\beta(t)\}.$$

Let $$W_\alpha = \bigcup_{\beta<\alpha} W_{\alpha\beta}.$$

First, using (a), choose $y_0: U \to A$ such that

$$\mathfrak{A} \models \bigwedge (\Phi^{x_0} \cap \Phi_{u_0})[z; x_0, y_0].$$

Next, using (b), we choose inductively functions $y_\alpha: U \to A$, $\alpha < \delta$, such that

(2) $$\mathfrak{A} \models \bigwedge (\Phi^{x_\alpha} \cap \Phi_{u_\alpha})[z; x_\alpha, y_\alpha]$$

and for all α, β,

(3) $$u \in W_{\alpha\beta} \text{ implies } y_\alpha(u) = y_\beta(u).$$

Suppose we already have chosen y_α, $\alpha < \gamma$, satisfying (2) and (3). We show how to choose y_γ. If $W_\gamma \cap U = 0$, we use (a) and choose y_γ such that (2) holds for $\alpha = \gamma$. In this case (3) is automatic for $\alpha,\beta \leq \gamma$. Suppose, on the other hand, that $U \cap W_\gamma = 0$. Since (3) holds below

γ, there is a function $y\colon U \to A$ such that

$$\alpha < \gamma \text{ and } u \in W_{\alpha\gamma} \text{ implies } y(u) = y_\alpha(u).$$

Also, for all $\alpha < \gamma$ and $w \in U \cap W_{\alpha\gamma}$, we have

$$\Phi^{x\alpha} \cap \Phi_w = \Phi^{x\gamma} \cap \Phi_w.$$

Hence in view of (2),

$$\mathfrak{A} \models \wedge\ (\Phi^{x\gamma} \cap \cup_{w\in U\cap W\gamma} \Phi_w)[z;\ x_\gamma,\ y].$$

Then using (b) we may choose $y_\gamma\colon U \to A$ such that

$$\mathfrak{A} \models \wedge\ (\Phi^{x\gamma} \cap \Phi_{u_\gamma})[z;\ x_\gamma,\ y_\gamma]$$

and $y_\gamma(w) = y(w)$ for all $w \in U \cap W_\gamma$. It then follows that (2) and (3) hold for all $\alpha,\beta \leq \gamma$. This completes the induction.

Now define the function $S\colon {}^TA \to {}^UA$ by

$$(Sx_\alpha)(u_\alpha) = y_\alpha(u_\alpha), \qquad \alpha < \delta.$$

It follows from (3) that S is a strategy. Also, for each α, $t < u_\alpha$ implies

$$u \leq u_\alpha \text{ implies } (Sx_\alpha)(u) = y_\alpha(u).$$

From this and (3) we obtain

$$\mathfrak{A} \models \wedge\ \Phi^x[z;\ x,\ Sx] \tag{4}$$

for all $x\colon T \to U$.

Suppose $i \in I$, $x\colon T \to U$, and

$$\mathfrak{A} \models \psi_i[z;\ x].$$

Then whenever $i \in J \in S_\omega I$,

$$\mathfrak{A} \models \sigma_i[z;\ x,\ S_Jx].$$

Therefore $\qquad \sigma_i \in \Phi^x(\{i\}), \qquad \sigma_i \in \Phi^x.$

Thus, by (4), $\qquad \mathfrak{A} \models \sigma_i[z;\ x,\ Sx].$

This shows that for all $x\colon T \to A$,

$$\mathfrak{A} \models \bigwedge_{i\in I} (\psi_i \to \sigma_i)[z;\ x,\ Sx],$$

and so S is a winning strategy for

$$\mathfrak{A} \models (T,\ U,\ <) \bigwedge_{i\in I} (\psi_i \to \sigma_i)[z].$$

This completes our proof.

It appears to be very awkward to state Theorem D in a more general form as we did Theorem C′. However, it will be seen from the proof of

Theorem D that the assumption that $\mathfrak{A}$ is $\mathfrak{p}$-saturated is stronger than necessary.

Proof of Theorem D. Let $z\colon V \to A$ and suppose

$$\mathfrak{A} \models \bigwedge_{J \in S_\omega I} (T, U, f) \bigwedge_{j \in J} (\psi_j \to \sigma_j)[z]. \tag{1}$$

Our plan is to introduce $\mathfrak{p}$ new variables to $\mathfrak{L}$ and, by substituting these new variables for the old variables in the right way, we shall unscramble the dependent quantifier (T, U, f). In this manner we shall get an auxiliary formula (4) below, which has a well-ordered quantifier and thus can be approximated using Theorem C.

Consider the set of all pairs $\langle x, u\rangle$ such that $u \in U$ and $x\colon f(u) \to A$. By (a) and the assumption that $|A| \leq \mathfrak{p}$, we see that there are at most

$$(\Sigma_{\mathfrak{m}<\mathfrak{n}}\mathfrak{p}^{\mathfrak{m}}) \cdot \mathfrak{p} = \mathfrak{p}$$

such pairs. Let

$$\langle x_\alpha, u_\alpha\rangle, \qquad \alpha < \mathfrak{p}$$

be an enumeration of all these pairs $\langle x, u\rangle$. As in the previous proof, let T_0 be the set of all variables $t \in T$ which occur in $\bigwedge_{i\in I} \sigma_i$, and let $T_1 = T - T_0$.

We shall now extend the language $\mathfrak{L}$ by adding some new variables. For each $\alpha < \mathfrak{p}$, add a new individual variable v_α. For each $t \in T_0$ and each $a \in A$, add a new individual variable $v_{t,a}$. Call the extended language thus formed $\mathfrak{L}'$.

For each $i \in I$ and $x\colon T \to A$, we modify the formula σ_i to form a new elementary formula $\sigma_{i,x}$ of $\mathfrak{L}'$ in the following way:

(2) Replace each free occurrence of a variable $t \in T_0$ in σ_i by the variable $v_{t,x(t)}$.

(3) Replace each free occurrence of a variable $u \in U$ in σ_i by the variable v_α, where α is such that $\langle x \mid f(u), u\rangle = \langle x_\alpha, u_\alpha\rangle$.

We now form a new quantifier (T', U', f') in the language $\mathfrak{L}'$. Let

$$T' = \{v_{t,a}\colon t \in T_0,\ a \in A\},$$
$$U' = \{v_\alpha\colon \alpha < \mathfrak{p}\},$$
$$f'(v_\alpha) = \{v_{t,x_\beta(t)}\colon \beta \leq \alpha, \quad \text{and} \quad t \in f(u_\beta) \cap T_0\}.$$

Notice that $\beta < \alpha$ implies $f'(v_\beta) \subset f'(v_\alpha)$. We have for each α,

$$|f'(v_\alpha)| \leq \Sigma_{\beta<\alpha}|f(u_\beta)|.$$

The right side is a sum of fewer than $\mathfrak{p}$ cardinals each $< \mathfrak{n}$. In case $\mathfrak{p} = \mathfrak{n}$, we have $\mathfrak{p} = \mathfrak{p}^{\mathfrak{m}}$ for all $\mathfrak{m} < \mathfrak{p}$; hence $\mathfrak{p}$ is a regular cardinal and the right side is $< \mathfrak{p}$. In case $\mathfrak{n} < \mathfrak{p}$, the right side is at most $|\alpha + 1| \cdot \mathfrak{n}$, which is $< \mathfrak{p}$. So in either case we have

$$|f'(v_\alpha)| < \mathfrak{p}.$$

It follows that there is a well ordering $<$ of $T' \cup U'$ of type $\mathfrak{p}$ such that

$$\alpha < \beta \text{ implies } v_\alpha < v_\beta,$$
$$f'(v_\alpha) = \{t \in T' : t < v_\alpha\}.$$

Then the quantifiers (T', U', f') and $(T', U', <)$ are the same.

Let

$$I' = \{\langle i,x\rangle : i \in I,\ x : T \to A, \text{ and } \mathfrak{A} \models \psi_i[z; x]\}.$$

Now consider the formula

$$(4) \qquad (T', U', <) \bigwedge_{<i,x>\in I'} \sigma_{i,x}.$$

Every *free* variable of this formula is also a free variable of the formula

$$(T, U, f) \bigwedge_{i\in I} \sigma_i,$$

and the same goes for predicate symbols. Thus by D(c), the formula (4) has fewer than $\mathfrak{p}$ free variables or predicate symbols. Since $\mathfrak{A}$ is $\mathfrak{p}$-saturated and $<$ is a well ordering of order type $\mathfrak{p}$, we may apply Theorem C to obtain

$$(5) \qquad \mathfrak{A} \models (\bigwedge_{J'\in S_\omega I'} (T', U', <) \bigwedge_{\langle j,x\rangle\in J'} \sigma_{j,x}) \to (T', U', <) \bigwedge_{\langle i,x\rangle\in I'} \sigma_{i,x}.$$

We shall establish two claims:

$$(6) \qquad \mathfrak{A} \models \bigwedge_{J'\in S_\omega I'} (T', U', <) \bigwedge_{\langle j,x\rangle\in J'} \sigma_{j,x}[z],$$

and

$$(7) \qquad \mathfrak{A} \models (T', U', <) \bigwedge_{\langle i,x\rangle\in I'} \sigma_{i,x} \to (T, U, f) \bigwedge_{I\in I} (\psi_i \to \sigma_i)[z].$$

Using (6), (5), and (7) in turn, we conclude that

$$\mathfrak{A} \models (T, U, f) \bigwedge_{i\in I} (\psi_i \to \sigma_i)[z],$$

and this will complete our proof.

Proof of (6). We shall use our assumption (1) at this time. Let $J' \in S_\omega I'$ and let

$$J = \{i \in I : \text{for some } x,\ \langle i, x\rangle \in J'\}.$$

By (1) there is a winning strategy S_J for

$$\mathfrak{A} \models (T, U, f) \bigwedge_{j\in J} (\psi_j \to \sigma_j)[z].$$

We shall define a winning strategy S' for

$$\mathfrak{A} \models (T', U', <) \bigwedge_{\langle j,x\rangle \in J'} \sigma_{j,x}[z].$$

For each $x'\colon T' \to A$ and $v_\alpha \in U'$, let

$$(S'x')(v_\alpha) = (S_J x'')(u_\alpha),$$

where

$$x''(t) = \begin{cases} x_\alpha(t) & \text{if } t \in f(u_\alpha) \cap T_1, \\ x'(v_{t,x_\alpha(t)}) & \text{if } t \in f(u_\alpha) \cap T_0, \\ \text{arbitrary} & \text{if } t \in T - f(u_\alpha). \end{cases}$$

If $x_1', x_2' \in {}^{T'}A$, $v_\alpha \in U'$, and

$$x_1' \restriction f'(v_\alpha) = x_2' \restriction f'(v_\alpha),$$

then we see from the above choice of x'' that

$$x_1'' \restriction f(u_\alpha) = x_2'' \restriction f(u_\alpha),$$

and hence

$$(S_J x_1'')(u_\alpha) = (S_J x_2'')(u_\alpha),$$

and

$$(S'x_1')(v_\alpha) = (S'x_2')(v_\alpha).$$

Thus S' is a strategy. Consider any $x'\colon T' \to A$ and $\langle j, x\rangle \in J'$. Since $\langle j, x\rangle \in I'$,

$$\mathfrak{A} \models \psi_j[z; x].$$

Define $x_1\colon T \to A$ by

(8) $$x_1(t) = \begin{cases} x(t) & \text{if } t \in T_1, \\ x'(v_{t,x(t)}) & \text{if } t \in T_0. \end{cases}$$

Then

$$\mathfrak{A} \models \psi_j[z; x_1],$$

so

(9) $$\mathfrak{A} \models \sigma_j[z; x_1, S_J x_1].$$

From (3) we see that all the variables in U' which are free in $\sigma_{j,x}$ are of the form v_α, where $x_\alpha \subset x$. So if v_α occurs free in $\sigma_{j,x}$, then

$$x_1(t) = \begin{cases} x_\alpha(t) & \text{if } t \in f(u_\alpha) \cap T_1, \\ x'(v_{t,x_\alpha(t)}) & \text{if } t \in f(u_\alpha) \cap T_0. \end{cases}$$

This means that

(10) $$(S'x')(v_\alpha) = (S_J x_1)(v_\alpha)$$

whenever v_α occurs free in $\sigma_{j,x}$. In passing from σ_j to $\sigma_{j,x}$ we replace t by $v_{t,x(t)}$ and u_α by v_α, so from (8), (9), and (10) it follows that

$$\mathfrak{A} \models \sigma_{j,x}[z; x', S'x'].$$

Therefore S' is the desired winning strategy, and (6) is proved.

Proof of (7). Let S' be a winning strategy for

$$\mathfrak{A} \models (T', U', <) \bigwedge_{\langle i,x\rangle \in I'} \sigma_{i,x}[z].$$

Let $b\colon T' \to A$ be the particular function defined by

$$b(v_{t,a}) = a \text{ for all } t \in T_0,\ a \in A.$$

Define $S\colon {}^TA \to {}^UA$ by

$$(Sx)(u) = (S'b)(v_\alpha), \qquad \text{where} \qquad \langle x_\alpha, u_\alpha\rangle = \langle x \restriction f(u), u\rangle.$$

S is a strategy for the quantifier (T, U, f), because if $x_1 \restriction f(u) = x_2 \restriction f(u)$, then for some α,

$$\langle x_1 \restriction f(u), u\rangle = \langle x_\alpha, u_\alpha\rangle = \langle x_2 \mid f(u), u\rangle,$$

hence

$$(Sx_1)(u) = (Sx_2)(u).$$

Let $x\colon T \to A$, and suppose $i \in I$ and

$$\mathfrak{A} \models \psi_i[z; x].$$

Then $\langle i,x\rangle \in I'$, and therefore

$$\mathfrak{A} \models \sigma_{i,x}[z; b, S'b].$$

Since $\sigma_{i,x}$ comes from σ_i by replacing u_α by v_α and t by $v_{t,x(t)}$,

and since $\qquad x(t) = b(v_{t,x(t)}),$

$$(Sx)(u_\alpha) = (S'b)(v_\alpha),$$

it follows that $\qquad \mathfrak{A} \models \sigma_i[z; x, Sx].$

Therefore, S is a winning strategy for

$$\mathfrak{A} \models (T, U, f) \bigwedge_{i \in I} (\psi_i \to \sigma_i)[z],$$

and (7) is proved. Our proof is complete.

From the proof of Theorem D we see that the hypothesis that $\mathfrak{A}$ is $\mathfrak{p}$-saturated can be weakened somewhat. For instance, let Φ be a set of elementary formulas containing Σ and closed under finite conjunction, substitution of free variables, and quantification by $\forall$ and $\exists$. Suppose $\mathfrak{L}$ has at least $\mathfrak{p}$ variables not occurring in $\bigwedge_{i\in I} \sigma_i$. Then Theorem D holds for any model $\mathfrak{A}$ of power $\leq \mathfrak{p}$ such that for every $\Phi' \subset \Phi$ of power $< \mathfrak{p}$, $\mathfrak{A}$ is Φ'-saturated. For example, if all the formulas in Σ are positive (contain no negations), we may take for Φ the set of all positive formulas; if none of the formulas in Σ contain the equality symbol, we may take for Φ the set of all formulas without equality.

We conclude this section with one more approximation theorem which differs from Theorems A–D because in the approximating formulas the existentially quantified variables are shifted to the right.

Consider two linear orderings $<_1$, $<_2$ of $T \cup U$. We shall say that $<_1$ is *stronger* than $<_2$ if for all $t \in T$ and $u \in U$,

$$t <_1 u \text{ implies } t <_2 u.$$

It is obvious that if $<_1$ is stronger than $<_2$, then for any formula ϕ,

$$\mathfrak{A} \models (T, U, <_1)\phi \rightarrow (T, U, <_2)\phi.$$

This is because any strategy for $(T, U, <_1)$ is also a strategy for $(T, U, <_2)$.

A set $\{<_k: k \in K\}$ of linear orderings of $T \cup U$ is said to be *directed* if for all $k_1, k_2 \in K$ there exists $k \in K$ such that $<_k$ is stronger than each of $<_{k_1}, <_{k_2}$. The set $\{<_k: k \in K\}$ is said to *converge* to the linear ordering $<$ of $T \cup U$ if for all $t \in T$ and $u \in U$, $t < u$ if and only if $t <_k u$ for all $k \in K$. Clearly, a directed set of linear orderings always converges to some linear ordering $<$, and $<$ is unique except for rearrangements within T and within U. If $\{<_k: k \in K\}$ converges to $<$, then $<$ is obviously stronger than each $<_k$.

If $u \in U$, let

$$T_u = \{t \in T: u < t\}, \quad U_u = \{w \in U: u < w\}.$$

We shall let $\exists^{\leq 1} u$ be the quantifier "there exists at most one u."

Theorem E. *Consider a formula*

$$(T, U, <) \bigwedge_{i \in I} (\psi_i \rightarrow \sigma_i)$$

such that (a)–(c) *of Theorem C′ hold, and* (d) *T is dense in the ordered set* $\langle T \cup U, < \rangle$.

Let $\mathfrak{A}$ be a model such that (e) *$\mathfrak{A}$ is Φ-saturated, where Φ is as in Theorem C; and* (f) *for all $u \in U$,*

$$\mathfrak{A} \models (\exists^{\leq 1} u)(\exists v)_{v \in T_u \cup U_u} \bigwedge_{i \in I} (\psi_i \rightarrow \sigma_i).$$

(That is, the interpretation of u is uniquely determined by the interpretations of the earlier variables.)

Then, for any directed set $\{<_k: k \in K\}$ of linear orderings of $T \cup U$ converging to $<$,

$$\mathfrak{A} \models \Big(\bigwedge_{k \in K} (T, U, <_k) \bigwedge_{i \in I} (\psi_i \rightarrow \sigma_i)\Big) \leftrightarrow (T, U, <) \bigwedge_{i \in I} (\psi_i \rightarrow \sigma_i).$$

Proof. Suppose $z: V \to A$ and

$$\mathfrak{A} \models \bigwedge_{k \in K} (T, U, <_k) \bigwedge_{i \in I} (\psi_i \to \sigma_i)[z]. \tag{1}$$

We first transform our formula into a more convenient form. We add new constants c_a, $a \in A$, to $\mathfrak{L}$, and consider the model $(\mathfrak{A}, a)_{a \in A}$ for the extended language. Let T_0, T_1 be as in the previous two proofs. Let I' be the set of all pairs $\langle i, x \rangle$ such that $i \in I$, $x: T_1 \to A$, and

$$\mathfrak{A} \models \psi_{i,x}[z; x].$$

For $\langle i, x \rangle \in I'$ let $\psi_i x$ be

$$\bigwedge_{t \in T_1} (t = c_{x(t)}),$$

a complete description of the function $x \upharpoonright T_1$ in terms of the constants c_a. Now for any interpretation $y: V \to A$ of the variables which coincides with z on $V - (T \cup U)$, we have

$$\begin{cases} \mathfrak{A} \models \bigwedge_{i \in I} (\psi_i \to \sigma_i)[y] \\ \text{if and only if} \\ (\mathfrak{A}, a)_{a \in A} \models \bigwedge_{\langle i, x \rangle \in I'} (\psi_{i,x} \to \sigma_i)[y]. \end{cases} \tag{2}$$

The model $(\mathfrak{A}, a)_{a \in A}$ is also Φ_u-saturated.

We see from the above discussion that we can assume without loss of generality that for each $i \in I$ there is a unique function $x_i: T_1 \to A$ such that

$$\mathfrak{A} \models \psi_i[z; x_i].$$

For if we prove the theorem with this extra assumption, then we may apply our result to $(\mathfrak{A}, a)_{a \in A}$, and using (2) conclude that the theorem holds in general.

We wish to prove

$$\mathfrak{A} \models (T, U, <) \bigwedge_{i \in I} (\psi_i \to \sigma_i)[z].$$

By Theorem C′, it suffices to prove, for all $J \in S_\omega I$,

$$\mathfrak{A} \models (T, U, <) \bigwedge_{j \in J} (\psi_j \to \sigma_j)[z].$$

Let $J \in S_\omega I$. Consider the functions $x_j: T_1 \to A$, $j \in J$. We shall say that $u \in U$ is a *critical point* (for J) if for some $i, j \in J$,

$$u = \inf \{t \in T_1: x_i(t) \neq x_j(t)\}$$

with respect to the ordering $<$. Since J is finite, the set of critical points is finite (and possibly empty). Let $u_1, \cdots, u_n$ be the set of critical points.

Consider the formula

$$(3) \qquad (\exists u_1 \cdots u_n) \bigwedge_{j \in J} (\psi_j \to \sigma_j).$$

This formula contains only finitely many free variables in U, say $w_1, \cdots, w_p$ (because each σ_j is elementary and no members of U occur in ψ_j). None of the w's is a critical point. In view of (d), it follows that for each w_r there exists $t_r \in T$ such that $w_r < t_r$ and for all $i,j \in J$,

$$x_i(t) = x_j(t) \text{ for all } t < w_r$$

implies $\quad x_i(t) = x_j(t)$ for all $t < t_r$.

Since the orderings $<_k$, $k \in K$ are directed and converge to $<$, there exist $k \in K$ such that

$$(4) \qquad w_r <_k t_r, \qquad r = 1, \cdots, p.$$

Since only finitely many variables $t \in T_0$ occur free in the formula (3), we may choose k such that in addition to (4) we have

$$(5) \qquad w_r < t \text{ implies } w_r <_k t$$

for all $t \in T_0$ free in (3).

It follows from (1) that for this k,

$$(6) \qquad \mathfrak{A} \models (T, U, <_k) \bigwedge_{j \in J} (\psi_j \to \sigma_j)[z].$$

Hence

$$(7) \qquad \mathfrak{A} \models (T, U, <_k)(\exists u_1 \cdots u_n) \bigwedge_{j \in J} (\psi_j \to \sigma_j)[z].$$

From (4), (5), and (7) it follows that

$$(8) \qquad \mathfrak{A} \models (T, U, <)(\exists u_1 \cdots u_n) \bigwedge_{j \in J} (\psi_j \to \sigma_j)[z].$$

Let

$$J' = \{i \in I: x_i = x_j \text{ for some } j \in J\}.$$

Then $u_1, \cdots, u_n$ is the set of all critical points for J' as well as for J. By (8) we have

$$\mathfrak{A} \models \bigwedge_{J \in S_\omega J'} (T, U, <)(\exists u_1 \cdots u_n) \bigwedge_{j \in J} (\psi_j \to \sigma_j)[z].$$

In the above formula, $(T, U, <)(\exists u_1 \cdots u_n)$ acts like the quantifier $(T, U, <')$, where $<'$ is obtained from $<$ by moving $u_1, \cdots, u_n$ to the end. It follows from Theorem C′ and the Φ-saturatedness of $\mathfrak{A}$ that

$$(9) \qquad \mathfrak{A} \models (T, U, <)(\exists u_1 \cdots u_n) \bigwedge_{j \in J'} (\psi_j \to \sigma_j)[z].$$

Let S_J be a winning strategy for (9).

Suppose $j \in J$, $x\colon T \to A$, and $x_j \subset x$. Then

$$\mathfrak{A} \models (\exists u_1 \cdots u_n) \bigwedge_{j \in J'} (\psi_j \to \sigma_j)[z; x, S_J x].$$

Moreover, for any $i \in I - J'$, we have $x_i \neq x_j$, so

$$\mathfrak{A} \models \neg\psi_i[z; x].$$

Hence $$\mathfrak{A} \models (\exists u_1 \cdots u_n) \bigwedge_{i \in I} (\psi_i \to \sigma_i)[z; x, S_J x].$$

Therefore there are functions $y_1, \cdots, y_n\colon {}^T A \to A$ such that whenever $j \in J$ and $x_j \subset x\colon T \to A$,

(10) $$\mathfrak{A} \models \bigwedge_{i \in I} (\psi_i \to \sigma_i)[z; x, S_J x, y_1 x, \cdots, y_n x].$$

By our hypothesis (e), $y_r x$ depends only on the values of $x(t)$ for $t < u_r$, $r = 1, \cdots, n$, so we may change the strategy S_J to a strategy S'_J by letting

$$(S'_J x)(u_r) = y_r x, \qquad r = 1, \cdots, u,$$
$$(S'_J x)(u) = (S_J x)(u) \qquad \text{otherwise.}$$

From (10) we see that S'_J is a winning strategy for

$$\mathfrak{A} \models (T, U, <) \bigwedge_{i \in J'} (\psi_i \to \sigma_i)[z].$$

Since $J \subset J'$, (2) holds. The theorem is proved.

In Theorem E we can, in certain cases, weaken the assumption that "$\mathfrak{A}$ is Φ-saturated" to "$\mathfrak{A}$ is Φ_u-saturated for all $u \in U$." This can be done, for instance, when $(T, U, <)$ has the property that for all $t \in T$ there exists $u \in U$ with $t < u$. To see this we note that in (7)–(9) of the proof of Theorem E, the quantifiers $(\exists u_1 \cdots u_n)$ can be moved to the left of some variable in the quantifier $(T, U, <)$.

2. Applications to Game Theory

Suppose T, U are two disjoint sets and $<$ is a linear ordering of $T \cup U$. Let A be a nonempty set and let

$$W \subset ({}^T A \times {}^U A).$$

Consider a game with two players, $\forall$ and $\exists$. The players play the game roughly as follows. $\forall$ chooses a function $x\colon T \to A$ and $\exists$ chooses a function $y\colon U \to A$. For each $t \in T$, $\forall$ knows only $y(u)$, $u < t$, when choosing $x(t)$, and for each $u \in U$, $\exists$ knows only $x(t)$, $t < u$, when choosing $y(u)$. $\exists$ wins the game if $W(x, y)$, and otherwise $\forall$ wins. The set W is called the *winning set* for $\exists$, and the game is denoted by

$$(T, U, <)W \text{ in } A.$$

For a linearly ordered game of this kind, we may speak of strategies for both players. An $\exists$-*strategy* is a function

$$S: {}^T A \to {}^U A$$

such that for all $x, x' \in {}^T A$, $u \in U$,

$$x(t) = x'(t) \text{ for all } t < u \text{ implies } (Sx)(u) = (Sx')(u).$$

Dually, an $\forall$-*strategy* is a function $R: {}^U A \to {}^T A$ such that for all y, $y' \in {}^U A$ and $t \in T$,

$$y(u) = y'(u) \text{ for all } u < t \text{ implies } (Ry)(t) = (Ry')(t).$$

A *winning strategy* for $\exists$ is an $\exists$-strategy S such that for all $x \in {}^T A$, $W(x, Sx)$. A winning strategy for $\forall$ is an $\forall$-strategy R such that for all $y \in {}^U A$, not $W(Ry, y)$.

The above definitions are essentially the same as in the previous section. In fact, if $\mathfrak{A}$ is a model and W is such that

$$W(x, y) \text{ if and only if } \mathfrak{A} \models \phi[z; x, y],$$

then $\exists$ has a winning strategy for the game $(T, U, <)W$ in $\mathfrak{A}$ if and only if

$$\mathfrak{A} \models (T, U, <)\phi[z],$$

and $\forall$ has a winning strategy for this game if and only if

$$\mathfrak{A} \models (U, T, <)\neg\phi[z].$$

In case T and U are finite, or even if the quantifier $(T, U, <)$ has only finitely many alternations, it is easily seen that in the game $(T, U, <)W$ in A exactly one player has a winning strategy. In case $<$ is a well ordering, it is still easy to see that at most one player has a winning strategy. However, Gale and Stewart [5] gave an example of a game where $<$ has order type ω and neither player has a winning strategy.

In the general case it is even possible that both players have winning strategies. Several simple examples are known. For example, see Malitz [10] for an example due to Galvin of a game where $<$ has order type ω^* and both players have winning strategies.

To understand the situation we must consider the notion of a playable pair of strategies. An $\forall$-strategy R and an $\exists$-strategy S are said to be a *playable pair* iff there exists a unique pair of functions $x: T \to A$, $y: U \to A$ such that $Sx = y$ and $Ry = x$. Thus if $\forall$ and $\exists$ use a playable pair of strategies, the game will have a unique outcome and exactly one player will win. It follows that if R, S are a playable pair, then at most one of them is a winning strategy.

In a well-ordered game (that is, a game where $<$ is a well ordering), every pair of strategies is playable. This is why at most one player has a winning strategy. However, for linearly ordered games there are, in general, pairs of strategies that are not playable.

Games that allow nonplayable pairs of strategies are unnatural. One way out of the difficulty is to pick sets $\mathcal{R}$, $\mathcal{S}$ of strategies such that every pair in $\mathcal{R} \times \mathcal{S}$ is playable, and to change the rules of the game by making $\forall$ choose a strategy in $\mathcal{R}$ and $\exists$ choose a strategy in $\mathcal{S}$. Then at most one player will have a winning strategy. It is not clear what the best choice of $\mathcal{R}$ and $\mathcal{S}$ is. For some of the approaches and difficulties involved, see [12], [15], [18], and [7].

We shall use an approach which is unfair to player $\forall$ but has the virtue of keeping the class of permissible strategies as large as we can. We shall say that an $\forall$-strategy R is *universally playable* iff for all $\exists$-strategies S, the pair (R,S) is playable. We shall consider games in which $\exists$ can choose any $\exists$-strategy, but $\forall$ must choose a universally playable $\forall$-strategy. This guarantees that the game has at most one winner. To show that there are plenty of universally playable strategies we now give some examples.

(1) *Finite strategies.* An $\forall$-strategy R is said to be *finite* if there is a finite set $U_0 \subset U$ such that Ry depends only on $y \upharpoonright U_0$; that is,

$$y \upharpoonright U_0 = y' \upharpoonright U_0 \text{ implies } Ry = Ry'.$$

(2) *Piecewise strategies.* An $\forall$-strategy R is said to be *piecewise* if there is a finite partition:

$$U = U_1 \cup \cdots \cup U_n,$$

of U into finitely many disjoint intervals U_i, (listed in increasing order), such that if t is not an upper bound of U_i, then $(Ry)(t)$ depends only on $y \upharpoonright U_1 \cup \cdots \cup U_{i-1}$. Intuitively, a piecewise strategy is played as follows. First $\forall$ chooses $x(t)$ for all t which are less than a member of U_1. Then $\forall$ looks at how $\exists$ plays through U_1, namely $y(u)$, $u \in U_1$. Then $\forall$ chooses $x(t)$ for all t which are upper bounds of U_1 but not of U_2. Then $\forall$ looks at $y(u)$, $u \in U_2$, and so on. Clearly such a strategy is universally playable. Finite strategies are obviously special cases of piecewise strategies.

(3) *Well-ordered strategies.* These are generalizations of piecewise strategies. R is a *well-ordered* strategy if there is a partition

$$U = \cup_{\beta<\alpha} U_\beta$$

of U into disjoint intervals U_β, where α is an ordinal, and $\beta < \gamma$ implies U_β is less than U_γ; for each t which is not an upper bound of U_β, $(Ry)(t)$ depends only on $y \restriction \bigcup_{\gamma<\beta} U_\gamma$.

Still more general kinds of universally playable strategies can be described. For instance, one can consider strategies like the well-ordered strategies except that the interval U_β depends on the previous moves $y(u)$, $u \in \bigcup_{\gamma<\beta} U_\gamma$, of $\exists$. We shall come across such a strategy in the next section.

(4) *Time-lag strategies.* Suppose that T is a real interval, $[0, \tau]$ or $[0, \infty]$, so we may regard T as an interval of time. An $\forall$-strategy R is said to be a *time-lag strategy* if there is an $\epsilon < 0$ such that, for all $t \in T$, $(Ry)(t)$ depends only on $y(u)$, where $u < t - \epsilon$. Time-lag strategies are well-ordered strategies of a very special kind, and if $T = [0, \tau]$, they are piecewise strategies. There are finite strategies that are not time-lag strategies, and vice versa.

Let us reexamine the results of the last section from our present viewpoint.

Consider a set

$$W \subset {}^T A \times {}^U A,$$

a model $\mathfrak{A}$ with universe A and a formula ϕ of $\mathfrak{L}$. We shall say that ϕ *represents* W in $\mathfrak{A}$ if all the free variables in ϕ are elements of $T \cup U$, and for all $x \in {}^T A$, $y \in {}^U A$ we have

$$W(x, y) \text{ iff } \mathfrak{A} \models \phi[x, y].$$

We first look at what Theorem C′ says.

***Theorem* 1.** *Consider a game*

$$(T, U, <)W \text{ in } A.$$

Suppose there is a model $\mathfrak{A}$ with universe A, and a formula $\bigwedge_{i\in I} (\psi_i \to \sigma_i)$ which represents W in $\mathfrak{A}$, such that all the hypotheses of Theorem C′ are satisfied by $\mathfrak{A}$ and

$$(T, U, <) \bigwedge_{i\in I} (\psi_i \to \sigma_i).$$

Then either $\exists$ has a winning strategy, or $\forall$ has a finite winning strategy.

Proof. By Theorem C′, if $\exists$ does not have a winning strategy, then for some $J \in S_\omega I$,

$$\mathfrak{A} \models \neg\, (T, U, <) \bigwedge_{j\in J} (\psi_j \to \sigma_j).$$

The formulas σ_j, $j \in J$, contain only finitely many free variables, and no $u \in U$ occurs in any ψ_j. Therefore in the above formula, the set

$U_0 \subset U$ of u's that are free in $\bigwedge_{j \in J} (\psi_j \to \sigma_j)$ is finite. We thus have

$$\mathfrak{A} \models (U_0, T, <) \neg \bigwedge_{j \in J} (\psi_j \to \sigma_j).$$

Let R be a winning strategy for the above game. Defining R' by $R'y = R(y \restriction U_0)$, we obtain a finite $\forall$-strategy R' such that for all $y\colon U \to A$,

$$\mathfrak{A} \models \neg \bigwedge_{j \in J} (\psi_j \to \sigma_j)[Ry, y].$$

Thus R' is a winning finite strategy for $\forall$ in the original game $(T, U, <)W$ in A.

Theorem E says something about time-lag strategies. Combining Theorems C′ and E we get a result about strategies, which are both finite and time lag.

***Theorem* 2.** *Consider a game*

$$(T, U, <)W \text{ in } A.$$

Suppose there is a model $\mathfrak{A}$ *with universe* A, *and a formula* $\bigwedge_{i \in I} (\psi_i \to \sigma_i)$ *which represents* W *in* $\mathfrak{A}$, *such that all the hypotheses of Theorem E are satisfied by* $\mathfrak{A}$ *and*

$$(T, U, <) \bigwedge_{i \in I} (\psi_i \to \sigma_i).$$

Then either $\exists$ *has a winning strategy, or* $\forall$ *has a winning strategy* R *such that* R *is both a finite strategy and a time-lag strategy.*

We remark that hypothesis (*f*) of Theorem E amounts to the following. For all $u \in U$ and all functions

$$x'\colon \{t \in T\colon t < u\} \to A,\ y'\colon \{w \in U\colon w < u\} \to A,$$

there is at most one element $y'(u) \in A$ such that there exist $x \supset x'$, $y \supset y'$ with $W(x, y)$.

Proof of Theorem 2. We first consider the linear orderings $<_\epsilon$, $\epsilon > 0$, of $T \cup U$ given by

$$u <_\epsilon t \text{ if and only if } u < t - \epsilon,$$

(where $<_\epsilon$ is the same as $<$ on T and on U). The set $\{<_\epsilon\colon \epsilon > 0\}$ is a directed set, and since no $u \in U$ has a least $t > u$ in T, the set converges to $<$. Assume that $\exists$ does not have a winning strategy for the game. Then by Theorem E, there is an $\epsilon > 0$ such that

$$\mathfrak{A} \models \neg (T, U, <_\epsilon) \bigwedge_{i \in I} (\psi_i \to \sigma_i).$$

By Theorem C′, there is a $J \in S_\omega I$ such that

$$\mathfrak{A} \models \neg (T, U, <_\epsilon) \bigwedge_{j \in J} (\psi_j \rightarrow \sigma_j).$$

Now arguing as in Theorem 1, there is a winning finite strategy R for $\forall$ in the game

$$(T, U, <_\epsilon)W \text{ in } A.$$

Then R is a winning strategy for $\forall$ in the original game

$$(T, U, <)W \text{ in } A,$$

and R is both a finite strategy and a time-lag strategy.

Instead of a two-valued game, one often considers a many-valued game, that is, a game in which the outcome is described by a numerical payoff instead of a winner. Our results on two-valued games also give information about many-valued games. The method we shall use for reducing many-valued games to two-valued games is familiar in the literature; for example, see [12]. Another possible approach would be via many-valued logic (see [1], for example).

We let $(T, U, <)$ be a linearly ordered quantifier as usual. But now we have a *payoff function*

$$\text{Val}: ({}^T A \times {}^U A) \rightarrow [-\infty, +\infty]$$

which maps pairs $\langle x, y \rangle \in {}^T A \times {}^U A$ to points of the extended real line. We consider a game

$$(T, U, <)\text{Val in } A$$

between two players $\forall$, $\exists$. This game is played exactly like the two-valued game, but instead of having a winner, the outcome is the payoff $\text{Val}(x, y)$. $\exists$ tries to minimize the payoff, and $\forall$ tries to maximize the payoff. The notion of a strategy is the same as for two-valued games, but there is no such thing as a winning strategy. Instead, we define the value of a strategy. For an $\exists$-strategy S, we define

$$\text{Val}(S) = \sup\{\text{Val}(x, Sx) : x \in {}^T A\}.$$

For an $\forall$-strategy R,

$$\text{Val}(R) = \inf\{\text{Val}(Ry, y) : y \in {}^U A\}.$$

Thus if $\exists$ plays S he is sure of a payoff at most $\text{Val}(S)$, and if $\forall$ plays R he is sure of a payoff at least $\text{Val}(R)$.

We define

$$\text{Val}(\exists) = \inf\{\text{Val}(S) : S \text{ is an } \exists\text{-strategy}\},$$

$$\text{Val}(\forall) = \sup\{\text{Val}(R) : R \text{ is an } \forall\text{-strategy}\}.$$

For well-ordered games we have

$$\mathrm{Val}(\forall) \leq \mathrm{Val}(\exists),$$

but in general this inequality fails (this corresponds to the fact that in a two-valued game both players may have winning strategies).

Now let us make $\forall$ play only universally playable strategies. We define

$$\mathrm{Val}^*(\forall) = \sup\{\mathrm{Val}(R) : R \text{ is a universally playable } \forall\text{-strategy}\}.$$

Obviously, $$\mathrm{Val}^*(\forall) \leq \mathrm{Val}(\forall).$$

If (R,S) are a playable pair, then we clearly have

$$\mathrm{Val}(R) \leq \mathrm{Val}(S).$$

It follows that $$\mathrm{Val}^*(\forall) \leq \mathrm{Val}(\exists).$$

We shall say that the game has a value, a, when

$$a = \mathrm{Val}^*(\forall) = \mathrm{Val}(\exists).$$

There are two common questions concerning many-valued games. One is whether the game has a value. The other is whether the players have optimal strategies. An $\exists$-strategy S is said to be *optimal* iff

$$\mathrm{Val}(S) = \mathrm{Val}(\exists).$$

We shall say that a universally playable $\forall$-strategy R is optimal iff

$$\mathrm{Val}(R) = \mathrm{Val}^*(\forall).$$

We shall now use Theorems 1 and 2 to obtain corresponding results for many-valued games. The idea is simply to consider the two-valued games

$$(T, U, <)(\mathrm{Val} \leq r) \text{ in } A,$$

where r runs over the real numbers and $(\mathrm{Val} \leq r)$ denotes the set

$$\{\langle x, y\rangle : \mathrm{Val}\langle x, y\rangle \leq r\}.$$

Suppose that for each $r \in [-\infty, +\infty]$, the formula ϕ_r represents the set $(\mathrm{Val} \leq r)$ in a model $\mathfrak{A}$. We then have

$$\mathrm{Val}(\exists) \leq r \text{ iff } \mathfrak{A} \models \bigwedge_{s>r} (T, U, <)\phi_s,$$

because $\mathrm{Val}(\exists) \leq r$ if and only if, for each $s > r$, $\exists$ has a strategy with value $\leq s$. Furthermore,

$$\mathfrak{A} \models \phi_r \leftrightarrow \bigwedge_{s>r} \phi_s.$$

***Theorem* 3.** *Consider a many-valued game*

$$(T, U, <)\text{Val in } A.$$

Suppose there is a model $\mathfrak{A}$ *with universe* A, *and for each* $r \in [-\infty, +\infty]$ *a formula* $\bigwedge_{i \in I_r}(\psi_i \to \sigma_i)$ *which represents the set* $(\text{Val} \le r)$ *in* $\mathfrak{A}$, *such that the model* $\mathfrak{A}$ *and the big formula*

$$(T, U, <) \bigwedge_{i \in I} (\psi_i \to \sigma_i), \ (I = \cup \{I_r : r \in [-\infty, +\infty]\})$$

satisfy the hypotheses of Theorem C′. Then:

(a) *The game has a value*

$$\text{Val}(\exists) = \text{Val}^*(\forall) = a \ (\textit{for some } a).$$

(b) $\exists$ *has an optimal strategy.*
(c) $\forall$ *has finite strategies with values arbitrarily close to* a.

Remark. If the hypotheses of the above theorem hold for all r in a dense subset $d \subset [-\infty, +\infty]$, then they hold for all $r \in [-\infty, +\infty]$. We need only define

$$I_s = \cup \{I_r : s < r \in d\}$$

for each $s \notin d$.

Proof of Theorem 3. Let $r > \text{Val}^*(\forall)$ and consider the two-valued game

$$(T, U, <)(\text{Val} \le r) \text{ in } A.$$

Since every finite $\forall$-strategy has value at most $\text{Val}^*(\forall)$, $\forall$ has no winning finite strategy for the above game. Hence $\exists$ has a winning strategy, say S_r, for the game. Then

$$\text{Val}(S_r) \le r.$$

Since this is true for all $r > \text{Val}^*(\forall)$, we have

$$\text{Val}(\exists) \le \text{Val}^*(\forall).$$

The other inequality is always true, hence (a) holds.

(c) Let $r < a$, and consider the two-valued game

$$(T, U, <)(\text{Val} \le r) \text{ in } A.$$

$\exists$ does not have a winning strategy for this game, so, by Theorem 1, $\forall$ has a winning finite strategy, R_r. We have

$$a \ge \text{Val}(R_r) \ge r,$$

and (c) is proved.

(b) Consider the two-valued game

$$(T, U, <)(\text{Val} \le a) \text{ in } A. \tag{1}$$

If $\exists$ has a winning strategy S for this game, then S is an optimal $\exists$-strategy for the game

$$(T,\ U,\ <)\mathrm{Val}\ \text{in}\ A.$$

So it suffices to prove that $\exists$ has a winning strategy for (1), in other words,

(2) $$\mathfrak{A} \models (T,\ U,\ <) \bigwedge_{i \in I_a} (\psi_i \rightarrow \sigma_i).$$

For each $r \in [-\infty, +\infty]$, let

$$J_r = \bigcup_{r<s} I_s.$$

Then by a previous remark,

$$\mathfrak{A} \models \bigwedge_{i \in I_r} (\psi_i \rightarrow \sigma_i) \leftrightarrow \bigwedge_{j \in J_r} (\psi_j \rightarrow \sigma_j).$$

Thus (2) is equivalent to

(3) $$\mathfrak{A} \models (T,\ U,\ <) \bigwedge_{j \in J_a} (\psi_j \rightarrow \sigma_j).$$

By Theorem C′, (3) holds if and only if for all finite $J \subset J_a$,

(4) $$\mathfrak{A} \models (T,\ U,\ <) \bigwedge_{j \in J} (\psi_j \rightarrow \sigma_j).$$

But each finite $J \subset J_a$ is included in J_r for some $r > a$. Moreover, since

$$a = \inf \{\mathrm{Val}(S) \colon S \text{ is an } \exists\text{-strategy}\}$$

we have

(5) $$\mathfrak{A} \models (T,\ U,\ <) \bigwedge_{j \in J_r} (\psi_j \rightarrow \sigma_j)$$

for all $r > a$. But when $J \subset J_r$, (5) implies (4). Hence (4) holds for all finite $J \subset J_a$. Therefore (3) and (2) hold, and our proof is complete.

By a similar argument we can prove a many-valued version of Theorem 2. For a many-valued game

$$(T,\ U,\ <)\mathrm{Val}\ \text{in}\ A,$$

we shall say that the moves of $\exists$ *depend uniquely on the previous moves* if the game has the following property:

For all $u \in U$ and all functions

$$x' \colon \{t \colon t < u\} \rightarrow A,\ y' \colon \{w \colon w < u\} \rightarrow A$$

there is at most one element $b \in A$ such that x', y' can be extended to a pair x, y with $y(u) = b$ and $\mathrm{Val}(x, y) < +\infty$.

This amounts to saying that the hypothesis (f) of Theorem E holds for the game

$$(T,\ U,\ <)(\mathrm{Val} < +\infty)\ \text{in}\ A.$$

***Theorem* 4.** *Consider a many-valued game*

$$(T,\ U,\ <)\text{Val in } A.$$

Assume that the hypotheses of Theorem 3 hold with "E" in place of "C'." Assume further that the moves of $\exists$ *depend uniquely on the previous moves. Then* (a), (b), *and* (c) *hold and also*

(d) $\forall$ *has (finite) time-lag strategies with values arbitrarily close to a.*

Proof. This follows at once from Theorems 2 and 3. We need only observe that for all $r < a$, all the hypotheses of Theorem E are satisfied by $\mathfrak{A}$ and

$$(T,\ U,\ <) \bigwedge_{i \in I_r} (\psi_i \rightarrow \sigma_i).$$

We now obtain some more special existence theorems. First we prove a lemma that gives a convenient example of a Φ-saturated model.

***Lemma* 5.** *Let M be a compact topological space. Let* $\mathfrak{M}$ *be the model*

$$\mathfrak{M} = \langle M, \cdots, P_\alpha, \cdots \rangle,$$

where the P_α *run over all the closed subsets of M as well as all the finite subsets of M. Let* Φ *be the set of all positive elementary formulas in which the identity symbol does not occur. Then* $\mathfrak{M}$ *is* Φ*-saturated.* (A formula is said to be positive iff its only connectives are $\wedge$, $\vee$.)

Proof. We first note that the least topology containing the topology M, such that each finite set is closed, is still compact. We may thus assume without loss of generality that every finite set is closed. We wish to show: (1) For every formula $\phi \in \Phi$ involving only variables from U, the set $\{y \in {}^U M : \mathfrak{M} \models \phi[y]\}$ is closed in ${}^U M$. Consider the set Δ of $\phi \in \Phi$ satisfying (1). Obviously all atomic formulas belong to Δ, and Δ is closed under finite conjunction and disjunction. Since the topology is compact, for any $U_0 \subset U$, the projection of an open subset of ${}^U M$ into ${}^{U_0} M$ is open, and the projection of a closed subset of ${}^U M$ into ${}^{U_0} M$ is closed. It follows that Δ is closed under the quantifiers $\forall u$, $\exists u$. Hence $\Phi \subset \Delta$.

Now let $\phi \in \Phi$, $y \in {}^U M$, and $u \in U$. We claim that the set

$$\{a \in M : \mathfrak{M} \models \phi[y, a]\}$$

is a closed subset of M. This is because $\phi \in \Delta$, so the set

$$\{z \in {}^U M : \mathfrak{M} \models \neg\, \phi[z]\}$$

is open, and hence if $\mathfrak{M} \models \neg\, \phi[y, a]$, then there are neighborhoods Y of $y \restriction (U - \{u\})$, Z of a, such that $\mathfrak{M} \models \neg\, \phi[z]$ for all $z \in Y \times Z$, and so

$\mathfrak{M} \models \neg\, \phi[y, b]$ for all $b \in Z$. Therefore, since M is compact,

$$\mathfrak{M} \models (\bigwedge_{\Gamma \in S_\omega \Sigma} \exists u \wedge \Gamma) \rightarrow \exists u \wedge \Sigma$$

whenever $\Sigma \subset \Phi$, and $\mathfrak{M}$ is Φ-saturated.

The converse of the above lemma is trivial. Indeed, if $\mathfrak{M}$ is Φ_0-saturated where Φ_0 is the set of all atomic formulas, then $\mathfrak{M}$ is obviously compact. For the case that M is Hausdorff, the above lemma becomes a special case of a theorem of Weglorz [19].

We now give an application of our results to games in compact spaces. We shall state only the version for many-valued games. The two-valued version is an obvious modification.

Corollary 6. *Consider a game*

$$(T, U, <)\text{Val in } M,$$

where M is a compact topological space, and for all $x\colon T \rightarrow M$ and all $r \in [-\infty, +\infty]$, the set

$$\{y \in {}^U M\colon \text{Val}(x, y) \leq r\}$$

is closed in the product topology ${}^U M$. Then conditions (a), (b), and (c) *of Theorem 3 hold. Indeed,* (c) *may be strengthened to:*

(c_F) *$\forall$ has finite strategies R with values arbitrarily close to $\forall$ such that the range of R, namely $\{Ry\colon y \in {}^U M\}$, is finite.*

Proof. Let I_r be the set of all pairs $\langle x, \phi\rangle$ such that $x \in {}^T M$, $\phi \in \Phi$ (where Φ is defined in Lemma 5), ϕ has only variables in U free, and

$$\{y \in {}^U M\colon \text{Val}(x, y) \leq r\} \subset \{y \in {}^U M\colon \mathfrak{M} \models \phi[y]\}.$$

The model $\mathfrak{M}$ is Φ-saturated by Lemma 5. For $m \in M$ let P_m be the predicate corresponding to the set $\{m\}$. For each $i = \langle x, \phi\rangle$ let ψ_i be the formula $\bigwedge_{t \in T} P_{x(t)}(t)$, and let σ_i be ϕ. Then the formula

$$\bigwedge_{i \in I_r} (\psi_i \rightarrow \sigma_i)$$

represents the set ($\text{Val} \leq r$) in $\mathfrak{M}$. Hence by Theorem 3, (a)–(c) hold. Using Theorem C′, we see that for each $r < a$, since

$$\mathfrak{M} \models \neg\, (T, U, <) \bigwedge_{i \in I_r} (\psi_i \rightarrow \sigma_i),$$

there is a $J \in S_\omega I_r$ such that

$$\mathfrak{M} \models \neg\, (T, U, <) \bigwedge_{j \in J} (\psi_j \rightarrow \sigma_j).$$

Therefore, $\forall$ has a finite strategy R with value $\geq r$ such that for all $y \in {}^U M$, there is a $j \in J$ for which Ry satisfies ψ_j in $\mathfrak{M}$. Since J is finite and only one x satisfies each ψ_j, the range of R is finite.

***Corollary* 7.** *Assume the hypotheses of Corollary 6. Assume further that T and U are each dense in $T \cup U$, M is a Hausdorff space, and whenever* $\mathrm{Val}(x, y) < +\infty$, *$y$ is continuous when U has the order topology. Then* (a)–(d) *hold.*

Proof. All the hypotheses of Theorem 4 are satisfied.

It is fairly easy to prove Corollaries 6 and 7 directly using the Tychonoff product theorem. These direct proofs are much easier than the proofs of Theorems C′ and E in Section 1, because of the simple nature of the model $\mathfrak{M}$—all its relations are unary and it is much more saturated than necessary.

Using Theorem D and Lemma 5, we can get a version of Corollaries 6 and 7 above for games of "incomplete information." We shall only give a rough sketch. Suppose T, U are disjoint sets and f maps U into the power set of T, as in Section 1. Let M be a compact space and let $\mathrm{Val}: {}^T M \times {}^U M \to [-\infty, *\infty]$ be such that for all $x: T \to M$, the set of all $y \in {}^U M$ with $\mathrm{Val}(x, y) \leq r$ is closed in the product topology ${}^U M$. Now consider the game G given by

$$(T, U, f)\mathrm{Val} \text{ in } M$$

in which the move of $\exists$ at u depends on the moves of $\forall$ for all $t \in f(u)$. It can be shown that $\exists$ has an optimal strategy for the game G. Moreover, if for each finite $U_0 \subset U$ we let G_{U_0} be the game which is like G except that $\exists$ does not have to make his moves at $u \not\subset U_0$ until all the moves of $\forall$ are known, then $\mathrm{Val}(\exists)$ for G is the supremum of $\mathrm{Val}(\exists)$ for G_{U_0}, $U_0 \in S_\omega U$. These claims are proved by an argument similar to the proof of Theorem 3, using Theorem D and Lemma 5. It is not clear what the best way to define a strategy for $\forall$ is when the quantifier is not linearly ordered.

3. *Examples*

Let us begin with some games in which the players move alternately and there are ω moves. If $\forall$ moves first, this situation can be represented by letting T be the set of even natural numbers, U the set of odd natural numbers, and $<$ the usual ordering. Some strong results concerning the question of when such games are determined are obtained in [2], [12], and [13].

The game of chess may be considered as a two-valued game where black ($\exists$) wins iff he checkmates white or there is a draw. Since there are only finitely many possible chess positions and every finite model is $\mathfrak{m}$-saturated for all $\mathfrak{m}$, Theorem 1 holds for this game. But for this game, Theorem 1 is a trivial consequence of the Koenig tree theorem, since each player has only finitely many possible moves at each time.

The above remarks also hold true for chess played on infinitely many boards, where at each time a player makes one move on some board, and the game ends with the first checkmate. This time a player has infinitely many possible moves at a given time, but only finitely many moves are essentially different, since there are only finitely many different positions appearing on the boards.

To get a less trivial example of Theorem 1 we need a game where $\exists$ has infinitely many possible moves at some time. One such game is the Japanese game of go-mo-ku. Ignoring some details in the rules, the game is played as follows. The board is an infinite square lattice of points. First $\forall$ places a black stone on a point, then $\exists$ places a white stone on another point, and the players continue taking turns in this way. The first player to get five connected stones in a row, either vertically, horizontally, or diagonally, wins, and otherwise the game is a draw.[2] We shall make it a two-valued game by declaring $\exists$ the winner in case of a draw. This game may be described using a model $\mathfrak{A} = \langle A, S_1, S_2 \rangle$, where A is the set of points on the board and S_1 and S_2 are the horizontal and vertical successor functions. The interpretations of the even variables $v_0, v_2, \cdots$ are the moves of $\forall$, and of the odd variables, $\exists$. (If someone moves on an occupied square, $v_m = v_n$, the first player to do this is the loser.) The winning set for $\exists$ can be described by an infinite conjunction $\bigwedge_{i \in I} \sigma_i$ of elementary formulas σ_i. However, the model $\mathfrak{A}$ is not $\aleph_0$-saturated, and hence Theorem 1 does not apply.

Let us modify the game of go-mo-ku by playing it on infinitely many infinite boards. This time the model $\mathfrak{A}$ is $\aleph_0$-saturated, and the hypotheses of Theorem 1 hold. Theorem 1 then tells us that either $\exists$ has a winning strategy or $\forall$ has a finite winning strategy. As a consequence, if $\forall$ has a winning strategy, then there exists an $n < \omega$ such that $\forall$ has a strategy which guarantees a win in n moves! This fact about go-mo-ku on infinitely many boards can be proved quite easily using the compactness theorem, since the existential quantifiers can be replaced by finitary Skolem functions.

The same result holds if the game is modified, for example, by changing the number five to six. There are more substantial ways in which the game can be modified and still satisfy Theorem 1. For example, let X be any

[2] As described, it is known that $\forall$ has a winning strategy. However, the actual game of go-mo-ku has the extra rule that a player may not form two open rows of length three. Our discussion here is still valid with this extra rule.

set of sequences of points on the first board, and let the game be modified by saying that ∃ wins iff either the sequence of all moves of ∀ does not belong to X, or else ∃ wins the game described previously. This time we verify the hypotheses of Theorem 1 by adding a constant to the model $\mathfrak{A}$ for each point of the first board—the new model is still $\aleph_0$-saturated—and observing that the winning set for ∃ can be described by a formula of the form

$$\bigwedge_{i \in I} (\psi_i \rightarrow \sigma_i).$$

Here only even variables are in the ψ_i's, and odd variables are in the σ_i's, and the ψ_1's describe the elements of X. Again, Theorem 1 tells us that either ∃ has a winning strategy or ∀ has a finite winning strategy; consequently, if ∀ has a winning strategy, he has one that, for some n, guarantees a win within n moves.

The corresponding question for games like go-mo-ku on a single board is beyond the scope of Theorem 1. It may be that ∀ has a winning strategy, but the number of moves it takes ∀ to win depends on the distance between the first moves of ∀ and ∃.

The standard example of a game with a linearly ordered quantifier is the game of pursuit. In this type of game, both players move through a metric space M during a time interval, say $[0, \infty)$. At each time the players know all the previous moves. The player ∃ tries to catch the player ∀, and the payoff is some measure of how well ∃ pursues ∀. In many of the examples of pursuit games below, the fact that ∃ has an optimal strategy is known from the literature (see [15] and [16]). Our results pitting arbitrary strategies for ∃ against finite or time-lag strategies for ∀ seem to be new. However, pursuit games in which each player has finite strategies with values arbitrarily close to a have been considered, for example, in [4]. Much of the literature on games of pursuit is from the point of view of differential games (see [7]), where differential equations play a major role.

Remark. It will be useful in what follows to observe that if T is an arbitrary topology on a set M, and T' is the new topology on M such that X is closed in T' iff $x = M$ or X is closed and compact in T, then T' is compact. This allows us to apply Corollaries 6 and 7 for games in an arbitrary topological space M with topology T, provided the hypotheses hold when we pass to the compact topology T'.

A metric space M is said to be *finitely compact* iff every closed bounded subset is compact. For example, any closed subset of Euclidean space is finitely compact.

Consider a finitely compact metric space M, with distance function δ.

Let C, the "capture set," be a closed subset of the product space $M \times M$. The two players $\forall$ (the evader) and $\exists$ (the pursuer) play the game by choosing paths

$$x: [0, \infty) \to M, \qquad y: [0, \infty) \to M.$$

At any time $s \in [0, \infty)$, $\forall$ knows all the earlier positions $y(r)$, $r < s$, of $\exists$, while $\exists$ knows all the earlier positions and the present position, $x(r)$, $r \leq s$, of $\forall$. We say that $\exists$ *captures* $\forall$ at time s if $\langle x(s), y(s) \rangle \in C$. To make the game reasonable, we are given initial positions $i_\forall$, $i_\exists$, and each player has a maximum velocity $v_\forall$ and $v_\exists$ (which may depend on his position). To play the game, the players begin at the initial positions and move without exceeding their maximum velocities. $\exists$ tries to capture $\forall$ as soon as he can, and $\forall$ tries to avoid being captured as long as he can. The payoff is the time of capture, or $+\infty$ if no capture occurs.

Here is a somewhat more precise description of the game. Take T and U, the sets of moves for $\forall$ and $\exists$, to be disjoint copies of the real interval $[0, \infty)$. Say

$$T = \{t_s: s \in [0, \infty)\}, \qquad U = \{u_s: s \in [0, \infty)\}.$$

Define the ordering $<$ on $T \cup U$ in the natural way within T and within U, and

$$t_r < u_s \text{ iff } r \leq s.$$

[We continue to write $x(s)$ for $x(t_s)$, and so on.] The maximum velocities are continuous functions

$$v_\forall: M \times M \to [0, \infty), \qquad v_\exists: M \times M \to [0, \infty).$$

We say that a path x *exceeds* the maximum velocity $v_\forall$ if there exist times $0 \leq s < s'$ such that

$$\frac{\delta(x(s), x(s'))}{s' - s} > v_\forall(x(s), x(s')).$$

We do not assume $v_\forall(p, q) = v_\forall(q, p)$, since it may take longer to go uphill than down. The definition for $v_\exists$ is similar. Any path that never exceeds the maximum velocity is obviously continuous.

Let's say that a path x for $\forall$ is *possible* if $x(0)$ is the initial position $i_\forall$ for $\forall$, and the maximum velocity $v_\forall$ is never exceeded by x. Possible paths for $\exists$ are defined analogously. A *strategy* for $\exists$ in this game is a function from the set of possible paths for $\forall$ into the possible paths for $\exists$, with the usual properties, and strategies for $\forall$ are defined dually.

Define the payoff by

$$\mathrm{Val}(x, y) = \begin{cases} +\infty & \text{if } \exists \text{ never captures } \forall, \\ s & \text{if } \exists \text{ first captures } \forall \text{ at time } s, \end{cases}$$

for all possible paths x, y. We claim that for this game the conclusions (a)–(d) of Theorems 3 and 4 hold [also (c_F) holds]. For ready reference we list (a)–(d) again here.

(a) The game has a value,

$$\mathrm{Val}(\exists) = \mathrm{Val}^*(\forall) = a \text{ (for some } a).$$

(b) $\exists$ has an optimal strategy.
(c) $\forall$ has finite strategies with values arbitrarily close to a.
(d) $\forall$ has (finite) time-lag strategies with values arbitrarily close to a.

To see this we represent the game in our previous framework by defining $\mathrm{Val}(x, y)$, where x, y are not both possible:

$$\mathrm{Val}(x, y) = +\infty \qquad \text{if } y \text{ is impossible,}$$
$$\mathrm{Val}(x, y) = 0 \qquad \text{if } y \text{ is possible and } x \text{ is impossible.}$$

We note that every possible path is continuous. Moreover, for each $s \in [0, \infty)$ the set of points $y(s)$, y a possible path, is bounded. It follows that for each x and r, the set $\{y\colon \mathrm{Val}(x, y) \leq r\}$, is closed in the product topology ${}^U M$ when we give M the topology whose closed sets are M itself and the closed bounded sets of the metric space. By our Remark, this topology on M is compact. Therefore the hypotheses of Corollaries 6 and 7 are satisfied, and the "expanded" game satisfies (a)–(d). To get back to our original game, we show how to replace an arbitrary strategy by one that is "just as good" and chooses only possible paths. For each impossible path $y\colon U \to M$, let s be the sup of the numbers r such that y is possible as far as r. If $s = 0$, let y^* be the path with constant value $i_\exists$. If $s > 0$, let y^* be the path such that $y^*(r) = y(r)$ for $r < s$, and

$$y^*(r) = \lim_{s' < s} y(s')$$

for $r \geq s$. If y is possible let $y^* = y$. Then for all y, y^* is possible. Given an $\exists$-strategy S, define S^* by

$$S^*x = (Sx)^*.$$

Then S^* is an $\exists$-strategy such that S^*x is always possible and

$$\mathrm{Val}(S^*) \leq \mathrm{Val}(S).$$

For each $\forall$-strategy R, define R^* in a similar way. Then R^*y is always possible, $\mathrm{Val}(R^*) \geq \mathrm{Val}(R)$, and if R is finite or time lag, so is R^*. Hence our original game also satisfies (a)–(d).

Our above discussion still holds if we change our criterion for a possible path, as long as the set Y of possible paths for $\exists$ is compact in the product topology ${}^U M$, and each $y \in Y$ is continuous from the left. (The continuity clause is needed only for the existence of time-lag strategies.)

In the above example, the payoff was the time of capture. If C is the diagonal set $\{\langle x, x\rangle : x \in M\}$, then $\exists$ captures $\forall$ when their positions coincide. Other natural criteria for the payoff are based on distance. If we choose a time s and define

$$\mathrm{Val}(x, y) = \delta(x(s), y(s))$$

for all possible paths x,y, we again have properties (a)–(d), since the game can be enlarged to satisfy the hypotheses of Corollaries 6 and 7. We also get the properties (a)–(d) if we define (for all possible paths x,y),

$$\mathrm{Val}(x, y) = \int_0^r \delta(x(s), y(s))\, ds,$$

or

$$\mathrm{Val}(x, y) = \sup\{\delta(x(s), y(s)) : 0 \leq s < r\},$$

where r is either finite or $r = +\infty$.

We now give some examples of games that do not satisfy the hypotheses of Corollary 6 but come close enough so we can at least prove that they have property (a) above and

(b_0) Either $\exists$ has an optimal strategy or $\forall$ has an optimal universally playable strategy.

Property (b_0) is clearly weaker than (b). First, consider any of the above examples, say the game with

$$\mathrm{Val}(x, y) = \sup\{\delta(x(s), y(s)) : 0 \leq s < \infty\}.$$

However, instead of a given initial position, we shall let the initial positions $x(0)$, $y(0)$ for *both* players be chosen by $\exists$. For future reference call this game G_1. It is obvious that in general $\exists$ will not have an optimal strategy for G_1, for there need not be an optimal way to choose the initial position. However, this game does have the properties (a) and (b_0).

To prove (a), suppose $r < \mathrm{Val}(\exists)$. For each initial position $x(0)$, $y(0)$, the game satisfies (a)–(d) and the value is $>r$. Therefore, for each initial position $x(0)$, $y(0)$, $\forall$ has a finite strategy $R(x(0), y(0))$ with value $\geq r$. Hence $\forall$ has a universally playable strategy R with value $\geq r$, played as follows: $\forall$ looks at the choice $\exists$ makes for $\langle x(0), y(0)\rangle$ and then plays $R(x(0), y(0))$. (R is not a finite strategy since the finite subset of U it uses depends on the first move of $\exists$.) This proves (a). To prove (b_0), suppose ∃ has no optimal strategy, that is, no strategy with value $\leq a$. Then repeating the above argument, we see that ∀ has a universally playable strategy with value $\geq a$. Since this strategy is optimal, (b_0) is proved.

We now consider a game G_2 which is just like G_1 except that the payoff is

$$\mathrm{Val}(x, y) = \limsup_{s \to \infty} \delta(x(s), y(s)),$$

for all possible paths x, y. We shall show that the game G_2 also has the properties (a) and (b_0). Moreover, the value a is the same for G_1 and G_2, and, if ∀ or ∃ has an optimal strategy for G_1, then he has an optimal strategy for G_2 (universally playable in the case of ∀).

We first note that the payoff function for G_2 is $\leq$ the payoff function for G_1. Thus if an ∃-strategy S has value r in G_1, it has value $\leq r$ in G_2. We shall show that for any universally playable ∀-strategy R with value r for G_1, there is a universally playable ∀-strategy R' with value $\geq r$ for G_2. From this all our claims follow at once. R' is played as follows. First, ∀ begins playing R. Sooner or later we must have

$$\delta(x(s), y(s)) > r - 1.$$

At the first natural number n_1 such that the above holds for some $s < n_1$, ∀ stops playing R. Now ∀ pretends that the time is 0 instead of n_1, and that ∃ has chosen the initial position $\langle x(n_1), y(n_1)\rangle$. ∀ then plays R under these assumptions. At the first natural number $n_2 > n_1$ such that

$$\delta(x(s), y(s)) > r - \tfrac{1}{2}$$

for some s, $n_1 \leq s < n_2$, ∀ again stops. He then continues in this manner. The strategy R thus described is clearly universally playable and has value $\geq r$.

Here is another variation of this example. With ∃ choosing the initial positions, consider the two-valued game in which, for possible paths x, y, ∃ wins iff the set

$$\{\delta(x(s), y(s)) : 0 \leq s < \infty\}$$

is bounded. For this game, either ∃ has a winning strategy or ∀ has a universally playable winning strategy. To see this, suppose ∃ does not have a winning strategy. Then for each $r > 0$, ∀ has a universally playable strategy $R(r)$ which guarantees that $\delta(x(s), y(s)) \geq r$, at some time s. Arguing as before, we can find a universally playable winning strategy R' for ∀.

There are some rather natural pursuit games which have values when we let ∀ use arbitrary strategies and make ∃ use universally playable strategies. For instance, consider the dual properties of (a)–(d).

(a′) Val(∀) = Val*(∃) = a (for some a);
(b′) ∀ has an optimal strategy.
(c′) ∃ has finite strategies with values arbitrarily close to a.
(d′) ∃ has (finite) time-lag strategies with values arbitrarily close to a.

For example, consider a pursuit game in a finitely compact metric space M with given initial positions and maximum velocities, but let the capture set $C \subset M \times M$ be open. Define the payoff for possible paths x, y by

$$\mathrm{Val}(x,y) = \inf\{s:\langle x(s), y(s)\rangle \in C\}.$$

This game has the properties (a′)–(d′). To see this we need only observe that the dual game

$$(U, T, <)(-\mathrm{Val}) \text{ in } M$$

can be enlarged to a game satisfying Corollary 7 by completing the definition of Val.

The game with the payoff

$$\mathrm{Val}(x, y) = \inf\ \{\delta(x(s), y(s)) : 0 \leq s < \infty\}$$

also has properties (a′)–(d′).

If we change the last two games by letting ∀ choose the initial positions $x(0)$, $y(0)$, then arguing as before we find that the games satisfy (a′) and:

(b_0'). Either ∀ has an optimal strategy or ∃ has an optimal universally playable strategy.

Similarly, (a′) and (b_0') hold for the game in which ∀ chooses the initial position and

$$\mathrm{Val}(x, y) = \liminf_{s\to\infty} \delta(x(s), y(s)).$$

Finally the two-valued game in which ∃ wins iff

$$\liminf_{s\to\infty} \delta(x(s), y(s)) = 0 \qquad (\text{or } \leq r)$$

is an example of a game in which either ∀ has a winning strategy or ∃ has a universally playable winning strategy.

References

1. C. C. CHANG AND H. J. KEISLER, *Continuous Model Theory*. Princeton: *Ann. Math. Studies 58*, 1966.
2. MORTON DAVIS, Infinite Games of Perfect Information (Advances in Game Theory), *Ann. Math. Studies 52* (1964), 85–102.

3. A. EHRENFEUCHT, Applications of Games to Some Problems in Mathematical Logic, *Bull. Acad. Polon. Sci.* (III)*5* (1957), 35–37.
4. W. H. FLEMING, The Convergence Problem for Differential Games, *J. Math. Anal. Appl. 3* (1961), 102–116.
5. D. GALE AND F. M. STEWART, Infinite Games with Perfect Information (Contributions to the Theory of Games, Vol. II), *Ann. Math. Studies 28* (1953), 245–266.
6. L. HENKIN, Some Remarks on Infinitely Long Formulas. Infinitistic Methods, *Proc. Symposium on Foundations of Mathematics*. Warsaw: Pánstwowe Wydawnictwo Naukowe, 1961, 168–183.
7. R. ISAACS, *Differential Games*, New York: Wiley, 1965.
8. H. J. KEISLER, Finite Approximations of Infinitely Long Formulas (Theory of Models, Berkeley Symposium of 1963), Amsterdam: North-Holland, 1965, pp. 158–169.
9. H. J. KEISLER, Some Applications of Infinitely Long Formulas, *J. Symbolic Logic 30* (1965), 339–349.
10. J. MALITZ, Problems in the Model Theory of Infinite Languages, Doctoral dissertation, Berkeley: Univ. of Calif., 1966.
11. M. MORLEY AND R. L. VAUGHT, Homogeneous Universal Models, *Math. Scand. 11* (1962), 37–57.
12. J. MYCIELSKI, Continuous Games with Perfect Information (Advances in Game Theory), *Ann. Math. Studies 52* (1964), 103–112.
13. J. MYCIELSKI, On the Axiom of Determinateness, *Fundamenta Math. 53* (1964), 205–224.
14. J. MYCIELSKI, Some Compactifications of General Algebras, *Colloq. Math. 13* (1964), 1–9.
15. C. RYLL-NARDZEWSKI, A Theory of Pursuit and Evasion (Advances in Game Theory), *Ann. Math. Studies 52*, 1964, 113–126.
16. P. P. VARAIYA, On the Existence of Solutions to a Differential Game, *J. SIAM Control*, *5* (1967), 153–162.
17. A. ZIEBA, An Example in Pursuit Theory, *Studia Math. 22* (1962), 1–6.
18. H. J. KEISLER, Ultraproducts and Saturated Models, *Indagationes Math. 26* (1964), 178–186.
19. B. WEGLORZ, Equationally Compact Algebras I., *Fundamenta Math. 59* (1966), 289–298.

Applications of Infinitary Languages to Analysis[1]

by R. D. KOPPERMAN

Throughout we use any set theory with the axiom of choice and proper classes. We also use the following notations: α, β will denote regular (infinite) cardinals; δ, ρ, ϱ any infinite cardinals; σ, τ sentences in the languages we are about to introduce; and other lowercase Greek letters will stand for ordinals. If R is a relation and B a set, then $R \mid B$ will denote the restriction of R to B. For binary relations R we write aRb for $\langle a, b\rangle \in R$. $c(A)$ will stand for the cardinality of A, and if $\mathfrak{J} = \langle A, R_\lambda\rangle_{\lambda<\mu}$ is a first-order structure, then $c(\mathfrak{J}) = c(A)$. For cardinals ρ, ϱ, $\rho^{\varrho} = \Sigma_{\delta<\varrho}\rho^{\delta}$.

The languages $L_{\alpha\beta}{}^{t}$, t a type (that is, a well-ordered set of nonnegative integers), are defined in much the same way as L^t except that conjunctions ($\wedge$) and disjunctions ($\vee$) of sets of formulas of cardinality less than α are allowed as is existential ($\exists$) or universal ($\forall$) quantification over sets of variables of cardinality less than β. More formally:

Definition. Let t be a type, α, β infinite regular cardinals. Let $V = \{v_\xi\colon \xi < \alpha + \beta\}$, $C = \{c_\lambda\colon t(\lambda) = 0\}$ be disjoint sets (whose elements are called the variables and constants of $L_{\alpha\beta}{}^{t}$, respectively). Then

$$E_0 = \{P_\lambda(x_0, \cdots, x_{t(\lambda)-1})\colon x_0, \cdots, x_{t(\lambda)-1} \in V \cup C,\ t(\lambda) > 0\} \cup \{x = y\colon x, y \in V \cup C\}.$$

For all ρ, $E_{\rho+1} = E_\rho \cup \{\neg F\colon F \in E_\rho\} \cup \{\vee S\colon S \subset E_\rho \text{ and } c(S) < \alpha\} \cup \{\wedge S\colon S \subset E \text{ and } c(S) < \alpha\} \cup \{(\exists Y)F\colon F \in E_\rho \text{ and } Y \subset V \text{ and } c(Y) < \beta\} \cup \{(\forall Y)F\colon F \in E_\rho \text{ and } Y \subset V \text{ and } c(Y) < \beta\}$, and for limit ordinals κ, $E_\kappa = \bigcup_{\rho<\lambda} E_\rho$. Finally, $L_{\alpha\beta}{}^{t} = E_{\alpha+\beta}$.

Certain abbreviations we use often are listed here. For $\vee\{F, G\}$ we write $F \vee G$, and so on. For $\wedge\{F_i\colon i \in S\}$ we often write $\wedge_{i\in S} F_i$, and

[1] This work was supported by National Science Foundation Grant NSF-GP-5710.

for $(\exists\{v_i: i < \omega\})F$ we write $(\exists v_0, v_1, \cdots)F$. Other similar abbreviations are used. From now on, all the letters u to z with or without subscripts will stand for variables.

We are interested in the problem of determining which concepts among those that cannot be axiomatized in the lower-predicate calculus can be axiomatized in our infinitary languages. In this paper several cases are considered and various methods developed to decide whether or not these concepts can be axiomatized within any of our languages. We formalize the idea of axiomatization in much the same way as is done for the lower-predicate calculus. First, satisfaction can be defined for $L_{\alpha\beta}{}^t$ in much the same way as it is defined for L^t (but using transfinite induction), and by $M(S)$ we denote the class of models of S. We also parallel definitions used in the lower-predicate calculus by stating that $K \in EC_{\Delta\alpha\beta}$ iff $K = M(S)$ for some set of sentences $S \subset L_{\alpha\beta}{}^t$ for some type t. $K \in PC_{\Delta\alpha\beta}$ iff for some type t, K is the class of all reducts of type t of elements of some $K' \in EC_{\Delta\alpha\beta}$. $K \in PC'_{\Delta\alpha\beta}$ iff for some type t, K is the class of all restricts of reducts of elements of some $K' \in EC_{\Delta\alpha\beta}$. In other words, $K \in PC'_{\Delta\alpha\beta}$ iff for some set of sentences $S \subset L^{t'}$, K is the class of structures obtained by removing certain relations from models of S and then cutting down their domains to make these domains coincide with one of their unary relations defined by S. (Formal definitions of these concepts may be found in [6].) If the set S referred to in any of the recent definitions contains only one element, the subscript Δ is removed; for example, if $K = M(S)$, we write $K \in EC_{\alpha\beta}$ instead of $K \in EC_{\Delta\alpha\beta}$ if $c(S) = 1$. We also say "K is a $PC_{\alpha\beta}$-class" for $K \in PC_{\alpha\beta}$, and so on.

It has been shown that metric spaces and metric algebraic structures (including Banach spaces, Banach algebras, Hilbert spaces, and others) are $EC_{\omega_1\omega_1}$-classes (see [5] and [7]). Extreme nonaxiomatizability results are sometimes found as well. In [6] it is shown that the class of complete uniform spaces is not a $PC'_{\Delta\alpha\beta}$-class for any α, β. This is also true of the class of topological spaces. Since this result appears nowhere in the literature, we shall prove it here. First we need an infinitary downward Löwenheim–Skolem theorem due to Hanf ([2]) and Karp ([4]):

***Theorem* (Downward L–S).** *Let $S \subset L_{\alpha\beta}{}^t$ be a set of sentences, $\mathfrak{J} = \langle A, R_\lambda\rangle_{\lambda<\mu}$, $\mathfrak{J} \in M(S)$. Then if $C \subset A$, $c(C) \leq \delta$, $\alpha \leq \delta$, $c(t) \leq \delta$, and $\delta^\beta = \delta$, there is a $B \subset A$ such that $\mathfrak{L} = \langle B, R_\lambda \mid B\rangle_{\lambda<\mu} \in M(S)$, $C \subset B$, and $c(B) \leq \delta$.*

Corollary. *If $S \subset L_{\alpha\beta}{}^t$ is a set of sentences and $\rho = \max(c(S)^\beta, \alpha^\beta)$, then if S has any models, S has models of cardinality $\leq \rho$.*

Let $\zeta = \{\langle X \cup T, X, T, \epsilon' \rangle : \langle X, T, \epsilon' \rangle \cong \langle Y, U, \epsilon \rangle$, where $\langle Y, U \rangle$ is a topological space, ϵ the usual element relation$\}$.[2]

***Theorem* 1.** *For no infinite regular cardinals α, β is ζ a $PC'_{\alpha\beta}$-class.*

Proof. Given α, β and any t, we must show that for no $S \subset L_{\alpha\beta}{}^t$ is $K = M(S)$ and ζ the class of restricts of reducts of elements of K. Assume the contrary, and let δ be a cardinal with the properties mentioned in the statement of the infinitary downward Löwenheim–Skolem theorem. Let N be a set such that $c(N) = \delta$ and $N \cap pN = \varnothing$ (where pN denotes the power set of N). Such a cardinal and set can be found. Then since $\langle N \cup pN, N, pN, \epsilon \rangle \in \zeta$, we must have an $\mathfrak{J} \in K$ the restrict of whose appropriate reduct is $\langle N \cup pN, N, pN, \epsilon \rangle$. Let $C = N \cup \{\{x\} : x \in N\}$. Then $C \subset A$, $c(C) = \delta$. Thus by downward L–S there is a $\mathfrak{L} \in K$, $\mathfrak{L} = \langle B, \cdots \rangle \subset \mathfrak{J}$ such that $C \subset B$ and $c(B) \leq \delta$. The restrict of the appropriate reduct of $\mathfrak{L}$ is $\langle X \cup T, X, T, \epsilon \rangle \in \zeta$. But $N \subset X$, $\{\{x\} : x \in N\} \subset T$. Since T contains arbitrary unions of its elements, $pN \subset T$, so $c(T) > \delta$. However, this contradicts the fact that $T \subset B$, $c(B) \leq \delta$.

However, the class of topological spaces with countable bases for their topologies is an $EC_{\omega_1\omega_1}$-class (and more generally, the class of topological spaces with bases of cardinality $< \alpha$ forms an $EC_{\alpha\alpha}$-class). To show this, we write the axioms for these spaces in terms of ϵ, X, T.

(1) $(\forall x)(T(x) \vee X(x) \wedge \neg(T(x) \wedge X(x)))$.
(2) $(\forall x)(\forall y)(x \in y \rightarrow X(x) \wedge T(y))$.
(3) $(\forall y)(\forall z)(T(y) \rightarrow ((\forall x)(x \in y \leftrightarrow x \in z) \rightarrow y = z))$.
(4) $(\exists x)(T(x) \wedge (\forall y) \neg (y \in x))$.
(5) $(\exists z)(T(z) \wedge (\forall y)(X(y) \rightarrow y \in z))$.
(6) $(\forall x)(\forall y)(\exists z)(\forall u)(u \in z \leftrightarrow u \in x \vee u \in y)$.
(7) $(\exists x_0, x_1, \cdots)(\forall y)(\forall z)((\bigwedge_{i<\omega} T(x_i)) \wedge (T(y) \wedge X(z) \wedge z \in y \rightarrow \bigvee_{i<\omega} (z \in x_i \wedge (\forall u)(u \in x_i \rightarrow u \in y))))$.
(8) $(\forall x_0, x_1, \cdots)(\exists y)(\forall z)(z \in y \leftrightarrow (\bigvee_{i\subset\omega} z \in x_i))$.

Axioms 1–3 make X, T disjoint and T a collection of subsets of X. They also limit the universe to elements of X and T. Axioms 4 and 5 put the empty set and X in T, while Axiom 6 (in the presence of Axioms 2 and 4) says that intersections of pairs of elements of T are in T. All that remains to make T a topology on X is the statement that arbitrary unions of elements of T are in T. This, by our theorem, cannot be written in any of our infinitary languages. Axiom 7 says that there is a countable set of elements $x_i \in T$ such that for each $y \in T$, $z \in y$, one of the x_i's, for example x_{i_z}, has the properties $z \in x_{i_z}$ and $x_{i_z} \subset y$. Thus $y =$

[2] I wish to thank H. J. Keisler, who pointed out an error in the original formulation of this class and thus of Theorem 1.

$\bigcup_{z \in yx i_z}$, so each element of T is the union of a collection of the x_i's. Now to see that the union of any collection $\{y_j: j \in J\} \subset T$ is an element of T, simply allow $y_j = \bigcup_{i \in I_j} x_i$, with $I_j \subset \omega$. Thus $\bigcup_{j \in J} y_j = \bigcup_{j \in J} (\bigcup_{i \in I_j} x_i)$, a (countable) union of the x_i's which is therefore in T by Axiom 8.

Certain algebraic concepts such as those of Noetherian ring, principal ideal domain, local ring, Euclidean domain, and torsion group, among others, cannot be axiomatized within the lower-predicate calculus. The first three of these, however, can be axiomatized within $L_{\omega_1\omega_1}$ (of appropriate type), and the last two can within $L_{\omega_1\omega_1}$. We prove some of these assertions here and leave others to the reader. We shall need some algebra to do this, and develop some of it below.

We first list definitions relevant to our work. A Noetherian ring is one in which each strictly ascending chain of ideals must be finite. An ideal I in a ring R is said to be generated by the set $A \subset R$ iff $A \subset I$ and each $x \in I$ can be written in the form $x = y_1a_1 + \cdots + y_na_n$ with $a_1, \cdots, a_n \in A$ and $y_1, \cdots, y_n \in R$. I is said to be countably (finitely) generated iff it is generated by some countable (finite) set A, and said to be principal iff it is generated by a singleton. A principal ideal domain is an integral domain in which each ideal is principal. A Euclidean domain is an integral domain $\langle R, +, \cdot \rangle$ together with a function $v: R \sim \{0\} \to \omega$ such that:

(1) For all a, b if $a, b \neq 0$, then $v(ab) \geq v(a)$.
(2) For all a, b there are c, d such that if $b \neq 0$, then $a = bc + d$ and $c = 0$ or $v(c) < v(b)$.

It can be shown (see [1] or any elementary text on abstract algebra) that if $\langle R, +, \cdot, v \rangle$ is a Euclidean domain, then $\langle R, +, \cdot \rangle$ is a principal ideal domain. We also need the following:

Lemma. *$\langle R, +, \cdot \rangle$ is a Noetherian ring iff every countably generated ideal is finitely generated.*

Proof. The statement that any ascending chain of ideals is finite is obviously equivalent to the fact that any countable ascending chain is finite, for any infinite ascending chain must contain a countable one. We shall show this statement equivalent to the statement of the lemma.

If there is a countable infinite ascending chain $A_0, A_1, \cdots$ of ideals, then the ideal generated by $a_0, a_1, \cdots$, where $a_i \in A_{i+1} \sim A_i$ for each i cannot be generated by any finite set of elements $b_0, \cdots, b_n$. For if so, $b_0, \cdots, b_n \in \bigcup_{i<\omega} A_i$, thus $b_0, \cdots, b_n \in A_r$ for some finite r. Thus $a_r \notin A_r$, and therefore not in the ideal generated by the b_j's, a contradiction. Thus if every countably generated ideal is finitely generated, there are no infinite countable ascending chains of ideals.

Conversely, if A is the ideal generated by $a_0, a_1, \cdots$ and is not generated by any finite set of the a_i's, let A_r be the ideal generated by $a_0, \cdots, a_r$. Obviously $A_0 \subset A_1 \cdots$, and clearly for an infinite number of integers s the inclusion $A_s \subset A_{s+1}$ is proper, for otherwise $A = \bigcup_{r<\omega} A_r = A_t$ (where t would be the largest integer such that the inclusion $A_{t-1} \subset A_t$ is proper). Thus if every countable ascending chain of ideals is finite, every countably generated ideal must be finitely generated.

A similar argument (see, for example, [8]) shows the well-known fact that a ring is Noetherian iff every ideal is finitely generated.

Corollary. *Every principal ideal domain is Noetherian.*

Proof. Every ideal, thus every countably generated ideal, is generated by one element.

It is well known and simple to verify that $\langle Z, +, \cdot, |\ \ | \rangle$ is a Euclidean domain (where $|\ \ |$ stands for absolute value) and that therefore $\langle Z, +, \cdot \rangle$ is a principal ideal domain and also a Noetherian ring. Now let $\langle {}^*Z, {}^*+, {}^*\cdot \rangle$ be an ultrapower of the integers and k an infinite nonstandard integer. For a general ring R we set $aR = \{ar : r \in R\}$. Then $(2^k){}^*Z \underset{\neq}{\subset} (2^{k-1}){}^*Z \underset{\neq}{\subset} (2^{k-2}){}^*Z \cdots$ is an infinite (strictly) ascending chain of ideals, so $\langle {}^*Z, {}^*+, {}^*\cdot \rangle$ is not a Noetherian ring, thus also not a principal ideal domain or a Euclidean domain under any v. Thus since $\langle {}^*Z, {}^*+, {}^*\cdot \rangle$ satisfies the same statements of the lower-predicate calculus as does $\langle Z, +, \cdot \rangle$, the first two concepts cannot be axiomatized within $L_{\omega\omega}$, and similar reasoning shows that the third also cannot.

We now show that the class of Noetherian rings is in $EC_{\omega_1\omega_1}$ by showing that the statement that every countably generated ideal can be finitely generated is expressible in our language $L_{\omega_1\omega_1}$ as follows:

$$N = (\forall x_0, x_1, \cdots) \bigvee_{i<\omega} \tau_i,$$

where

$$\begin{aligned}\tau_i = (\exists y_0, \cdots, y_{i-1})((\textstyle\bigwedge_{n<\omega}((\forall z_0, \cdots, z_n)\ (\exists v_0, \cdots, v_{i-1})\\ (z_0x_0 + \cdots + z_nx_n = v_0y_0 + \cdots + v_{i-1}y_{i-1}))) \wedge ((\forall v_0, \cdots, v_{i-1})\\ \textstyle\bigvee_{n<\omega}(\exists z_0, \cdots, z_n)(x_0z_0 + \cdots + z_nx_n = v_0y_0 + \cdots + v_{i-1}y_{i-1}))).\end{aligned}$$

τ_i says that there are i elements of the ring such that every linear sum of products of the x_i's can be written in terms of these y_j's and, conversely, each linear sum of products of the y_j's can be written in terms of the x_i's. In other words, τ_i says that the ideal generated by $\{x\phi, z_1, \cdots\}$ is generated by i elements. Thus the rings satisfying N must be precisely the Noetherian rings. Now let $P = (\forall x_0, x_1, \cdots)\tau_1$. Then clearly $P \rightarrow N$, so each ring satisfying P must be Noetherian. Thus each ideal in such a ring must be finitely generated, therefore countably generated. But P says that each countably generated ideal (thus every ideal) is principal.

This brings us to the question of what applications such axiomatizations have when they exist. In part, this question asks how "good" these languages are. It is known that compactness fails, often spectacularly (see [2]) for many of these languages, leaving in doubt the meaning and usefulness of the most basic semantical notions. Completeness (for single sentences) holds in some cases and fails in others (see [3]). In general, the semantics of these infinitary languages have not been shown to have many virtues. One virtue, however, is the existence of a downward Löwenheim–Skolem theorem, given above. A second, also due to Hanf, is a weak upward Löwenheim–Skolem theorem.

***Theorem* (*Upward* L–S).** *For each pair of regular cardinals α, β, and type t, there is a number $H(\alpha, \beta, t)$ such that $H(\alpha, \beta, t)^\beta = H(\alpha, \beta, t)$ and if $K = M(S)$, $S \subset L_{\alpha\beta}{}^t$ a set of sentences and for some $\mathfrak{J} \in K$, $c(\mathfrak{J}) \geq H(\alpha, \beta, t)$, then for each cardinal δ there is a $\mathfrak{L} \in K$ such that $c(\mathfrak{L}) \geq \delta$.*

The number $H(\alpha, \beta, t)$ has come to be known as the Hanf number of $L_{\alpha\beta}{}^t$.

These Löwenheim–Skolem theorems also enable us to establish an infinitary Vaught's condition. First we need some definitions:

Definition. Let $\mathfrak{J}$ be a structure of type t. Then $T_{\alpha\beta}(\mathfrak{J}) = \{\sigma \in L_{\alpha\beta}{}^t: \mathfrak{J} \in M(\sigma)\}$. For two such structures, $\mathfrak{J} \equiv_{\alpha\beta} \mathfrak{L}$ iff $T_{\alpha\beta}(\mathfrak{J}) = T_{\alpha\beta}(\mathfrak{L})$.

Clearly $\equiv_{\alpha\beta}$ is an equivalence relation.

Definition. Let K be a class of structures of type t. Then K is $\alpha\beta$-complete iff for all $\mathfrak{J}$, $\mathfrak{L}K$, $\mathfrak{J} \equiv_{\alpha\beta} \mathfrak{L}$. A set $S \subset L_{\alpha'\beta'}{}^t$ is $\alpha\beta$-complete iff $K = M(S)$ is $\alpha\beta$-complete, and S is $\alpha\beta$-complete in cardinality ρ iff L is $\alpha\beta$-complete, where $L = \{\mathfrak{J} \in M(S): c(\mathfrak{J}) = \rho\}$.

***Theorem* 2 (*Infinitary Vaught*).** *Let $S \subset L_{\alpha\beta}{}^t$ be a set of sentences. If S is $\alpha\beta$-complete in some cardinality $\rho = \rho^\beta \geq \max(\alpha^\beta, c(S)^\beta)$, then K is $\alpha\beta$-complete, where $K = \{\mathfrak{L} \in M(S): c(\mathfrak{L}) \geq \min(H(\alpha, \beta, t), \rho)\}$.*

Corollary. *Let $S \subset L_{\alpha\beta}{}^t$ be a set of sentences and $\varrho = \max(c(S)^\beta, \alpha^\beta)$. Then if S has no models of cardinality $< \varrho$ and S is $\alpha\beta$-complete in cardinality ϱ, then S is $\alpha\beta$-complete.*

Proof. Let $\varrho = \rho$ in the statement of the theorem. Then $\rho = \rho^\beta$ and $K = M(S)$, and the corollary is immediate.

Before proving the theorem, we show a counterexample to a stronger conjecture. The class V of nontrivial real vector spaces can be shown to be an $EC_{\omega_1\omega_1}$-class. Set $V = M(\sigma)$. All elements of V have cardinality $\geq 2^\omega$, and $2^\omega \leq \omega_1{}^\omega = \omega_1{}^{\omega_1} \leq (2^\omega)^\omega = 2^{\omega x \omega} = 2^\omega$, so all elements of V have cardinality $\geq \omega_1{}^{\omega_1}$ and σ is categorical in each cardinality $> \omega_1{}^{\omega_1}$, for if $U \in V$, $c(U) > 2^\omega$, and B is a basis for U, then $c(U) = 2^\omega c(B) = c(B)$. Thus any two such spaces over the reals of the same cardinality have bases which can be put in one-to-one correspondence, and this correspondence extends to an isomorphism of the spaces. However, σ is not $\omega_1\omega_1$-complete, for a sentence τ_1 can be written in our language to say that U has dimension 1. In fact, $\tau_1, \cdots, \tau_{\omega+1}$ may be written in $L_{\omega_1\omega_1}{}^v$ (v the appropriate type), where τ_i, $i \leq \omega$, says that our space is of dimension i and $\tau_{\omega+1}$ says it is uncountable in dimension. Any of these may be adjoined to our axiom σ for real vector spaces and a consistent theory will result. The corollary to the infinitary Vaught's condition and the continuum hypothesis (CH) tell us that the addition of any of these sentences to σ gives us an $\omega_1\omega_1$-complete theory. This is true since for all $i \leq \omega$, all models of $\{\sigma, \tau_i\}$ are isomorphic, and for $\{\sigma, \tau_{\omega+1}\}$, CH can easily be seen to imply that those of cardinality 2^ω are. (Methods used in [4] can be applied to eliminate the use of CH here.)

We use the following trivial lemma in the proof of Theorem 2:

Lemma. *Let E be an equivalence relation on a class K and let $L \subset K$. If $(\forall a)(\forall b)(a,b \in L \rightarrow aEb)$ and $(\forall a)(a \in K \rightarrow (\exists b)(b \in L \wedge aEb))$, then $(\forall a)(\forall b)(a,b \in K \rightarrow aEb)$.*

Proof of Theorem 2. Let K be as in the statement of the theorem, $L = \{\mathfrak{J}: \mathfrak{J} \in M(S) \text{ and } c(\mathfrak{J}) = \rho\}$, $E = \equiv_{\alpha\beta}$. E, and by the statement of our theorem, L, satisfy the conditions of the lemma. Now let $\mathfrak{J} \in K$, $\mathfrak{J} \in M(\sigma)$, $\mathfrak{L} \in L$. If we can show $\mathfrak{L} \in M(\sigma)$, the proof will be completed because σ is arbitrary, so $\mathfrak{J} \equiv_{\alpha\beta} \mathfrak{L}$. This we shall proceed to do. By upward L–S (if necessary) there is a $\mathfrak{D} \in M(S \cup \{\sigma\})$ such that $c(\mathfrak{D}) \geq \rho$. We now adjoin to our language constants $c_0, \cdots, c_\lambda, \cdots \lambda < \rho$ and let $T = S \cup \{\sigma\} \cup \{c_\lambda \neq c_\mu: \lambda < \mu < \rho\}$. Then by the corollary to downward L–S we can find $\mathfrak{C} \in M(T)$ such that $c(\mathfrak{C}) \leq \rho$. But since all models of T must have cardinality at least ρ, we must have $c(\mathfrak{C}) = \rho$, so since $\mathfrak{C} \in M(S)$, $\mathfrak{C} \in L$. Thus $\mathfrak{L} \equiv_{\alpha\beta} \mathfrak{C}$, so $\mathfrak{L} \in M(\sigma)$.

Of course, if $\mathfrak{J} \cong \mathfrak{L}$, $\mathfrak{J} \equiv_{\alpha\beta} \mathfrak{L}$, so it must hold that if S is categorical in cardinality ρ, then K is $\alpha\beta$-complete.

It is interesting to note that although the lemma was used in the proof of Theorem 2, the generalized continuum hypothesis (GCH) is required to show that the conditions of the lemma are satisfied by $K = M(S)$ and so on, for arbitrary sets of sentences $S \subset L_{\alpha\beta}{}^t$. More precisely,

GCH is required to show in general that if $\mathfrak{I} \in M(S)$, $c(\mathfrak{I}) \geq \rho = \max(c(S)^\beta, \alpha^\beta)$, then for some $\mathfrak{L} \equiv_{\alpha\beta} \mathfrak{I}$, $c(B) = \rho$. To show this, we need the fact (easily established by induction on the $E\rho$ from which our language $L_{\alpha\beta}{}^t$ was originally formed) that $c(L_{\alpha\beta}{}^t) = c(t)^\alpha(\alpha\beta)^{\alpha\beta}$.

Theorem 3. *Let $S \subset L_{\alpha\beta}{}^t$ be a set of sentences, $\rho = \max(c(S)^\beta, \alpha^\beta)$, and assume* GCH *holds or $\alpha \leq \beta$. Then if S has no models of cardinality $< \rho$ and $\mathfrak{I} \in M(S)$, there is a $\mathfrak{L} \equiv_{\alpha\beta} \mathfrak{I}$ such that $c(\mathfrak{L}) = \rho$.*

Proof. First we assume that $\alpha \leq \beta$. We note that $c(T_{\alpha\beta}(\mathfrak{I})) = 2c(T_{\alpha\beta}(\mathfrak{I})) = c(L_{\alpha\beta}{}^t)$, since all are infinite and for each $\sigma \in L_{\alpha\beta}{}^t$, either $\sigma \in T_{\alpha\beta}(\mathfrak{I})$ or $\neg\sigma \in T_{\alpha\beta}(\mathfrak{I})$. But $c(L_{\alpha\beta}{}^t) = c(t)^\alpha(\alpha\beta)^{\alpha\beta} \leq (\alpha c(S))^\alpha\beta^\beta$ (assuming, as we must, that every relation in t is referred to in S). Since $(\alpha c(S))^\alpha\beta^\beta \leq c(S)^\alpha(2^\beta)^\beta = c(S)^\alpha 2^\beta \leq c(S)^\beta\alpha^\beta = \rho$, by downward L–S we have a $\mathfrak{L} \in M(T_{\alpha\beta}(\mathfrak{I}))$ such that $c(\mathfrak{L}) \leq \rho$. $T_{\alpha\beta}(\mathfrak{I}) \subset T_{\alpha\beta}(\mathfrak{L})$, so (as in the case of the lower-predicate calculus) $\mathfrak{I} \equiv_{\alpha\beta} \mathfrak{L}$; thus $\mathfrak{L} \in M(S)$, and $c(\mathfrak{L}) = \rho$, since all models of S have at least that cardinality, and we are through in this case.

Otherwise, assuming GCH, one can easily show that $\alpha^\beta = \alpha\beta$ (see [9]). We allow E, K, L to be as in the proof of Theorem 2, $\mathfrak{I} \in K$. We have that $c(T_{\alpha\beta}(\mathfrak{I})) = c(t)^\alpha(\alpha\beta)^{\alpha\beta} \leq \alpha c(S)\alpha\beta\alpha\beta = c(S)\alpha\beta = (c(S)_\beta)\alpha\beta = c(S)^\beta\alpha^\beta$. But now by downward L–S we can find a $\mathfrak{L} \in M(T_{\alpha\beta}(\mathfrak{I}))$ such that $c(\mathfrak{L}) \leq \rho$. The proof is now completed as in the previous case.

The use of GCH in the preceding proof is essential as shown by the following example. If GCH fails, let δ be the first cardinal such that $\delta^+ < 2^\delta$. Now consider structures of the form $\mathfrak{I} = \langle A, C, B, c_0, \cdots, c_\rho, \cdots\rangle_{\rho<\delta}$ which satisfy the following statements of $L_{\delta+\omega}{}^s$ ($s = \langle 1, 1, 2, 0, \cdots, 0, \cdots\rangle$ is the appropriate type):

(1) $(\forall x)((C(x) \vee B(x)) \wedge \neg(C(x) \wedge B(x)))$ (B and C are disjoint and exhaust all elements).

(2) $(\forall x)(B(x) \to \vee \{x = c_i\colon i < \delta\})$ (B consists precisely of the c_i's).

(3) $\wedge \{\neg(c_i = c_j)\colon i < j < \delta\}$ (the c_i's are unequal).

(4) $(\forall x)(\forall y)(C(x) \wedge C(y) \to (x = y \leftrightarrow (\forall z)(z \in x \leftrightarrow z \in y))$ (extensionality for elements of C).

(5) $(\forall x)(\forall y)(x \in y \to B(x) \wedge C(y))$ (each element of C is a subset of B).

(6) We want $c(\mathfrak{I}) \leq \delta^+$. Thus let X be a collection of the c_i's and define $f_X(y = c_i) = (y = c_i)$ if $c_i \in X$, $f_X(y = c_i) = \neg(y = y)$ if $c_i \notin X$. Let $\sigma_X = (\exists x)(\forall y)(y \in x \leftrightarrow \vee \{f_X(y = c_i)\colon i < \delta\})$. In essence, σ_X says that X is in C. We now add axioms of the form σ_X for δ^+ different subsets X of B.

We note that $\rho = \max(c(S)^\omega, \delta^{+\omega}) = \delta^+$ in this case (where S is the set of all the axioms mentioned in 1–6 above), and that S, as assumed throughout, mentions all the relations of s. It remains to be seen that $M(S)$ contains an element $\mathfrak{L}$ for which we have no $\mathfrak{J}$ such that $c(\mathfrak{J}) = \delta^+$, and $\mathfrak{J} \equiv_{\delta+\omega} \mathfrak{L}$. But this is true of $\mathfrak{L} = \langle pB \cup B, pB, B, \epsilon, c_0, \cdots, c_\lambda, \cdots \rangle_{\lambda<\delta}$, since $\mathfrak{L}$ satisfies *all* axioms of the form σ_X and is the only model of axioms in S to do this.

We also give the following more direct application of an axiomatization in one of these languages. The set $P_{\alpha\beta}{}^t$ of positive sentences in $L_{\alpha\beta}{}^t$ is defined to be the smallest subset of $L_{\alpha\beta}{}^t$ containing E_0 and closed under $\vee$, $\wedge$, $\exists$, and $\forall$. This definition can easily be made inductive and it can be shown that if $\mathfrak{L}$ is a homomorphic image of $\mathfrak{J}$, and $\mathfrak{J} \in M(S)$, $S \subset P^t$, then $\mathfrak{J} \in M(S)$.

Referring back to our definition of Noetherian ring as a ring satisfying N, we see that since all the ring axioms, as well as the statement N, are in $P_{\omega_1\omega_1}{}^r$ (r the type of a ring), the homomorphic image of any Noetherian ring is Noetherian. This result can be established by standard algebraic methods as well, although the proof is a bit more difficult.

References

1. R. A. DEAN, *Elements of Abstract Algebra.* New York: Wiley, 1966.
2. W. P. HANF, *Some Fundamental Problems Concerning Languages with Infinitely Long Expressions,* Ph.D. thesis, Berkeley: Univ. of Calif., 1962.
3. C. R. KARP, *Languages with Expressions of Infinite Length.* Amsterdam: North-Holland, 1964.
4. C. R. KARP, Completeness Proof in Predicate Logic with Infinitely Long Expressions, *J. Symbolic Logic 32* (1967).
5. R. D. KOPPERMAN, The $L_{\omega_1\omega_1}$-Theory of Hilbert Spaces, *J. Symbolic Logic 32* (1967), 295–304.
6. R. D. KOPPERMAN, On the Axiomatizability of Uniform Spaces, *J. Symbolic Logic 32* (1967), 289–294.
7. R. D. KOPPERMAN, Applications of Infinitary Languages to Metric Spaces, to appear in the *Pacific J. Math.*
8. D. G. NORTHCOTT, *Ideal Theory.* New York: Cambridge, 1965.
9. A. TARSKI, Sur les Classes d'ensembles closes par rapport à certaines operations elementaires, *Fundamenta Math. 16* (1930), 181–304.

On Completing Ordered Fields

by DANA SCOTT

Every ordered field, not only the field of rationals, can be completed— in a suitable sense. This no doubt follows from the fact that an ordered field is a *uniform space*, but we shall show here that the completion process has a simple algebraic interpretation. The first step is to define what we mean by a *complete* field in a way applicable to arbitrary cardinalities, for the usual Dedekind notion of completeness for fields implies isomorphism with the reals. The definition that is appropriate is as follows:

Definition. A given ordered field is called *complete* if it has no proper extension to an ordered field in which the given field is order-dense.

If K and L are ordered fields and $K \subseteq L$, then K is *dense* in L (order-dense) if between any two distinct elements of L there lies an element of K. We say K is *cofinal* in L if every element of L is exceeded by an element of K. If K is cofinal in L, it is easy to see that it is also *coinitial* in the sense that for $\epsilon \in L$, $\epsilon > 0$, there always exists $\delta \in K$ with $0 < \delta < \epsilon$. Note, however, that K can be cofinal in L without being dense. [Give a non-Archimedean ordering to $K = Q((t))$, the field of formal power series. Let $L = \bar{K}$ be the real-closure of K, and ask yourself what lies between $\sqrt{t}$ and $2\sqrt{t}$.] Note also that every ordered field is cofinal in its real-closure, because easy estimates on the roots of a polynomial are always rationally computable from the coefficients.

We shall establish two results that seem to answer the obvious questions about fields complete in the sense of our chosen definition.

Theorem 1. *Given any ordered field K, there is a complete ordered field $\hat{K}$ in which K is dense. Any other complete ordered field in which K is dense is isomorphic to $\hat{K}$ by a unique isomorphism that is the identity on K.*

It follows that if K is dense in L, then K is dense in $\hat{L}$. Thus $\hat{K}$ and $\hat{L}$ are isomorphic. This makes L isomorphic to a subfield of $\hat{K}$. This isomorphism is the identity on K and is unique—because density implies that each element of L is determined by the cut it makes in the ordered set K. Thus in many senses $\hat{K}$ is a maximal ordered field in which K is dense. Note that if K is the field of rationals, then clearly $\hat{K}$ is isomorphic to the reals.

***Theorem* 2.** *If K is dense in L, then passing to the real-closures we have $\bar{K}$ dense in $\bar{L}$.*

From Theorem 2 it follows that if K is real-closed, then so is $\hat{K}$. Or better, $\hat{K}$ is real-closed if and only if K is dense in its real-closure $\bar{K}$. Because if $\hat{K}$ is real-closed, then $K \subseteq \bar{K} \subseteq \hat{K}$, which means K is dense in $\bar{K}$. On the other hand, if K is dense in $\bar{K}$, then since K is dense in $\hat{K}$, the theorem implies $\bar{K}$ is dense in $\hat{K}$. Therefore, $\hat{K}$ is dense in $\bar{\hat{K}}$, and so $\hat{K} = \bar{\hat{K}}$, which shows that the field is real-closed. [We note that the example of $Q((t))$ mentioned above shows that not every ordered field is dense in its real-closure.]

Proof of Theorem 1. Given an ordered field K we first extend K to an ordered field M in which *every* cut in K is filled. In other words, if sets $A,B \subseteq K$ are such that $A < B$ (that is, every element of A is less than every element of B), then there is at least one element $x \in M$ with $A < x < B$. The existence of such an M is very easy to establish. One can use the compactness theorem of first-order logic, or use the ultrapowers, or use the enlargements employed for nonstandard models of analysis, or simply adjoin indeterminates one after another until all the cuts are filled. Of course, M is a miserable field with many too many elements. The next step is to form a more reasonable quotient field of subring of M.

Let F be the subring of all *K-finite* elements of M; that is, F consists of those $x \in M$ for which there exists a $y \in K$ with $|x| < y$. We let I be the ideal of *K-infinitesimal* elements of F; that is, I consists of those $x \in F$ for which $|x| < y$ for *all* $y \in K$ where $y > 0$. Now I is a maximal ideal of F and we let $K' = F/I$. It is easy to see that K' is an ordered field and that K is isomorphic to a subfield by the obvious injection. Let us simply make $K \subseteq K'$. Now K' is less miserable than M for K is *cofinal* in K'. Furthermore, for every cut $A < B$ in K, there will exist $x \in K'$ with $A \leq x \leq B$, when A and B are *nonempty*. But generally K' is still too large to be $\hat{K}$; we shall find our completion as a subfield of K'.

To this end let K^+ be the set of strictly positive elements of K, and let $\hat{K}$ be the set of $x \in K'$ such that for every $a \in K^+$ there is an element of K between x and $x + a$. Note that $\hat{K}$ contains not only K but also all subfields of K' in which K is dense. Furthermore, K is dense in $\hat{K}$, because if $x, y \in \hat{K}$ and $x < y$, then we can choose $a \in K^+$ with $a \leq y - x$ (K is coinitial in K'). Next take $b \in K$ with $x < b < x + a$, which puts b between x and y. If we can only show that $\hat{K}$ is a subfield of K', then $\hat{K}$ will be *the* maximal subfield of K' in which K is dense, which is a more pleasant characterization of $\hat{K}$.

Well, let us show first that $\hat{K}$ is closed under *addition*. Suppose $x, y \in \hat{K}$ and $a \in K^+$. Choose $b, c \in K$ so that $x < b < x + \frac{1}{2}a$ and $y < c < y + \frac{1}{2}a$. Then $x + y < b + c < (x + y) + a$, and we see why $x + y \in \hat{K}$.

To show that $\hat{K}$ is closed under *minus*, let $x \in \hat{K}$ and $a \in K^+$. By the above, since $-a \in K \subseteq \hat{K}$, we know $x - a \in \hat{K}$. Thus for some $b \in K$ we have $x - a < b < (x - a) + a = x$. Hence $-x < -b < -x + a$, and we see why $-x \in \hat{K}$.

To show that $\hat{K}$ is closed under *product*, it is enough to consider $x, y \in \hat{K}$ with $x, y > 0$. First pick $b \in K^+$ with $b \leq a/2y$. Next pick $c \in K^+$ with $c \leq a/2(x + b)$. This is all arranged to make $by + cx + bc \leq a$. Now take $d, e \in K$ with $x < d < x + b$ and $y < e < y + c$. We find

$$xy < d \cdot e < x \cdot y + by + cx + bc \leq x \cdot y + a,$$

and we see why $x \cdot y \in \hat{K}$.

Finally, to show that $\hat{K}$ is closed under *inverse*, let $x \in \hat{K}$, $x > 0$, and let $a \in K^+$. Choose $b \in K^+$ so that $b \leq ax^2/(1 + ax)$, and pick $c \in K$ with $x - b < c < x$. Since this proof was found working backward, we are not surprised that

$$0 < \frac{x}{1 + ax} = x - \frac{ax^2}{1 + ax} \leq x - b < c < x,$$

whence $x^{-1} < c^{-1} < x^{-1} + a$, which shows us why $x^{-1} \in \hat{K}$.

Let us now establish the completeness of $\hat{K}$. Suppose $\hat{K} \subseteq L$ and $\hat{K}$ is dense in L. Then K is dense in L also. Let $x \in L$ and let

$$A = \{y \in K : y \leq x\},$$
$$B = \{y \in K : x < y\}$$

be the cut in K determined by x. Now in K' there is an element x' such that $A \leq x' \leq B$. We note that $x' \in \hat{K}$ because if $a \in K^+$, then for some $b \in K$ we have $x < b < x + a$. This means $b \in B$ while $b - a \in A$. Therefore, $x' \leq b \leq x' + a$. Now either the strict inequalities hold, or if not, $x' \in K$ and we can modify b to make the inequalities strict.

Hence $x' \in \hat{K}$. But then $x' \in L$ also, and in view of the density of K in L, it follows, from the fact that the two elements determine the same cut, that $x = x'$. This puts $x \in \hat{K}$; therefore, $L = \hat{K}$.

It is now time to reveal the nature of $\hat{K}$. The elements of $\hat{K}$ are in a one-to-one correspondence with the cuts in K that are *never* invariant under a nonzero translation by an element of K. We could have indeed constructed $\hat{K}$ this way. But then the proof that $\hat{K}$ is a field is quite tiresome. We have side-stepped this issue by starting with M (better, K') in which the axioms for a field are already satisfied. Then $\hat{K}$ can be a subfield. The necessary algebra is not avoided, however, because we still had to prove that $\hat{K}$ was closed under the field operations.

There is still one step missing, unfortunately: the uniqueness of $\hat{K}$. For this it seems best to use the cuts. Suppose L is another complete ordered field in which K is dense; then we can map each element $x \in L$ uniquely and one to one to an element $f(x) \in \hat{K}$ so that

$$\{y \in K : x < y\} = \{y \in K : f(x) < y\}.$$

This mapping is the identity on K. One can then proceed directly to show that this mapping preserves order, addition, minus, and products of positive elements. This is enough to conclude that L is mapped onto a subfield. But since L is complete, it must be mapped *onto* K.

Proof of Theorem 2. Suppose K is dense in L. We wish to show that $\bar{K}$ is dense in $\bar{L}$. (Obviously we are assuming that $\bar{K} \subseteq \bar{L}$, which is reasonable because $K \subseteq \bar{L}$ and $\bar{L}$ is real-closed.) Note that since L is cofinal in $\bar{L}$ and K is dense in L, then K is also cofinal in $\bar{L}$. To establish the denseness of $\bar{K}$ in $\bar{L}$ it is enough to prove:

(*) for each $x \in \bar{L}$ and $\eta \in K^+$, there exists $y \in \bar{K}$ with $|x - y| < \eta$

For if $u, v \in \bar{L}$ and $u < V$, then let $x = \frac{1}{2}(u + v)$ and choose $\eta \in K^+$ with $\eta \leq \frac{1}{2}(v - u)$. Then whenever $|x - y| < \eta$, obviously y must lie between u and v. So, by (*), some element of $\bar{K}$ lies between u and v.

Our proof of (*) will be based essentially on the principle that the roots of a polynomial depend continuously on the coefficients. Roughly, we take a polynomial which x satisfies with coefficients in L, then modify the coefficients ever so slightly to lie in K in such a manner that the new polynomial has a root within η of x which, of course lies in $\bar{K}$. It is possible to make this argument precise as it stands, but the following proof is slightly more elementary.

Let $f(x) = 0$ where

$$f(t) = t^n + a_1t^{n-1} + \cdots + a_{n-1}t + a_n$$

with the $a_i \in L$. Now we can assume that $f(t)$ has no multiple roots and that it is *monotonic* in a neighborhood of x, say for t where $|x - t| \leq \eta' \leq \eta$. Thus $f(x - \eta')$ and $f(x + \eta')$ have opposite signs. Choose $\epsilon \in K^+$ so that $\epsilon < \min(|f(x - \eta')|, |f(x + \eta')|)$. Next choose $k \in K^+$ so large that $|x \pm \eta'|^i \leq k$ for $i = 0, \cdots, n - 1$. We can now pick $b_i \in K$, $i = 1, \cdots, n$, so that $|a_i - b_i| \leq \epsilon/nk$ for each i. Let

$$g(t) = t^n + b_1 t^{n-1} + \cdots + b_{n-1}t + b_n,$$

and note that

$$|f(x \pm \eta') - g(x \pm \eta')| \leq \sum_{i=1}^{n} |a_i - b_i| \, |x \pm \eta'|^{n-i} \leq \sum_{i=1}^{n} \left(\frac{\epsilon}{nk}\right) \cdot k = \epsilon.$$

Hence $g(x - \eta')$ has the same sign as $f(x - \eta')$, and $g(x + \eta')$ has the same sign as $f(x + \eta')$. Therefore, $g(t)$ changes sign between $x - \eta'$ and $x + \eta'$. Hence $g(y) = 0$ for some $y \in \bar{K}$ with $|x - y| < \eta' \leq \eta$, and the proof is complete.

Historical remarks. The results presented in this paper were obtained in the summer of 1961 while the author was a Miller Research Fellow at the University of California at Berkeley. The author profited at that time very much from conversations with A. Robinson and G. Kreisel. The paper was never published before because no application was apparent, and, in any case, the results are rather elementary. However, since several people have asked about them, the author is glad to have this opportunity to present them.

After reading a draft of the paper, E. Zakon kindly pointed out that similar results for ordered Abelian groups were formed by L. W. Cohen and Casper Goffman [*Trans. Am. Math. Soc. 67* (1949), 310–319]. Indeed, the idea of using the special cuts goes back to R. Baer [*J. Reine Angew. Math. 160* (1929), 208–226], who calls them Dedekindean cuts. We have in effect reproved some of the Cohen–Goffman results (sec. 2 of their paper) and extended the method to fields. They do not, for some reason, stress the fact that the original structure is order-dense in its completion and, further, their notion of completeness has to do with convergent (transfinite) sequences, but the notion proves to be equivalent to ours. They do, however, prove the interesting fact that the groups (and hence the real-closed fields) constructed by H. Hahn's method of formal power series are complete. Although the algebra is very simple, it is not at once obvious that the cuts they use for the additive structure are also appropriate for the full field structure. That, in a (rather small) nut shell, is the contribution of the present paper, for whatever it is worth.

A Nonstandard Theory of Topological Groups

by ROHIT PARIKH

We shall take the theory of topological groups in [3] and show how certain structures receive natural nonstandard characterizations. We shall assume familiarity with [3].

Let $\mathcal{G}$ be an abstract group. Let X be a transitive set containing $\mathcal{G}$. Put $A = X \cup P(X) \cup P(P(X)) \cdots$ [where $P(X)$ = the power set of X]. If $\{a_i\}$ is an enumeration of A, let $\mathfrak{M}$ be the structure $\langle A, \epsilon, \{a_i\}\rangle$. Let $\mathfrak{M}^* = \langle A^*, e^*, \{a_i\}\rangle$ be an enlargement of $\mathfrak{M}$ in the sense of Robinson. Most of our results will be results about such an $\mathfrak{M}^*$. Notice that we do not need to include any group structure or topology on $\mathcal{G}$ explicitly, as it comes with $\mathfrak{M}$. If we consider two or more groups we shall assume they are simultaneously embedded in the transitive set X.

Occasionally we shall need to assume that $\mathfrak{M}^*$ is κ-saturated for a suitable cardinal κ. The situation is even more interesting if we assume that $\mathfrak{M}^*$ is saturated because any two structures definable in $\mathfrak{M}^*$, if elementarily equivalent, will be saturated and of the same power, and hence isomorphic. Generally, such an isomorphism will not be in the model $\mathfrak{M}^*$.

If we are assuming the axiom of choice, then assuming the existence of a saturated extension $\mathfrak{M}^*$ of $\mathfrak{M}$ does not involve any additional loss of generality. For consider the sets constructible in $\mathfrak{M}$. They form a model of $ZF + AC$ in which $\mathfrak{M}$ and quantifiers over $\mathfrak{M}$ retain their usual meaning but in which the G.C.H. holds for cardinals larger than $\overline{\overline{A}}$. Hence there are plenty of saturated structures, elementarily extending $\mathfrak{M}$.

Since the structure $\mathfrak{M}^*$ is not a standard model of set theory, its elements are not, intuitively, sets. Let us agree that the elementary embedding $\mathfrak{M} \to \mathfrak{M}^*$ is the identity map on A. Then for $a \in A$ the symbol a will denote both the element $a \in A^*$ and the subset $\{x \mid x \in A^*$

and $\mathfrak{M} \models x \in a\}$ of A^*. The symbol a^* will denote the set $\{x \mid \mathfrak{M}^* \models x \in a\}$. If a is infinite and $\mathfrak{M}^*$ is κ-saturated, $\kappa > \overline{\overline{A}}$, then $\overline{\overline{a^*}}$ will be at least κ and hence the subset $a \subseteq A^*$ will never be of the form b^* for any $b \in A$. In other words, all infinite subsets of A are external in $\mathfrak{M}^*$.

We shall make no distinction between ϵ and ϵ^*.

Suppose now that $\mathcal{G}$, x, e is a group. Then $\mathcal{G}^*$, x^*, e will also be a group elementarily extending $\mathcal{G}$; $\mathcal{G} \prec \mathcal{G}^*$. Now suppose $\mathfrak{F}$ a family of subsets of $\mathcal{G}$ such that $A \in \mathfrak{F} \rightarrow e \in A$. Define:

$$J_1 = \cap\, A^*\colon A \in \mathfrak{F},$$

$$J_0 = \text{subgroup of } \mathcal{G}^* \text{ generated by } J_1 \text{ and } \mathcal{G},$$

$$\mathfrak{I} = \{A\colon A \subseteq \mathcal{G} \text{ and } p \in A \rightarrow J_1 \cdot p \subseteq A^*\}.$$

Theorem 1. *$\mathcal{G}$, $\mathfrak{I}$ is a topological group iff J_1 is a normal subgroup of J_0. The topology is Hausdorff iff*

$$J_1 \cap \mathcal{G} = \{e\}.$$

Moreover, $J_1 = \mu(e)$.

Proof. It is clear from the definition of $\mathfrak{I}$ that $\phi, \mathcal{G} \in \mathfrak{I}$ and $\mathfrak{I}$ is closed under finite intersections. Suppose now that, for each α, $A_\alpha \in \mathfrak{I}$. Suppose $p \in \cup A_\alpha$. Then there is a β such that $p \in A_\beta$. Hence $J_1 \cdot p \subseteq A_\beta^* \subseteq (\cup A_\alpha)^*$. Thus $\mathfrak{I}$ is a topology on $\mathcal{G}$.

We claim that if $A \in \mathfrak{F}$, then $e \in \mathrm{int}(A)$.

For let $\mathfrak{K}$ consist of finite intersections of members of $\mathfrak{F}$. Then for each $A \in \mathfrak{K}$ there is a $B \in \mathfrak{K}$ such that $B \cdot B \subseteq A$. Otherwise the formulas $p \in B$, $q \in B$, $p \cdot q \notin A$, with B ranging over $\mathfrak{K}$, would be finitely satisfiable in $\mathfrak{M}$ and hence simultaneously satisfiable in $\mathfrak{M}^*$ by p, $q \in J_1$ such that $pq \notin A^*$. But this contradicts $pq \in J_1 \cdot J_1 \subseteq J_1 \subseteq A^*$.

Now, for $A_0 \in \mathfrak{K}$, choose $A_1, A_2, \cdots \in \mathfrak{K}$ such that $A_{i+1}{}^2 \subseteq A_i$. Then if $V = \cup_{n=1}^{\infty} A_1 \cdot A_2 \cdots A_n$, then $V \subseteq A_0$, and if $p \in V$, then $J_1 \cdot p = p \cdot J_1 \subseteq V^*$. Thus V is open in $\mathfrak{I}$ and $e \in V \subseteq A = A_0$, so $e \in \mathrm{int}(A)$.

This gives $J_1 = \mu(e)$. For we have

$$\mu(e) = \cap\, A^*\colon e \in \mathrm{int}(A) \subseteq \cap\, A^*\colon A \in \mathfrak{F} = J_1.$$

But if $e \in A$ and $A \in \mathfrak{I}$, then $J_1 \subseteq A^*$. Hence

$$J_1 \subseteq \cap\, A^*\colon A \in \mathfrak{I} \qquad \text{and} \qquad e \in A = \mu(e).$$

Thus $J_1 = \mu(e)$. Since J_1 is a normal subgroup of J_0, multiplication will be continuous at all standard points iff it is so at e. But let U be any standard neighborhood of e. Then $U \supseteq J_1$. Hence $U \supseteq J_1 \cdot J_1{}^{-1}$. But J_1 contains an open (nonstandard) neighborhood of e. Hence $\mathfrak{M}^* \models$

there are open neighborhoods V, W of e such that $V \cdot W^{-1} \subseteq U$. Hence $\mathfrak{M} \models$ there are $\cdots \subseteq U$. Thus $\mathcal{G}$, $\mathfrak{J}$ is a topological group.

The topology is Hausdorff iff monads are pairwise disjoint iff e is the only standard point in its own monad J_1.

The fact that these conditions are necessary was proved by Robinson.

Theorem 2. *Given $\mathcal{G}$, $\mathfrak{J}$ a topological group. Then $\mathcal{G}$, $\mathfrak{J}$ is locally compact iff there is a neighborhood U of e such that $U^* \subseteq J_0$.*

Proof. Trivial. J_0 are precisely the near-standard elements of $\mathcal{G}^*$.

1. Local Isomorphism

Let $\mathcal{G}$, e, $\mathcal{G}'$, e', be two topological groups. They are locally isomorphic if there is a map f from a neighborhood U of e to a neighborhood V of e', which preserves products and inverses and is a homeomorphism between U and V.

Theorem 3. *$\mathcal{G}$, e, $\mathcal{G}'$, e' are locally isomorphic iff there is a standard one-to-one function f which maps $\mu(e)$ isomorphically onto $\mu(e')$.*

Proof. Clearly, if a local isomorphism f exists between $\mathcal{G}$ and $\mathcal{G}'$, then it must create a one-to-one correspondence between small neighborhoods of e and e'. Thus

$$\begin{aligned} f[\mu(e)] &= \bigcap f(U)^*\colon U \text{ standard, open, } e \in U, \\ &= \bigcap V^*\colon V \text{ standard, open, } e' \in V, \\ &= \mu(e'). \end{aligned}$$

Conversely, suppose there is a standard, one-to-one function f mapping $\mu(e)$ isomorphically onto $\mu(e')$. Then the set A defined by

$$A = \{(p, q)\colon f(p), f(q), f(pq), f(qp), f(p^{-1}), f(q^{-1}) \text{ are defined and } f(pq) = f(p)f(q) \cdots\}$$

is a standard subset of $\mathcal{G}^* \times \mathcal{G}^*$ containing $\mu(e) \times \mu(e)$ and hence must contain a standard neighborhood $V \times V$ of (e, e) in the product topology. Otherwise the formula $(p, q) \notin A$ and the formulas $(p, q) \in V \times V$: V ranging over standard neighborhoods of e are finitely satisfiable and hence simultaneously satisfiable, giving $(p, q) \in \mu(e) \times \mu(e) - A$. Restrict f to V.

$f[V]$ is a standard set containing $\mu(e')$ and is therefore a neighborhood of e'. To show now that f is a local isomorphism suppose $U_1 \subseteq V$ is a standard open set and $p \in U_1$. Then U_1p^{-1} is a neighborhood of e and by the argument above

$$f[U_1p^{-1}] = (f[U_1] \cdot f(p)^{-1}) \cap f[V]$$

is a neighborhood of e' and $f[U_1]$ is a neighborhood of $f(p)$. Thus $f[U_1]$ is a neighborhood of each of its points, and is therefore open.

Thus f is open. By a symmetrical argument f is continuous. Thus f is the required local isomorphism.

Remark. The requirement in the theorem above that f be standard cannot be dropped. For suppose $\mu(e)$, $\mu(e')$ are elementarily equivalent and $\mathfrak{M}^*$ is saturated. Now consider a model $\mathfrak{M}_1$ of the same power as $\mathfrak{M}$ and such that $\mathfrak{M} \prec \mathfrak{M}_1 \prec \mathfrak{M}^*$ and $\langle \mathfrak{M}_1, \mu_{\mathfrak{M}_1}(e) \rangle \prec \langle \mathfrak{M}^*, \mu_{\mathfrak{M}^*}(e) \rangle$. Such a model exists by the downward Löwenheim–Skolem theorem. Now take a saturated extension of $\langle \mathfrak{M}_1, \mu_{\mathfrak{M}_1}(e) \rangle$ of the same power as $\mathfrak{M}^*$. Let it be $\langle \mathfrak{M}_2^*, \mu_{\mathfrak{M}_2}(e) \rangle$. Then $\mathfrak{M}_2^*$, $\mathfrak{M}^*$ being saturated of the same power, are isomorphic, with an isomorphism that preserves $\mathfrak{M}$ and hence $\mu(e)$. Thus $\mu(e)$ is saturated in $\mathfrak{M}^*$, even though it is not definable in it. But now the $\mu(e)$, $\mu(e')$ above must be isomorphic. This gives at most $2^{\aleph_0}$ isomorphism types. However, the number of local isomorphism types for topological groups is much larger.

2. Construction of the Dual Group

Let $\mathcal{G}$, 0 be an Abelian topological group, $\mathcal{H}$, 0′ a connected Abelian group. Robinson has given a nonstandard proof that if U is a neighborhood of 0 in $\mathcal{H}$, then $\bigcup_{n \in N} U^n = \mathcal{H}$.

Consider Hom($\mathcal{G}$, $\mathcal{H}$) = all continuous homomorphisms from $\mathcal{G}$ to $\mathcal{H}$. These form a group in the obvious way, letting

$$(f + g)(x) = f(x) + g(x).$$

The constant function 0′ is the identity in Hom($\mathcal{G}$, $\mathcal{H}$), denoted O.

For the topology we take the following to be the neighborhoods of O. Given a compact $C \subseteq \mathcal{G}$ and an open $U \subseteq \mathcal{H}$, $0' \in U$, the corresponding neighborhood of O is the set $\{f : f[C] \subseteq U\}$.

With this definition $\mu(O)$ will be $\{f : f[J_0] \subseteq \mu(0')\}$. By Theorem 1, Hom($\mathcal{G}$, $\mathcal{H}$) is a topological group.

Suppose now that $\mathcal{H}$ = the complex numbers of modulus 1, under multiplication and $\mathcal{G}$, is locally compact. To show that Hom($\mathcal{G}$, $\mathcal{H}$) is locally compact, notice first that every element of $\mathcal{H}^*$ is near-standard. Let U be a symmetric neighborhood of 1 in $\mathcal{H}$, $\bar{U} \subsetneq \mathcal{H}$, C a compact neighborhood of 0 in $\mathcal{G}$. Then let

$$A^* = \{f : f(C) \subseteq U\}^*$$
$$= \{f : f(C^*) \subseteq U^*\}.\ A^* \text{ is a neighborhood of } 0.$$

If $f \in A^*$, let $g = {}^0f$. We have to show g continuous. First $g(C) \subseteq \bar{U} \subsetneq \mathcal{K}$.

Suppose W, a symmetric neighborhood of $0'$, $= 1$. Then $\exists n$, $W^n \supseteq U$. Choose U_1 such that $U_1{}^n \subseteq C$. Then

$$g(U_1) \subseteq W, \text{ otherwise}$$
$$g(U_1{}^n) = (g(U_1))^n \text{ would have points not in } \bar{U}.$$

Hence g is continuous.

Now $f - g^*$ clearly takes J_0 in $\mu(0') = \mu(1)$. So f is near-standard. Hence $\mathrm{Hom}(\mathcal{G}, \mathcal{K})$ is locally compact.

From now on we write $\mathcal{G}' = \mathrm{Hom}(\mathcal{G}, \mathcal{K})$, where $\mathcal{K}$ = complex numbers of modulus 1.

Theorem 4. *If $\mathcal{G}$ is compact, $\mathcal{G}'$ is discrete; if $\mathcal{G}$ is discrete, $\mathcal{G}'$ is compact.*

Proof. Suppose $\mathcal{G}$ is compact. We have to show that $\mu(O)$ in $\mathcal{G}'^*$ is just O. But

$$\mu(O) = \{f : f(J_0) \subseteq \mu(1)\}$$
$$= \{f : f(\mathcal{G}^*) \subseteq \mu(1)\}$$

Suppose now $f(x) \neq 1$ for some x. Then there is an $n \in N^*$, $f(x^n) \notin \mu(1)$. Hence $f \notin \mu(O)$.

Suppose $\mathcal{G}$ is discrete. To show that every $f \in \mathcal{G}'^*$ is near-standard, given f take $g = {}^0f$. g is automatically continuous. Then $f - g^* \in \mu(O)$. Hence f is near-standard.

3. Construction of the Haar Measure

Let $\mathcal{G}$, $\mathfrak{J}$ be a locally compact group. Let $V \subseteq \mu(e)$ be an infinitesimal neighborhood of e. Fix a compact standard set C and given any compact, standard, set C' define

$$m(C') = {}^0\!\left[\frac{l(C')}{l(C)}\right],$$

where $l(A)$ = least member of N^* such that there is an internal covering of A^* by l sets of the form $V^* \cdot p$.

If C has interior, then it follows from the Heine–Borel property that $l(C')/l(C)$ is finite and $m(C')$ is defined.

Theorem 5. (a) $m(A \cdot p) = A$.

(b) *If* A, B *are disjoint*, $m(A \cup B) = m(A) + m(B)$.

Proof

(a) is obvious from definition.

(b) follows from the fact that a set of the form $V^* \cdot p$ cannot simultaneously intersect A^* and B^*, otherwise ${}^0p$ would exist and be in $A \cap B$.

Suppose now that $\mu(e)$ is a normal subgroup of $\mathcal{G}^*$. Then e has small neighborhoods invariant under inner automorphisms. In fact, given a standard neighborhood U,

$$\bigcap_{p \in \mathcal{G}^*} p^{-1} \cdot U^* \cdot p \supseteq \bigcap_{p \in \mathcal{G}^*} p^{-1} \cdot \mu(e) \cdot p \supseteq \mu(e).$$

Hence

$$\bigcap_{p \in \mathcal{G}^*} p^{-1} \cdot U^* \cdot p \text{ is an } \mathfrak{M}^*\text{-neighborhood of } e.$$

But

$$\bigcap_{p \in \mathcal{G}^*} p^{-1} \cdot U^* \cdot p = \Big(\bigcap_{p \in \mathcal{G}} p^{-1} \cdot U \cdot p\Big)^*$$

so

$$\bigcap_{p \in \mathcal{G}} p^{-1} \cdot U \cdot p \text{ is an } \mathfrak{M}\text{-neighborhood of } e.$$

Thus e has arbitrarily small neighborhoods invariant under inner automorphisms. Take an infinitesimal one, V. The corresponding measure is right-invariant. To see left-invariance note that

$$l(p \cdot A) = l(p \cdot A \cdot p^{-1} \cdot p) = l(p \cdot A \cdot p^{-1}) = l(A)$$

using the invariance of V in the last step. Thus we get

$$m(p \cdot A) = m(A)$$

and

Theorem 6. *If* $\mu(e)$ *is a normal subgroup of* $\mathcal{G}^*$, *then* $\mathcal{G}$ *is unimodular.*

The converse is also true. We leave the proof to the reader.

References

1. W. A. J. LUXEMBURG, *A New Approach to the Theory of Monads* (Tech. Rept. 1). Pasadena: California Institute of Technology, 1967. (See also this volume.)
2. M. MORLEY AND R. VAUGHT, Homogeneous Universal Models, *Math. Scand.*, *11* (1962), 37–57.
3. A. ROBINSON, *Non-Standard Analysis* (Studies in Logic and the Foundations of Mathematics). Amsterdam: North-Holland, 1966.

Nonstandard Analysis in Topological Algebra

by ARTHUR L. STONE

The main concern of this paper is a method for turning topological questions about groups, rings, and fields into algebraic questions about certain homomorphisms. We characterize group, ring, and field topologies in the terminology of nonstandard analysis, and there are some applications to type V field topologies.

We shall not have recourse to Robinson's *enlargements* ([11], pp. 30–40) but use a simpler concept, that of *adequate* ultrapower (Section 1). Much of nonstandard analysis can be phrased in terms of adequate ultrapowers.

It is intended that this paper be readable by the nonspecialist in model theory or nonstandard analysis.

Preliminaries

Recall that a *filter* on an index set I is a set $\mathbf{\Delta}$ of subsets Δ of I such that

$$\Delta_1 \in \mathbf{\Delta} \text{ and } \Delta_2 \in \mathbf{\Delta} \text{ imply } \Delta_1 \cap \Delta_2 \in \mathbf{\Delta},$$

$$\Delta_1 \in \mathbf{\Delta} \text{ and } \Psi \subseteq I \text{ imply } \Delta_1 \cup \Psi \in \mathbf{\Delta}.$$

A filter is called *proper* if it does not contain the empty set, and a maximal proper filter is called an *ultrafilter*. It is not difficult to prove that a filter $\mathbf{\Delta}$ on I is an ultrafilter if and only if whenever $\langle \Psi_1, \cdots, \Psi_n \rangle$ is a finite partitioning of I into disjoint sets, exactly one of $\Psi_1, \cdots, \Psi_n$ is an element of $\mathbf{\Delta}$.

Using the axiom of choice, it is easy to show that every proper filter can be extended to an ultrafilter. If I has infinite cardinality χ, then there are $2^{2^{\chi}}$ ultrafilters on I (see, for example, [5], p. 130). A *principal* ultrafilter on I is one of the form $\{\Delta \subseteq I \mid \iota \in \Delta\}$ for some fixed ι. Clearly, not all ultrafilters on an infinite set are principal.

Ultrapowers

An *n-ary relation* R on a set K is a subset of the Cartesian product K^n. A *relational structure* consists of a set K together with a set of relations on K. For example, groups, rings, and fields are relational structures: we may identify a binary operation $\cdot$ on K with the ternary relation which is the set of triples k_1, k_2, k_3 for which $k_1 \cdot k_2 = k_3$. Now let K be a relational structure. (We employ a familiar abuse of language, using the same symbol for the set K and the relational structure K.) Let I be an infinite index set and let K^I denote the set of functions $\mathbf{k}\colon I \to K$. Given an ultrafilter $\mathbf{\Delta}$ on I, we define equivalence classes $^\star\mathbf{k}$ in K^I by

$$\mathbf{k}_1 \in {^\star\mathbf{k}_2} \text{ if and only if}$$
$$\{\iota \in I \mid \mathbf{k}_1(\iota) = \mathbf{k}_2(\iota)\} \in \mathbf{\Delta}.$$

Let $*^I{}_{\mathbf{\Delta}}K$ or, for brevity, simply $*K$ denote the set of these equivalence classes. If R is a relation on K, we define a relation $*R$ on $*K$ by

$$\langle {^\star\mathbf{k}_1}, \cdots, {^\star\mathbf{k}_n}\rangle \in *R \text{ if and only if}$$
$$\{\iota \in I \mid < \mathbf{k}_1(\iota), \cdots, \mathbf{k}_n(\iota) \in R\} \in \mathbf{\Delta}.$$

In the special case where R corresponds to a binary operation $\cdot$, this is equivalent to

$$^\star\mathbf{k}_1 \cdot {^\star\mathbf{k}_2} = {^\star\mathbf{k}_3} \text{ if and only if}$$
$$\{\iota \in I \mid \mathbf{k}_1(\iota) \cdot \mathbf{k}_2(\iota) = \mathbf{k}_3(\iota)\} \in \mathbf{\Delta}.$$

(We have used the same symbol for the operation on K and on $*K$.) With these relations $*R$, one corresponding to each relation R on K, we call $*K$ the *ultrapower* of K determined by I and $\mathbf{\Delta}$.

In the special case where K is a field, K^I has a natural ring structure and it is easy to see that $*K$ is K^I modulo the maximal ideal consisting for all functions $\mathbf{k}$ for which $\{\iota \in I \mid \mathbf{k}(\iota) = 0\} \in \mathbf{\Delta}$. (That this is an ideal follows from the fact that $\mathbf{\Delta}$ is a filter, and maximality follows from the maximality of $\mathbf{\Delta}$.) Hence if K is a field, so is $*K$. After a few definitions we shall be able to say much more.

Let $\langle\cdots, R, \cdots\rangle$ be the set of relations defining a relational structure on set K. Then an *atomic formula* in the language of K is an expression of the form $\langle k_1, \cdots, k_n\rangle \in R$, where each k_i is either an element of K or a variable that ranges over the elements of K. An *elementary sentence* in the language of K is an assertion built up from such atomic formulas by means of the connectives *and*, *or*, *not*, *implies*, and the quantifiers $\forall$ (for all) and $\exists$ (there exist)—where $\forall$ and $\exists$ apply only to variables which range over the *elements* of K. (For a more careful description, see, for example, [10], pp. 3–11. For simplicity we have overlooked a distinction that is usually made between the relations on K and the symbols in the language of K which stand for those relations).

The canonical embedding of K in an ultrapower $*K$ is obtained by mapping each element k of K to the equivalence class $^\star\langle k\rangle$, the equivalence class of the constant function with value k. If S is an elementary sentence in the language of K, let $*S$ denote the sentence in the language of $*K$ obtained by replacing in S each relation R by the relation $*R$, each element k by the element $^\star\langle k\rangle$, and each variable that ranges over the elements of K by a variable that ranges over the elements of $*K$.

Proposition. *If an elementary sentence S is true for K, then the sentence $*S$ is true for $*K$.*

This proposition is due to Łos [7] and (in a form closer to the above) to Frayne, et al. [4]. Another source for the proof (which is by induction on the length of S) is Kochen [8], p. 266. As consequences of this proposition, we have that ultrapowers of groups, rings, ordered groups $\cdots$ are again (respectively) groups, rings, ordered groups $\cdots$ (associativity, commutativity, existence of identity, and so on, are asserted by elementary sentences). But not all properties of relational structures can be expressed by elementary sentences. Ultrapowers of Noetherian rings, for example, are usually non-Noetherian.

1. Adequate Ultrafilters and Adequate Ultrapowers

In the sections that follow it will be necessary simultaneously to discuss convergence with respect to many topologies on a given structure K, some of them first countable and some of them not. It is perhaps surprising that we can do this. Note, for example, that a sequence (= function on an initial segment of the ordinal numbers) of uncountable length can converge in a first countable space only if it is eventually constant.

We shall use filters. Recall that a filter is said to *converge* to a point of a topological space if and only if it contains the neighborhood filter of the point. Where $\mathbf{k}: I \to K$ and $\mathbf{\Delta}$ is a filter on I, $\mathbf{k}[\mathbf{\Delta}]$ will denote the filter on K generated by the sets $\mathbf{k}\Delta = \{k(\iota)\}_{\iota \in \Delta} (\Delta \in \mathbf{\Delta})$. It is easy to show that if $\mathbf{\Delta}$ is an ultrafilter on I, then $\mathbf{k}[\mathbf{\Delta}]$ must be an ultrafilter on K.

Definition. An ultrafilter $\mathbf{\Delta}$ on an index set I will be said to be *adequate* for a set K if every ultrafilter on K is of the form $\mathbf{k}[\mathbf{\Delta}]$ for some function $\mathbf{k}: I \to K$.

Every filter is the intersection of the ultrafilters that contain it. Consequently, if we have a topology on K and $\mathbf{\Delta}$ is adequate for K, then the neighborhood filter of a point a is the intersection of the filters $\mathbf{k}[\mathbf{\Delta}]$ which converge to a. This gives us the beginnings of a method for describing all the topologies on K—when we have an adequate ultrafilter.

Theorem 1.1. *Let K have cardinality χ and I have cardinality $\cdot\, 2^{\chi}$. Then there exist ultrafilters $\mathbf{\Delta}$ on I which are adequate for K.*

Proof. Let K have cardinality χ. Let I be the set of all pairs $\langle\langle\cdots, S_\alpha, \cdots\rangle, \langle\cdots, k_\alpha, \cdots\rangle\rangle$, where $\langle\cdots, S_\alpha, \cdots\rangle$ is a finite partitioning of K and $\langle\cdots, k_\alpha, \cdots\rangle$ is a set of representative elements: $k_\alpha \in S_\alpha$ for each α. Then I has cardinality 2^χ. For every ultrafilter $\mathbf{D}$ on K define a function $\mathbf{k}_\mathbf{D}: I \to K$ by

$$\mathbf{k}_\mathbf{D}(\langle\langle\cdots, S_\alpha, \cdots\rangle, \langle\cdots, k_\alpha, \cdots\rangle\rangle) = k_\alpha$$

if and only if $S_\alpha \in \mathbf{D}$.

Since $\mathbf{D}$ is an ultrafilter, $\mathbf{k}_\mathbf{D}$ is well defined. Let $\mathbf{k}^{\leftarrow}$ denote the inverse image function associated with a function $\mathbf{k}$. Let $\mathbf{\Psi}$ be the filter on I generated by the inverse images $\psi = \mathbf{k}_\mathbf{D}{}^{\leftarrow}(D)$, where D ranges over the elements of $\mathbf{D}$ and $\mathbf{D}$ ranges over the set of ultrafilters on K. Straightforward computation shows that $\mathbf{\Psi}$ is a proper filter. (Use the fact that if $\mathbf{D}_1, \cdots, \mathbf{D}_n$ are distinct ultrafilters on K, then there exist partitionings $\langle S_1, \cdots, S_n\rangle$ of K with $S_1 \in \mathbf{D}_1, \cdots, \mathbf{S}_n \in \mathbf{D}_n$.) It is easy to show that any ultrafilter $\mathbf{\Delta}$ which contains $\mathbf{\Psi}$ is adequate for K.

We shall call the ultrapower $*^I{}_\mathbf{\Delta}K$ an *adequate ultrapower* (for K) if the ultrafilter $\mathbf{\Delta}$ is adequate for K.

Remark. Let $\mathbf{P}S$ denote the set of all subsets of a set S. The ultrapower $*K$ is adequate for the sets K, $\mathbf{P}K$, $\mathbf{PP}K, \cdots$ if and only if $*K$ is an enlargement of K in the sense of Robinson.

2. A Preliminary Lemma

A *ring topology* on a ring K is a topology for which the operations addition, subtraction, and multiplication are continuous. Given a topology on K, a subset S is said to be *bounded away from zero* if S has empty intersection with some neighborhood of zero.

Definition. A topology $\mathbf{T}$ on a ring K will be said to be of *type V* if $\mathbf{T}$ is a Hausdorff ring topology and whenever A and B are subsets of K bounded away from zero then $A \cdot B = \{a \cdot b \mid a \in A,\ b \in B\}$ is also bounded away from zero. When a topology $\mathbf{T}$ on K is given, an element $^\star\mathbf{k}$ of an ultrapower $*^I{}_\mathbf{\Delta}K$ will be said to be an *infinitesimal* if the ultrafilter $\mathbf{k}[\mathbf{\Delta}]$ converges to zero.

***Lemma* 2.1.** *If* **T** *is a type V topology on a field K, then the set of infinitesimals in an ultrapower* $*K = *^{I}{}_{\mathbf{\Delta}}K$ *forms the maximal ideal of a valuation ring in* $*K$.

Proof. Note first that if $^{\star}\mathbf{k}_1 = {}^{\star}\mathbf{k}_2$, then $^{\star}\mathbf{k}_1[\mathbf{\Delta}] = \mathbf{k}_2[\mathbf{\Delta}]$. For $^{\star}\mathbf{k}_1 = {}^{\star}\mathbf{k}_2$ only if for some $\Delta_0 \in \mathbf{\Delta}$, $\mathbf{k}_1(\iota) = \mathbf{k}_2(\iota)$ for every $\iota \in \Delta_0$, and the collection $\{\mathbf{k}_1(\Delta) \mid \Delta \in \mathbf{\Delta} \text{ and } \Delta \subseteq \Delta_0\}$ is a base for $\mathbf{k}_1[\mathbf{\Delta}]$. Similarly, $\{\mathbf{k}_2(\Delta) \mid \Delta \in \mathbf{\Delta} \text{ and } \Delta \subseteq \Delta_0\}$ is a base for $\mathbf{k}_2[\mathbf{\Delta}]$.

Let **T** be a type V topology on field K, let $*K = *^{I}{}_{\mathbf{\Delta}}K$ be an ultrapower, and let $^{\star}i$ denote the set of infinitesimals. That $^{\star}i$ is a subring of $*K$ is immediate from the fact that addition, subtraction, and multiplication are continuous. Let $^{\star}A$ be the set of elements $^{\star}\mathbf{a}$ in $*K$ such that $^{\star}\mathbf{a}^{-1} \notin {}^{\star}i$. (We might say that $^{\star}A$ is the set of elements $^{\star}\mathbf{a}$ such that $\mathbf{a}[\mathbf{\Delta}]$ is eventually bounded away from infinity.) Then $^{\star}i \subseteq {}^{\star}A$. For if $^{\star}\mathbf{k}$ is an element of $^{\star}i$ but not of $^{\star}A$, then $^{\star}\mathbf{k}^{-1}$ is also an element of $^{\star}i$. But then we should have $^{\star}\mathbf{k} \cdot {}^{\star}\mathbf{k}^{-1} \in {}^{\star}i$, and $\mathbf{k} \cdot \mathbf{k}^{-1}[\mathbf{\Delta}]$ is the principal ultrafilter generated by $\{1\}$, which does not converge to zero.

By construction $^{\star}A \cup {}^{\star}A^{-1} = *K$, and the elements of $^{\star}A$ not in $^{\star}i$ are the units of $^{\star}A$. Therefore we shall be done if we can show that $^{\star}A$ is a ring and that $^{\star}i$ is an ideal of $^{\star}A$. That $^{\star}A$ is closed under multiplication is a consequence of the assumption that **T** is of type V. (Roughly, if the product of sets bounded away from zero is bounded away from zero, then the product of sets bounded away from infinity is bounded away from infinity.) If the ideal property does not hold—if we should have $^{\star}\mathbf{a} \in {}^{\star}A$ and $^{\star}\mathbf{k} \in {}^{\star}i$ with $^{\star}\mathbf{a} \cdot {}^{\star}\mathbf{k} \notin {}^{\star}i$—then we should also have $({}^{\star}\mathbf{a} \cdot {}^{\star}\mathbf{k})^{-1} \in {}^{\star}A$ and $^{\star}\mathbf{a} \cdot ({}^{\star}\mathbf{a} \cdot {}^{\star}\mathbf{k})^{-1} = {}^{\star}\mathbf{k}^{-1} \in {}^{\star}A$. But this last would contradict the definition of $^{\star}A$. Finally, if $^{\star}A$ is not closed under addition—if we should have $^{\star}\mathbf{a}$ and $^{\star}\mathbf{k}$ in $^{\star}A$ with $^{\star}\mathbf{a} + {}^{\star}\mathbf{k} \notin {}^{\star}A$—then $({}^{\star}\mathbf{a} + {}^{\star}\mathbf{k})^{-1} \in {}^{\star}i$, $^{\star}\mathbf{k} \cdot ({}^{\star}\mathbf{a} + {}^{\star}\mathbf{k})^{-1} \in {}^{\star}i$, and $^{\star}\mathbf{a} \cdot ({}^{\star}\mathbf{a} + {}^{\star}\mathbf{k})^{-1} \in {}^{\star}i$. Since $^{\star}i$ is closed under addition, this would imply $({}^{\star}\mathbf{a} + {}^{\star}\mathbf{k}) \cdot ({}^{\star}\mathbf{a} + {}^{\star}\mathbf{k})^{-1} \in {}^{\star}i$. But $({}^{\star}\mathbf{a} + {}^{\star}\mathbf{k}) \cdot ({}^{\star}\mathbf{a} + {}^{\star}\mathbf{k})^{-1}[\mathbf{\Delta}]$ is, again, the principal ultrafilter generated by $\{1\}$, which does not converge to zero. This last contradiction completes the proof.

Henceforth where **T** is a type V topology on a field K and $*K$ is an ultrapower of K, by the valuation ring and ideal determined by **T** in $*K$ we shall mean the structures $^{\star}A$ and $^{\star}i$ of the preceding proof. And we shall regard K as canonically embedded in $*K$; that is, we drop the distinction between k and $^{\star}\langle k\rangle$.

Examples

1. The order topology on an ordered field K is of type V. By the proposition above, ultraproducts of ordered fields are ordered fields. The valuation ring $^{\star}A$ determined by the order topology, in an ultrapower $*K$, turns out to be the set of K-bounded elements of $*K$;

that is: ${}^\star A$ consists of those elements ${}^\star\mathbf{a}$ in $*K$ for which there exist k_1 and k_2 in K with $k_1 < {}^\star\mathbf{a} < k_2$ in $*K$. And the ideal ${}^\star i$ determined by the order topology turns out, appropriately, to be the set of K-infinitesimal elements of $*K$: for every ${}^\star\mathbf{k} \in {}^\star i$, for all negative k_1 and positive k_2 in K we have $k_1 < {}^\star\mathbf{k} < k_2$ in $*K$.

2. Let v be a valuation on a field K and let A and i be the valuation ring and ideal determined by v in K. Every valuation topology is of type V. Let $*K = *^I{}_{\mathbf{\Delta}} K$ be an ultrapower. Then there is a canonical embedding of the ultrapower $*A = *^I{}_{\mathbf{\Delta}}A$ in $*K$. (If we think of A as a unary relation on K, this is a special case of the definition of relations $*R$ in $*K$ in the Preliminaries.) The proposition, again, implies that $*A$ is a valuation ring in $*K$. Assume that the valuation topology is nondiscrete and let ${}^\star A$ be the valuation ring it determines in $*K$. It turns out that $*A$ is properly contained in ${}^\star A$. The ring $*A$ determines a valuation on $*K$ which extends v. Statements similar to those of the preceding example hold for ${}^\star A$ and ${}^\star i$.

3. Applications

A *field topology* on a field K is a ring topology on K for which the function $a \rightsquigarrow a^{-1}$ is continuous at every nonzero a.

Proposition 3.1. *Every type V topology on a field is a field topology.*

Proof. Let $\mathbf{T}$ be a type V topology on a field K. Let $*K = *^I{}_{\mathbf{\Delta}}K$ be an adequate ultrapower, and let ${}^\star A$ and ${}^\star i$ be the valuation ring and ideal determined by $\mathbf{T}$. As part of the definition, a type V topology is a ring topology. Hence we have only to show that the function $a \rightsquigarrow a^{-1}$ is continuous at every nonzero element a of K. Since $\mathbf{\Delta}$ is adequate for K, the function $a \rightsquigarrow a^{-1}$ is continuous at a if and only if whenever $\mathbf{k}[\mathbf{\Delta}]$ converges to a, $\mathbf{k}^{-1}[\mathbf{\Delta}]$ converges to a^{-1}. The filter $\mathbf{k}[\mathbf{\Delta}]$ converges to a if and only if $a - {}^\star\mathbf{k} \in {}^\star i$. Suppose we do not have continuity at the nonzero element a. Then for some ${}^\star\mathbf{k}$ in $*K$, $a - {}^\star\mathbf{k} \in {}^\star i$ and $(a^{-1} - {}^\star\mathbf{k}^{-1}) \notin {}^\star i$. Then $(a^{-1} - {}^\star\mathbf{k}^{-1})^{-1} = a \cdot {}^\star\mathbf{k}/(a - {}^\star\mathbf{k})$ is in ${}^\star A$. Since a is nonzero, we also have $a \notin {}^\star i$ and ${}^\star\mathbf{k} \notin {}^\star i$, hence $a^{-1} \in {}^\star A$ and ${}^\star\mathbf{k}^{-1} \in {}^\star A$. Then

$$\frac{a \cdot {}^\star\mathbf{k}}{a - {}^\star\mathbf{k}} \cdot a^{-1} \cdot {}^\star\mathbf{k}^{-1} = \frac{1}{a - {}^\star\mathbf{k}} \in {}^\star A.$$

But this last would contradict our initial assumption: $a - {}^\star\mathbf{k} \in {}^\star i$. So we have shown that $\mathbf{T}$ is a field topology.

A subset S of a topological field is said to be *bounded* if for every neighborhood N_1 of zero there is a neighborhood N_2 of zero with $N_2 \cdot S \subseteq N_1$.

Proposition 3.2. *For a field topology* $\mathbf{T}$ *on* K *the following conditions are equivalent:*

(a) $\mathbf{T}$ *is of type* V.
(b) *The inverse of a set bounded away from zero is always bounded.*

Proof. That (b) implies (a) is proved by Kaplansky ([6*c*], lemma 4, p. 910). For the converse, let $*K = *^I{}_{\mathbf{\Delta}}K$ be an adequate ultrapower of a field K, and let ${}^\star A$ and ${}^\star i$ be the valuation ring and ideal determined by a type V topology $\mathbf{T}$. If S is any set bounded away from zero, then no ${}^\star\mathbf{k}$ in $*S$ is in ${}^\star i$; hence $*S^{-1} = (*S)^{-1}$ is contained in ${}^\star A$. Then, since ${}^\star i$ is an ideal of ${}^\star A$, ${}^\star i \cdot (*S^{-1}) \subseteq {}^\star i$. If there were a neighborhood N_1 of zero such that for no neighborhood N_2 of zero do we have $N_2 \cdot S \subseteq N_1$, then we should be able to construct a function $\langle k_\iota \cdot s_\iota^{-1}\rangle_{\iota \in I}$ with $s_\iota \in S$ for every $\iota \in I$ and ${}^\star\langle k_\iota\rangle_{\iota\in I}$ an element of ${}^\star i$—and so that $\langle k_\iota \cdot s_\iota^{-1}\rangle_{\iota\in I}$ has no values inside N_1. Since this would contradict ${}^\star i \cdot (*S^{-1}) \subseteq {}^\star i$, we have proved the proposition.

Kaplansky uses condition (b) of Proposition 3.2 for the definition of type V [6]. Propositions 3.1 and 3.2 justify the modified definition given in Section 2.

For the proof of the next proposition we shall need an additional fact about ultrapowers. If $\mathbf{\Delta}$ is an ultrafilter on set I and $\mathbf{\Delta}'$ is an ultrafilter on set H, then the collection of sets of the form $\{\langle\iota, \eta\rangle \in I \times H \mid \iota \in \Delta_\eta \text{ and } \eta \in \Delta'\}$, $\Delta' \in \mathbf{\Delta}'$ and $\Delta_\eta \in \mathbf{\Delta}$ for every $\eta \in \Delta'$, forms the base for an ultrafilter $\mathbf{\Delta}''$ on the Cartesian product $I \times H$. With this construction of $\mathbf{\Delta}''$, for any relational structure K the double ultrapower $*^H{}_{\mathbf{\Delta}'}(*^I{}_{\mathbf{\Delta}}K)$ is naturally isomorphic to $*^{I\times H}{}_{\mathbf{\Delta}''}K$. For proof see, for example, [8], p. 230.

Proposition 3.3. *The nondiscrete type* V *topologies on a field* K *are noncomparable: No one is a refinement of another.*

Proof. Let $\mathbf{T}$ and $\mathbf{U}$ be type V topologies on K with $\mathbf{T} \subseteq \mathbf{U}$. (We think of $\mathbf{T}$ and $\mathbf{U}$ as collections of open sets.) Let $*K = *^I{}_{\mathbf{\Delta}}K$ be an adequate ultrapower and let ${}^\star A$ and ${}^\star i$, ${}^\star B$ and ${}^\star j$ be, respectively, the valuation rings and ideals determined by $\mathbf{T}$ and $\mathbf{U}$ in $*K$. Since $\mathbf{T} \subseteq \mathbf{U}$ we have ${}^\star i \supseteq {}^\star j$. Then the rings ${}^\star A$ and ${}^\star B$ determine the same valuation topology on $*K$. (For proof see [2], p. 136, Proposition 33.) Let ${}^\star\mathbf{T}$ denote this topology on $*K$. Let $\mathbf{\Delta}'$, on an index set H, be an ultrafilter which is adequate for $*K$. Then, using the notation above, $*^H{}_{\mathbf{\Delta}'}(*^I{}_{\mathbf{\Delta}}K)$ is isomorphic to ${}^{I\times H}{}_{\mathbf{\Delta}''}K$. Let ${}^{\star\star}C$ and ${}^{\star\star}Ⓚ$ be the valuation ring and ideal in $*^H{}_{\mathbf{\Delta}'}(*^I{}_{\mathbf{\Delta}}K)$ determined by ${}^\star\mathbf{T}$. We shall see that ${}^{\star\star}Ⓚ$ determines the original topologies $\mathbf{T}$ and $\mathbf{U}$.

First let $Ⓚ = \langle k_{\iota,\eta}\rangle_{\iota\in I,\eta\in H}$ be a function defined on $I \times H$, with values in K, such that the $\mathbf{\Delta} - \mathbf{\Delta}'$ equivalence class ${}^\star\langle{}^\star\langle k_{\iota,\eta}\rangle_{\iota\in I}\rangle_{\eta\in H}$ is an element of ${}^{\star\star}Ⓚ$. We shall see that then the ultrafilter $Ⓚ[\mathbf{\Delta}'']$ contains every $\mathbf{T}$-neighborhood N of zero in K. Let ${}^\starⓀ$ denote the indexed set $\langle{}^\star\langle k_{\iota,\eta}\rangle_{\iota\in I}\rangle_{\eta\in H}$: We may think of ${}^\starⓀ$ as a function from H to $*K$. Then since ${}^{\star\star}ⓚ \in {}^{\star\star}Ⓚ$ we have that ${}^\starⓚ[\mathbf{\Delta}']$ converges to zero with respect to ${}^\star\mathbf{T}$ in $*K$. This happens only if for every nonzero ${}^\star\mathbf{a}$ in $*K$ eventually (over $\mathbf{\Delta}'$) we have ${}^\star\langle k_{\iota,\eta}\rangle_{\iota\in I}/{}^\star\mathbf{a}$ an element of ${}^\star i$. In particular, choosing 1 for ${}^\star\mathbf{a}$, there is some $\Delta' \in \mathbf{\Delta}'$ such that for every $\eta \in \Delta'$, ${}^\star\langle k_{\iota,\eta}\rangle_{\iota\in I} \in {}^\star i$, hence $\{\{k_{\iota,\eta}\}_{\iota\in\Delta}\}_{\Delta\in\mathbf{\Delta}}$ converges to zero in K with respect to $\mathbf{T}$. Then for any given $\mathbf{T}$-neighborhood N of zero, for every $\eta \in \Delta'$ there is a $\Delta_\eta \in \mathbf{\Delta}$ so that $\{k_{\iota,\eta} \mid \iota \in \Delta_\eta\} \subseteq N$. Then if we let Δ'' be the set $\{\langle\iota,\eta\rangle \mid \eta \in \Delta'$ and $\iota \in \Delta\eta\}$ we have $ⓚ(\Delta'') \subseteq N$. Hence $ⓚ(\Delta'')$ contains the $\mathbf{T}$-neighborhood filter of zero in K.

Next we find that if S is any subset of K which is not in the $\mathbf{T}$-neighborhood filter of zero, then for some ⓚ with ${}^{\star\star}ⓚ \in {}^{\star\star}Ⓚ$ we have $S \notin ⓚ(\mathbf{\Delta}'')$. For if S is not a $\mathbf{T}$-neighborhood of zero, then the complement of S meets every $\mathbf{T}$-neighborhood of zero. Then for every nonzero ${}^\star\mathbf{a} \in *K$ we may construct a function $\mathbf{k}\colon I \to K$ with the image $\mathbf{k}(I)$ contained in the complement of S and with ${}^\star\mathbf{k}/{}^\star\mathbf{a} \in {}^\star i$. Then ${}^\star\mathbf{k}$ is in the ${}^\star\mathbf{T}$-neighborhood of zero determined by ${}^\star\mathbf{a}$. Then since $\mathbf{\Delta}'$ is adequate for $*K$, using this function $\mathbf{k}$ we may construct a function $ⓚ\colon I \times H \to K$ with ${}^{\star\star}ⓚ \in {}^{\star\star}Ⓚ$ and with the image $ⓚ(I \times H)$ contained in the complement of S — so that $S \notin ⓚ(\mathbf{\Delta}'')$.

By the two preceding paragraphs, the intersection $\bigcap \{ⓚ(\mathbf{\Delta}'') \mid {}^{\star\star}ⓚ \in {}^{\star\star}i\}$ is the $\mathbf{T}$-neighborhood filter of zero in K. Since our argument is symmetrical in $\mathbf{T}$ and $\mathbf{U}$, this implies $\mathbf{T} = \mathbf{U}$: Type V topologies on K are comparable only when equal.

Theorem 3.4 (**Approximation Theorem for Type *V* Topologies**). *Let* $\mathbf{T}_1, \cdots, \mathbf{T}_n$ *be distinct nondiscrete type V topologies on a field K. Let* $a_1, \cdots, a_n$ *be elements of K, and let* $N_1, \cdots, N_n$ *be neighborhoods* N_i *of* a_i *in* $\mathbf{T}_i (i = 1, \cdots, n)$. *Then there is an element k of K in the intersection* $\bigcap_{1\le i\le n} N_i$.

Proof. Let $*K = *^I{}_{\mathbf{\Delta}}K$ be an adequate ultrapower of the field K. Let $\mathbf{T}_1, \cdots, \mathbf{T}_n$ be distinct nondiscrete type V topologies on K, and let ${}^\star A_1, \cdots, {}^\star A_n$ and ${}^\star i_1, \cdots, {}^\star i_n$ be the corresponding valuation rings and ideals in $*K$. For $i = 1, \cdots, n$ let $\rho_i\colon {}^\star A_i \to {}^\star A_i/{}^\star i_i$ be the natural ring homomorphism with kernel ${}^\star i_i$. Then each ρ_i is a place from $*K$, and we may apply the approximation theorem for places (for example, [12], p. 30). Since K is contained in each ${}^\star A_i$ and K has zero intersection with each ${}^\star i_i$, there is a natural embedding of K in each of the residue fields ${}^\star A_i/{}^\star i_i$. Then given $a_1, \cdots, a_n$ in K, by the approximation theorem for places there is an element $^\star\mathbf{k}$ in the intersection of the rings $^\star A_i$ such that $\rho_i(^\star\mathbf{k}) = a_i (i = 1, \cdots, n)$. Now straightforward checking shows that $\mathbf{k}[\mathbf{\Delta}]$ converges to a_i with respect to $\mathbf{T}_i (i = 1, \cdots, n)$. Hence for any set $\{N_1, \cdots, N_n\}$ of neighborhoods of the respective points, in the respective topologies, for some Δ in $\mathbf{\Delta}$ we have $\mathbf{k}(\Delta) \subseteq \bigcap_{1 \leq i \leq n} N_i$.

Special cases of the preceding theorem are the approximation theorem for valuations (for example, [2], p. 134) and the approximation theorem for absolute values (for example, [2], p. 136).

Where L is an algebraic extension of a field K, we shall say the topologies $\mathbf{U}_1$ and $\mathbf{U}_2$ on L are *conjugate* over K if there is an isomorphism of L over K which carries the open sets of $\mathbf{U}_1$ onto those of $\mathbf{U}_2$. A topology $\mathbf{U}$ on L is said to be an *extension* of a topology $\mathbf{T}$ on K if $\mathbf{T}$ is the topology induced by $\mathbf{U}$ on K.

Proposition 3.5. *If L is a finite algebraic extension of a field K and $\mathbf{T}$ is a type V topology on K, then the number of type V extensions $\mathbf{U}$ of $\mathbf{T}$ to L is bounded by $[L: K]$.*

Proposition 3.6. *If L is a normal extension of a field K and $\mathbf{T}$ is a type V topology on K, then the type V extensions $\mathbf{U}$ of $\mathbf{T}$ to L are conjugate.*

With the proposition on page *287* and Lemma 2.1, these two propositions are immediate consequences of similar statements that hold for valuation rings (see, for example, [2], pp. 141, 152).

4. **Fundamental Theorems**

Where $*K = *^I{}_{\mathbf{\Delta}} K$ is a fixed ultrapower of a set K and S is a subset of K, we may identify the ultrapower $*S = *^I{}_{\mathbf{\Delta}} S$ with the subset $\{^\star\mathbf{k} \in *K \mid \mathbf{k}(I) \subseteq S\}$ of $*K$. (This is a special case of the definition of the relations $*R$ discussed in the Preliminaries.) We use this identification for the following.

Definition. Where $*K = *^I{}_{\mathbf{\Delta}} K$ is an ultrapower of a set K, the *quasi-discrete* topology on $*K$ is the smallest topology containing all the sets $*S$, S a subset of K. (Again, we think of a topology as a collection of open sets.)

Note that since the ultrapower operation preserves complements, the basic open sets $*S$ are also closed.

A *partial function* (*group homomorphism, ring homomorphism*) from a set (group, ring) A is a function (group homomorphism, ring homomorphism) defined on a subset (subgroup, subring) of A. We shall use the symbol $\mapsto$ for partial function. Where $*K = *^I{}_{\mathbf{\Delta}} K$ is an ultrapower of a set K and $\mathbf{T}$ is a Hausdorff topology on K, we shall use $\mathrm{st}_{\mathbf{T}}$ to denote the partial function $*K \mapsto K$ defined by

$$\mathrm{st}_{\mathbf{T}}({}^{\star}\mathbf{k}) = a \text{ if and only if } \mathbf{k}[\mathbf{\Delta}] \text{ converges to } a.$$

Remarks. In the special case where $*K$ is an ultrapower of the real field K and $\mathbf{T}$ is the usual topology, $\mathrm{st}_{\mathbf{T}}$ is the *standard part* partial function of Robinson's nonstandard analysis ([9]; [10], pp. 224–270). Robinson uses arbitrary nonstandard models, whereas for the methods of this paper ultrapowers seem to be necessary. Let βK be the Stone–Čech compactification of a group, ring, or field K, regarded simply as a discrete space. Using the Wallman approach (see, for example, Gillman and Jerison [5]), we can think of βK as the set of ultrafilters on K. Then there is a natural map t: $*^{I}{}_{\mathbf{\Delta}}K \rightarrow \beta K$ defined by $t({}^{\star}\mathbf{k}) = \mathbf{k}[\mathbf{\Delta}]$. The map is onto βK exactly when $\mathbf{\Delta}$ is adequate for K, and the quasi-discrete topology turns out to be the t-inverse image of the Stone–Čech topology. A Hausdorff topology $\mathbf{T}$ on K determines a partial function $s_{\mathbf{T}}$ on βK by $s_{\mathbf{T}}(\mathbf{k}[\mathbf{\Delta}]) = a$ if and only if $\mathbf{k}[\mathbf{\Delta}]$ converges to a. The theorems of this section are concerned with the following diagram:

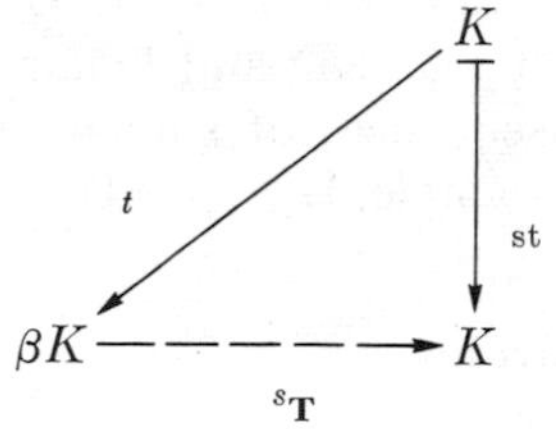

Given a partial function st, we wish to know if there is a well-behaved topology $\mathbf{T}$ for which the corresponding $s_{\mathbf{T}}$ makes the diagram commute.

It is difficult when K has algebraic structure to put corresponding structure on βK. In a sense, the central method of this paper is to replace βK by an approximation, $*K$, on which algebraic structure is easily defined, and to do with $*K$ things we wish we could do with βK.

Where φ is a function from L to K and $*$ denotes the ultrapower determined by a fixed ultrafilter $\mathbf{\Delta}$ on an index set I, the function $*\varphi$: $*L \rightarrow *K$ is defined by

$$\varphi({}^{\star}\mathbf{l}) = {}^{\star}(\varphi\mathbf{l}) \text{ for every } {}^{\star}\mathbf{l} \in *L.$$

***Lemma* 4.1.** *Let* $\mathbf{U}$ *be a Hausdorff topology on a set* L, *let* $\mathbf{T}$ *be a Hausdorff topology on a set* K, *and let* $* = *^{I}{}_{\mathbf{\Delta}}$, *where* $\mathbf{\Delta}$ *is adequate for* L. *Then a function* φ: $L \rightarrow K$ *is continuous with respect to* $\mathbf{U}$ *and* $\mathbf{T}$ *if and only if the* *composite partial functions* $\varphi\ \mathrm{st}_{\mathbf{U}}$ *and* $\mathrm{st}_{\mathbf{T}} *\varphi$ *are equal, that is, if and only if this diagram commutes:*

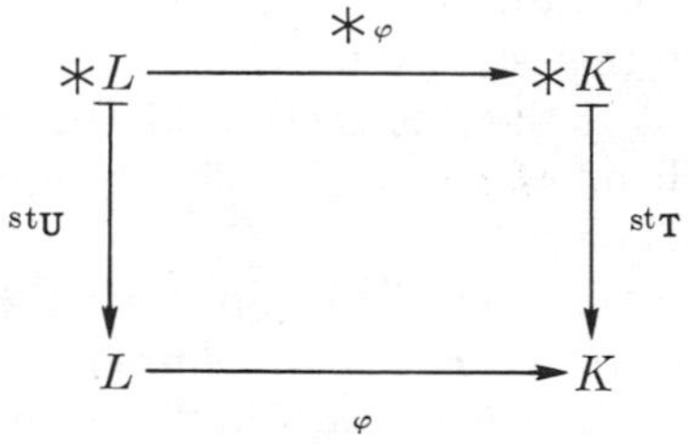

Proof. The function φ is continuous if and only if whenever a filter $\mathbf{\Psi}$ on L converges to an element l, then $\varphi[\mathbf{\Psi}]$ converges to $\varphi(l)$. Since every filter is the intersection of the ultrafilters that contain it, we need only look at the ultrafilters $\mathbf{\Psi} = \mathbf{l}[\mathbf{\Delta}]$, where ${}^\star\mathbf{l} = *L$.

In most of the applications which follow, K will be a group, ring, or field; L will be the Cartesian product $K \times K$; $\mathbf{U}$ will be the product topology; and φ will be one of the binary operations on K.

Where $*K$ is an ultrapower of a structure K, we shall say that a partial function st: $*K \mapsto K$ is *over* K if st is defined at least on K (embedded in K) and $\mathrm{st}(k) = k$ for every element k in K.

Theorem 4.2. *Let* $*K = *^I{}_{\mathbf{\Delta}}K$ *be an adequate ultrapower of a group* K. *If* $\mathbf{T}$ *is a Hausdorff group topology on* K, *then* $\mathrm{st}_{\mathbf{T}}$ *is a partial group homomorphism over* K *with quasi-discrete closed kernel. Conversely, if* st: $*K \mapsto K$ *is a partial group homomorphism over* K *with quasi-discrete closed kernel, then there is a Hausdorff group topology* $\mathbf{T}$ *on* K *with* $\mathrm{st} = \mathrm{st}_{\mathbf{T}}$. *Furthermore, where* $\mathbf{T}$ *is a Hausdorff group topology on* K *and* ${}^\star i$ *is the kernel of* $\mathrm{st}_{\mathbf{T}}$,

(a) *The neighborhood filter of the identity of* K *is* $\bigcap \{\mathbf{k}[\mathbf{\Delta}] \mid {}^\star\mathbf{k} \in {}^\star i\}$.
(b) *The closure of a subset* S *of* K *is the set* $\mathrm{st}_{\mathbf{T}}(*S \cap \mathrm{Dom}(\mathrm{st}_{\mathbf{T}}))$.

Remark. The lemma sets up a one-to-one correspondence between the Hausdorff group topologies $\mathbf{T}$ on K and the quasi-discrete closed subgroups ${}^\star i$ of $*K$ which are normal in the subgroup of $*K$ generated by ${}^\star i$ and K. It can be shown that the correspondence is natural in the sense of Eilenberg and MacLane [3].

Proof. Let $*K = *^I{}_{\mathbf{\Delta}}K$ be an adequate ultrapower of the group K. With a view to the applications which follow, we write K as an additive group, although we shall not use commutativity. Let $\mathbf{T}$ be a Hausdorff group topology on K. The addition and subtraction are continuous with respect to $\mathbf{T}$; hence if $\mathbf{k}_1[\mathbf{\Delta}]$ converges to a_1 and $\mathbf{k}_2[\mathbf{\Delta}]$ converges to a_2, then $(\mathbf{k}_1 + \mathbf{k}_2)[\mathbf{\Delta}]$ converges to $a_1 + a_2$ and $(k_1 - k_2)[\mathbf{\Delta}]$ converges to $a_1 - a_2$. From this it is immediate that $\mathrm{st}_{\mathbf{T}}$ is a partial group homomorphism. For every constant function $k: I \to K$, the principal ultrafilter $k[\mathbf{\Delta}]$ converges to k, so that $\mathrm{st}_{\mathbf{T}}$ is over K. And the kernel of $\mathrm{st}_{\mathbf{T}}$ is quasi-discrete closed, since it is the intersection of the basic open-closed sets $*N$, N a $\mathbf{T}$-neighborhood of zero in K. This completes the proof of the first assertion of the lemma.

The converse will take longer. To begin, let st: $*K \mapsto K$ be a partial group homomorphism over K. For S any subset of K let $S' = \mathrm{st}(*S \cap \mathrm{Dom(st)})$. Call a subset C of K *closed* if and only if $C' = C$. Straightforward checking shows that this defines a topology on K, which we label $\mathbf{T}$. Note that for every $k \in K$ we have $*\{k\} = \{k\}$ and $\mathrm{st}(\{k\}) = \{k\}$, so that singleton sets are closed: $\mathbf{T}$ is a $T - 1$ topology. The next eight claims lead us to the point where we can apply Lemma 4.1 to show that $\mathbf{T}$ is a group topology.

Where there is no other indication, the words "convergence," "neighborhood," and "open" refer to $\mathbf{T}$.

1. If $\mathrm{st}(^\star\mathbf{k}) = a$, then $\mathbf{k}[\mathbf{\Delta}]$ converges to a. For if $\mathrm{st}(^\star\mathbf{k}) = a$, then for any closed set C which excludes a, $^\star\mathbf{k} \not\in *C$ (since $C = C'$) and $C \not\in \mathbf{k}[\mathbf{\Delta}]$; hence the ultrafilter $\mathbf{k}[\mathbf{\Delta}]$ contains the complement of C. Therefore, $\mathbf{k}[\mathbf{\Delta}]$ contains every open neighborhood of a.

For every a in K let $\mathbf{N}_a$ denote the neighborhood filter of a and let $\mathbf{B}_a = \bigcap \{\mathbf{k}[\mathbf{\Delta}] \mid \mathrm{st}(^\star\mathbf{k}) = a\}$. By Claim 1, $\mathbf{B}_a$ contains $\mathbf{N}_a$.

2. A subset S of K is open if and only if $S \in \mathbf{B}_a$ for every element a of S. For if S is open, then $S \in \mathbf{N}_a \subseteq \mathbf{B}_a$ for every a in S. Conversely, if $S \in \mathbf{B}_a$ for every a in S, let C be the complement of S. If we had $^\star\mathbf{k} \in *C$ and $\mathrm{st}(^\star\mathbf{k}) = b$ in S for some $^\star\mathbf{k}$, then $S \in \mathbf{B}_b$; hence $S \in \mathbf{k}[\mathbf{\Delta}]$. But $^\star\mathbf{k} \in *C$ if and only if $C \in \mathbf{k}[\mathbf{\Delta}]$; that is, we should have both C and S in the proper filter $\mathbf{k}[\mathbf{\Delta}]$, a contradiction. From this it follows that $C' \subseteq C$ and, since st is over K, $C' = C$, S is open.

3. For every a in K, $\mathbf{B}_a = \mathbf{B}_0 + a$. This follows from the fact that st is a group homomorphism.

Now let $^\star i$ be the kernel of st and assume that $^\star i$ is quasi-discrete closed.

4. For every $^\star\mathbf{k} \in *K$, $^\star\mathbf{k} \in {}^\star i$ if and only if $\mathbf{B}_0 \subseteq \mathbf{k}[\mathbf{\Delta}]$. For if $^\star i$ is quasi-discrete closed, then there is a collection $\mathbf{D}$ of subsets D of K with $^\star i = \bigcap_{\mathbf{D}} *D$. That is, $^\star\mathbf{k} \in {}^\star i$ if and only if $D \in \mathbf{k}[\mathbf{\Delta}]$ for every D in $\mathbf{D}$. Then $\mathbf{D} \subseteq \mathbf{B}_0$. Hence $\mathbf{B}_0 \subseteq \mathbf{k}[\mathbf{\Delta}]$ implies $^\star\mathbf{k} \in {}^\star i$. The converse is immediate from the definition of $\mathbf{B}_0$.

5. For $a \neq b$, $\mathbf{B}_a$ and $\mathbf{B}_b$ contain disjoint sets. Suppose the contrary, that $a \neq b$ and $\mathbf{B}_a$ and $\mathbf{B}_b$ contain no disjoint sets. Then $\mathbf{B}_a \cup \mathbf{B}_b$ generates a proper filter, contained in some $\mathbf{k}[\mathbf{\Delta}]$ (since $\mathbf{\Delta}$ is adequate), and by the preceding claim we should have $\mathrm{st}(^\star\mathbf{k}) = a = b$.

6. For every subset S of K, $S'' = S'$ and therefore S' is the closure of S. (This is not immediate from the definition of $\mathbf{T}$. At this point in the proof it is perhaps still conceivable that the closure of a set S may be the union of a nontrivial ascending chain S', $S''S'''$, $\cdots$). Since st is over K we always have $S \subseteq S'$. To show containment the other way, let $a \in S''$, for an arbitrary subset S of K. Then for some ${}^\star\mathbf{b} \in *S'$ we have $\text{st}({}^\star\mathbf{b}) = a$. Without loss of generality we may assume that the image $\mathbf{b}(I)$ is contained in S'. Then for every $\iota \in I$ there is some ${}^\star\boldsymbol{c}_\iota \in *S$ with $\text{st}({}^\star\boldsymbol{c}_\iota) = \mathbf{b}(\iota)$. And we may assume that each $\boldsymbol{c}_\iota$ has image contained in S. Then the ultrafilter $\mathbf{b}[\boldsymbol{\Delta}]$ contains $\mathbf{B}_0 + a$, and for every $B \in \mathbf{B}_0$ for some $\Delta \in \boldsymbol{\Delta}$ we have $\mathbf{b}(\Delta) \subseteq B + a$. Similarly, for every $\iota \in I$ and every $B \in \mathbf{B}_0$ there is a $\Delta \in \boldsymbol{\Delta}$ with $\boldsymbol{c}_\iota(\Delta) \subseteq B + \mathbf{b}(\iota)$. For each B in $\mathbf{B}_0$ let

$$H(B) = \{\boldsymbol{c}_\iota(\eta) \mid \mathbf{b}(\iota) \in B + a \text{ and } \boldsymbol{c}_\iota(\eta) \in B + \mathbf{b}(\iota);\ \iota, \eta \in I\}.$$

The sets $H(B)$, $B \in \mathbf{B}_0$, generate a proper filter on K. Let $\mathbf{k}[\boldsymbol{\Delta}]$ be an ultrafilter which contains every $H(B)$, $B \in \mathbf{B}_0$. (Again we have used the fact that $\boldsymbol{\Delta}$ is adequate.) Then for every $B \in \mathbf{B}_0$ there is a $\Delta \in \boldsymbol{\Delta}$ with $\mathbf{k}(\iota) - \mathbf{b}(\iota) \in (B + \mathbf{b}(\iota)) - \mathbf{b}(\iota) = B$. (At this point the method breaks down if we try to apply it to semigroups.) Now it is easy to show that $\text{st}({}^\star\mathbf{k}) = a$. Since the image of $\mathbf{k}$ is in S, we have ${}^\star\mathbf{k} \in *S$, and $a \in S'$—which establishes the claim.

7. For every $a \in K$, $\mathbf{B}_a = \mathbf{N}_a$; hence $\mathbf{T}$ is Hausdorff and $\text{st} = \text{st}_{\mathbf{T}}$. For suppose we do not have $\mathbf{B}_a \subseteq \mathbf{N}_a$. Then some B in $\mathbf{B}_a$ contains no neighborhood of a, and a is in the closure of the complement of B. Let S be the complement of B. By Claim 6 there is some ${}^\star\mathbf{k} \in *S$ with $\text{st}({}^\star\mathbf{k}) = a$. But then $S \in \mathbf{k}[\boldsymbol{\Delta}]$, which contradicts the definition of $\mathbf{B}_a$. With Claims 1, 4, and 5, this establishes 7.

Employing the natural identification of $*(K \times K)$ with $(*K) \times (*K)$, let $\text{st} \times \text{st}\colon *(K \times K) \mapsto K \times K$ be the Cartesian product partial function. Again, straightforward checking shows that we obtain a topology $\mathbf{U}$ on $K \times K$ if we call a subset M *closed* when $M = M' = \text{st} \times \text{st}\ (*M \cap \text{Dom}(\text{st} \times \text{st}))$. For a and b in K let $\mathbf{B}_{a,b} = \bigcap \{(\mathbf{k} \times \mathbf{l})[\boldsymbol{\Delta}] \mid \text{st}({}^\star\mathbf{k}) = a \text{ and } \text{st}({}^\star\mathbf{l}) = b\}$. Then a subset U of $K \times K$ is open in $\mathbf{U}$ if and only if $\langle a, b\rangle \in U$ implies $U \in \mathbf{B}_{a,b}$. (The proof is just as for Claim 2.)

8. $\mathbf{U}$ is the product topology on $K \times K$ determined by $\mathbf{T}$ on K. For a filter converges in a product space if and only if its projections converge in the component spaces. Therefore, applying Claim 7 we have for every $a,b \in K$, $\mathbf{B}_{a,b} = \bigcap \{(\mathbf{k} \times \mathbf{l})[\boldsymbol{\Delta}] \mid (\mathbf{k} \times \mathbf{l})[\boldsymbol{\Delta}]$ converges to $\langle a, b\rangle$ in the product topology$\}$ = the product topology neighborhood filter of $\langle a, b\rangle$.

9. $\mathbf{T}$ is a group topology on K. For since st is a partial group homomorphism, this diagram commutes when we let φ be addition or subtrac-

tion in K:

$$\begin{array}{ccc} *(K \times K) = (*K) \times (*K) & \xrightarrow{\;*\varphi\;} & *K \\ \Big\downarrow{\scriptstyle \mathrm{st} \times \mathrm{st}} & & \Big\downarrow{\scriptstyle \mathrm{st}} \\ K \times K & \xrightarrow{\;\varphi\;} & K \end{array}$$

Hence by Lemma 2.1, addition and subtraction are continuous with respect to **T**.

Straightforward checking shows that when we begin with a Hausdorff group topology **T** on K and associated partial function $\mathrm{st}_{\mathbf{T}}$, if we define a subset S of K to be *closed* if $S = S' = \mathrm{st}_{\mathbf{T}}\,(*S \cap \mathrm{Dom}(\mathrm{st}_{\mathbf{T}}))$, then we recover the topology **T**. Consequently, in Claims 7 and 6 we have already verified the assertions (a) and (b) of the theorem, and our proof of the theorem is complete.

Let an *algebra*, for the moment, be a set K together with a collection of operations (unary, binary, ternary, or n-ary) which are everywhere defined. Then an *equational class* is a class of all algebras for which the operations satisfy some given set of equations. It is not difficult to see that the methods of Theorem 4.2 will apply to any equational class for which the members are groups with respect to one of the operations. For example,

Theorem 4.3. *Let* $*K$ *be an adequate ultrapower of a ring* K *and let* **T** *be a Hausdorff ring topology on* K. *Then* $\mathrm{st}_{\mathbf{T}}$ *is a partial ring homomorphism over* K *with quasi-discrete closed kernel. Conversely, if* $\mathrm{st}\colon *K \mapsto K$ *is a partial ring homomorphism with quasi-discrete closed kernel, then there is a ring topology* **T** *on* K *with* $\mathrm{st} = \mathrm{st}_{\mathbf{T}}$.

We omit the straightforward proof.

The class of fields is not an equational class, since the function $a \to a^{-1}$ is not everywhere defined. We have, however, the following proposition. By *local ring* we mean ring with unique maximal ideal.

Theorem 4.4. *Let* $*K = *^I{}_{\Delta}K$ *be an adequate ultrapower of a field* K *and let* **T** *be a Hausdorff ring topology on* K. *Then*

(a) **T** *is a field topology if and only if the domain of* $\mathrm{st}_{\mathbf{T}}$ *is a local ring.*
(b) **T** *is a type V topology if and only if the kernel of* $\mathrm{st}_{\mathbf{T}}$ *is the maximal ideal of a valuation ring in* K.

[The valuation ring in (b) need not be $\mathrm{Dom}(\mathrm{st}_{\mathbf{T}})$. In fact, it can be shown that $\mathrm{Dom}(\mathrm{st}_{\mathbf{T}})$ is a valuation ring in $*K$ if and only if **T** makes K locally compact.]

Proof. (a) Lemma 4.1 continues to hold if we let φ be a partial function, if by continuity we mean continuity on the domain of φ. Let $\varphi(a) = a^{-1}$ for every nonzero a in K. Then the diagram of Lemma 4.1 commutes if and only if whenever $^\star\mathbf{k} \in \mathrm{Dom}(\mathrm{st}_\mathbf{T})$ and $\mathrm{st}(^\star\mathbf{k}) \neq 0$, then $^\star\mathbf{k}^{-1} \in \mathrm{Dom}(\mathrm{st}_\mathbf{T})$. That is, if and only if all the noninfinitesimal elements of $\mathrm{Dom}(\mathrm{st}_\mathbf{T})$ are units in $\mathrm{Dom}(\mathrm{st}_\mathbf{T})$.

(b) In one direction this is Lemma 2.1. To go the other way, by Proposition 3.1, we have only to show that if $^\star i = \mathrm{Ker}(\mathrm{st}_\mathbf{T})$ is the maximal ideal of a valuation ring, then $\mathbf{T}$ is a type V topology. Let B and C be subsets of K which are bounded away from zero, and let $^\star i = \mathrm{Ker}(\mathrm{st}_\mathbf{T})$ be the maximal ideal of the valuation ring $^\star A$ in $*K$. Then if $B \in \mathbf{b}[\boldsymbol{\Delta}]$ and $C \in \mathbf{c}[\boldsymbol{\Delta}]$, $\mathbf{b}[\boldsymbol{\Delta}]$ and $\mathbf{c}[\boldsymbol{\Delta}]$ cannot converge to zero: $^\star\mathbf{b} \notin {}^\star i$ and $^\star\mathbf{c} \notin {}^\star i$. Then $^\star\mathbf{b}^{-1}$ and $^\star\mathbf{c}^{-1}$ are elements of $^\star A$. Therefore, $^\star\mathbf{b}^{-1} \cdot {}^\star\mathbf{c}^{-1} \in {}^\star A$ and $\mathbf{b} \cdot \mathbf{c}[\boldsymbol{\Delta}]$ does not converge to zero. From this we obtain that $B \cdot C$ is bounded away from zero: $\mathbf{T}$ is of type V.

References

1. J. AX AND S. KOCHEN, Diophantine Problems over Local Fields, *Am. J. Math. 87* (1965), 605–630, 631–698.
2. N. BOURBAKI, *Algèbre Commutative.* Paris: Hermann, 1964, Chap. 6.
3. S. EILENBERG AND S. MACLANE, General Theory of Natural Equivalences, *Trans. Am. Math. Soc. 58* (1945), 231–294.
4. T. FRAYNE, A. MOREL, AND D. SCOTT, Reduced Direct Products, *Fundamenta Math. 51* (1962), 195–226.
5. L. GILLMAN AND M. JERISON, *Rings of Continuous Functions.* Princeton, N.J.: Van Nostrand, 1960.
6. I. KAPLANSKY, a. Topological Methods in Valuation Theory, *Duke Math. J., 14* (1947), 527–541; b. Topological Rings, *Bull. Am. Math. Soc. 54* (1948), 809–826; c. Polynomials in Topological Fields, *Bull. Am. Math. Soc. 54* (1948), 909–926.
7. J. LOS, Quelques remarques, théorèmes et problèmes sur les classes définissables d'algèbres, in Skolem, et al., *Mathematical Interpretations of Formal Systems.* Amsterdam: North-Holland, 1955.
8. S. KOCHEN, Ultraproducts in the Theory of Models, *Ann. Math. 74* (1961), 221–261.
9. A. ROBINSON, Non-Standard Analysis, *Indagationes Math. 23* (1961), 432–440.
10. A. ROBINSON, *Introduction to Model Theory and the Metamathematics of Algebra.* Amsterdam: North-Holland, 1963.
11. A. ROBINSON, *Non-Standard Analysis* (Studies in Logic and the Foundations of Mathematics). Amsterdam: North-Holland, 1966.
12. A. ZARISKI AND P. SAMUEL, *Commutative Algebra*, Vol. II. Princeton, N.J.: Van Nostrand, 1960.

k-Fold Preordered Sets

by J. L. B. COOPER

1. Introduction

The question of finding criteria which guarantee that a preordered set has an order-preserving map to the real numbers occurs in a number of contexts, for instance, in the study of measurement of subjective probability and of preferences: In the article [1] on the foundations of thermodynamics, criteria depending on topological properties of the space and of the ordering are given. Such a map is possible only for a linear preorder of states of a thermodynamic system if the system does not contain thermally insulated parts. The thermodynamic problem suggests the question of finding criteria in order that a preorder be generated by k entropies, that is, by an order-preserving map to R^k; the problem of ordering preferences suggests an analogous problem, when preferences of incomparable objects are involved. This problem will be discussed here. To begin with, we shall give a purely combinatorial criterion which results in a proof of existence of an order-preserving map to a nonstandard model of R^k (or, equally, of N^k). Next criteria will be given, in terms of composition of systems, for the mapping to be additive. Finally, topological criteria are given for a mapping to be a product of k continuous linear mappings, and, as a consequence, a criterion for the existence of an order-preserving map to R^k is found.

Notation. A preorder on a set S means a transitive relationship, which will be denoted by the symbol $\rightarrow$. If $x \rightarrow y$ and $y \rightarrow x$ both hold, we write $x \sim y$. If $x \rightarrow y$, but $y \rightarrow x$ is false, we write $x > y$. $x \geq y$, as usual, means that either $x > y$ or $x = y$: $\geq$ is a partial order; and $<$ or $\leq$ are used correspondingly in the usual way.

A preorder $\rightarrow$ is *linear* if for any x, y in S at least one of $x \rightarrow y$ or $y \rightarrow x$ must hold.

Generalizing this, we shall say that a preorder $\rightarrow$ on S is *k-fold* if for any finite subset of S there are k linear preorders, $\rightarrow(1), \rightarrow(2), \cdots \rightarrow(k)$ such that for x, y in $x \rightarrow y$ if and only if $x \rightarrow (r)y$ for $r = 1, 2, \cdots, k$.

An example of a k-fold preorder is the standard partial order on R^k: $x \geq y$ if and only if $x_r \geq y_r$ for $r = 1, 2, \cdots, k$.

In this case the criterion given in the definition applies to the whole of S, not merely to the finite parts, if $x \rightarrow (r)y$ is read $x \geq y$. This is not true for the preorder of R^k defined by

$$x \geq (\text{st})y \text{ if } x_r > y_r \text{ for } r = 1, 2, \cdots, k \text{ or if } x = y.$$

2. A Characterization of k-Fold Preorders

Theorem 1. *If $\rightarrow$ is a k-fold preorder, on a set S, S has an order-preserving map to a nonstandard model of R^k (or of N^k). $\rightarrow$ is the product of the k linear preorders generated by the projections of this map.*

Any finite subset σ of S has an order-preserving map to N^k: that one which x maps into $(n_1, n_2, \cdots, n_k)$ if n_r is the number of distinct classes of elements equivalent for the relationship $a \sim (r)b$ all of whose elements satisfy $a \rightarrow (r)x$. Let M be the set of all order-preserving maps of finite subsets S to N^k, and let M_σ be the set of maps whose domains contain σ. Then M_σ is a filter base on M: $M_{\sigma_1} \cap M_{\sigma_2} = M_{\sigma_1 \cup \sigma_2}$. Let $\mathfrak{U}$ be an ultrafilter on M which is finer than M_σ, and let $^*N^k = (N^k)^M/\mathfrak{U}$; that is, $^*N^k$ consists of classes of maps from M to N^k, each class consisting of a set of maps any two of which are equal on some set of $\mathfrak{U}$.

$^*N^k$ is a nonstandard model of N^k, and hence, since N^k has a k-fold partial order, so has $^*N^k$. Indeed, if $f,g \in {^*N^k}$ and $F \in f$, $G \in g$, then if F_r, G_r denote the rth projections of these maps, one or the other of the sets of ψ for which

$$F_r(\psi) > G_r(\psi), \qquad F_r(\psi) = G_r(\psi), \qquad F_r(\psi) < G_r(\psi)$$

is in $\mathfrak{U}$. If the first is in $\mathfrak{U}$ we write $f^* > (r)g$ and the k linear preorders so defined induce as their product a k-fold partial order in $^*N^k$ which we designate $^*\geq$.

For any $x \in S$ define $F(x) \in (N^k)^M$ by

$$\begin{aligned} F(x)(\psi) &= \psi(x) \qquad \text{if } \psi \in M_{\{x\}} \\ &= a \qquad \text{otherwise,} \end{aligned}$$

where a is a fixed element of N^k. The class in $^*N^k$ containing $F(x)$ is independent of a; call it $\phi(x)$.

The relation $\phi(x) \; ^*\geq (r)\phi(y)$ is a linear preorder in S; write it $x \geq (r)y$.

Now, if $x \to y$, then for any $\psi \in M_{\{x,y\}}$ and any r, $\psi_r^{(x)} \geq \psi_r(y)$ so that

$$\text{(1)} \qquad \{\psi : F_r(x)(\psi) \geq F_r(y)(\psi)\} \supset M_{\{x,y\}} \in \mathfrak{U}.$$

Consequently, $\varphi(x) \mathbin{*}\!\geq (r)\phi(y)$ and hence $x \to (r)y$. Conversely, if $x \geq (r)y$ for all r, then (1) holds, so that $\psi_r(x) \geq \psi_r(y)$ for all ψ in a set $U \in \mathfrak{U}$. U can be chosen so that it contains $M_{\{x,y\}}$ and then, because ψ is order-preserving, it follows that $x \to y$.

This proves the theorem. As an immediate corollary we find:

If S is any set with a k-fold preorder, then there is a nonstandard model of N^k which contains a set order isomorphic with S.

Even quite simple k-fold orders require nonstandard models of N^k, or of R^k, for their realization. An example is the partial order on R^k, $x \geq (\text{st})y$.

This partial order cannot be realized by any order-preserving map onto R^k with its standard order. If η is an infinitesimal in a nonstandard model $^*R$, with $\eta > 0$, the order is realized by the map $(x_r) \to (x_r + \eta \sum_1^k x_s)$.

3. Additivity of Ordering Functions

In thermodynamics and in other applications it is important to investigate order-preserving maps with certain additivity properties. We shall discuss these here in terms of a natural situation in which systems can be brought together to form larger systems. A physical model for the composition of k-fold ordered systems in thermodynamics is as follows. Each individual system consists of simple thermodynamic systems (for example, gases) interacting dynamically but thermally insulated, say $A_1, A_2, \cdots, A_k$. A composed system is formed by bringing together n such systems in such a way that all the systems $A_r^1, A_r^2, \cdots, A_r^n$, for any one r, interact thermally. The problem then is to define the order-preserving function so that it is additive for composed systems.

Definitions. Two preordered sets are isomorphic if they have a one-to-one order-preserving mapping.

We now go on to the definition of composition. The definition will be restricted to isomorphic sets, which is sufficient for the present discussion: Once the existence of an additive mapping is proved for compositions of isomorphic sets, the extension to nonisomorphic sets is not difficult. Note that the definition of a composition given below involves, essentially, an induction on the number of systems involved.

Let $S_1, S_2, \cdots, S_n$ be n k-fold preordered isomorphic sets. Their composition $[S_1, S_2, \cdots, S_n]$ is a k-fold preordered set with the following properties:

(a) There is a one-to-one map of $S_1 \times S_2 \times \cdots \times S_n$ onto $[S_1, S_2, \cdots, S_n]$; we write $[s_1, s_2, \cdots, s_n]$ for the element corresponding to $(s_1, s_2, \cdots, s_n)$.

(b) If $s_r \rightarrow t_r$ for each r, then $[s_1, s_2, \cdots, s_r] \rightarrow [t_1, t_2, \cdots, t_r]$.

(c) If $[s_1, \cdots, s_{r-1}, s_r, s_{r+1}, \cdots, s_n] \rightarrow [s_1, s_2, \cdots, s_{r-1}, t_r, s_{r+1}, \cdots, s_n]$, then $s_r \rightarrow t_r$.

(d) If $(t_1, \cdots, t_n)$ is a permutation of $(s_1, \cdots, s_n)$ [more precisely, if there is a permutation π of $(1, 2, \cdots, n)$ such that, for each r, $t_{\pi(r)}$ is the element corresponding to s_r in the isomorphism of S_r to $s_{\pi(r)}$], then

$$[t_1, t_2, \cdots, t_n] \sim [s_1, s_2, \cdots, s_n].$$

(e) If the set $S_1, \cdots, S_n$ is partitioned into subsets $\{A_1, \cdots, A_r\}$, $\{B_1, \cdots, B_{n-r}\}$, then each of these subsystems has a composition $[A_1, \cdots, A_r]$, $[B_1, \cdots, B_{n-r}]$ and $[S_1, \cdots, S_n]$ is isomorphic in the natural correspondence to the composition of these two compositions. In particular, this means that if

$$[a_1, a_2, \cdots, a_r] \rightarrow [b_1, b_2, \cdots, b_r],$$
$$[a_1, a_2, \cdots, a_r] \rightarrow [a'_1, \cdots, a'_r],\ [b_1, \cdots, b_{n-r}] \rightarrow [b'_1, \cdots, b'_{n-r}],$$

then $$[a_1, a_2, \cdots, a_r b_1, b_2, \cdots, b_{n-r}] \rightarrow [a'_1, \cdots, a'_r, b'_1, \cdots, b'_{n-r}],$$

with a corresponding extension of c.

We now prove the following theorem.

***Theorem* 2.** *If a k-fold ordered set S is such that, for any n, the composition of n systems isomorphic to S exists, then there is an order-preserving map of S to a nonstandard model of R^k such that, for any n,*

$$[a_1, a_2, \cdots, a_n] \rightarrow [b_1, b_2, \cdots, b_n]$$

if and only if $\phi(a_1) + \cdots \phi(a_n) \geq \phi(b_1) + \cdots + \phi(b_n)$.

We begin by showing that such a map exists for any finite subset σ of S.

A mapping to a nonstandard model of R^k is additive and order-preserving for the preorder if for each r the rth component is additive and order-preserving for the rth linear preorder. It is therefore sufficient to prove the theorem on the hypothesis that the preorder on σ is linear.

In that case, there must be a minimal element, say a_0, for the preorder.

Let us say that a is comparable with b and that $m/n > [a{:}\,b] > p/q$

if there exist positive standard integers m, n, p, q such that

$$[n[a_0], m[b]] \rightarrow [m[a_0], n[a]], \; [p[a_0], q[a]] \rightarrow [q[a_0], p[b]],$$

where the symbol $[n[a], m[b]]$ stands for an element of the $m + n$-fold composition consisting of n repetitions of a and m of b.

Let a_1 be a minimal element among the elements not equivalent to a_0. Let a_2 be minimal among the elements not comparable to a_1 and a_3 minimal among those not comparable to a_1 or a_2, and so on.

Assign to a_1 the number 1, to a_p the number ω^{p-1} where ω is an infinite real number; and if a is comparable to a_{p+1}, assign to it the number $x\omega^p$, where

$$x = \inf \left\{\frac{m}{n} : \frac{m}{n} > [a : a_{p+1}]\right\}.$$

It is not difficult to see that this construction follows, for each set of comparable elements, the procedure of the classical construction (essentially that of Eudoxus) for lengths of lines: and that the assignment is additive: If $\phi(a)$ designates the number assigned to a, then $[a, b] \rightarrow [c, d]$ if and only if $\phi(a) + \phi(b) \geq \phi(c) + \phi(d)$, and similarly for compositions involving more than two elements.

This argument establishes the existence of additive maps to a nonstandard model of R^k, including some infinite elements, for any finite set $\sigma \in S$. If M_σ denotes the set of maps which include σ in their domain, we can proceed as in the proof of Theorem 1: Similar arguments then prove the existence of a map additive over the whole of S whose image is in some nonstandard model of R^k.

4. Orderings of Topological Spaces

In any preordered set S a topology can be defined in terms of the preorder, taking as basis of open sets the open intervals, that is, the sets which have one or other of the forms

$$]a, b[\; = \{x : b > x > a\} \;]\rightarrow, a[\; = x : a > x\},$$
$$]a, >[\; = \{x : x > a\}.$$

We call this topology the interval topology, and write $\{S, >\}$ for the corresponding topological space.

If S has a topology T, we say that the preorder $\rightarrow$ is continuous at a in T if the identity map is continuous on (S, T) to $(S, >)$ at a and that it is continuous if it is continuous everywhere.

In what follows, we adopt the notation that if sets A, B are such that for all $a \in A$, $b \in B$ $a \rightarrow b$ or $a > b$ holds, then we write $A \rightarrow B$ or $A > B$, respectively; and also write $a \rightarrow B$, $A \rightarrow b$, and so on.

***Theorem* 3.** *In order that $\rightarrow$ be continuous it is necessary and sufficient that for each a, b such that $a > b$ there are neighborhoods $N(a)$, $N(b)$ of a and b, respectively, which are such that*

$$N(a) > b \text{ and } a > N(b). \tag{1}$$

If this holds, then $N(a)$, $N(b)$ can be chosen so that

$$N(a) > N(b). \tag{2}$$

An equivalent condition is that in any nonstandard extension of E the $a > b$ implies that $\mu(a) > \mu(b)$, where $\mu(a)$ is the monad of a.

Suppose that $\rightarrow$ is continuous and that $a > b$. If there is a c such that $a > c > b$, then $N(a) =]>, c[$, $N(b) =]c, >[$ are neighborhoods of a and b, respectively, for T which satisfy (2) and so (1). If there is no such c, $N(a) =]>, b[$, $N(b) =]a, >[$ are disjoint and open in T and satisfy (2).

Now suppose that (1) holds. If $a > c$ there is a neighborhood $N_a(c)$ of c such that $a > N_a(c)$; and if $c > b$, there is a neighborhood $N_b(c)$ such that $N_b(c) > b$. It follows that the intervals defining the $>$ topology are open in T, and so that $\rightarrow$ is continuous; and then (2) follows from the argument above.

The relation (2) must imply that $^*N(a) > {}^*N(b)$ for the extensions of $N(a)$ and $N(b)$ and it follows that $\mu(a) > \mu(b)$. The converse follows similarly.

Corollary. *$\rightarrow$ is continuous at a if whenever $c > a > b$ there is a neighborhood $N(a)$ of a such that $c > N(a) > b$.*

We shall now consider the problem of when a k-fold ordering is generated by k continuous linear preorders.

Definition. A point a is r-separated for a k-fold preorder $\rightarrow$ if, whenever $a \rightarrow (r)b$, there exists b' such that $a \rightarrow b' \geq b$ and $a \rightarrow (r)b' \geq (r)b$, and if whenever $c \rightarrow (r)a$, there exists c' such that $c \geq c' \rightarrow a$ and $c \geq (r)c' \rightarrow a$.

***Theorem* 4.** *If the preorder $\rightarrow$ is continuous and r-separated at a, then $\rightarrow(r)$ is continuous at a.*

A k-fold continuous preorder for which all points are r-separated for all r is a product of k continuous linear preorders.

If a b exists as in the definition, choose the corresponding b'. Because of the continuity of $\rightarrow$ there is a neighborhood of a, $N(a)$ say, such that $N(a) > b'$ and so $N(a) > (r)b' > (r)b$ holds. With the corresponding result for $c \rightarrow (r)a$, we find that any open interval for the rth ordering which contains a also contains some neighborhood of a: and hence the rth ordering is continuous at a. If no b with the properties specified in the definition exists, we need consider only r intervals of the form $]>, c[$, where $c > a$; and if neither b nor c exists, the only open r-interval containing a is the entire space.

The second part follows immediately since, if all points are regular for all r, all the linear preorders involved are continuous.

The significance of the requirement that points be r-separated is illustrated by the following counterexample. Let the square $|x_1| \leq 1$, $|x_2| \leq 1$ in the (x_1, x_2)-plane be ordered as follows: Let each of the sets $A = \{(x_1, x_2): x_1 + x_2 \leq 0\}$, $B = \{(x_1, x_2): x_1 + x_2 \leq 0\}$ be ordered by the strict ordering of R^2, and let $B > A$. This ordering is continuous, and is the product of the linear orderings induced by mapping the square into R^2, with the strict ordering of R^2, so that (x_1, x_2) goes into (x_2, x_2) in A and into $(x_1 + 2, x_2 + 2)$ if in B. The two linear preorders are discontinuous at any point of the line $x_1 + x_2 = 0$; and this is due to the fact that the preorder is not separated at these points.

Although the separation condition in this theorem cannot be relaxed, the continuity condition can be weakened; and this is important since the standard ordering of R^k is not itself continuous. We shall now discuss a wider class of orders on a topological space.

Definition. If $\rightarrow$ is a preorder on a topological space S, the corresponding partial order, and if G is the graph of $>$, then $\rightarrow$ and $>$ will be said to be compatible with the topology if $\overline{G^0} \supset G$, where, as usual, G^0 is the interior of G in $S \times S$.

The condition that $a,b \in G$ is that, in every nonstandard extension of $S, \mu(a) > \mu(b)$. Since $\mu(a) > \mu(b)$ and $\mu(b) > \mu(c)$ imply that $\mu(a) > \mu(c)$, G^0 is the graph of a preorder; and since $a,b \in G^0$ and $b,a \in G^0$ imply that both points are in G and this is impossible, G is the graph of a strict partial order. We write this ${}^0\!>$.

$a \,{}^0\!> b$ if and only if there are open neighborhoods $N(a)$, $N(b)$ of a and b such that $N(a) > N(b)$: and if $x \in N(a)$ and $y \in N(b)$ it follows that $x \,{}^0\!> y$; thus G^0 is a continuous order.

From these considerations, and the last theorem, we can deduce the following theorem.

Theorem 5. *If a k-fold preorder $\rightarrow$ on a topological space is compatible with the topology, and all points are r-separated for $r = 1, 2, \cdots, k$, then there exist k continuous linear preorders $\rightarrow(r)$, $r = 1, 2, \cdots, k$, such that if H is the graph of the relation $x > (r)y$, $r = 1, 2, \cdots, k$ and G is the graph of $x > y$, then $H = G^0$, $\bar{H} \supset G$.*

In particular, if the preorder is closed, then there are k continuous linear preorders which have $\rightarrow$ as their product; that is,

$$x \rightarrow y \text{ if and only if } x \geq (r)y \text{ for } r = 1, 2, \cdots, k$$

Here, following Nachbin [2], we say that a preorder is closed if its graph is closed.

Finally, combining these results with those of [1], we find:

Theorem 6. *Let $\rightarrow$ be a preorder on a Hausdorff space which is separable (that is, equal to the closure of some sequence of points in it). Let all points of the space be r-separable for all r. Then if $\rightarrow$ is continuous, there are k continuous functions $\phi_1, \phi_2, \cdots, \phi_k$ on the space to the real line such that*

$$x \rightarrow y \text{ if } \phi_r(x) > \phi_r(y) \text{ for } r = 1, 2, \cdots, k,$$

and if $\rightarrow$ is closed and compatible with the topology, $\varphi_i \cdots \varphi_k$ can be found so that

$$x \rightarrow y \text{ if and only if } \phi_r(x) \geq \phi_r(y) \text{ for } r = 1, 2, \cdots, k.$$

References

1. J. L. B. COOPER, The Foundations of Thermodynamics, *J. Math. Anal. Appl.* *17* (1967), 172–193.
2. L. NACHBIN, *Topology and Order*. Princeton, N.J.: Van Nostrand, 1965.